MW00338930

MANAGING FOR PROFIT IN THE SEMICONDUCTOR INDUSTRY

ROBERT MCIVOR

PRENTICE HALL, Englewood Cliffs, N.J. 07632

The publisher offers discounts on this book when ordered in bulk quantities. For more information, write:

Special Sales/College Marketing
College Technical and Reference Division
Prentice Hall
Englewood Cliffs, New Jersey 07632

Printed in the United States of America

10 9 8 7 6 5 4 3 2 1

ISBN 0-13-551722-2

Prentice-Hall International (UK) Limited, *London*
Prentice-Hall of Australia Pty. Limited, *Sydney*
Prentice-Hall Canada Inc., *Toronto*
Prentice-Hall Hispanoamericana, S.A., *Mexico*
Prentice-Hall of India Private Limited, *New Delhi*
Prentice-Hall of Japan, Inc., *Tokyo*
Simon & Schuster Asia Pte. Ltd., *Singapore*
Editora Prentice-Hall do Brasil, Ltda., *Rio de Janeiro*

Foreword

As managers, we need to know at least a little about everything in order to best interface with our many specialists in integrating their work into a cohesive and productive whole. I have tried to fashion this book to best support that need, producing a tool box, if you will, of those things I have been fortunate enough to have been exposed to and found to be of value in the course of my own career and those which we developed within our own organization in response to our particular needs. One of our primary obligations as managers, as I see it, is to assist in the training, education, and development of our people and much of the material contained herein has been oriented to that purpose. Much of it has benefited from exposure in the formal classroom environment, critiqued and refined over several years. Most, if not all of it, has been practically applied in some form or another in real-life situations. As such, I hope it will be of value to other management practitioners as well as the student, to the finance man who wishes to understand manufacturing a little better, the engineer who would like to feel less uncomfortable with accounting practices and jargon, the production control specialist with a need and desire to know more of technology, or those managers and students who simply wish to better understand the semiconductor business.

If, in some small way, what has been produced here helps to increase the size or improve the quality of our cadre of well-rounded general practitioners in manufacturing and operations management, needed now more than ever by all organizations, then it will have served its purpose. If we are to reverse or at least arrest further erosion of our industrial base—the wealth creating infrastructure upon which our standard of living depends—it is upon them that the heaviest burden shall fall. There is much to be done and little time remaining in which to do it. To succeed in such a formidable challenge they will need all the help we are capable of placing at their disposal.

As a practicing manager, my role in contributing to the social science we call management, like that of my many colleagues in industry, is to take the work of the academic, and sometimes that of the consultant, test it for applicability, modify it to our purpose, and then apply it in a practical manner in our particular working environment.

I cannot and do not by any means claim to have originated all of the material in this book. Some of it is the work of others much more gifted than I, and where the source of the work is accreditable, I have respectfully and gratefully acknowledged this. Where, for whatever reason, this has not been possible, I hope the originators will be satisfied with the knowledge that their work has found at least one satisfied customer. As a writer, I have a singular and somber obligation not to claim credit for the work of others. As a practitioner, I share in the obligation to ensure that what has been shown to be useful in the real life crucible of the factory be widely exposed and applied.

Table of Contents

INTRODUCTION x
Industrial Competitiveness: Are We Losing the Global Battle? If So, Why? Or Doesn't It Matter Anyway? x
We Are Losing! It Does Matter! How Do We Fix It? xiii
About the Structure of the Book xxi

CHAPTER 1: MACROECONOMIC FACTORS, THE BUSINESS CYCLE, AND MANAGING DURING RECESSION 1-1
The 1929 Wall Street Crash and the Great Depression 1-2
The Business Cycle 1-5
Economic Legacies of World War II 1-7
Postwar International Economic Cooperation 1-13
Preconditions Forming the Explosive Mixture 1-17
Exchange Rates and the Trade Deficit 1-22
Guidelines for the Management Practitioner 1-30
New Innovative Instruments 1-32
Terrible Tuesday 1-41

THE TECHNOLOGY

CHAPTER 2: PRODUCT AND PROCESS INNOVATION 2-1
New Product Definition 2-1
New Product Marketing 2-4
Project Management 2-7
Advantages of PERT 2-15
New Product Pricing 2-18
Why Relative Market Share? 2-19
Which Market Share? 2-19
Cash Not Profit 2-20
The Learning or Experience Curve 2-21
Opportunity Curve Summary 2-22
Price Volume Sensitivity Curve 2-23
Further Thoughts on the "Learning Curve" 2-23
Guidelines for the Pragmatic Practitioner 2-27

CHAPTER 3: NEW PRODUCT DESIGN 3-1
Designing for Performance 3-1
Signs of Stress 3-4
The Role of Design in the New Product Introduction Process 3-5
Organizing for the Task 3-7
The War on Waste 3-8
Statistical Process Control—A Definition 3-18
Operating Principles Summary 3-20
Quality Definitions 3-20
Innovation 3-21

CHAPTER 4: THE MANUFACTURING PROCESS 4-1
Technology Overview 4-1
Typical N-Channel Silicon-Gate Process 4-16
Layout Design Rules 4-29
Basic Semiconductor Physics 4-30
Manufacturing Process Baseline 4-36

CHAPTER 5: PRODUCTION SYSTEMS 5-1
Just In Case (JIC)—Push System Versus Just In Time (JIT)—Pull System 5-1
Preferred Inventory Profile 5-3
Comparison of Traditional Versus Modern Manufacturing Methods 5-5
A Comparison of Functional, Modular, and IMC Systems 5-6

CHAPTER 6: MANUFACTURING'S ROLE IN PROVIDING TOTAL CUSTOMER SATISFACTION 6-1
The Ingredients of Total Customer Satisfaction 6-1
The Obstacles in Achieving Total Customer Satisfaction 6-2
Focusing on the Customer 6-4
Engineering Hold and Short Cycle Time Manufacturing 6-18
Manufacturing Excellence for Total Customer Satisfaction 6-27
Organization as a Task Focused System 6-30
Where Do We Go From Here? 6-34
Developing the Strategic Alliances 6-39
Organizational Considerations in the Next Phase in the Evolution of Modules 6-42

THE MEASUREMENT SYSTEM PROFIT AND LOSS ACCOUNTING AND SEMICONDUCTOR ECONOMICS

CHAPTER 7: COMPONENTS AND STRUCTURE OF P&L OPERATING STATEMENT 7-1
Cost Grouping and Variation in Margin 1 7-2
Actual or M2 (Margin 2) Costs 7-3
Summary 7-6

CHAPTER 8: PRODUCT COST STRUCTURE, PRICING, AND OVERHEAD RECOVERY 8-1
Margin 2 (M2) Costs 8-3
Wafer Cost 8-3
Die Cost 8-6
Test Cost 8-7
Technology/Cost Sensitivity 8-7
P&L Hints 8-14
Inability to Compensate for Savage ASP Erosion 8-15
Experience Curve Position 8-15
New Product Support 8-15
Experience Curve Analysis—The Progress Function 8-16
Examples of Tools to Improve Yield (Reduce Product Cost) 8-16
Test Systems Layout Utilization and Efficiency 8-21
Mathematical Test Capacity Model 8-24
Final Test 8-25
Probe Test 8-27
Calculations 8-27
Product Transfer Pricing 8-30
Transfer Pricing 8-34

BUSINESS AND STRATEGIC MANAGEMENT

CHAPTER 9: COST ACCOUNTING FOR SHORT CYCLE-TIME MANUFACTURING . . . 9-1
The Old Way—A Traditional Cost Accounting System . . . 9-1
The New Way . . . 9-2
What Should be Measured? . . . 9-3
Measuring Manufacturing Performance . . . 9-7
Goal Focused Action—Visibility/Execution/Control . . . 9-14
Conclusion . . . 9-14
Cycle-Time Tutorial . . . 9-16

CHAPTER 10: DEFINITION OF TERMS . . . 10-1
Operating Statement Definitions . . . 10-1
Line Item Definitions . . . 10-2

CHAPTER 11: BUSINESS FORECASTING . . . 11-1
What is a P&L Forecast? . . . 11-1
Why Do We Forecast? . . . 11-1
What, When, and How Do We Forecast and For What Future Periods? . . . 11-2

CHAPTER 12: INTEGRATED BUSINESS INFORMATION SYSTEM (IBIS) . . . 12-1
Visibility, Execution, and Control . . . 12-1
The Sequence of Events in the Cycle . . . 12-16
The Changing Nature of Demand . . . 12-16
Forecasting . . . 12-17
Making and Meeting Aggressive Commitments . . . 12-19
On-Time Delivery . . . 12-19
Implementing IBIS . . . 12-24
System Goals . . . 12-27
Utility Program Suites . . . 12-28
System Users . . . 12-28
System Implementation . . . 12-29
System Development Guidelines . . . 12-29
File Responsibility . . . 12-31

CHAPTER 13: MANAGING FOR PROFIT/BUSINESS STRATEGY . . . 13-1
Wafer Fabrication . . . 13-1
Pricing Strategy . . . 13-3
Foregone Opportunity . . . 13-3
Point of Sale Buying Criteria . . . 13-4
Strategy . . . 13-4
Strategy—A Definition . . . 13-5
Some Important Aspects of Strategic Thinking . . . 13-9
Be Committed to Winning . . . 13-9
Know Your Adversary . . . 13-10
What Do We Have to Work With? . . . 13-10
Leadership Myths . . . 13-11
Commitment . . . 13-11
Examples of Important Leadership Studies . . . 13-12
Theory X/Theory Y . . . 13-12
Bringing Structure to Strategy . . . 13-12
Production Planning and Control—Inventory Control . . . 13-20

CHAPTER 14: QUALITY AND STATISTICAL PROCESS CONTROL IN INTEGRATED CIRCUIT MANUFACTURING **14-1**
A General Discussion and Specific Applications Example 14-1
Quality Conformance 14-1
Examples of Charts Used in Characterizing and Controlling Processes 14-4
Basic Statistics 14-20

CHAPTER 15: COMPUTER INTEGRATED MANUFACTURING **15-1**
Why Do We Need CIM? 15-3
How Is It Implemented? 15-5
Bits, Bytes, and Blocks 15-7
Networks 15-8

CHAPTER 16: SOFTWARE AND CIM **16-1**
Introduction—Why CIM? 16-1
Defining the System—The Desired End Result 16-2
Building the System—How CIM? 16-4
A Typical Application 16-5
Productivity and Cycle-Time 16-6
The Evolution of CIM—Where It Began! Where It's Going! Where It's At! 16-6
The Digital and Analog Worlds Start to Converge 16-8
The Evolution of the Personal Computer 16-8
The Transition Period—Today and Beyond 16-9
Application Software 16-10
Operating Systems 16-10
Designing the Data Base Structure—The Foundation Upon Which All Else is Built 16-13
The Mechanics of the Search Process 16-14
An Example of a Commercially Available Relational Data Base Management System 16-16
Data Base Standards 16-18
CIM Strategies—Order Out of Chaos 16-19
The Essential Components of CIM—The Building Blocks 16-20
Rules For Selecting Software 16-20
The Software Development Process 16-21
Programming Evolution 16-22
Bugs, Viruses, and Logic Bombs 16-23
Strategic Alliances and Partnerships 16-24
DEC (Digital Equipment Corporation) 16-25
AT&T (American Telephone and Telegraph)/SUN (Stanford University Network) 16-26
Conclusion 16-27
MRP 16-29
Appendix—The Relational Data Model 16-29
Noble Experiments—A Case Study in CIM 16-32
From Craftsman's Guild to CIM—Old Habits Die Hard 16-35

CHAPTER 17: ARTIFICIAL INTELLIGENCE AND EXPERT SYSTEMS **17-1**
XCON—Expert Configurer 17-6
Adopted from Artificial Intelligence Symposium, 1986 17-8
The Human Brain as a Model 17-9
Processes of the Brain 17-17
Mental Faculties 17-19
Summary 17-22

CHAPTER 18: SUMMARY AND CONCLUSIONS **18-1**
World Class or Closed 18-1

APPENDIX A: MILITARY PRODUCTS **A-1**
A Case Study in the Application of Modern Manufacturing Methods to the Manufacture of Integrated Circuits in Compliance with MIL-M-38510F and MIL-STD-883C Specifications A-1
MIL-M-38510F—Qualification Milestones A-4
Military Product Acronyms A-10
National/International Standards, Etc.—Integrated Circuits A-11
International Equivalents A-12

APPENDIX B: PRIMARY TEST AREA PRODUCT FLOW **B-1**

INDEX **I-1**

Introduction

INDUSTRIAL COMPETITIVENESS: ARE WE LOSING THE GLOBAL BATTLE? IF SO, WHY? OR DOESN'T IT MATTER ANYWAY?

The semiconductor industry, like many others which have preceded it, is currently experiencing the onslaught of global competition, led mainly by ''Japan Inc.'' and the ''Four Tigers of the Orient''—Singapore, Korea, Hong Kong and Taiwan. If history is any guide, the outcome is predictable: Asian global economic domination of yet another industry. The precedents are as numerous and diverse as cameras, watches, domestic appliances, radios, VCRs, stereo equipment, steel production, ship building, textiles, automobiles and, most recently, semiconductor dynamic RAM memory products.

According to at least one school of economic thought, however, there is no cause for concern. What we are experiencing, according to their reasoning, is merely a transition, entirely consistent with the normal course of economic development, from an industrial to a postindustrial or service economy, a process which should be encouraged, not resisted. After all, they argue, for every blue-collar job we lose to foreign competition, we gain at least one in the highly skilled, highly paid white-collar service sector to assure us tenure in our God-given place in the sun. The scaremongers among us, this school would caution, should show more restraint. Recall the Luddites who resisted, in vain, the transition from an agricultural to an industrial economy. History proved them wrong, didn't it?

Then there is the ''If you can't beat them, join them'' brigade. Yes, there is a problem but we cannot compete cost effectively on our own turf, so let's play on theirs and move manufacturing offshore, keeping the highly skilled service jobs here. This way, we will still own manufacturing and that's what really matters.

There is the ''Let's bash the government'' brigade. Yes, we too agree there is a problem, but it's all their fault. What we need are protective trade barriers against unfair competition based on low cost labor and capital, and so on.

Will history repeat itself? Shall we retain ownership of offshore manufacturing and service employment onshore, or will manufacturing simply be the thin edge of the wedge? Are our national governments really to blame? The danger of course is that these kinds of analyses and conclusions could be wrong or at best incomplete, and any action we choose to take in response to these perceptions or not, as the case may be, might turn out to be inappropriate.

There is another school of thought, to which this writer subscribes, which concludes that there will be two classes of factory in the future—world class and closed—the closed ones being in the United States and Western Europe. Furthermore, the service employment, 70 percent of which is directly associated with manufacturing, will also migrate to foreign shores, and since it is not held to be the fault of government, we should not appeal to them for its resolution. The case for this school of thought, the self-help brigade, without benefit of rose-tinted spectacles or whipping boy, is presented on their behalf as follows.

In the first industrial revolution, as agriculture became more productive as a result of capitalization, resources were released to fuel the growth in industrialization. This cannot be said of industrial productivity in the United States and Western Europe today in relation to our Asian competitors. At least in one respect then, the link in the transition between industrialization and service economy and between an agrarian economy and industrialization is different. Britain, no longer a world-class power, militarily or economically, obviously did not retain the advantage of being first to industrialize. It can be argued that the second industrial revolution originated in the United States. Will it flourish elsewhere? If a service economy is so desirable, why do we have budget deficits and balance of trade problems which necessitate us borrowing yen and deutsche marks to buy products manufactured in Japan and Germany with technology exported from America and the rest of Western Europe?

After the Second World War, with European and Asian economies in ruins, the Marshall Plan was established to lend money to these countries to buy products which only the United States was capable of producing, bringing 30 years of unparalleled prosperity and economic growth to the United States. Do we not now have at least a form of the Marshall Plan—in reverse?

Perhaps herein lies a clue to a different analysis and prognosis. Like Britain before it, suffering from the legacy of presiding over the greatest empire the world has ever seen, upon which "the sun would never set," did the United States become complacent while others diligently and intelligently rebuilt their economies? At the same time, did the Japanese and other Asian Pacific countries perceive the opportunity to achieve by economic means what they failed to achieve militarily? Is the Third World War now being fought—in the economic arena? Can this be why industrial productivity is no longer increasing at the same rate in the United States as in Germany or Japan, who incidentally have virtually no MBA factories but produce engineering and manufacturing graduates in the same proportions that the United States and Great Britain produce legal and financial graduates? Like the British before them, has the U.S. become a nation of administrators, preoccupied with perpetuating status quo, with defending the "establishment" and competing only for existing wealth rather than channeling their resources into creating new wealth? Has 30 years of preoccupation with improving standardization and marketing what our factories can produce rather than learning to build, more competently than anyone else, what global markets really want, left us unable to compete in a rapidly changing world? Like Samson, has our greatest strength become our greatest weakness? If this is so, is it we, management, who are at fault?

By contrast, if we look to Japan, we see a different scenario. Japan is an indigenously poor nation. It imports 70 percent of its food and 90 percent of its energy and raw materials. How else can she sustain and improve the standard of living of her people but by importing raw materials, adding value to them more effectively than anyone else and then exporting them as finished goods to world markets? Would it be so astonishing that they perceived this and developed a long-term strategy to be successful in doing so, building manufacturing, marketing and engineering competence, layer by painstaking layer, over the last four decades? Can it be that our problem is simply that they must be good at what they do while we, for a variety of reasons, think we need not be so committed? In effect, did they blame others for their misfortune and miserable lot in life, or did they use the only resource they had at their disposal, the brains God gave them, to do something about it, developing manufacturing, marketing and engineering excellence in the process? If we now believe that having a healthy onshore manufacturing infrastructure is important to our continuing economic well-being, can we in turn learn from them as they did from us and further improve on the "state of the art" to our relative advantage, by building on our cultural strengths instead of deluding ourselves into a "postindustrial economy" false sense of security or blaming others, including our governments? This book is a humble contribution in support of that quest.

It has been developed in support of the proposition that in a highly capital-intensive industry, (high fixed cost of doing nothing) market share is a prerequisite to profitability. Market share can only be won on a product utility, quality, on-time delivery, price (cost) and service basis. Only world-class factories can provide these competencies in a non-mutually exclusive way, and these distinctive competencies must be established in a manner which is difficult to copy or emulate by developing methods and skills which are deeply embedded in the manufacturing, marketing and engineering infrastructure and culture of an enterprise. Manufacturing in this context is used in its broadest sense, from new product definition to shipping the finished product to the customer. This chronology of events has been paralleled in the structure of the book in order to provide continuity.

The work is neither a pure technical text on semiconductor technology nor on general management principles but a blend of both, of mechanics and management, of people and technology, because even the most state-of-the-art technology is nothing without people. Its theme is transition, from the old order to the new, from economies of scale to economies of scope, from standardization and cost reduction to mix management and revenue maximization, from labor-intensive production systems to knowledge-intensive ones, from inventory profligate functional manufacturing systems to just-in-time and short-cycle manufacturing methods, from inspecting out rejects quality systems to building in quality using real-time feedback process control, from offshore escape to onshore renewal, using the most contemporary manufacturing techniques at our disposal. The first part of the material deals with making the best use of what we have available to us today in terms of manufacturing technology, systems, methods, and so on. The second part is more futuristic, dealing with those resources still in their evolutionary stages of development such as computer integrated manufacturing (CIM), expert systems and artificial intelligence.

The vehicle chosen, integrated circuits, will hopefully serve as a role model for the semiconductor industry in its own right. Its importance as a core competence of so many other businesses and indeed industries is such, however, that hopefully the subject matter will also be of interest and value outside the semiconductor industry environment. A company, an industrial enterprise, is a living organism and like any other organism from the beginning of life on earth, it must continually evolve and adapt to a changing environment or perish. Like King Canute, we can command the waves to retreat, get wet, or move our chair. Technology is relatively easy to transfer. It's what people do with it that really matters. As managers and leaders, it is incumbent upon us to find ways to wield our people into a cohesive force, united in a common purpose, just as the Japanese have done. Only by doing this can we regain our stature in world leadership.

WE ARE LOSING!
IT DOES MATTER!
HOW DO WE FIX IT?

Throughout the remainder of this text I shall try to avoid simply stating the obvious: that we in the western hemisphere are losing the battle of global industrial competitiveness. Hopefully, this is already apparent. There is ample evidence, balance of trade and budget deficits, consistently high levels of apparently chronic unemployment, diminishing productivity growth, loss of domestic and international market share and so on., in an alarming range of industries, including semiconductors, for there to be little lack of consensus on this point. There is much less agreement, however, as to its cause and even less as to its cure, except to move manufacturing offshore to low labor cost regions of the world while appealing to our governments to intervene with tariff barriers and reciprocal trade peace treaties. Other than this, most opinions appear to share a common theme—that others have an advantage, some would claim an unfair advantage—that it's someone else's fault and nothing can be done until "they" fix it. What will be presented here does not subscribe to that fatalistic view.

Human nature being what it is, no one likes to be beaten, especially fairly, and there is perhaps an understandable if not condonable tendency in these circumstances to call foul play and appeal to the referee. We have all seen this—in professional tennis tournaments, in football and soccer matches, in political elections, in semiconductor dumping allegations, in our own homes—especially those with young children and teenagers. What we are seeing at work is something we might describe as problem pathology, the process manifested by that element of the human psyche which makes us reluctant to acknowledge the existence of a problem, especially one whose origins, if pursued, could be shown to be traceable back to our own personal shortcomings. Only when the problem has become serious enough, perhaps even reached crisis proportions, do we finally acknowledge its existence and proceed to the next stage. Then the ritual of problem rationalization begins. Yes, there is a problem but it's someone else's fault. In our global competition context, it's cheap foreign labor, the Japanese work ethic in particular and Asian culture in general, the strength of the dollar, lower capital costs, the under-valued yen or deutsche mark and so on, anything in fact which is both plausible and difficult to disprove—in effect, a search for, and presentation of excuses to hide behind. Within our factories it's someone upstream who screwed up, those idiots in quality control, a dumb management decision, our sullen, lazy workforce. Only when all conceivable extraneous possibilities have been eliminated and the problem still persists are we then willing to look inwardly for the cause—usually because it's the only possible explanation remaining—that it might just be our own management or leadership competence which is lacking. Only then are we willing to consider the possibility that we are losing, not because others have what Adam Smith described as a naturally endowed comparative advantage, fair or otherwise, but because we simply are not as good. While it may indeed be true that some or all of these rationalizations contribute to our difficulties, we would be better advised to operate on the assumption that to a great extent these things must be regarded as given. Wishing them away will not make them go away. In any event, they are more likely to be second-order effects rather than first-order causes. The Japanese, the Koreans, and the Taiwanese, have not been dealt a better hand than anyone else. At best it is only different. They simply play the cards they have been dealt better. Real champions, world-class players, neither need the referee to help them win nor to blame him if they lose.

It may well be true that Asia has lower labor costs, for example, although most recent information suggests this is no longer true with respect to the Japanese, and while labor cost is important, it is only one of many components of competitiveness. Only when we have reached this point, when we are willing to sign up for ownership of a situation or problem in its entirety, good and bad, can we possibly begin to properly address its solution. Only in this way can we meaningfully consider the complete spectrum of possible solutions available to us, not just those which are expedient. How much time would be saved, how much damage would be avoided if we could admit this as an opening possibility, rather than as a last resort by process of elimination. The healing process cannot begin until we are willing to admit that we are ill. Moving manufacturing offshore rather than fixing our problems at home may well be subsequently seen to be such an expedient solution when and if all of the service activity associated with it follows. So much for our service economy future. If this ultimately transpires, and there is already incontrovertible evidence that it will, the consequences will be an economy which subsists on growing potatoes, cabbages and exporting raw materials rather than importing them, adding value and then exporting finished products. Historically, such an economy was called a colony. That global, multinational or transnational corporations may continue to flourish in such an economic scenario in the form of "hollow corporations"—at best nothing more than final assembly plants and at worst simply product distribution centers—is debatable. Even so, nation states are not likely to go along with this scenario. (Without income from employment, people cannot continue to purchase goods indefinitely, not even imported ones.)

It is somewhat of a paradox that while many of our manufacturing corporations in the western hemisphere deploy more of their manufacturing operations offshore to take advantage of lower labor costs, more Asian enterprises are constructing manufacturing facilities in the United States and Western Europe to avoid tariff barriers, the strong yen and dumping allegations in an effort to increase their penetration of these markets, even at the expense of short-term return on investment. There are already well established examples of this practice—demonstrating that they can succeed in an environment in which we not only fail, but blame for our failure—further testimony, if any were needed, that they collectively make better use of what they have then we do. Is management the uncommon factor? While it may be strategically expedient to temporarily deploy more manufacturing activity offshore in order to remain economically viable in the short and medium term, if the time bought by this strategy is not used to regroup onshore, then the longer-term consequences of such a strategy could be dire indeed. Such an approach can only be condoned as a means to an end, not as an end in its own right. Sustained profits, society's stamp of approval of an enterprise's activities, will soon carry a stigma if the employment which helps to create these profits is foreign.

Those who wish to use this time in preparation for battle rather than capitulating, those who wish to compete rather than complain, will hopefully find some of the ammunition they need in this book. But be warned: it will be no easy task. Our malaise has flourished for decades in a culture of complacency; a fortress America and the world owes us a living mentality, the so-called British disease. To fix it will call for a fundamental reappraisal of every facet of business conduct, beginning with a critical re-examination of a company's system of values and beliefs, its very culture itself; that component of an enterprise's corporate character which can be most difficult to change and for which the probability of successfully changing it is not encouraging. We are talking about the need for very substantial self-imposed change. Change, if it is to occur successfully, must first be preceded by receptivity to the need for change. Otherwise any change will be resisted by well-established and deeply entrenched bastions of those who believe that what has stood us in good stead since the Second World War best be left alone. As in all great campaigns, the first battles are likely to be political, winning popular support for the cause, beginning with the most senior levels of leadership in industry, government, and education. Change is something to be embraced, not resisted. It is already too late for that. The human race committed itself, some might say condemned, to a process of continuous change when we cast aside our spears for ploughs and then these in turn for our factory robots. Change has been our traveling companion ever since. Only its pace, its amplitude and the consequences of not keeping in step with it have escalated. Those who adjust best to the process—to the imperatives of change—those who make it work for them rather than resist it, can be world class. Only those who are world class can be sure of economic survival.

I have tried to present our own particular journey towards world-class status systematically and in chronological order, dealing with each important component, as I saw it, as thoroughly as time and space permitted. Solutions which were developed and successfully applied to the kinds of problems which are by no means unique to the semiconductor industry are described, the principles of which may work at least in part, or in modified form, in other industries. In all of this, I have also tried to avoid being trite. This is not a book for the person who aspires to "one minute management" success. There are indeed important moments in everyone's career, those flashes of enlightenment when all is clear, when some decision, albeit one you have wrestled with both consciously and subconsciously for months, becomes intuitively obvious, but we all know that nothing worthwhile is easily or quickly achieved in practice, especially in manufacturing. As Einstein said, even genius is 1 percent inspiration and 99 percent hard work. (The eloquence if not the essence of this casual utterance on the great man's part was subsequently improved upon with the substitution of the word perspiration for hard work by someone who remains anonymous). To become world class, to at least arrest further erosion of our industrial base, if not repatriate what has already gone, will be a long hard campaign; genius is too scarce a commodity to depend on. If we, the live-now, pay-later, credit-card-binging generation insist on having the next generation accept a reduced rather than improved standard of living in order to service the debt we have incurred, the least we can do is leave them with the means to do so.

Becoming world class is too formidable a quest to be undertaken for its own sake, for the purely egotistical reason of being able to say, "We are best," for example. Its ultimate purpose is profitability, and I have tried to present each section of the text in an integrated fashion, subordinate to that paramount goal. Only by being profitable can an enterprise continue to fund the changes necessary to become world class. With customers selecting a much narrower range of suppliers, in many cases only one, only by being world class in today's fiercely competitive global environment can any organization hope to continue being profitable by being one of the chosen few. This virtuous circle can only be forged by translating the desire to be world class into action; by first defining what being world class means, by communicating this to everyone concerned and then by inculcating this need into the shared culture of the company. How this is done will vary according to the prevailing circumstances and current culture of any specific enterprise. One possible approach, invoked successfully by ourselves and others, is to use the realization that nothing is more effective in uniting people in a common purpose than the existence of a common, external threat, manifesting itself in loss of market share and deteriorating profitability, the potential consequences of which can be communicated to everyone in tangible terms, losing jobs.

There is a fine distinction here between using fear as a motivator, effective if not necessarily enlightened nor enduring, and not insulating people from the sometimes potentially grim realities of life. As has been said, "Nothing concentrates the mind so fully as the prospect of the hangman's noose." Under these circumstances most people are likely to respond constructively to almost any alternative presented to them. If being world class is that alternative, then as was advocated earlier, what that means needs to be understood and communicated to all concerned. Market share, a prerequisite to profitability in any capital intensive enterprise, and those competencies with which market share is won and held—product utility, quality, on-time delivery, price (cost) and service—must be quantified in terms of world class standards and actual performance measured accordingly. High performance is not necessarily guaranteed by setting high standards—but will not be attained without them. To the Japanese, a high standard is what is theoretically possible minus some small allowance for life's imperfections. It is not, as we have come to willingly accept by custom and practice, historical performance plus 10 percent, especially if historical performance falls far short of what is theoretically possible. This approach perpetuates mediocrity, not excellence. Contrary to historical precedent, these parameters must be considered to be mutually inclusive rather than exclusive. This is particularly true with respect to winning and holding market share in mature commodity products. But perhaps the most important component in winning more market share is that of new product definition, design, development and release to production, and this too is fully discussed in the text. There is some threshold, the proportion of total revenue accruing from new products, above which a business can be considered to be intrinsically healthy and below which much therapy may be required, 40 percent being suggested as a rule-of-thumb value for this figure of merit. As will be demonstrated later, there is no question that businesses so positioned can grow, even during recession. The importance of this particular competence, of being able to introduce new products quickly and flawlessly, cannot be overstressed.

Profit strategy is also explored in depth, presenting the argument that a profit strategy which has low cost as its only or primary component, may not in itself be adequate. Revenue maximization, again in a global context, is at least equally important and a vigorous effort to solve the mix management problems usually associated with product proliferation may well be preferable to foregoing this approach in favor of the vulnerability associated with unnecessarily restricted product rationalization.

The kind of data base framework required to manage mix is described in the Integrated Business Information System (IBIS) and Forecasting sections. Reconciliation of external business and internal operation variables in a common electronic database environment is needed in order to provide visibility and control the execution of what needs to be done, when, how, and by whom, in order to deliver a wide spectrum of products, to a wide range of customers, in varying quantities, on time and at the right cost and quality.

The way in which the manufacturing operation is organized to provide these things, in a nonmutually exclusive way, has also been discussed at length in terms of focused factories (modules)—in building layers of competence and in managing change from the old order to the new, from offshore escape to onshore renewal—in comparative terms. The vision of being world class is indispensible to the process of change, and it must be quantified in terms of communicable goals, but in itself is not enough. There must be a systematic approach to practical realization of the vision. There must be strategy, there must be discipline in the execution of the strategy, and there must be leadership, the indispensible catalytic ingredient in harnessing widespread commitment behind the cause.

(Our own humble efforts in striving for this kind of cohesion are summarized in Chapter 6—Manufacturing's Role in Providing Total Customer Satisfaction.)

Our competition—the Japanese and the Four Tigers of the Orient—are truly formidable opponents; but they are not indomitable, they are simply thorough. They understand the importance of market share, global market share, as a fundamental prerequisite to profitability in capital-intensive industries with high fixed costs. They long ago realized that to win globally they had to dominate at least two of the three major markets in the world—Japan itself, the United States and Europe. (Other markets, such as India and China, were not worth the effort—until now!) Japan, they could take care of, retaining almost exclusive ownership for themselves. They knew that the fight to wrest U.S. market share from indigenous U.S. companies would not be a quick knockout, that they would have to be prepared to go the distance in a 15-round fight, so they got in shape first by sparring in Europe, a much weaker opponent. (Confucius say "Fight by all means if attacked, but don't pick one unless you think you can win.") If he were alive today he might have (hopefully) added, "Especially against sleeping giant, lest history repeat itself." Europe saw so-called "predatory" pricing at least five years before the U.S. did. The harbinger of ill fortune was evident even then for those receptive to the signals. They also know how to win market share, competing on cost, quality, reliability and on-time delivery, and by designing innovative new products—until recently, not so much from a product functionality point of view, but from one of process innovation, although even this is changing. The camera-toting copiers are not just copying anymore.

They understand the opportunity curve (what used to be called the learning or experience curve, expressions which concealed more than they revealed) possibly better than we do. Volume creates the opportunity, and the incentive, to reduce cost, but more importantly, unlike ourselves who only took some of the potential benefits of this strategy by sitting back and waiting for costs to fall of their own accord as volume increased, they perceived that the full benefit could only be realized by providing the means to drive costs down when it matters most—up front during a new product introduction cycle and by minimizing the duration and therefore maximizing the frequency of the "learning cycle." They understand the virtuous circle of pricing in such a way as to win that market share (volume), based not on the current costs of an unefficient, underloaded factory, but on loaded, highly efficient, factory costs in the future, and therefore creating the circumstances which are most conducive to loading their factories with the volume at which they can be profitable at these prices: a desired end result, self-fulfilling strategy. This strategy may well lead to predatory pricing, but if predatory pricing means fiercely competitive, is dumping an entirely appropriate description of its effect? (Dumping is defined as (1) selling at a price lower than the cost of manufacture or (2) at a lower price in a second market.)

Business Portfolio Management, based primarily on the work done by the Boston Consultancy Group, appears to be yet another area in which they have learned their lessons well, using cash flow surplus from well-established products or captive geographic markets to fund penetration into other products and markets while still in the embryonic stage of their development. Preventing competition from establishing a foothold in a developing market at the outset is much less costly than letting them in and having to extricate them later. Keeping their cash cows healthy, by continuing to invest in productivity and quality improvements if not in capacity, rather than milking them dry, is yet further confirmation of their astuteness.

They also understand that dollar capacity is a function of mix and that unit capacity is a function of yield. The higher the yield, the greater the capacity and the lower the minimum acceptable price at which business can profitably be taken in order to totally consume that capacity. They thoroughly address the need to determine the price at which the market share required to fully consume the factory capacity, or plan to have available, can be won. From this they establish what the product costs need to be to take business profitably at these prices, what needs to be done to achieve these costs; then they execute! The alternative, underloaded factory cost plus desired margin, does not give rise to acceptable average selling prices in a highly competitive market. It is neither by accident nor by good luck (or naturally endowed or politically bestowed structural comparative advantage) that they can produce three times as much saleable output, for the same amount of bricks, mortar and raw silicon as we can. Where they are fastidious, we are extremely wasteful. They understand what it takes to get high yield, productivity and quality. So do we. They execute with relentless commitment and rigorous discipline. We don't. They bring more capacity on-stream, after they have exhausted productivity improvements, not before. We throw bucks or brawn before brains at the problem. They pursue productivity improvements in all of the "factors of production," land, labor (both direct and indirect), capital (equipment, floor space), material and knowledge. We sometimes cannot see beyond direct labor.

They dominate the industry by understanding the overall economics and by relentlessly pursuing 5, 10, and even 20 year objectives while we diddle with outmoded accounting systems, defunct values and a preoccupation with the next 30 to 90 days' financial results. The sense of frustration caused by the current level of incompatibility and inadequacy of current accounting practice with the needs of modern manufacturing approaches is perhaps reflected in the following unkind, but hopefully amusing if not strictly accurate definition of an accountant. "An accountant is someone who does not have the skills required to play the game, so he is allowed to participate by keeping the score. He reciprocates, however, by keeping the score in a way that no one else can understand."

That they have refined this strategic approach to a "fine art" in high volume, commodity product manufacturing is why we feel compelled to seek safe refuge in so-called niche markets such as application specific integrated circuits (ASICs), and so on. This is not strategic brilliance. It is capitulation. What are niche markets today are growth markets tomorrow, and the prices at which they are currently profitable will not be sustained; the Japanese and their proteges will take care of that as they have done so often in the past. We don't know how to build the small-scale semiconductor plants which this kind of stand-alone profit strategy would require to be viable. We only know how to build large ones which require high volume to absorb overhead and reduce unit cost, so any niche market strategy must of necessity be complemented by a high volume, commodity product strategy. (Alternatively, when we are not so gracefully driven out of the niche markets, there's always the service sector—for a while.)

So much for the self-criticism and extolling the virtues of others. What do we do now Batman? How do we repel the "Oriental onslaught"? We can start by swallowing our pride and be willing to learn from them as they did from us and then in turn surpass them, as they surpassed us. This process must begin within the industry itself. We must stop rationalizing failure and be willing to admit that we are losing, not because others have structural advantages, but simply because they are more competent than we are in an overall context, in setting global objectives, in defining strategies to realize these objectives, and in executing these strategies with almost military precision, especially in manufacturing. They are more productive, not because they are more efficient than we are, but because they are more effective. There is no reason whatsoever why we cannot be at least as effective. There is good reason to believe that we can be even more so, but we have to believe in ourselves first. If we allow ourselves to be convinced that the outlook is so bleak that nothing can be done about it, then we are surely condemned and will be sentenced accordingly, but by ourselves, not by the competition. Positive thinking doesn't always achieve results, but negative thinking never does. Neither can we win with a defensive strategy, by retreating into the trenches and keeping our heads down until the bullets stop flying. When that happens, not only the battle, but the war will be over. These battles may be fought in the field, but the war will be won or lost back in the factories. The Japanese were quick to realize that the most powerful marketing strategy is one predicated on world-class factories. We need nothing less to win. They also realized that achieving manufacturing excellence would be as difficult as it is important, so they committed their best people to the task. In their culture, the manufacturing profession is held in high esteem, to which only the most able may aspire. In ours, it is considered to be employment not worthy of a "scholar and a gentleman."

In creating these factories, we must first establish a clear vision of what business we are in, identify the key competencies required to be successful in that business, develop strategies to create or acquire these competencies, and then execute with unflinching determination. A word of caution about the fashionable trend to mergers and acquisitions as a means to correct some weakness or to exploit some opportunity. The 140-pound weakling rarely develops true strength with mail-order bolt-on biceps. There are few successful substitutes for hard work. Strength sought without sustained effort is usually nonenduring if not elusive. Sometimes it's better to stick to your knitting.

We must also stop seeing ourselves as victims, trapped by adverse circumstances, capable of doing nothing more than perpetuating status quo and complaining instead of questioning "conventional wisdom." of not being willing to test our system of values and beliefs lest they have outlived their usefulness, or thinking we can buy our way out of trouble. Our customers will be very happy to tell us what they need from us in terms of performance, both now and in the future, in order for them in turn to remain competitive. It is our obligation to listen carefully, then find ways of reaching these standards, as the Japanese have already done, with new approaches if necessary, if the old ones are not good enough to take us there. If we focus on the appropriate desired end results, and measure our progress towards them, then behavior will change accordingly. Productivity must be harnessed as the great engine of change, not just direct operator productivity, but total productivity, the productivity of the whole system, from designing new products to shipping to the customer in high volume. We can no longer afford the luxury of complacency about the way we do things. There is always a better way, and if the need is great enough, the effort to find it and the courage to apply it will be forthcoming.

There are vast opportunities to increase productivity in any business, sometimes to an embarrassing extent. We are all aware of examples of things being done differently, unconventionally if you will, and producing staggering results. Almost invariably, the opportunity and skill already exist. What was missing was motivation, not because it too did not already exist, even in abundance, but because it was stultified. If unleashed, it usually proves to be a significant source of creativity and innovation to fuel the productivity engine. If we can organize ourselves such that we can employ the total person, rather than limit an individual's contribution to that of human robot, we would find solutions to many of our problems of lack of competitiveness.

The key to unlocking this resource is that most vital component of management called leadership. The continued use of the term *management* in itself implies control, setting boundary limits, authoritative pressure, compulsion and coercion, overcoming reluctance, close supervision, pushing from behind, prescribing in great detail not only what needs to be done but how it's to be done, and so on. Management in this sense is of course required to some degree, but without the necessary measure of leadership, it will stultify rather than stimulate. It has come to have negative connotations with its emphasis on the less attractive side of human nature. Perceived in this way, it can precipitate and reinforce adversarial relationships. Leadership, on the other hand, appeals more directly to positive human qualities: the need to belong to a group, to accomplish, to be appreciated, to identify with, be part of and contribute to a common enterprise. Only leadership can create the circumstances in which motivation is allowed to flourish to its full potential, by empowering people, not supervising them, to achieve new levels of performance not previously considered possible, by allowing as much self-determination as is practically permissible to be brought to bear on the task. Enough work has been done on this for us to be willing to at least consider, if not accept, that leadership, contrary to popular myth, is not a talent granted by God to the chosen few. Like any other component of management, it is a process at the disposal of those who wish to pursue it. It is a tool and, like any other tool, it requires skill; skills which can be learned in a structured and systematic fashion.

It is the process of setting appropriate objectives, of leading the activity of forging well-reasoned and articulated strategies to achieve these objectives, by people and through people, by winning their commitment, their hearts and minds, to the vision, and the application of their considerable skills to the task. It is the process of empowering "ordinary" people to achieve extraordinary results, usually by having more faith in them than they sometimes have in themselves. Our use of labels helps illustrate the use and abuse of this force. Those of us who are not independently wealthy and have to work for a living are "compensated" for doing so. The Webster dictionary definition of this word "a psychological mechanism by which feelings of inferiority, frustration, or failure in one field are counterbalanced by achievement in another," implies reluctance. The word *remuneration*, on the other hand, "to pay an equivalent for a service or expense" implies reward for services freely and willingly rendered. *Direct labor* is another widely used term not designed to endow dignity and respect.

While there is much we must do in the way of self-help, that is not to say that our national governments are exonerated or do not have a role to play, but we should not require them to help those who are not willing to help themselves; the "lame ducks" as Mrs. Thatcher described them. The problem is now so serious, however, especially in the semiconductor industry, that some form of temporary defensive intervention may be indispensable, if only to buy time for a more appropriate solution, of the kind which does not lend itself to being accused of rewarding failure and perpetuating mediocrity such as tariff barriers or trade reciprocity mandates. (This is nothing more than fiscal fiddling while Rome burns.) In the longer term a cohesive and collaborative offensive, rather than defensive program on the part of industry, government and the educational establishment, to allow our industries to compete at least on equal terms with Japan Inc., et al., is required. This is possible, indeed imperative, even in our free enterprise "nonintervention-in-industry" culture, without violating the sacred tenets, or at least to a lesser extent than do tariff barriers. The semiconductor industry is of central importance to many other industries, such as data processing, telecommunications, artificial intelligence, and the original equipment manufacturers' (OEM) electronics equipment. Sovereign states are dependent upon many of these, not only for servicing their huge administrative needs in "managing" their economies, but also in defense of the realm.

These functions are obviously too important to be strategically dependent on technology which is exclusively in foreign ownership.

There is too much at stake for us not to be passionately committed to winning. Excellence is what it will take and there is no excellence without passion. Meanwhile, while we wait patiently for the helping hand, let's proceed and practice self-help. These competencies such as new product definition, design and project management, product costing and pricing, managing mix, focused factories, computer integrated manufacturing, just-in-time materials management techniques, short cycle manufacturing methods and statistical process control, broadly embraced in this preface are now each discussed in more depth in the remainder of the text. Last but by no means least, I have tried to review and chronicle the role which strategy, leadership and motivation must play in making all of these competencies productive. Let it not be said that we do not practice what we preach.

Let's not complain, let's compete—and rise to the challenge!

ABOUT THE STRUCTURE OF THE BOOK

As was stated earlier, this book is about **functional integration**. This is not a topic normally taught in our business schools and engineering colleges, yet it is the way things are in the real world of the factory, especially those in pursuit of excellence. It is the key to future success, perhaps survival, for many businesses. In order to provide a structure to this process of integration, I have chosen to build on what I call the **Strategic Hierarchy of Business Imperatives**, as shown in the following chart. The terms used in this structure are familiar ones. Where I hope to add a different perspective is in the relationship these terms have to each other and in the way they are treated in more depth within the body of the text. The structure of the book follows this relationship, in which the prerequisite condition for each imperative is shown in vertically descending order, as follows:

1. The super, superordinate goal of business, is not profit . . . but to satisfy society's needs . . . the Noble Goal.

2. Profit is a derived benefit of servicing these needs successfully. It is society's "stamp of approval" of the enterprise's contribution: a mandate to continue in business.

3. In a high fixed cost business such as semiconductors, winning and holding market share to amortize these costs is a prerequisite to profit.

4. Market share can only be won and held by providing **total customer satisfaction**. This, like manufacturing excellence, cannot be defined and measured in terms of a single entity . . . but only in terms of its ingredients.

5. The ingredients of total customer satisfaction are:

a. product portfolio (new products)
b. quality/reliability
c. price/cost
d. 100 percent on-time delivery
e. total service

6. Having products in one's portfolio which most closely meet the application needs of the customer base is the paramount ingredient. If not satisfied, distinctive competence in any other ingredient is academic.

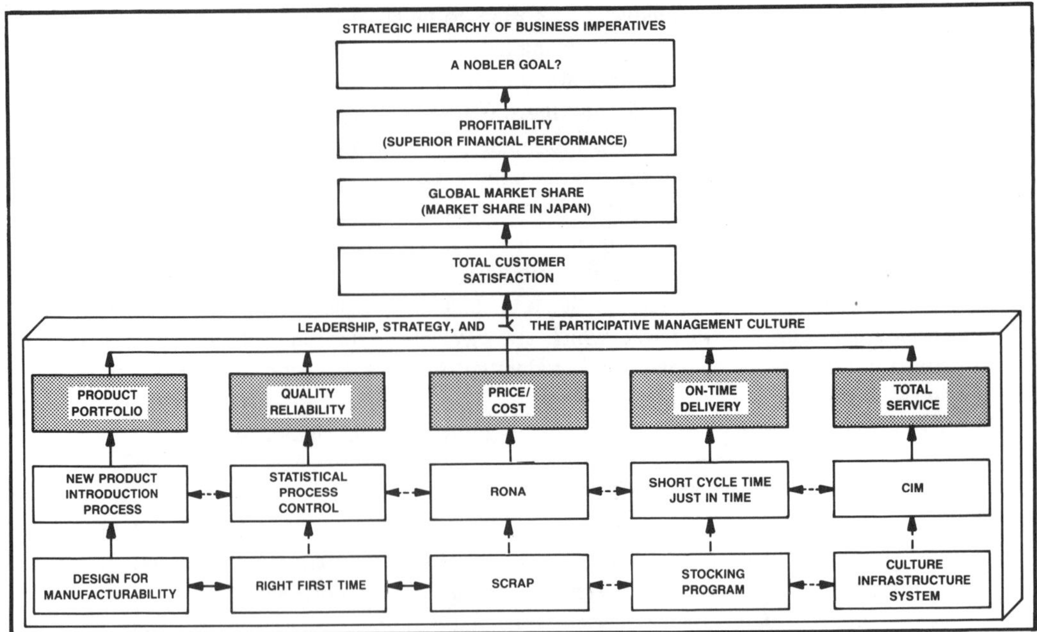

7. These ingredients must be provided inclusively—not exclusively. To fail to provide any one ingredient is to deny total customer satisfaction.

8. These ingredients must be provided on more than one product, to more than one customer. That means we have to learn how to **manage mix**.

9. It is on these **five ingredients** that a business is measured by its customers! It is on these same five ingredients which an organization should measure itself. (Our customers do not care about our cycle-time, market share, or overhead recovery for example—only our performance on these five ingredients.) These others are internal, secondary parameters—not primary.

10. To focus and improve performance on these same five ingredients of total customer satisfaction imperative is to contribute to all of the strategic imperatives! (Market share and profit are not imperatives—they are derived benefits of the extent to which the total customer satisfaction imperative is achieved.)

Unlike market share, or profit before tax, which are too universal to be meaningful and too far removed from the factory floor to be useful, everyone in an organization can relate their everyday contribution to these five "bridging imperatives" of total customer satisfaction in a measurable and meaningful way. Collectively they constitute "manufacturing excellence" in its broadest sense. How do we define and measure the manufacturing capability of a business, including excellence, in a quantitative way? If there is no scale against which to calibrate, how do we know when we have achieved excellence, or be able to measure where we are in relation to it? Like total customer satisfaction, which cannot be defined as a single entity, or be measured and represented by a single number such as market share, or profit in percentage points, manufacturing too has to be defined in terms of its major ingredients or components which can be measured quantitatively. These components are: **QUALITY AND RELIABILITY, COST,** and **ON-TIME DELIVERY**.

Every functionally specialized organization affects all of the five ingredients of total customer satisfaction, but of the five, these are the three in which manufacturing

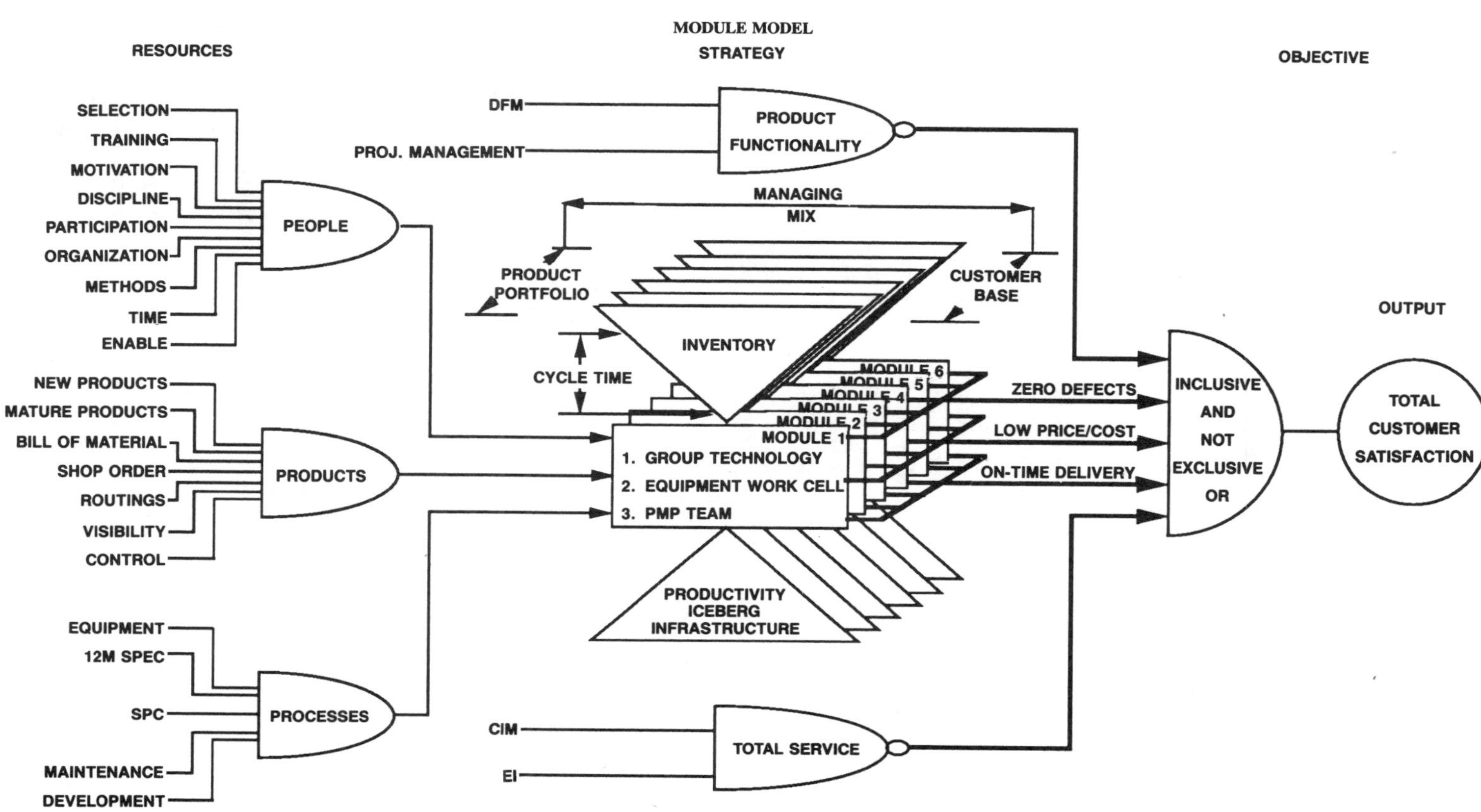

SHORT CYCLE TIME MANUFACTURING
RESOURCES
MODULE MODEL
STRATEGY
OBJECTIVE
OUTPUT
SELECTION
TRAINING
MOTIVATION
DISCIPLINE
PARTICIPATION
ORGANIZATION
METHODS
TIME
ENABLE
PEOPLE
NEW PRODUCTS
MATURE PRODUCTS
BILL OF MATERIAL
SHOP ORDER
ROUTINGS
VISIBILITY
CONTROL
PRODUCTS
EQUIPMENT
12M SPEC
SPC
MAINTENANCE
DEVELOPMENT
PROCESSES
DFM
PROJ. MANAGEMENT
PRODUCT FUNCTIONALITY
MANAGING MIX
PRODUCT PORTFOLIO
CUSTOMER BASE
CYCLE TIME
INVENTORY
MODULE 6
MODULE 5
MODULE 4
MODULE 3
MODULE 2
MODULE 1
1. GROUP TECHNOLOGY
2. EQUIPMENT WORK CELL
3. PMP TEAM
PRODUCTIVITY ICEBERG INFRASTRUCTURE
CIM
EI
TOTAL SERVICE
ZERO DEFECTS
LOW PRICE/COST
ON-TIME DELIVERY
INCLUSIVE AND NOT EXCLUSIVE OR
TOTAL CUSTOMER SATISFACTION

plays a leading role, unlike new product introduction, where manufacturing plays a supporting role to design and marketing's leading roles. **It is these components or ingredients which should provide the focus for cohesive action.**

What is Excellence?

Excellence is what is theoretically possible—minus some small allowance for life's imperfections. (The benchmarking technique measures actual performance relative to the best that is currently being achieved . . . not the best that is possible.) How do we apply this general definition to the specific ingredients of total customer satisfaction?

Product Portfolio. For new product introduction, excellence is: defining and designing products which appeal to the customer by satisfying his particular application need to a greater degree than a competitor's product; in the shortest possible design to manufacturing cycle-time: with zero redesign iterations, that is, Right First Time; at the lowest possible development and manufactured product cost.

Quality. For the quality component, the answer is obvious. It's zero defects, or zero PPM and while perfection is unattainable, we know how to continue to approach it asymptotically. Product quality is a function of **the quality of the process**. The process in this context means the **design** and **manufacturing** process. Design for Manufacturing (DFM) and Statistical Process Control (SPC) preceded by Right First Time (RFT) are the paths we must follow in improving the competence in both of these respectively.

Price/Cost. With regard to cost, the superordinate measurements are **profit** and **RONA** (Return on Net Assets) but this again is too remote for everyone in an organization to relate to. Zero waste, however, of material, capacity, and time is more tangible.

On-Time Delivery. For on-time delivery, excellence is 100 percent—on all products, to all customers, at all times. On-time delivery is a function of many things, but the manufacturing organizations' main contribution to it is **cycle-time**—not just the manufacturing process cycle time, but the cycle time of everything which manufacturing controls. But cycle-time, both theoretical and actual, since we shall have different manufacturing flows for different products, is a function of **mix**. (Total cycle-time—the time which elapses between order entry to shipping the product—including ''white space'' cycle-time, is a responsibility shared by all of the members of the enterprise.) So how do we avoid the convenient but dangerous practice of reporting averages and the accuracy but obscurity in detail which measuring every product cycle-time would cause? The solution is to report a **cycle-time ratio**—the ratio of actual cycle-time to theoretical cycle-time—**for a given mix**. The cycle-time of what? A device? A lot? What lot size? The answer in this case must be the cycle-time of the quantity that the line is optimized or designed to process.

Total Service. Total service requires satisfying relatively minor customer needs not explicitly and inclusively satisfied by the other ingredients such as: interfacing with customers in a professional and courteous manner; helping out when they are in trouble, even when there is no contractual obligation to do so; responding to unforecasted demand perturbations; responding promptly to requests for information, and so on.

It is the treatment and integration of these which the rest of this book is about.

1

Macroeconomic Factors, The Business Cycle, and Managing During Recession

INTRODUCTION

While most of the material in this text deals with the process of renewal within a manufacturing enterprise, addressing the development of these competencies required to be able to compete as a world-class manufacturer, it is probably fitting that we at least attempt to deal with the factors which form the external business environment in which the enterprise must operate. Winning has at least as much to do with understanding the rules of the game, the other players, and the state of the playing field as internal, operational skill. While an individual company can, to some extent at least, manage supply and demand at the micro level, it obviously cannot do so at the macroeconomic level. Forces at work here must be accepted as given. Any business operating internationally will be affected by all of these to some extent. When acting in isolation, some of these factors, such as fluctuating exchange rates or inflation, for example, may affect profitability in a marginal way. Particularly adverse combinations of two or more of them, such as those forming the conditions of deep recession, can be fatal. While these forces cannot be controlled by the individual business, action can be taken to reduce a business's exposure and vulnerability.

In this analysis, we shall consider these major factors—the business cycle, inflation, exchange rate fluctuation, government policy mechanisms, other world-class competition, protectionism and trade barriers, the role of the stock market, and money supply—which in the aggregate, create the environment in which both domestic and international business is conducted. Since national economies are at least in part the summation of individual businesses, we may find that there are lessons here for the government policy maker as well as for the business leader. We shall try to develop an understanding of these conditions, this macroeconomic environment, by tracing the evolution of its development during the years immediately following the Second World War, when much of the foundation of the world economy as we know it today were laid.

In a business upturn, markets are still usually generous and benevolent, even against world class competition in paying a premium over cost plus waste and turning a blind eye to less than competent management. In a downturn, however, going through a recessionary phase in the business cycle—the purging process—a business is exposed to the supreme test. Since 200 years of tracking this phenomena tells us that the next recession is coming—the only uncertainty is when—this particular state in the cycle, starting with the worst of these downturns so far experienced, the Great Depression of 1929, will be explored at some length. Since at the time of writing, the 1987 Wall Street Crash is very much in vogue, with much speculation in the media on why it occurred, its relationship to, and what it portends for the economy in the future, will be examined by way of comparison.

THE 1929 WALL STREET CRASH AND THE GREAT DEPRESSION

On Monday, October 28, 1929, the Wall Street Crash as it has come to be known, entered our history books when the stock market, as reflected on the Dow Jones, fell from 298 points to 230. An unprecedented 22 percent fall, and was followed by a further drop of 14 percent by the following day, continuing downwards to an all time low of 198 by the 13th of November. The market continued its downward plunge over the next two years. While the popular belief is that the crash actually started at this point, the market had in fact immediately prior to this plummeted from a high of 381 points down to 198.69 before recovering again back up to 294.07 points in what was to become known as the "sucker's rally." This initiated a cascading series of events. One of the first was the collapse of the banking system in the United States, which culminated in the Great Depression. During this time, the United States gross national product fell 50 percent and unemployment rose to 25 percent. By 1932, some 9,000 banks, 40 percent of those in existence had failed and the market, bottoming out at 41.22 points, had lost 90 percent of its value. Even though stock markets and national economies were not nearly so interdependent then as they are today, the effects of this were soon felt across the world. Then, as now, the market reflected, rather than caused, a malaise in the underlying economy. Almost certainly, the underlying cause was a process of escalating protectionism precipitated by attempts to balance the federal government budget. Consistent with the principles of prudent financial management, it is considered desirable to reduce one's expenditure as income reduces. Prior to Keynes, in times of economic adversity, especially recession, this was the conventional wisdom which governments attempted to follow in balancing their budgets. In an escalating spiral of tit for tat retaliation—so-called "beggar thy neighbor" tactics—the Smoot-Hauley Tarriff Act was signed into law by President Hoover in June 1930. In a like fashion, as more than just a handful of the 535 members of the U.S. Congress prepare the Omnibus Trade and Competitiveness Act, the same propensity towards protectionism exists today.

While somewhat alarmed by the speed and intensity of the downward plunge, governments in the early stages elected not to intervene. That they did nothing, despite the apparent need for them to do otherwise, was due largely to the advice they were given by their economic advisors. Consistent with the dogma of the day, the body of knowledge which then constituted what has come to be known as classical economics, it was the popular belief that these upward and downward perturbations were entirely natural and unavoidable as the economy adjusted in its self-perpetuating drive to achieve dynamic equilibrium. In keeping with Say's Law—the belief that supply creates its own demand—that the very act of production generates the income necessary to consume that which is produced—situations of inadequate demand could not exist, and this dynamic equilibrium would therefore, eventually be reached **at the level of full employment** further re-enforcing the no-intervention policy. Say's Law asserted that since all revenue was returned to the factors of production in the form of rent, wages, and interest, this income would automatically be spent on consumption, either directly or indirectly, through investment. This, discussed later at more length, was subsequently shown to be an erroneous assertion by British economist, John Maynard Keynes.

Under such advice, governments watched and waited. Only when this particular downturn went deeper and lasted longer than previous ones to the extent that the economy appeared to be stuck at the bottom of the cycle, circumstances the persistence of which refuted what classical orthodoxy said could not exist, did intervention begin. In fact, as late as 1936, GNP (gross national product) had only recovered to 95 percent of what it was prior to the crash and unemployment remained at 17 percent. Only when governments finally accepted, contrary to the conventional economic wisdom of the day, that the economy could reach a state of dynamic equilibrium **at a level less than full employment** did the search for instruments with which to intervene begin.

The first of these attempts focused on interest rates as a demand priming mechanism. During the Hoover administration, interest rates declined from 6 percent prior to the crash to 1.5 percent by 1931. This reduction, however, failed to produce the desired effect due to what is now understood to be the asymmetrical effect of interest rates on demand. While strong demand can be reduced by increasing interest rates, sucking money back out of the economy into central banks, the reverse effect—stimulating demand by reducing interest rates to flush money out of central banks into the hands of investors and consumers—was not realized to the same extent. On the one hand, in the face of such low prices, it still did not appear attractive enough for businesses to borrow for investment purposes, even at such low rates. On the other hand, in attempting to stimulate individual consumer demand, common sense should have told the economic pundits that people without jobs cannot consume—no matter how much paper money is stacked in bank vaults, at whatever low interest rates. The "poor," unattractive to bankers as a lending risk at the best of times, only borrow to finance the consumption of immediate needs as a last resort. It often seems that in the minds of the very learned, common sense has to leave to make room for all that knowledge.

The second major attempt at positive government intervention, now in the Roosevelt administration, took the form of action to raise prices, hoping to make borrowing, for both investment and consumption, more attractive. This action consisted of freeing the dollar from its link with gold, the private hoarding of which, in wishful anticipation of its appreciation in dollars—not surprising in times of such economic distress—was thought to be restricting demand and growth by keeping the money supply too tight. With this in mind, Roosevelt prohibited the private hoarding of gold and instructed the banks to discontinue gold being redeemed in exchange for dollars. On the gold standard, the amount of money in the economy was regulated by the amount of gold in deposit in banks and as such, the private possession of gold, rather than dollars, was considered to be restricting demand and therefore holding down prices. To further discourage this practice, the Treasury was instructed to raise the price it was willing to pay for gold. But since the private possession of gold had already been disallowed, any benefit from this action could only apply to the newly mined quantities of the mineral and did not result in a windfall increase in wealth in dollars to the consumer to spend on increased consumption, as was the original intent. Also, since other currencies still remained on the gold standard—and were still therefore convertible to gold—the value of these currencies rose against the dollar; that is, a given amount converted to more dollars. In effect, this action simply resulted in a depreciation of the dollar. Although not the original intention, exports were made less expensive, but the benefit of this in an economy not at that time heavily oriented to exports was very limited.

Yet another attempt to directly intervene in the price-setting mechanism occurred under the auspices of the National Recovery Act. The concentration of economic power associated with the evolution of corporate oligopolies was seen as a mechanism which could be used to raise prices; a fairly dramatic departure from the conditions of perfect competition, where no supplier or consumer commands sufficient market share to determine price, the point at which supply and demand are considered to be in equilibrium. With market share, economies of scale, and some power to hold wages down, these oligopolies could be profitable, at least temporarily, at low prices. In conditions of weak demand, each firm would lower prices in order to gain an advantage over other firms in the industry. Others would then respond in like fashion, giving rise to an escalating downward spiral on prices and wages. While the mechanics were different, the end effect on prices was the same as for conditions of perfect competition. Unlike perfect competition, however, these lower prices did not necessarily result in an increase in demand. The National Recovery Act's plan to use this economic power to raise prices required these firms to collaborate in agreeing to set minimum prices, with trade unions accorded similar rights on wages. In so doing, the National Recovery Act was in fact condemning the reduction of price due to competition on the basis that it was not, at that time, in the public interest; endorsing in a way, the potential abuse of monopoly power. To re-enforce this strategy, the antitrust laws then in existence were not enforced. Such code-making provisions of the National Recovery Act were repealed by the Supreme Court in May 1935.

Attempts to prime demand using welfare spending were also tried. In the 1930s, wages from employment were, for many people, their only source of income. As unemployment rose, the full effect of this was transmitted into reduced demand, which in turn, further reduced employment and perpetuated the vicious circle. Some welfare programs to provide people with jobs were attempted but on a scale far removed from welfare as we know it today and its effect on reflating demand was negligible. The end result of this process for many businesses, as is the case in all recessions, was bankruptcy. (Aggregate demand and falling prices are key characteristics to which we shall return later.) It was under these conditions that the capitalist system was most vulnerable to attack. Perceived failures and inherent weaknesses of the system—those of recession and its associated high levels of unemployment, which classical theory said could not exist, and oligopoly, a departure from the assumption of conditions of perfect competition, provided much grist for the Marxist mill. It would seem that with public sector spending in the seven largest OECD countries averaging 42 percent of GDP, at the same time that Russia and China strive to introduce more private enterprise into their economies, that the pure capitalist and socialist systems are on a path of convergence towards more mixed economies. In Russia's case, however, with its Perestroika initiative (restructuring)—market forces determine all but a few staple prices, with the state continuing to own all property. With no labor, stock or capital markets, and the continuation of the one-party system, it remains to be seen how this will be achieved.

Thanks to Keynes, who in refuting Say's Law in his treatise "The General Theory of Employment, Interest, and Money" showed that there could be a preference for holding or hoarding money—a liquidity preference—in which money was held out of circulation and that shortages of demand could arise; that the economy could therefore reach dynamic equilibrium—a steady state—at levels less than full employment. Governments now were finally convinced of the need to intervene and the policy instrument—deficit spending on public works to create employment and therefore reflating demand by increasing purchasing power in the economy—was born. Its success meant that the capitalist system lived to fight another day. It has since become apparent however that this state of affairs cannot be sustained without unleashing inflationary forces due to wage-price escalation. Also, it was implicit in this treatment that the deficit would be driven positive in the upcycle. Even squirrels have the good sense to put something away for the winter.

THE BUSINESS CYCLE

The cyclical nature of national economies—called the business cycle—had already been observed and indeed studied prior to the Great Depression. A whole series of explanations as to its cause had already been proposed and discarded by this time. One of the earliest, understandable if not credible in an economy still early in the transition from one predominantly dependent on agriculture to an industrial one, was that of sun spots. This cyclical pattern of the economy was seen to be almost exactly in phase with periodic bursts of solar activity. Every seven years or so, great solar flares radiating for hundreds of thousands of miles outwards from the sun were believed to coincide with and were therefore believed to be the cause, of good harvests, the benefits of which rolled over into the rest of the economy. The period of these economic cycles is now in the range of three to five years, with the postwar average at three. With hindsight, we now know this early hypothesis to be a misassociation of cause and effect.

A more contemporary explanation, based on what we think we understand of the effects of change on the supply and demand relationship, allows us to construct a more plausible explanation of the series of events in the cycle (inflation, recession, depression, recovery) as follows. Let's assume for the purposes of our exercise that we are at the leading edge of an upturn in the cycle. Perhaps our government, having learned from the Great Depression what interventive action is appropriate to kick the cycle of bottom—courtesy of Mr. Keynes—has just awarded a large tax cut, or announced some great public works program in order to restore consumer confidence and release more purchasing power into the economy to increase demand. (More precisely perhaps, to convert some latent, intrinsic demand into effective demand: people do not stop wanting German BMWs and Japanese video recorders just because they cannot afford them.)

At this point then, consumer confidence and purchasing power will, for whatever reason, be growing reasonably strong, manifested in healthy demand. Having just come out of the bottom of the cycle, one could reasonably accept at this point that demand will now be running somewhat ahead of supply. Through amplified demand signals, increasing consumer confidence and purchasing power will eventually be transmitted to the supply side of the equation. Suppliers and potential suppliers, who immediately prior to this were in a state of restraint, will obviously try to respond to this increasing demand by increasing factory output. In the early stages, they will be calling into production resources already in place to support a higher level of output from the previous high point in the cycle, but now unused at the lower level of demand. On the human resource side, for example, one can understand employers working their existing pool on overtime, rather than permanently adding to their head count.

Only when all of these resources—people, capital equipment, material—are absorbed, and demand still exceeds supply, will the supplier be favorably disposed to call upon the open market for more. Again, due to the prior state of affairs, these resources are likely to be available in relative abundance—and therefore relatively inexpensively. (In the case of human resources though, perhaps not in the required skills mix.) Since capital investment will also have suffered in the downturn, funds at low interest rates will be available. Raw material too will be plentiful at a reasonable price. As these resources are brought into productive use, incremental income from the increased employment cumulatively reinforces the increasing demand.

In trying to respond to these increasing sales opportunities, the competition among suppliers for claims on until now, surplus to requirement resources will begin, progressively reducing their availability and therefore pushing up the price at which they continue to be available. This effect, rather grandly called the theory of marginal utility, more popularly, the law of supply and demand, simply states what is perhaps intuitively obvious, that the utility of any product or service, all else being equal (which in economics seems never to be the case) diminishes with increasing availability; it is the utility of the last or least wanted unit—the unit at the margin—which determines the value of all units. (More on this with respect to money as a commodity later.) An escalating spiral of the cost of these resources—interest rates on capital, wages, and price of raw materials—is now underway. The boom is on!

The government too will want some of the action, competing with the private sector for these very same resources to support its own obligations and pet projects such as defense, social security, health care, and education. At this point and beyond, it will also be cooperating by managing the money supply to fund this growth, buying back bonds previously sold to the central banks when, in the previous upturn, it saw fit to reduce liquidity; cautiously aware that too little will limit growth opportunities—but that too much will encourage demand beyond the capacity of the economy's ability to supply, the result of which would be inflation and devaluation of the coin of the realm. (In an international context, it is typical at this point for the government's current account in trade to go into deficit and for exchange rates to change.)

As the general upward movement in the cycle continues, a point is eventually reached where the increasing cost of incremental resources—higher interest rates, wages, material costs—due to their decreasing availability, is beyond the point where the additional revenue and profit from their use exceeds the cost of their acquisition and are therefore beyond the economically viable threshold. At this point, the rate of growth will decelerate and the curve will flatten out. The economic engine is now at full throttle and no more power is available—whatever the call for more—and is incapable of expanding further under these conditions. Rising costs may now have reached the point where fear of inflation—the deterioration in the purchasing power of the currency over time—precipitates action from government to cool down the overheating economy by reducing effective demand. This it may do by starting the process of buying back the bonds it so willingly sold at the beginning of the up-cycle or by increasing taxation in order to reduce the amount of money in circulation, changing the relative proportions of effective and intrinsic demand. Alternatively, a factor independent of government intervention, like a critical nonavailability of the correct mix of human skills mentioned earlier may bring about an end to the growth phase. Again, for whatever reason, a cumulatively reinforcing series of events now cascades through the downward cycle in a similar, but reverse direction, to that which occurred in the upward cycle. (So far, continuous expansion without inflation—the Holy Grail of both economists and politicians—has eluded their grasp.)

As purchasing power and effective demand are reduced, inventories which cost money to fund will start to accumulate. The business operating statement will suffer an erosion in profit margins due to reduced sales. Management will attempt to protect this margin by reducing expenditure and inventories (in some cases, including paper clips).

This takes the form of cutting back on manufacturing run-rates. (In a high fixed-cost business, this kind of action may only succeed in replacing the problem of high inventory carrying cost with the problem of low fixed overhead recovery—only now, the business will have less inventory available to respond to any windfall sales opportunity which may occur.) Eventually a point will be reached where layoffs will again be considered necessary, reducing purchasing power even further, and so the process cumulatively reinforces itself on its downward journey. (The purists held that there was an intrinsic, self-correcting mechanism in the downward cycle. As interest rates fell, eventually a point would be reached below which new investment would become economically viable, thus arresting then reversing the downward trend.) Again, having learned from the 1929 experience not to take this mechanism for granted, a point will be reached where the government may again decide to intervene, stimulating demand with deficit spending and so ensuring that the cycle repeats itself, with each successive upward and downward perturbation superimposed on a generally upward, underlying trend in the longer term, ad infinitum.

There was also a view, following a study of business cycle activity by Wesley C. Mitchel, University of California, which concluded that every business cycle was due, not to some singular, common, recurrent theme, but rather to some unique, pre-emptive series of events and set of conditions not forecastable a priori; and as such, these cyclical perturbations could neither be prevented nor cured. As we also learned in the years following 1929, while every upturn may carry the seeds of its own destruction, the downturn and plateau at the bottom need not necessarily carry the seeds of its own salvation or recovery and that appropriate government intervention may therefore be necessary.

But what action is appropriate if an administration already has an embarrassingly high deficit from a previous downturn and, not having studied Keynes or squirrels, has not been prudent enough to reduce it during the upside in the economic cycle? Or the country has a serious trade imbalance with foreign countries? Or both? (Budget deficit spending, like other economic strategies, is not exempt from the law of diminishing returns.) All governments, for obvious reasons, want continuous growth in their economies as measured in GNP—preferably without the boom or bust cyclical perturbations. They also want full employment, low interest rates, and so on. The fulfillment of these objective—or at least the promise to—is what gets politicians elected. We shall return to this topic later when we explore macroeconomic management of the domestic economy. Prior to this, however, we shall attempt to develop at least a basic understanding of the infrastructure of the international economy.

ECONOMIC LEGACIES OF WORLD WAR II

The Marshall Plan

Unlike Britain, which had fought longer, committed itself more completely, organized its economy on a war-time footing more thoroughly than any other nation, and in consequence emerged from World War II in a significantly impoverished condition, the United States emerged far stronger economically (and in consequence, politically and militarily) than when it went in. The United States standard of living in fact actually improved during the war, in part because more people were employed, but also because the necessities of war had compelled the country to intensify the discovery and economic development of its vast natural resources.

The British on the other hand had so depleted their resources in throwing everything into the war effort that Britain's chief economic adviser at the time, John Maynard Keynes, was obliged to report to his government that the country was so short of money that only victory, or something like it, would have to be achieved in 1944—or the war effort would need to be curtailed. In 1945, Keynes compared the losses suffered by both nations, finding that British casualties in total were almost three times those of the United States, with those either killed or missing in action almost three and a half times as great; whereas 55 percent of Britain's labor force had been engaged in war production in June of 1944, the comparable number in the United States was only 40 percent; that Britain had lost 35 times the foreign invested capital which the United States had lost (the beginnings of the death throws of colonialism). Whereas the consumption of nonmilitary goods and services had declined by 16 percent in Britain during the war years, it had increased by 16 percent in the United States; the British Commonwealth fleet fell from 40 million tons to 19.5 million tons as the United States merchant fleet shipping capacity increased fourfold from 12 million tons to 50 million tons. The United States in fact emerged from the war far richer than any nation had ever been before.

It was under such circumstances that America displayed unparalleled generosity (and true economic genius) in playing its ace card. Every first-year student of economics, contrary to Say's Law, knows that there is no need for supply without effective demand, and with the cessation of the war effort, the consumption of military products the American factories were geared to supply would rapidly diminish. There is, in turn, no effective demand without purchasing power. General Marshall, as Secretary of State, persuaded Congress to extend the Roosevelt lend-lease program into peace time to these nations, devastated by war, who were in need of and willing to avail themselves of aid in rebuilding their economies. All but the USSR and the Eastern Block satellite countries accepted this generous offer.

The genius lay in the fact that the United States lent money to others to buy products which only the U.S. factories were then capable of producing. In reality, this was a practical demonstration on the grandest possible scale of Adam Smith's principle of "the invisible hand" at work—that action motivated by self-interest can result in the greatest possible good—even though this may not have been the original intention. As poetically paraphrased by Alexander Pope—"Thus God and nature made the general frame . . . and bade self-love and social be the same." American factories, having developed considerable momentum in manufacturing military hardware, for which there was now obviously much less demand, were diverted to manufacturing consumer products for which there was much pent-up demand, backed up with savings accumulated during the war years, not only for their own domestic market, but for the rest of the world as well, thus avoiding the slump which would otherwise have followed the abrupt cessation of the war.

Whatever Happened to "Fortress America" and the "Mighty Dollar?"

At the end of the war, with the rest of the industrialized world's economies in ruin, there was no need for American industry to be efficient, far less world class. There was effectively no competition and America could sell everything its factories were capable of producing. There was no need then for short cycle-time manufacturing; statistical process control; just-in-time materials management; design for manufacturability and all the other waste reduction and quality improvement techniques which we now know to be in the world-class manufacturer's tool box. Manufacturing under these conditions did not need to be world class in today's terms. It only needed to be adequate, more often than not, only barely. This is why "prophets" such as Duran and Deming were "not heard in their own land" and had to find markets for their products elsewhere—most notably, Japan. Our motives in dealing with this is not in a history lesson for its own sake. The point is that there are parallels today to this situation, namely: that there is a transition in economic power, based on industrial supremacy, from the United States to Japan, similar to that which occurred between Britain and the United States 40 years ago—a process to which both nations are adjusting only with great difficulty. Did lack of competition lead to complacency? Did the legacy of the Vietnam War, which was financed by printing money, rather than by increased taxation, further reinforced by the oil cartel price hike producing the double digit inflation of the 1970s, and then the unbridled profligacy of the early 1980s, start the United States on a path, the outcome of which will be no different than Britain's? While the underlying reasons and the mechanics of the process may be different, the outcome may well be the same.

The United States is now much less independent and autonomous than it was then. Despite its still vast natural resources the U.S. has a budget deficit of 160 billion dollars. It has a trade deficit of 170 billion dollars. The consumer debt in the U.S. is at 600 billion dollars and the corporate debt is estimated at 700 billion dollars with a serious deterioration in debt to equity ratios as a result of the crash. The U.S. federal debt is 2.25 trillion dollars, 400 billion of which is owed to foreigners, financed mainly by foreign funds, which the U.S. consumer uses to purchase foreign goods. With a rapidly devaluing currency, the U.S. is clearly a nation living beyond its means. In the space of a few short years, the U.S. has switched from being the world's largest creditor nation to the largest debtor. Do we not now have the Marshall plan—in reverse? It was Britain's inability and America's unwillingness to accept the role of world financial and economic leadership which helped to cause the 1929 stock market crash to develop into a severe global recession. Are there not distinctly similar parallels in the relationship between the United States and Japan today? No where is the attrition of the U.S. autonomy and independence more evident than in the special economic relationship which, for a variety of reasons, has evolved with Japan since the Second World War. While starting from almost diametrically opposed ends of the cultural, political, and economic spectrum, each finds itself in a mutually dependent, symbiotic relationship with the other—a relationship many Americans and Japanese find uncomfortable. The practical reality of the matter, however, is that they need each other.

Not naturally well endowed with natural resources—circumstances which precipitated the Japanese abortive invasion of Manchuria in 1931—the Japanese were quick to realize that they could achieve by economic means, via America, what they failed to militarily via Manchuria. A nation which has to import 70 percent of its food and 90 percent of its energy has nothing going for it but its people. In such circumstances, the strategy which they needed to pursue was clear—to develop value adding manufacturing competence better than anyone else. This strategy required access to a source or sources of raw material and a large market for the end product. Both of these it found in the United States—rich in natural resources and technology, with the largest, most voracious consumer market in the world. In return, the Japanese were willing, up to a point, to fund the almost chronically endemic, U.S. postwar budget deficits. (This special relationship was described in a *Business Week* article by Norman Jonas, October 5, 1987, as the "Nichibei Economy," a combination of the Japanese words meaning "sun country" for Japan and "rice country" for America.) Does not Japan now have the currency reserves to lend money to the less developed countries (and some developed ones as well) to buy products which only Japan is capable of producing? With the "hollowing out" of America's industrial base, there are in many cases, no alternatives—not even low quality, high price ones—to German and Japanese products. In consequence, the United States' faces a double dilemma in this respect. The first is to keep interest rates low enough to encourage consumption and investment at the same time, keeping them high enough to continue to attract the foreign capital necessary to finance the budget deficit. The second is in letting the dollar fall low enough to reduce the trade deficit by reducing imports but still high enough not to frighten off foreign lenders. Over 200 years ago, Americans fought and died to throw off the shackles of colonialism—only it seems, to inflict this status upon themselves. We can only hope Keynes was right when he said, "there is a great deal of ruin in a nation."

Other Postwar Legacies

There were of course other legacies of the war which helped to shape the world's economic and political arena. The British, for example, fully employed during the war years, expected no less in peacetime. As had been the case in America, there was also much pent-up demand, released as the public began to redeem the war bonds which had been used to finance the war effort. Welfare economics, whose origins can be traced back to Bismarck's Germany of the 1880s, further developed in Lloyd George's Britain of the early 1900s, where welfare, funded by taxation, was seen to be socially if not economically justifiable, was used to insulate the British from the rigors of unemployment as the nation adjusted back to a peacetime economy during the postwar years. Such developments did not gain a foothold in the United States until the years of the Great Depression. Its acceptance was slow since classical economics argued that the marginal utility of money, unlike goods and services, did not reduce with increasing availability—that it in fact remained constant and therefore additional increments did not render any less satisfaction. There was, therefore, no case for the redistribution of wealth from the rich to the poor since the rich did not enjoy additional wealth any less with increasing income than would the poor. ("Satisfaction" of course, means different things to different people. Smith's view of this with regard to the rich being that "the chief satisfaction of wealth is the parade of wealth.") Not until Pigout, who succeeded Marshall at Cambridge University, showed in "The Economics of Welfare Spending" that the marginal propensity of money did in fact decline, just as for other goods and services; that the "poor" would in fact get more satisfaction from successive increments than would the rich, was the economic objection to welfare programs removed.

This era also saw the laying of the foundation which forms the basis of the macroeconomic statistics so readily available today. These statistics are plugged into economic models which, unlike scientific ones, deal with variables which are hard to define or defy unanimity of expert agreement, assuming relationships which are not always well understood. Neither do we humans always warrant the credit which economists give us for being "rational," an assumption without which their mathematical models would not work. (George Marshall defined the so-called "dismal science" of economics or political economy as "the study of man in the ordinary business of life." Involving people as it does, it is at best a social rather than a pure science.) As a net result of these developments, the postwar years saw an unprecedented accumulated pent-up demand backed up by highly dispersed purchasing power and the development of the means, or so thought economists and politicians, to manage their economies rather than passively waiting for the economic cycle to run its "natural" course. It is to this "management" we now turn.

As we have seen from our studies of the business cycle, economic activity is known to be intrinsically cyclical, with these cycles, while superimposed on a longer term, upward trend, increasing in both amplitude and frequency. We also saw that while each downturn may not carry the seeds of its own correction, having a propensity to get stuck at the bottom, the upward cycle does indeed seem to carry, if left uncorrected, the seeds of its own destruction. The pattern is also changing in that in each successive cycle, the level of inflation in the up-cycle and the level of unemployment in the trough exceeds those of the previous ones. Since much uncertainty about the economy could be avoided if economic performance could be linearly extrapolated from the past, or if the effects of government policies could be predicted, one can assume that these cycles are to be avoided if possible. This being so, let's now look in more depth at the tools available to government policy makers to modulate the effects of these perturbations in the pursuit of economic goals.

Not surprisingly, economic policies—and the tools applied in their name—are a function of the goals being pursued. Almost certainly included in any list of these goals would be steady and continuous growth in GNP. On this much at least, governments and their oppositions are usually in agreement. Such a happy state of affairs makes political life so much easier since debates about which government department or program has to get by with less, or whether or not to increase taxation in order to make the government's budget balance, can be avoided. With a bigger cake, there is more for all. There is usually much less unanimity on what comes next on the list of goals since, for governments as for businesses, the more of these goals that are pursued, the less likely, due to mutually exclusive interdependence, they are to be achieved. Additions to the list, not necessarily in any order of preference or priority might be: full employment; no inflation; low taxation; low interest rates; favorable exchange rates; vigorous investment; positive balance of payments; little or no government borrowing—many of the factors which we mentioned in the introduction to this chapter. We shall see that even if the government's economic advisors could provide them with a formula to achieve these in a mutually inclusive way without trade-offs—this economic nirvana—the politics of any given situation would almost certainly prevent it. While some of these goals can be achieved directly, just for the asking, and equally, almost any one can be achieved in isolation, some must be pursued by more indirect means. Perhaps even more importantly, the more goals that are added, the greater is the difficulty in achieving them due to increased complexity and interaction.

We saw from our study of the business cycle, for example, how in an economic upturn, continuously increasing output, especially if the economy is at or near its full output potential, tends to be inflationary, as the cost of a diminishing supply of uncalled resources increases. This could be corrected in the past by allowing unemployment to rise—now politically if not economically unacceptable if this is also on the list of policy goals. (Governments tend to be somewhat flexible in their definition of what constitutes full employment. One such definition is NAIRU—the non-accelerating inflation rate of unemployment. This is considered by monetarists to be the "natural rate of unemployment" below which any further attempts to reduce unemployment, running a budget deficit to stimulate demand, for example, will cause inflation to rise continuously as expectations of inflation are revised upwards.) In any event, the reduction in demand associated with rising unemployment is now much diminished due to the unemployment welfare cushion. Yet another of the many examples of this mutual exclusivity principle is taxation. Lower taxation cannot be achieved without lower public spending or more government borrowing. We can see therefore that the more goals that are pursued in a nonmutually exclusive way, the greater the degree of difficulty in achieving them.

Broadly speaking, governments pursue each of these policy goals using policy instruments—economic variables such as taxation, prime interest rates, deficit spending (usually measured as a percentage of GNP) over which they have direct control—with one such instrument mainly associated with each individual goal. These instruments and goals fall broadly into two categories, the first being that of **fiscal policy**—dealing with issues affecting the public purse—income, in the form of taxation and expenditure—and any associated mismatch, that is, the public deficit. The second main branch is that of **monetary policy**—dealing with these issues concerning interest rates and the supply of money in the economy. (These categories also serve to broadly divide economists and politicians into two schools of thought—Keynesians and monetarists.)

In the 1970s, when governments began to realize that full employment and inflation were, with the instruments that they then had at their disposal, mutually exclusive goals, a third branch of policy, in the form of **incomes policy**, was added. It was to become evident, however, that this type of intervention only served to further distort, and not fix, the interaction of instruments and goals. Mixing and matching the use of these instruments allows flexibility in the way the goals are pursued but does not add to the number which can be pursued without compromise.

Then came the realization that interest rates affect not just investment and demand but also exchange rates since, with the advent of electronic funds transfer, capital can now move across international boundaries much faster, and certainly more so than the physical transportation of the goods of international trade. During the 1980s, a combination of an expansionary fiscal policy, funded by budget deficits financed to some significant extent by yen-backed dollars, and a tight monetary policy in the form of higher interest rates has come to be called Reaganomics. More simply, prosperity through consumption and happy talk. Vast quantities of foreign capital, drawn by these high rates, contributed to the problem of an already large and rapidly growing trade balance deficit by forcing up the exchange rate of the dollar and making exports more expensive and imports cheaper. This in turn, as we shall discuss later, contributed to the unstable conditions which pre-empted the Wall Street Crash of Monday, October 19, 1987.

All of this is compounded by measurement difficulties. For example, what is the budget deficit? There are several variations of the definition: (1) **actual** or **primary**—that which excludes the interest payments on government borrowing, (2) **structural**—what the deficit would be if the economy was operating at its full potential output, and (3) **inflation-adjusted**—which measures the extent to which the deficit is adding to the real value of the government's outstanding debt. (The current account consists of the trade balance of goods plus the net of positive and negative financial effect of services and debt, and so on.) Money supply is (1) notes and coins and (2) all liquid financial assets, so called M1 and M2 respectively. (Currency held by foreigners, both private individuals and banks, is not included in these figures.) Neither are economists in agreement that deficit spending actually achieves any real, lasting benefit, protagonists citing the crowding out theory—the null and void effect of deficit spending—that the increase in interest rates generated by deficit spending eventually offsets the benefit of short-term increase in demand by lower consumption and higher interest rates in the longer term. Monetarists too have their difficulties in being able to reach agreement, their particular chicken and egg problem being interest rates and supply of money—which is the dependent and which is the independent variable? Should interest rates be manipulated to control the supply of money or vice-versa?

Macroeconomic Management of the World Economy

We saw in the previous section how difficult it was for an independent government to achieve all of its economic policy goals. We shall now see how these difficulties are further exacerbated in being integrated into an interdependent, global trading, and financial system.

POSTWAR INTERNATIONAL ECONOMIC COOPERATION

The Bretton Woods Conference

The belief that national economies benefit through international trade with each other is one of the oldest tenets of economics. It is predicated on the international extension of the principle of comparative advantage, first articulated by Adam Smith, that individuals, firms, or countries will benefit by specializing in those areas of economic endeavor where they have the greatest advantage—or least disadvantage—over their competition. If a country uses imports or quotas to insulate itself from the rest of the world, its competitiveness will be distorted and it will then be unable to judge wherein its distinctive competence or comparative advantage lies and it will lose accordingly. This argues that it is in fact in the best self-interest of a country to open its markets to foreign competition—even if it is not granted access to others in return. Not to do so is to deny the consumer freedom of choice which may also carry an economic levy in the form of higher cost. In the words of Smith's metaphor: "It is the maximum of every prudent master of a family, never to attempt to make at home what it will cost him more to make than buy . . . what is prudence in the conduct of every private family can scarce be folly in that of a great kingdom." (Not all that long ago, the original 13 states in the American confederation had their own currency and tariffs, in some cases as high as 50 percent).

As a result of the Bretton Woods Conference, conducted under postwar circumstances most conducive to international economic cooperation, three multilateral institutions were established, the common goal of which, consistent with the free trade principle, was to develop and oversee a liberal, world trading system and a commensurately liberal financial support infrastructure. These were: (1) the International Monetary Fund (IMF) whose function is to supervise the international monetary system, (2) the World Bank, originally called the International Bank for Reconstruction and Development, to act as the financial intermediary for the reconstruction of Europe, and (3) the International Trade Organization (ITO) to police a more open trading system. As originally conceived, this latter institution was considered by some of the participants to have too much power and was perceived as a threat to their autonomy—which indeed it was—in a way that the IMF and the World Bank was not. As a result, it was never ratified and was replaced by the General Agreement on Trade and Tariffs (GATT), an interim agreement administered by a small institution consisting of 94 member countries monitoring the trade policies of its members and trying to resolve trade disputes. That this has had a favorable effect would seem to be evident in that tariffs, which on non-manufactured goods were on average about 40 percent in 1947, are now about 6 percent. As we shall see later, tariffs on manufactured goods tend to be cloaked in a more subtle guise.

Then, as is still the case today, the world economy's most pressing problems were: (1) exchange rate volatility, (2) protectionism, and (3) developing country debt. The need to solve these problems forms the basis of the need for continuing international economic cooperation, the aims of which are: (1) to increase the probabiliy of the participating country goals being as compatible as possible with each other, (2) to make any chosen policy collectively more powerful, and (3) to enable individual governments to use the fact that they have given international commitments to defend their policies from domestic opposition. That is the economic rationale. The political difficulty in doing so due to lack of communication and absence of trust is often illustrated in economic circles by way of an analogy called **"the prisoners dilemma,"** the gist of which is as follows.

The dilemma assumes that two prisoners, who were partners in crime, are, each unknown to the other, offered the same deal. If both prisoners confess, they will each be sentenced to ten years in jail. If only one confesses, he will be sentenced to one year while the other will receive 20. If both deny the crime, they will be charged with a lesser crime, the sentence for which is three years each.

Each prisoner then is left to reflect on his best course of action, fully aware that what makes best sense for him as an individual, guided by self-interest, depends on the position taken by the other—which he cannot know in advance. We can represent these positions and all of the possible outcomes associated with them, in a table.

First Prisoner	Sentence	Second Prisoner	Sentence	Combined Sentence
Confess	1	Deny	20	21
Deny	3	Deny	3	6
Confess	10	Confess	10	20
Deny	20	Confess	1	21

It is clear from this table that it is in their best mutual interest for both prisoners to deny the crime, each, in so doing, being sentenced to only three years, for a combined sentence of six. However, given that they cannot communicate in order to agree on this strategy, and even if they could collaborate, there would still be the uncertainty about whether or not the other could be trusted to stick to his position. In seeing the situation from a purely best self-interest point of view, each believes that under these circumstances, there can only be a win/lose, rather than a win/win outcome to the dilemma—that one man's gain can only be at the expense of the other's loss, and so each convinces himself that regardless of the position taken by the other, it is in his best interest to confess, thus for sure avoiding the maximum 20-year sentence, probably taking ten, with a chance of getting off with only one.

This little exercise illustrates that in situations in which independent economic agencies attempt to collobrate, that Mr. Smith's "invisible guiding hand" may not produce the best mutually beneficial result. In the real world of international politics, even where a mutually beneficial economic outcome might be evident, such as agreement on exchange rates, one can readily appreciate the political difficulties such as lack of communication, enduring commitment, and trust preventing its realization. It is also possible that mutually undesirable goals can be pursued very effectively.

Hamada Diagrams

Economists have tried to develop tools to help governments coordinate international macroeconomic policy on the premise that this leads to a more mutually beneficial outcome

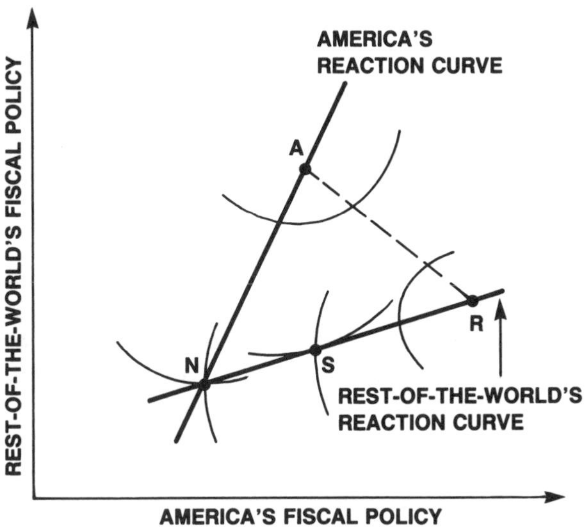

Figure 1-1 Economic Bargin-Hunting

than any one country can achieve independently. Their first hurdle is to convince politicians that this is indeed the case; their second is to show them how. In the former, they have employed game theory, the latter, econometric models. One such attempt is the Hamada Diagram, developed by Professor Koichi Hamada of Tokyo University, shown in Figure 1-1, in which the horizontal axis represents one country's budget deficit (country A), the vertical axis, the budget deficit of the rest of the world. Every point within these axes, therefore, represents a different combination of country A and the restof the world's fiscal policies. Acting from a basis of best self-interest, country A would attempt to optimize its position by choosing a point such as A on the chart, where the rest of the world's fiscal policy is more expansionary than its own, giving country A the desirable combination of GNP growth and a strong current account. The rest of the world, however, also acting in what it perceives to be its own best self-interest, would choose a point such as R, where country A is more expansionary than the rest of the world. Around the points A and R, known as "bliss" points, are "indifference curves" which define the area in which each is indifferent to the fiscal policy of the other—A in the case of country A and R in the case of the rest of the world, bearing in mind that both want to optimize their respective "state of bliss."

Let's suppose that country A is confronted by the predetermined fiscal policy of the other, represented by a line parallel to the horizontal axis. Country A now has to comprehend this in forming its own fiscal policy in order to reach its highest possible indifference curve. This would occur where the horizontal line is tangential to one of its indifference curves. "Reaction curves" are then defined by formulating country A's response to each hypothetical rest of the world's fiscal policy and likewise the rest of the world's reaction curve.

On the matter of trust, even if countries can, at least ostensibly, reach agreement on their macroeconomic policies, there are certain principles which have been established to ensure against the possibility of both flagrant and subtle abuse. The non-discrimination or MFN, most favored nation treatment, holds that countries should treat all of their trading partners with equanimity—that if a country sees fit to impose a tariff, it should do so across the board in order to prevent a downward escalating spiral of retaliatory and counter-retaliatory tariffs. The transparency rule requires that countries should replace disguised and unquantifiable protectionism with unambiguous, straightforward tariffs. Reciprocity requires that countries should make reciprocal reductions in their tariff barriers. Then there are various forms of the subtle abuse referred to earlier such as nontariff barriers (NTB), prohibitions, quotas, volume export restraints (VER), health and safety regulations. A devaluation of the dollar is in fact a none too subtle form of import tariff.

The 1987 Crash—Bloody Monday (Financial Meltdown)

On Friday, October 16, 1987, following a bull market which had lasted for five years, the Dow Jones Index, which had stood at a record high of 2722.42 on Tuesday, August 25, fell 108.36 points to 2614.42, with a record 343 million shares being traded. On the following Monday, the index fell a further 508 points—the largest drop ever in a single day—to 2106 points, representing a 23 percent reduction and wiping 500 billion dollars of equity value of the market, the total reduction in this period being one trillion dollars. On that Monday, 604 million shares—almost double the previous record set on the Friday—were traded. The final actual number might have been even higher but the system went into overload and was all but completely shut down. Following so soon after the Chernoble experience—the term *financial meltdown* was coined. While the market regained 289 points across the next two days—a temporary recovery which subsequently dissipated—the fear causing the situation to feed on itself had already set in. The real crisis however, took place on Tuesday, the 20th, when during one particularly crucial period, stock, stock options, and stock index futures trading all but ceased on all of the exchanges. Unknown to the general public, desperate behind the scenes action was being taken to prevent a total degeneration of the financial system from which, if left unchecked, it was unlikely to recover. (This is described in a blow-by-blow account in the following article from the *Wall Street Journal*, Friday, November 20, 1987).

Following in the aftermath of the crash, indeed while the stock market was still crashing, many opinions were offered as to its cause and what it signaled for the economy in the future. In reading the press and listening to the media, one could be forgiven for thinking that there seemed to be as many different opinions as there were experts. Immediately after the crash, there were many public utterances to the effect that as a result of changes introduced after the 1929 crash and subsequent depression in the U.S. and world economy, such stock market perturbations were less likely to effect the economy so adversely. Legislation which had for example, separated commercial banks and brokers and restricted investor borrowing to 50 percent of stock purchases—in 1929 it was 78 percent, made cascading economic collapse unlikely.

Knowing what we now know about business cycles, the effects of government fiscal and monetary policy, the economic legacies of World War II, the increasing interdependence of the world economy, and Mitchel's analysis that each cycle is due to a unique set of preconditions, we can now reconstruct and analyze the crash of Monday, October 19, 1987 in a systematic way rather than adding to the proliferation of opinions shot from the hip in the heat of battle. More importantly, what if anything, can we deduct by way of implications for the future?

That the situation was explosive, there can now be no doubt, and by way of analogy, we shall use what we know about explosions to structure our analysis. We know for example, that for a explosion to occur, there must first be a combination of elements, which while possibly harmless in themselves, in combination form an unstable, potentially explosive mixture. We also know that we then need a trigger mechanism—a spark—to ignite the combustible mixture. We then need a supply of materials, which while not necessarily contributing to the initial preconditions required for combustion, amplify its effect by adding fuel to the fire after it has started. In effect, our task is to separate the many factors involved into those which were pre-emptively causative and those which were merely consequential in their effect. The important issues are: What were merely symptoms as distinct from causes? What primed the explosion? What was the trigger mechanism? What factors were amplifiers?

PRECONDITIONS FORMING THE EXPLOSIVE MIXTURE

The State of the Economic Engine Prior to the Crash

The expression ''dynamic equilibrium'' is one borrowed by economists from the pure physical sciences to describe the state of the economy at any particular time. In its original context, a physical system is considered to be in a state of dynamic equilibrium if its output, however that is defined, is in a steady state, regardless of any changes which may be occurring at the inputs to the system. A jet aircraft for example, flying at 500 miles per hour at 30,000 feet is in such a state. In this case, the desired output is defined as the speed—500 miles per hour. As such, only one of the many variables is defined as an output and all others, either by intent or default, are inputs. This state of dynamic equilibrium is preserved so long as any fluctuation in the desired output, within pre-defined limits, is corrected or compensated for by appropriate changes in the inputs. In some cases, this action is fulfilled automatically by coupling the output back to the input or inputs through an automatic servo-control feedback loop so that any deviation in output is detected, transmitted back to the input and an offsetting correction made at the input. Let's consider a second case, however, in which we include the fuel consumption in miles per gallon as a desired output in addition to the speed. We have now increased our expectation of the system by making the output goal, or goals, more difficult to achieve. We have complicated our system in that fuel, clearly only an input in the first case, now has an additional role in that it is also a factor in the output of the second. We have introduced duality in the definition of this parameter.

It is not too much of a stretch of the imagination to consider the economy as an engine. Of all of the parameters, the variables associated with the control and measurement of performance of our economic engine, only GNP is invariably an output. It is the direction and rate of change in this parameter which determines whether an economy is in a state of growth, plateau, recession, or depression. All others can be defined as inputs, outputs, or both. This is as much a matter of politics as of economics. Full employment for example, may be considered to be a desired output of the economic system in the form of a policy goal or, on the other hand, as an input in the form of a policy instrument to control inflation. Interest rates too can be considered, in being defined as a policy goal, as an output; or on the other hand, as an input control instrument affecting consumption and investment.

As we know, any engine can be mismanaged to the point of damage—or even explosion. Our primary purpose here is to assess the condition of the economic engine immediately prior to the stock market alarm bell of October 19th; to see how well this was reflected by the market and to assess how well it will fulfill our output expectations in the future. Like any engine, its future performance is not independent of the manner in which it has been used and maintained in the past. While a physical, mechanical engine does not have an infinite lifetime, no matter how well cared for, our economic engine is more of an organic one, with new cells being born (we hope) as others die off.

"Reaganomics"

On taking office in 1980, the Reagan administration inherited an economic engine whose condition could be described in terms of the economic parameters prevailing at the end of the Carter administration. For simplicity, let's set up a check list of these engine parameters showing how they stood at the end of the Carter administration and how they stood in late 1987, towards the end of Mr. Reagan's second term, as follows:

	1980	1987
1. Inflation—consumer price index (%)	13.0	4.5
2. Expansion of GNP (%)	2.0	2.4
3. Unemployment (%)	7.0	6.8
4. Interest rates (%)	11.0	8.0
5. Personal disposable income ($)	2200	2400
6. Rising stock market (Willshire 500)	500	2400
7. Business investment (%)	12.0	11.5
8. Savings (%)	6.5	3.8
9. Trade deficit (billions)	- 30	- 160
10. Budget deficit (billions)	- 60	- 160
11. U.S. debt (billions)	+ 105	- 250
12. Exchange rates dollar to yen/deutsche mark	277/1.98	149/1.85
13. Interest payments on federal debt (billions)	52.58	138.68
14. Top rate personal income tax (%)	51	48

How these parameters have trended over the course of the intervening years is shown in the following charts. The Reagan adminstration's economic strategy—what has come to be known as Reaganomics—consists essentially of cutting taxes and reducing government spending to encourage investment and saving, the intention presumably being to return a higher portion to the private sector. As Mr. Reagan was to belatedly discover, reducing taxes is a policy goal which can be achieved, or resisted, at the stroke of the pen—but to reduce public spending requires consensus much resisted by vested interests. Democratic governments operate by consensus—not omnipotence, and Mr. Reagan was to discover he had less power than he thought he had on taking office and with defense, at an "inviolate" 6.5 percent of GNP (290 billion dollars), this did not leave much scope for cuts elsewhere. Mr. Reagan in fact, "bet the farm" on tax cuts, hoping to force Congress into budget cuts. In reality, what happened was that taxes were reduced but government spending was not. The result was that interest rates rose, pulling in foreign money to fund the budget deficit due to reduced revenue from tax cuts. This pushed up the value of the dollar, made exports more expensive, imports cheaper, resulting in a growing foreign trade deficit. The net result was that the incumbent administration added a new twist to economic policy—**deficit spending during an upturn in the economic cycle**—something more than distinctly Keynsian.

During its first term in office, the Reagan administration focused, not surprisingly, on reducing inflation as the primary if not exclusive policy goal of the system. As we already know, one such goal can be pursued in isolation, usually with a high probability of success. Indeed, under the guidance of the then Chairman of the Federal Reserve Board, Paul Volcker, appointed during the previous Carter administration, the goal of reducing inflation was fairly quickly realized by tightening credit to slow demand. Perhaps not surprisingly, unemployment and interest rates rose to 10 percent and 13 percent respectively during the same time. The classic treatment for inflation has always been, and regrettably remains, a good dose of unemployment. As a result, the economy entered the deepest recession since World War II. With the inflationary forces showing signs of being unleashed at the end of the second term of the Reagan administration, the wheel has gone full circle. What began with recession, preceded by double digit inflation, will almost certainly end with recession preceded by inflation. However, with such a large deficit going in, recalling the law of diminishing returns, more of the same won't work either to prevent the next downturn or to kick it off bottom when its gets there.

No doubt encouraged by the success in reducing inflation, despite the price paid, the administration then loaded the system with the other policy goals to which they were pledged upon taking office. To the policy goal of reducing inflation were now added: increasing GNP by restoring positive economic growth; reducing taxation; reducing government spending; reducing regulation; and restoring the United States' autonomy and prestige on the world's economic stage, all of which added up to a very commendable, but formidable task. The reader is reminded from the previous section that the more economic goals that are pursued, the greater the number, as a general rule, of policy instruments required and, due to complex interaction, the lower the probability they will be achieved in a nonmutually exclusive way. (From this we might conclude that the expectations placed on the system were totally unrealistic right from the outset.)

In October 1987, after five years of economic expansion, the economic engine, operating at a high level of utilization of real resources—the characteristics of the top of the cycle described earlier—was considered to be at its maximum potential. This, in conjunction with the falling dollar, had justifiably raised fears of rising inflation in the future. In fact, upon taking office on August 11, 1987, the new Federal Chairman, Allan Greenspan, had already initiated an anti-inflationary monetary policy. To illustrate, when Mr. Greenspan took office, the yield on 30-year Treasury bonds was 8.8 percent. On October 19th, this had risen to 10.5 percent. The federal funds rate increased from 6.5 percent to 7.6 percent, money supply growth rate declined from 9.8 percent in the preceding 12 months to an annual rate of 4.2 percent while in the same time frame, bank reserves had also fallen. On October 19th, when the stock market crashed, this tight-money, inflation-fighting policy was thrown into reverse, the flood gates of liquidity being thrown open to prevent a market crash almost certainly becoming an economic recession. By mid-December, the direction was being reversed yet again with almost all of the reserves the Fed had pumped into the system having been drained back to the pre-September levels. The federal funds rate rose from 6.1 percent in early November to 7.25 percent by December 1. Only by such violent use of the accelerator and brake could the economic engine be kept under control. With failure to agree on corrective action on the budget deficit, a standoff between an overly optimistic president, who would not raise taxes, and an obdurate Congress which would not reduce spending—a combination of loose fiscal and tight monetary policy—the prospect of Gramm-Rudman Act being invoked increased.

The Budget Deficit

Without doubt, one of the other major preconditions of our explosive mixture was, and remains, the United States' budget deficit—a situation with which the financial markets were very uncomfortable and on which they were to eventually demand corrective action. While we now understand why a budget deficit might exist, and even be acceptable, during a downturn in the business cycle to stimulate demand, how can a deficit which has grown to such troublesome proportions during the longest ever, peacetime economic expansion, possibly be defended? How can such a situation possibly develop? More, importantly, how can it be corrected—and prevented—in the future? Why does it appear to be so difficult to fix, that the U.S. government must resort to legislation in the form of the 1985 Gramm-Rudman Act, compelling it to achieve by law what it fails to achieve by consensus. The Gramm-Rudman Act initiates virtually automatic spending cuts if certain, preagreed thresholds are exceeded. With a projected deficit for 1987 of $150 billion, a probable $179 billion in 1988, $192 billion in 1989, and $100 billion in 1990 the Gramm-Rudman thresholds are $156, $156, and $100 billion, respectively.

At least part of the explanation has already been offered by Mr. Reagan's grossly overoptimistic economic goals and an unrealistic strategy—prosperity through consumption and happy talk—setting expectations of the American economic engine, loading it with goals which, for reasons we now understand, it could not possibly fulfill in a non-mutually exclusive way. But to what extent if any are the other arms of the administration culpable? Are Congress and the Federal Reserve exonerated from blame? The deficit was created by a serious mismatch between government revenue and spending. It obviously could have been prevented—and for sure can only be cured—by either an increase in revenue in the form of higher taxation (or the sale of public assets) or a reduction in public spending, or a combination of both. Why did the two sides of the equation so greatly diverge?

Much of the explanation can be found in the U.S. budget preparation machinery and processes. For good constitutional reasons, the budget process is structured in such a way that the concentration of power—and therefore the potential abuse of power—is avoided by sharing the responsibility for economic policy making between the President, Congress, the Treasury Secretary, and the Federal Reserve Board, all of which is enclosed within a system of checks and balances. Each has virtually independent, though not necessarily complementary roles. As such, what may be good politically, where concentration of power is to be avoided, is almost certainly not good in terms of macroeconomic policy making, where cohesion of policy goals and policy instruments is essential. Where there is no absolute power, neither is there absolute ownership and accountability.

The budget preparation process for the fiscal year beginning October 1, begins in the autumn and fall of the preceding year with the Office of Management and Budget (OMB). This organization prepares and coordinates the President's economic forecast and budget report, usually presented to Congress in January. This report consists of an economic forecast upon which the President's spending plans for the various government departments—and any associated deficit—are based. Obviously, the quality of the budget is a function of the quality of the economic forecast on which it is based. If the forecast is wrong, the budget will not balance, even if this is the intent. However, whatever the quality and merits of this submission, Congress has the prerogative—and frequently the penchant—to veto it.

Congress, drawing on its own economic sources and resources, by means of the Congressional Budget Office (CBO), then proceeds to produce its own budget. The House of Representatives and the Senate, both of whom have their own budget committees, coordinate the budget spending of a multitude of individual departments, each with its own vested interest to protect. These two committees must then agree upon a single budget resolution, approved by both houses, by April 15. This resolution defines outlays or spending amounts and the authority to spend specific amounts for specific purposes. This resolution disregards the income side of the equation—the sourcing of these funds—

and does not require, indeed has no provision, for presidential approval. The source of the funds to be spent is addressed in an almost entirely separate process which starts in the House of Representatives, where appropriation bills, one for each major spending category such as defense, social security, and medicare are raised. These bills are then passed to both the House of Representatives and Senate for approval, and then on to the President, who must either sign them into law or veto them in their entirety. The two sides of the equation—the budget resolution and the sum of the appropriation bills—are then subjected to an additional legislative process by Congress called reconciliation. Due to be completed by the end of June, it frequently isn't. In these circumstances Congress then passes a continuing resolution bill, granting spending authority until such time as the reconciliation process is complete. This then is how U.S. fiscal policy is forged. The other major policy instrument, that of monetary policy, is managed as follows.

While under the Constitution, Congress has formal responsibility for monetary policy, it is in reality administered by the Federal Reserve. Created by Congress in 1914, this board consists of a chairman and six other members, all appointed by the President. The Chairman of the Board is required to present the Board's policies and targets for monetary growth before Congress twice a year. This organization has a very high degree of autonomy—not because of the authority vested in it by Congress—but because Congress accepts, if not respects, the financial market's expectation that it be largely independent of the incumbent administration. The size of the money supply and its rate of growth are "controlled" using the following instruments: (1) ratio of reserves to deposits, (2) discount rate—the interest rate charged on loans by the regional Federal Reserve Banks to banks in their respective areas, and (3) open market operations—controlled not by the Board—but by a seven-member plus five-voting-member Federal Open Market Committee (FOMC). The present Chairman of the Federal Reserve Bank of New York—the Government's central bank and lender of last resort on behalf of the Fed—through which open market operations are conducted, is Mr. Gerald Corrigan.

This dispersal of economic power leaves the U.S. Treasury Secretary with little part to play in either fiscal or monetary policy and does not enable him to represent the U.S. in international negotiations from a position of great authority. In the macroeconomic context, this process in effect leaves America without a cohesive fiscal policy mechanism and as such, it must rely more heavily than might otherwise be desirable on monetary policy alone in determining its macroeconomic policy in controlling the economy. In effect, fiscal power is diffused while monetary power is concentrated.

Commenting on the recently agreed budget "compromise" in the *Wall Street Journal*, Tuesday, November 24, 1987, Republican Senator from Colorado, Bill Armstrong, called the deal a "lead ballon," describing it as "one part tax hike (mainly on corporations and investors), one part defense cut—and enough cheap cosmetics to make Mae West blush." More somberly, the article concluded, "certainly the impression that no one is in charge in Washington is one of the big reasons for market uneasiness, and even a $30 billion compromise could help if it provided evidence that Congress is ready to deal with the bankruptcy of the budget process. But the dawn of realism the budget compromise is not. It is better seen as an exercise in creative irresponsibility." The market reprimand of the 19th was not so much that there was no captain at the helm, but that there were too many. There was a domestic saving to investment or spending gap which the government could provide incentives for foreign money to fund in one of two ways: (1) raise yields, which when attempted caused Wall Street to smell recession or (2) make assets cheaper by devaluing the dollar.

Fixed, Floating, or Target Zone Management?

If floating exchange rates appear to cause governments as much grief as they do individual businesses operating in the global arena, perhaps we should not have departed from the practice of establishing a currency's value in relation to some fixed standard such as gold. Until 1971 gold was the standard for the dollar. Mr. Baker, the U.S. Treasury Secretary at the time, suggested using a list of commodities, possibly including gold as a fixed standard for the dollar. While there are indeed many advantages with such an approach in terms of avoiding the uncertainty associated with the value of the currency in the future, eliminating the volatility caused by speculative capital movements in anticipation or response to a currency's value changing, it suffers from the major perceived disadvantage of reducing an administration's autonomy in managing monetary policy. As we saw earlier, this was all that the U.S. had any real control of in managing its economic policy. Under a fixed system, the amount of money in the economy automatically adjusts in accordance with the state of the current account balance. As the current account goes into surplus, the currency which foreigners surrender in return for these purchases increases the money supply, albeit tending to reduce the value of the currency. The reverse effect occurs as the account goes into deficit. (In fact, under the gold standard, following the closing of the current account balance at the end of each fiscal month, gold as the reserve against which the amount of money in circulation was controlled was physically transferred to and from sovereign central banks.) Rightly or wrongly, governments are not comfortable with these adjustments in the international balance of trade influencing the amount of currency in free circulation and its purchasing power. Under a floating system, governments can control the size and rate of growth of their money supply independent of the current account by simply letting the exchange rate of their currency rise or fall accordingly. (Under these conditions, unlike in a fixed system, it is possible to have a strong currency and a trade deficit simultaneously, as was the case for the dollar in the early 1980s.)

Any currency's value, under fixed or floating systems, is simply its purchasing power. If for example, for whatever reason, the dollar's purchasing power falls in relation to the yen say, then obviously more dollars will be required to pay for the same amount of goods as can be purchased with the same amount of yen. The exchange rate of any two currencies is simply, therefore, the point at which their purchasing power is equal. There are many factors which determine this purchasing power, one of the main ones being the quantity of it in circulation—as per the marginal utility of money—the law of supply and demand. Central banks are aware of this too and intervene accordingly to manipulate the value as they see fit. A currency whose value increases because of central bank intervention to prop it up is like an athlete who is on steroids. His strength is not natural and disappears when the steroids cease. Governments who choose to fight the currency market in this way usually lose. Inflation too affects it, requiring economists to talk in terms of real and nominal exchange rates, according to whether they are adjusted for inflation or not.

The disadvantages of an entirely free, floating system in which currency markets determine the exchange rate between currencies, independent of governments, are many; the main one being that often the governments do not like the market's outcome. Much uncertainty is associated with the market process as currencies fluctuate and are expected to fluctuate in the future, as the market shows their relative values in relation to changing economic conditions in different countries. Perhaps the second major disadvantage is the extent to which it can help the case for protectionism, leading to a downward escalating spiral of tit for tat retaliation. Also, money is not just a commodity invented to facilitate the process of trade; it is also the unit of value by which other commodities such as goods, services, and assets are valued. As the value of the currency changes, so too does the value, in monetary terms, of these other things. In the U.S., the Fed Chairman and the Treasury Secretary are supposed to be accountable to the electorate in this respect. In reality, they are heavily influenced by currency traders, one of Washington's most powerful but least visible special interest groups.

As a compromise to these extremes, managed exchange rates is an alternative approach in which currencies are free to adjust in relation to each other in response to market forces within predefined limits. The European Economic Community (EEC) is an example, where the European Current Unit (ECU) is valued in terms of a basket of mixed currencies, with each currency allowed to fluctuate between predetermined limits: the so-called "snake." It was to seek such a compromise that the New York Plaza meeting of September 22, 1985, when the finance ministers of five major industrial economies met and agreed that the dollar was overvalued. (Mr. Reagan's view was that the other currencies were undervalued—particularly the yen and the Deutsche mark). At the Louvre Accord, February 1987, the seven largest OECD countries met yet again and agreed to drive it down by various means, including intervention on foreign exchanges to sell dollars. The dollar in fact was already falling, even prior to the New York meeting, demonstrating that the substance of these meetings, in the absence of any change to any of the participants underlying fiscal and monetary policy, dealt only with the symptoms rather than the causes of exchange rate instability.

The Double-Edged Sword

Contrary to the popular, but erroneous belief that a strong currency is always desirable and should be maintained at all times, almost at any cost, the rate of exchange of a currency can have a *double* double-edged sword effect, both when it is too strong and when it is too weak. On the one hand, a strong currency reflects a sign of confidence in the real or perceived strength of the underlying economy. There is a self-perpetuating effect associated with this in that there is no reluctance or apprehension to conduct international trade or to hold wealth in that currency, or assets valued in that currency, thereby increasing the demand and therefore the value or strength of it. On the consumer side, a strong currency renders imported goods more affordable in relation to domestic products. The downside however is that it makes the exporting of goods and services more difficult since foreigners must convert more of their domestic currency and discretionary purchasing power to meet the relatively higher dollar prices. In fact, it was the heavy burden of the combined effect of the strong dollar of the early 1980s in conjunction with weak manufacturing and marketing competence, which set corporate America off on its restructuring and takeover spree as a solution to its lack of competitiveness problem. A strong dollar also helps to make domestic markets more vulnerable to foreign competition.

A weak currency, on the other hand, also carries with it both advantages and disadvantages. On the credit side, a weak dollar does indeed lower the relative price of American products in overseas markets, enabling American industry to be more competitive, at least with that ingredient of total customer satisfaction. This is particularly effective with regard to raw materials where low price is high on the customer's hierarchy of decision criteria. It is much less effective on manufactured products where it takes much more than low price to induce Hans in Germany and Oko in Japan to buy products which the U.S. consumer is disinclined to purchase. (According to a government source estimate, as few as 250 companies account for 80 percent of U.S. exports.) On the debit side, imports become relatively more expensive—a benefit, albeit dubious, to the incumbent administration perhaps with its hopefully favorable effect on reducing the balance of trade deficit. This, however, carries the risk of fueling inflation through higher prices—a penalty to the domestic consumer, who has in effect to decide whether to pay a tariff mark-up or forego choice in favor of a domestic product. Again, like Hans and Oko, there is evidence that the U.S. consumer is equally disinclined to buy American products, preferring instead to pay the tariff penalty.

The Sword of Damocles

Despite a devaluation of the dollar, which had been falling against the yen and the Deutsch mark—without the help of the New York and Louvre Accord meetings—since June 1984, the U.S. trade balance, contrary to economic precedence, continued to deteriorate for reasons clearly not associated with the J-curve effect. The grim truth is that American industry was not and is not producing products which American consumers, far less foreigner consumers, are willing to buy, almost at any price. The J-curve effect, in attempting to describe the relationship between trade accounts and exchange rates, says that when exchange rates change, prices change first with quantities traded adjusting only after some delay, since the price change only effects future transactions, while earlier transactions at the higher price continue to be fulfilled. This is the same effect as a price reduction by an individual business where the price of orders on the existing backlog is honored as new orders are entered for shipment in the future, at a lower price. As the currency continues to fall, a series of these J-curves ripple through, delaying the reduction of the trade balance. This is reinforced by delays caused in anticipating further deterioration of the currency. Devaluing a currency is in fact the very worst way to regain competitiveness, with no guarantee that it will even work. As the following charts show, the dollar has been falling since mid-1985 while the trade deficit, in surplus from post-World War II until 1981, continues to grow. Even if devaluation does work, an inescapable effect is that the standard of living for all falls. Other less widespread effects include the rising cost of foreign travel, both for pleasure and for business. The former may simply be a disappointment, the latter competitively detrimental if it leads to businesses cutting back on visiting their foreign customers. Also, the purchasing power of salaries paid to U.S. executives overseas will diminish. American assets become less expensive to buy, for foreigners as well as local nationals. If an administration is running a budget deficit, interest rates, and stock price to earnings ratios will have to be higher to continue to draw the funds necessary to finance these shortfalls. A weak currency also stimulates foreign suppliers to compete even more intensely in order to retain hard won market share, and if necessary even at the expense of lower margins. In both extremes, either too strong or too weak, the flames of protectionist rhetoric are fanned. Perhaps the single most important consideration though, especially to foreign lenders, is that a depreciating currency, like inflation, erodes the real value of the assets they own or the debt owed to them.

Wall Street

Riding on the back of the longest ever peacetime economic expansion, albeit financed by debt funded by foreigners, the bull market had gone five years without a "correction"—whatever that means—and a downturn in both the market and the economy could, from past experience of the economic cycle, be considered long overdue. According to general classical market theory, "efficient markets" capture the collective perceptions and actions of all individuals in the aggregate, comprehending information about future prospects for the economy. Another more cynical view is that of the "popular delusion and the madness of crowds" or mob psychology theory, which considers the market to be an untamed beast. Reality, no doubt, lies somewhere in between. There are obviously people from all walks of life in the market, from the individual, private investor, to the large, professional institutions. What category their behavior fits into is probably a function of their motives in being there. There are those who participate in the original spirit of the system—a bridge between those in industry who require capital and those with funds they wish to invest. Acting often in what sometimes amounts to no more than good faith, these investors back their judgment about a company's markets, products, and management. In return for the cash made available for these productive purposes, the stock taken in exchange represents a partial claim on ownership of the company. As such, this process forms a vital link in the wealth-creating process. While liquidity of this system has been improved with the advent of innovative instruments such as "junk" bonds, stock index futures, program trading, and portfolio insurance, one wonders if this has not polluted the system by creating a secondary, more dominant use of it—that of providing traders with a means to skim margin from high volume share traffic. This concentration of power in the hands of a few may have tilted the balance more in favor of the "beast." Since the market, no matter what polite euphemisms we use to disguise the ugliness, is fueled by greed on the way up, and fear on the way down, perhaps "correction" simply means unjustifiable greed. In 1960, daily traffic in shares amounted to three million per day. By the mid-1980s, this number had risen to 600 million. Even at infinitesimally small margins, this kind of volume generates large commissions, begging the question—how much liquidity is too much? Another possibly undesirable quality of the market which seems to have developed is its attraction for many of the best business school graduates, intent on being yuppie millionaires by age 30, who might otherwise be usefully employed in productive jobs in industry. Yet another, potentially much more serious concern, is the apparent structural inability of the system to handle this new traffic.

The stock market however is not just a mechanism for allocating the flow of capital to industry—it is also the temperature gauge of the economic engine. Its behavior on Monday, October 19, was more in response to apprehension and lack of confidence than to any real crisis. Its behavior on the following day, however, does not bode well in the event that there is one.

Throwing a Party . . . on Borrowed Money

If the stock market, in addition to its function of allocating investment funds to industry, is also the barometer of the economic engine, statements like "overvalued" and "due for a correction" which appeared in the media to explain the slide, suggested that it was in some way disconnected from an underlying economy, the reality of which was much less than the rosy picture which had been painted. From a low of 774.42 in 1982, the market had risen to an all time high of 2722.42 by August 1987, including a spectacular 800 points in the ten months immediately preceding the crash. Was the American economy really so obscenely healthy—or was the temperature gauge wrong? It should now be apparent beyond all reasonable doubt, that the gauge grossly overstated the reality. But if so, why? Was the gauge itself faulty; did it correctly measure a false signal; or was the overheating boiler plain for all to see— but ignored? Why was the speculative euphoria allowed to run unchecked for so long?

Following the double digit inflation of the late 1970s, and then the deepest postwar recession of 1981/1982, one might reasonably surmise that the beleaguered U.S. electorate were of the opinion that they had already stoically endured more than enough economic adversity and that a party was long overdue. By great good fortune, Sir Ronald, ably assisted by squire Volcker, had just grievously wounded, some believed fatally, the evil, inflation breathing dragon, and was there to oblige. On looking around the magic kingdom, it was not difficult to find signs justifying the release of the pent-up party spirit. Unemployment, interest rates, in addition to inflation, were falling. It would have been equally easy to find at least as many signs advocating continued restraint, but no one wanted to be a kill-joy. A party was called for and a party there would be. But to party, one needs money—or credit.

Like old Mrs. Hubbard, Sir Ronald looked in the U.S. domestic savings pantry and to his dismay, found that the cupboard was bare. Compared to the Japanese and German consumer who saves 16 percent and 12 percent of after-tax income respectively, the U.S. figure is in the order of 3 percent. No matter, thought Sir Ronald, our expansive economic policy—prosperity through consumption—will pay for it out of future revenue. In the meantime, we can print more of the stuff—and borrow the difference. Squire Volcker will oblige on the former and the economically cautious Japanese and Germans have lots of it sloshing around looking for hiding places to keep it out of their inflation-shy economies. Besides, corporate America lost sufficient market share, both at home and in the world's markets, to finally realize its lack of industrial competitiveness, and has already begun to fix this by restructuring and corporate takeovers, both friendly and otherwise. Corporate earnings were improving, so this must be the correct treatment.

Sir Ronald settled himself in the driver's seat of the "American Dream" machine, pushed the accelerator to the floor, gunned the economic engine—and began his reckless dash to immortality in the history books—taking Congress and the rest of the country, party poopers or no, along with him on the party circuit. The Federal Reserve supported both of these grand strategies, those of industrial renewal through restructuring and takeovers and prosperity through consumption, by printing money at a fast clip: the money supply growing by 12 percent in 1985 and then further by 15 percent in 1986. With the money supply spigot open, and with inflation low, the stock market had little competition from more tangible wealth investments such as real estate or recapitalizing factories for these funds.

Fueled by recently introduced valuation concepts, tailor-made for the new takeover industry, such as break-up value and private market value, plentifulness of money, easy debt, low margin requirements—5 percent down and 50 percent margin—and increasing equity value, stocks continued to rise well beyond traditional valuation criteria, fostering the belief that the bull market would go on forever. The increasing equity "wealth effect" of rising share values, had also helped to fuel consumption and encouraged both individual and business borrowing to rise to record levels. So strong was this belief that contrary to economic precedent, when interest rates rose in April 1987 and then again in August and September, the market faltered briefly, chose to disregard these signals, then resumed rising again. Normally, when interest rates rise, the combination of relatively high rate of return with the low risk associated with government bonds makes them a relatively more attractive investment in relation to stocks, diverting the flow of funds from stocks to bonds. Even as stocks were seen to become less attractive by these criteria—the Standard and Poors stock index was trading at 23 times earnings; price to earnings ratios of 14.5 times earnings; annual dividends of 2.2 percent—half the postwar average; stocks trading at three times book value; Japanese stocks trading at 60 times earnings—and still rising—stocks continued to be much sought after. There were also many instances of spectacular, speculative successes which further fueled the euphoria. The government, contrary to what might have been expected, did nothing to regulate this euphoria by raising margin requirements, as it had been inclined to do in the past, preferring instead that the market itself accept this regulatory responsibility—which it did not. Besides, it was not in the administration's best interest to contradict the market's proclamation that everything was hunky dory.

It is one thing however for foreigners to stand idly by seeing their hard earned money being spent on the wealth-creating process. It is quite another to see it being spent on partying. With the continuously deteriorating trade deficit the message to them was clear—America was consuming more than it was producing. This kind of situation can only be corrected by consuming less or producing more. With the economy at an estimated 85 percent utilization, a level which to all intents and purposes, is flat out, the former was the only option. Failure to agree on reducing the budget deficit only served to confirm the emphatic refusal of the U.S. economy to stop living beyond its means. Becoming concerned about the depreciation of the assets in which they had already invested, the availability of these lender's funds started to dry up—leaving the U.S. with a dilemma—raise interest rates to continue to attract the foreign funds necessary to finance the deficit, not an action, in a pre-election year, likely to escape the attention of the market or the electorate—or bomb the dollar, a course more likely to go unnoticed until too late. Either way, the party was well and truly over. Mr. Greenspan, who had very prudently initiated a secret study weeks before the crash on how the Federal Reserve should respond to various potential crises should they arise, including a stock market crash, had already tried raising interest rates. The market smelled recession and sounded the alarm bell. Mr. Greenspan briefly capitulated, flooded the market with money to belay the panic, then quietly drained it back out again—and the international market then applied the only remaining option—bomb the dollar. After every party comes the hangover—and the bill. Where stock collateral was used to finance debt, those who thought they had died and were well on their way to heaven may discover they have to stop over in purgatory for a spell.

Other Contributory Factors

One of these many other factors was Volcker's departure from the Federal Reserve, being perceived as a desire on the part of the incumbent administration, for easier money and a lower dollar, making the holders of large quantities of dollars and dollar assets, extremely nervous. There had been a distinct lack of progress on international cooperation—particularly on major currency exchange rates. Then there was all the protectionist sabre rattling on Capitol Hill in the form of Dan Rostenkowski's Ways and Means Committee Bill, disallowing, among other things, interest payment deductions on takeover borrowing. The U.S. had by then virtually closed its capital account, cutting back on aid to less developed countries (LDCs). Treasury Secretary Baker, in public dialogue with the West Germans that weekend, criticizing their intransigence in taking a more expansionary stance on their fiscal policy, was reported to have threatened to let the dollar fall, making foreign investors even more nervous. An indiscreet comment was made by SEC Chairman, David Ruder, to the effect that he was prepared to intervene to halt trading under certain conditions. Corporate third-quarter actual earnings much less than their rosy forecast had just been declared. Last, but by no means least, in the face of all of this uncertainty and volatility, there was perceived to be a leadership vacuum, the president's stature and respect having been seriously eroded by the Iran affair and the Bork fiasco.

These then were the conditions of "dynamic equilibrium" immediately prior to the market issuing its warning of the 19th. Many of these parameters were not in themselves healthy, neither did they in aggregate reflect a strong underlying economy. They had not however been overnight in the making and as such, could be ruled out in terms of explaining the market's perception of the underlying instability becoming critical, and other circumstantial events, in tipping the balance, have to be identified in causing the market to issue its dire warning that all was not well. These events, the trigger for the explosion, finally brought the situation to a point where the market saw Capitol Hill rapidly running out of options—became unwilling to wait any longer for the government to take action—and intervened. What were these events? What was the straw which finally broke the camel's back?

The Trigger (Spark)

There are people on Wall Street who know little, and care even less, about economics and industrial competitiveness than they do about rates of return on capital—preferring to play on the government bonds/corporate stocks rate of return see-saw than follow the fortunes of companies in which they have invested. Like greedy pigs at the trough, people who have never been near a factory floor to see for themselves how apallingly archaic and inefficient the real American wealth-creating process is, were to receive their come-uppance. When the market crashed, there was no "invisible guiding hand" governing their behavior, only a lot of greedy little fists which, like the monkey trying to grab the nuts in the bottle, could not release their grasps to free themselves from the self-imposed trap. Two events, one having a direct effect on greed, the other on fear, almost certainly provided the spark.

On Wednesday, October 14, the Democrats on the House Ways and Means Committee agreed to tax changes that would make corporate takeovers much less attractive. Also, when the trade deficit numbers came in, they were much worse than expected. The Dow Jones fell a record 95 points that day. Interest rates went up; the rate on 30-year Treasury Bills rose to 10.4 percent—when stocks were yielding on average less than 3 percent—institutional money started to flow out of stocks and into bonds and foreign currency. In a system unintentionally programmed to avalanche under certain conditions, these very conditions were encountered. On Friday, October 16, the market fell another 108 points. The bubble of speculative euphoria was burst and the chain reaction had begun.

Amplifier (Highly Combustible Fuel for the Fire)

By Monday greed, confidence, and trust fled the field—only to be replaced by fear and panic. As stock values continued their rapid fall, a rush of sellers converged on the market, eager to dispose of their hot potatoes—only to find an almost total absence of buyers. Chartered to deal with this type of situation, but almost certainly not in this magnitude, the NYSE specialists stepped in to buy the stocks no one else wanted. Already holding large amounts in anticipation of future corporate takeovers, their inventories swelled to unprecedented levels, rapidly depleting their capital and purchasing power in the process. In need of extended credit, many were shocked to find on appealing to their credit sources, the big New York banks, that they refused to oblige. Fearful of loan defaults where stock equity had been used as collateral, these institutions were already making margin calls to lenders. As in 1929, the banks again played a key role in the disintegration.

Yet another major factor which added to the chaos was that of program trading and portfolio insurance—the simultaneous trading of stocks and stock index futures by means of computer, a practice which the Big Board Chairman, John Phelan, had felt cause to publicly express concern about as early as mid-summer 1986, fearing that the volatility which these techniques would bring to the market could lead to a "financial meltdown." At an estimated 30 percent of transaction activity, as investors tried to buy high priced options almost at any cost as a hedge against the collapsing stock prices, the Big Board unilaterally restricted the use of electronic order routing systems, designed to give the small investor access to the system but commandeered by the arbitrageurs, which were overwhelming the system with traffic it was not originally designed to carry. The increasing complexity due to the introduction of new derivative instruments such as stock-index options and futures increased the range of the product portfolio to the point that volume and mix management became a problem for a system not originally designed to handle it. Many of these new techniques were afterthought add-ons bringing volatility to the system. The machine became the master.

Forecasting—The Stock Market as Leading Indicator

While forecasting is indeed an "inexact science," share prices as reflected in the monthly average of the Standard and Poors Index of 500 common stocks has been shown to be an extremely reliable leading indicator of what lies ahead for the economy and business. A study by the National Bureau of Economic Research has ranked the market at the top of several widely followed barometers of the probable future economic scenario. Of eight recessions since the Second World War, each has been preceded by sustained declines in the stock market by lead times averaging about eight months. So too has the Commerce Department Index—consisting of 11 components, one of which is the stock market values. Also included in this particular index are jobless insurance claims and a gauge of business activity based on delays in deliveries. History shows that while there is no cause for concern over a dip of one or two months, those of three or four months are a different matter.

There are basically two schools of thought as to whether the 1987 crash would lead to a recession in 1988. The main argument of those against being that it would set a precedent by being the first postwar recession in a presidential election year. Despite some very elegant econometric forecasting models, most forecasts usually boil down to such rule-of-thumb bases. Most economists would probably agree however that the real issue is not whether but when, and if not in 1988, this can only be at the cost of rising inflation. The market may not be that patient. The case for sooner rather than later also has some significant precedents in its favor. This economic expansion has already lasted two years longer than the average, not just since the war, but for this century. In this time frame, there have been eight declines in the Dow Jones of equal or greater severity as the October 1987 slide. In seven of these, the economy slumped within one year of the downturn in the market, the exception being the one during World War II when, despite the economy running full bore on a war-time footing, the market slumped 40 percent. Also, with approximately 25 percent of the American electorate participating in the market in some form, the effect of a drop of such severity on consumer confidence cannot be lightly discarded. What has proved to be a timely and reliable indicator, the money supply, went down prior to each slump. High plant and equipment investment, and low unemployment, also tend to immediately precede the downturn reflecting, as we saw from our business cycle analysis, a high level of utilization of economic resources. Also, since debt has risen from 1.4 GNP to 1.7 of GNP during the Reagan administration—the highest level since the Great Depression—this can no longer be relied upon to sustain demand indefinitely.

No doubt confused by all of the conflicting expert opinions, businessmen will do what they have always done—simply disregard what all of the experts say and scrutinize their own favorite barometers instead. Some of these barometers, such as crawl charts, bookings forecast, changes in size, shape, quality of backlog, price erosion—volume affected to lesser extent are discussed in later chapters.

GUIDELINES FOR THE MANAGEMENT PRACTITIONER

Productivity—Not Profligacy

Our purpose in this analysis has been to develop an understanding of the major factors which shape both the domestic and world macroeconomic environment in order to comprehend, proactively where possible, reactively where not, the effects of formulating appropriate policies and strategies internal to the business. With our observations so far we might include the following. That national economies are cyclical and that economists and politicians do not know how to make them behave otherwise. Further that the next downturn is coming the only uncertainty is when. The stock market does not always faithfully reflect the underlying economic reality. The world economy is becoming progressively more complex and interdependent. Everyone loses in trade bashing. The probable outcome of an administration's economic policy and goals can be anticipated within reasonably well-defined limits. The economic pendulum has now swung from one extreme to the other—from an untrammeled, free running business cycle and economy of the 1930s to a fully "managed" one. Because of the latter a company can anticipate to some degree the probable outcome of an administration's economic policy and should attempt to posture itself accordingly. Those who do not will almost certainly be punished. Corporations for example which chased cheap foreign labor offshore now get to pay import tariffs with a devalued dollar.

In circumstances of such volatility and uncertainty, how does a firm posture itself appropriately to ride the boom and slump roller coaster? The first step in the process must be in guarding against future complacency and being lulled into a false sense of security during both the upturn and the plateau at the top of the cycle. This is so often the time and circumstances under which bad practices are allowed to develop: when profligacy reigns supreme; when inventory is allowed to accumulate; when growth gets fueled by capital spending funded by borrowing rather than by productivity improvements and reduced inventory carrying costs; when organizations overstaff and accumulate deadwood. Then when the downturn arrives, companies find that their break-even cost is too high, and their response time, due to long manufacturing cycle-times, is too slow—when its already too late to do anything about it. Almost invariably, by the time these cost-cutting actions have run their course, the next upside arrives, resulting in such companies losing out twice—once on the way in, once again on the way out—when demand is again rising but the capacity to support it does not exist.

The second step is to resist the temptation to blame extraneous events, which while possibly true, cannot be changed and are the same for everyone. The process of successive elimination associated with hiding behind excuses usually identifies the real cause of poor performance last. It is the management competence specific to each company which distinguish those who weather the storm from those who flounder—not the state of the playing field, or the competition or the rules of the game.

The third, perhaps most important step, in these uncertain conditions, is to realize that manufacturing excellence will fix problems which fiscal (or monetary) policy fiddling won't. A company can take steps to reduce its vulnerability and reduce the width of the window of uncertainty, by using manufacturing as a strategic weapon rather than as a tactically employed, necessary evil. The absolute minimum duration that a company is exposed to the uncertainty of external factors is the sum of the new product introduction cycle-time plus the manufacturing cycle-time. To reduce these cycle-times is not just to reduce the carrying cost of inventory. It is also to reduce vulnerability to exchange rate fluctuations for companies doing business internationally and those who incur their major costs in dollars, but whose income is in a basket of mixed foreign currencies. It is to protect against the erosion of income, due to inflation, in time between the booking of an order and the invoicing of it. To reduce vulnerability to surprise moves by the competition. In the war of the Titans, it is better to be agile than big—ask the dinosaurs. We like quick, easy, spectacular fixes. That is why corporate restructuring and takeovers were so appealing. We treat and manage each discipline and function separately—that is why our response time to changing conditions is too long. Japan manages its economy, as it does their businesses, as a total and flexible system.

Recession need not inhibit individual company growth and profitability. A downturn will affect price more than unit demand. It will affect older more mature products than new. The cost-effective producer can take much more price attrition punishment and still retain, even expand, market share. The successful innovator of new products using design for manufacturability, statistical process control, and just-in-time materials management can maximize margin, taking market share in the downturn when the competition is preoccupied with simply surviving. This is exactly what the Japanese do!

Intrinsic demand in this world is, to all intents and purposes, infinite. Every human being on the planet has unsatisfied needs in some form. Demand is not what needs to be managed but satisfied. Only the value-adding manufacturing process can satisfy these needs. As such, it warrants much more attention than it gets. Restoring this competence, the renewal of the industrial base, is what the rest of this text is about. All of the fiscal fiddling while Rome burns is symptomatic of the U.S. having lost sight of the basics, just as Britain did in using the revenue from North Sea oil to fund unemployment. Those who lose focus are usually in for a rude awakening. The U.S. does not have a balance of trade deficit just because the dollar was too strong but because American industry is not providing what the consumer demands. There is too much reliance on demand side monetarism and not enough on supply side competence. The principle of comparative advantage is as true now as it was in Smith's day. It differs only in that it is no longer a function of naturally endowed resources, which the U.S. has in abundance, but of value-adding competence, which it does not. It is the progressive atrophying of this value-adding competence in the industrial base which is the root cause of the U.S. economic distress—the net result of complacency, arrogance, and preoccupation on the part of corporate America with the fight for a bigger share of the existing wealth rather than with continuing to refine the process of creating it. The party is over, America. Now it's time to get back to work—on the factory floor. For the readers still with us who are so inclined, you are invited to join us on our tour.

Stock Index Futures

As in any other futures contract, a stock index future contract is a contractual commitment to make or take delivery of an underlying commodity by some predetermined time in the future, at a predetermined price—the points value of that future price being quoted daily, just as is the current index price, on the Index and Markets Division of the Chicago Mercantile Exchange. Believing in safety in numbers and the law of compensating errors, index portfolios were already popular with the risk-adverse professional money managers. Such contracts can be traded or settled any time prior to the expiration of the delivery date but, unlike stocks, do not necessarily require the change of ownership of the commodity or stocks upon which it is based, but can be settled in cash.

These futures differ from conventional stocks in other ways which make their use attractive to traders and investors. In fact, in only a few short years, because of their convenience and low cost, the volume of transactions in these has grown to approximately equal that of stocks. Unlike stocks, which pay dividends, futures do not. On the other hand, trading in futures contracts does not require ownership of the underlying commodity. The cost of the transaction to the buyer is only a small proportion of the total contract value when the opening of the contract is established and incremental costs are normally low. They differ from stocks in another important respect in that they can be sold "short" in a fallng market. (Selling "short" is the practice of "selling" a stock one does not own when prices are falling with the intention of buying the stock back again at a lower price. SEC regulations were changed to prohibit this practice with respect to stocks after the 1929 crash.)

A stock index futures contract is defined and valued as: $500 times the value of the index in question, most typically the Standard and Poors for example, on the day the bargain is struck. This $500 dollar constant is called the "contract multiplier." Each contract then, can be considered to represent 500 "shares" of the index. For example, if the S&P stands at 240.00 points, the "underlying value" of a contract struck on that day would be: $240.00 \times \$500 = \$120{,}000$. The "contract value" would be the same equation, with the futures price substituted for the stock price. Let's say the futures price was $242.00. In that case, the contract value would be: $242 \times \$500 = \$121{,}000$. To establish a contract, both buyer and seller simply post a small proportion of the contract value—called the "initial margin"—with the exchange's clearinghouse. This is not a down payment, but rather a performance bond to establish the credit worthiness of the participants. Each day then that the contract remains outstanding, the buyer and seller's respective initial margins are adjusted in accordance with fluctuations in the stock market to future market index price. This adjustment is called "variation margin," with the loser on the day depositing additional cash with the clearinghouse commensurate with each day's unrealized losses; the winning party being free to draw unrealized gains. Since the clearinghouse is an intermediate buyer and/or seller between the two parties, each is free to liquidate his or her position at any time by making an offsetting closing transaction. The day the contract expires, final profits and losses between buyer and seller are settled in cash based on the closing price of the S&P Index. At this point, the futures price used in the contract value equation is the stock index price of that day—since the contract now has no unelapsed future time—so the contract value then equals the underlying value.

Apart from the low cost and the convenience, what's in it for seller and buyer which makes index futures trading such an attractive and widespread practice? If the seller owns the underlying stock and is nervous of a fall in its value in the future, this can be partially offset with the margin received from the buyer of a futures contract in the event that this does indeed happen. The seller in this case, owning the stock, is called a hedger. The buyer on the other hand is in effect buying the opportunity to gain from a rise in the underlying stock price—without incurring the full cost associated with owning the stocks. For example, before the crash, the Chicago clearinghouses required an initial margin of $5,000 per contract from traders as the market crashed. The gamble involved is simply that the seller bets that stock index price will fall and the buyer bets that it will rise. The low cost and convenience of index futures, however, attracted a second class of trader, the pure speculator. The speculator was more numerous by far than the cautious, institutional hedger, they neither owned the underlying stock nor cared about the well-being of the companies it represented and, free from the burden of ownership, were only interested in the prospect of potentially large gains at low cost. Willing to take high risks, they bet on a rise or fall of the futures, and added to the market euphoria. In a relatively stable market, potential gains/losses are normally modest. A crashing market, however, spelled disaster for the buyer—being called upon to put up an additional variation margin of $500 per point drop, and contrary to the initial intent—also for the seller. At the market's peak in August 1987, an S&P futures contract was worth $171,000. Factoring in the 120-point fall which occurred during October, that same contract's value had fallen to $120,500 at a variable margin cost to the buyer of $60,000. On the 19th alone, the market was flooded by a wave of selling of these futures to the tune of four billion dollars against two billion in stocks. As this wave of selling pushed futures prices below stocks, many insurers simply stopped trading.

The margin put up by the seller (hedger) could be regarded as the premium on an insurance policy, the theory being that as stocks fall, the holder of the stocks loss is offset by additional variation margin from the buyer. The reality, because index futures, unlike stocks, can be sold short in a falling market, was somewhat contrary to this expectation. As stock prices fell on the New York exchange, and kept on falling, margin calls were made on investors whose portfolios were funded with debt. Owners in this position tried to sell stocks to cover the margin calls with equity. As the market continued to fall, the speculators, placed in similar circumstances, tried to do likewise with their futures contracts on the Chicago Mercantile. With a flood of sellers—and no buyers however, these actions only served to reinforce each other, pulling prices of stock indices and stock index futures downwards in an escalating spiral. Occurring in two separate markets, the panic was exacerbated by communication difficulties as the rumors about an impending closure of the Big Board spread.

Stock Index Options

A more complicated variation of stock index futures are stock options, available in two forms: "calls" and "puts." A call gives the buyer the right, but not the obligation, to exercise, thereby receiving in cash the amount by which the underlying index is above the call's strike price. A "put" gives the buyer the right, but not the obligation, to receive any amount by which the underlying index is below the "put's" strike price. There are two generic forms of these: the American, where the buyer can exercise at any time during the life of the option and the European, which can only be exercised at the date of expiration. Options differ from futures in that the contractual obligations are not equivalent for sellers and buyers. For the buyer, to exercise is a right—but not an obligation. Sellers, however, are under an unconditional obligation to respond whenever the buyer chooses to exercise. The potential cash value to an option buyer when he exercises is called the exercise or intrinsic value. Where this value is positive, the buyer is said to be in-the-money, negative—out-of-the-money and even-on-the-money.

"Junk" Bonds

Two major rating services, Moody's and Standard and Poors, rate bonds—a loan made by an investor to a company which requires funds—into two categories: investment and noninvestment. This classification considers many factors including the size of the issue, the company's credit history, and capital structure. A high yield or "junk" bond is thus by definition one that is either unrated or fails to meet the investment grade criteria.

Portfolio Insurance and Program Trading

Where the more cautious institutional investors sold futures, involving some 60 billion dollars, mainly in pension funds, it was called portfolio insurance. Where SIFs were used as a surrogate for stocks, buying future contracts when the cost relative to the underlying stock index was low and selling when relatively more expensive, taking into account the cost associated with the foregone profit in the least risk alternative investment—T-bills, under computer control, this practice was called program trading. These computers determined when the time was right for the switch. When the S&P futures market closed on Tuesday, October 20, hit by a flood of sellers and no buyers, no prices could be established on many leading stocks and as a result, future index prices could not be calculated. The insurance policies proved to be worthless.

In the futures pits, professional traders called "locals," who normally accept the portfolio insurance obligation, compete with each other to service orders flowing onto the exchange but are under no obligation to do so—that is, to keep transacting. With trading on 91 stocks halted, and rumors that closure of the Big Board was imminent, stock-index markets, fluctuating wildly became the only price indication mechanism of U.S. stocks and the premium or price of these stock options rose, as everyone grabbed for the lifeboats. Many of theses traders were overwhelmed and simply stopped trading.

The NYSE specialists, the weak link in the financial chain, are granted a virtual monopoly on specific stocks in return for which they are obliged to maintain a "fair and orderly" market by regulating supply and demand—buying stock in a down market when many or even all customers want to sell into a market where there are few or even no buyers and selling in an up market when customers want to buy but there are few or even no sellers. In a volatile market, the Big Board has the prerogative to halt trading if buying or selling waves threaten to overwhelm these specialists.

The Reagan Era Will End With Many Economic Gains ...

Inflation Cooled Off

Year-to-year change in CPI, in percent

14%
12%
10%
8%
6%
4%
2%
0
(Reagan)
'75 '77 '79 '81 '83 '85 '87

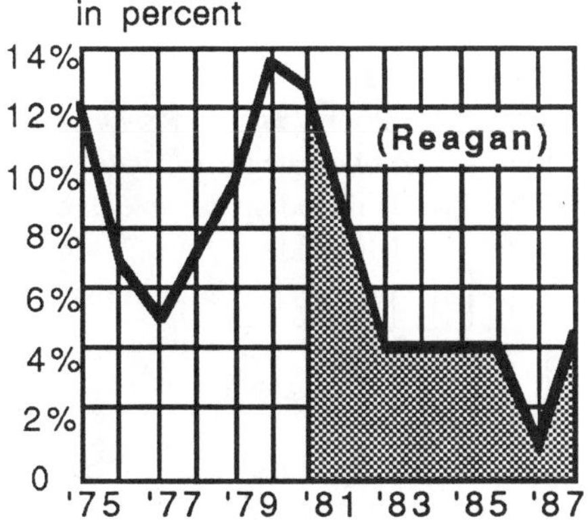

Expansion Continued

Annual change in real GNP, in percent

8%
6%
4%
2%
0
-2%
-4%
(Reagan)
'75 '77 '79 '81 '83 '85 '87

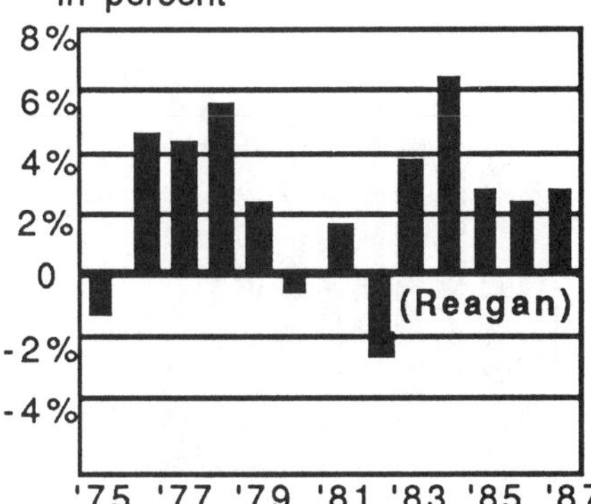

Joblessness Fell

Average annual unemployment rate in percent

10%
9%
8%
7%
6%
5%
'75 '77 '79 '81 '83 '85 '87

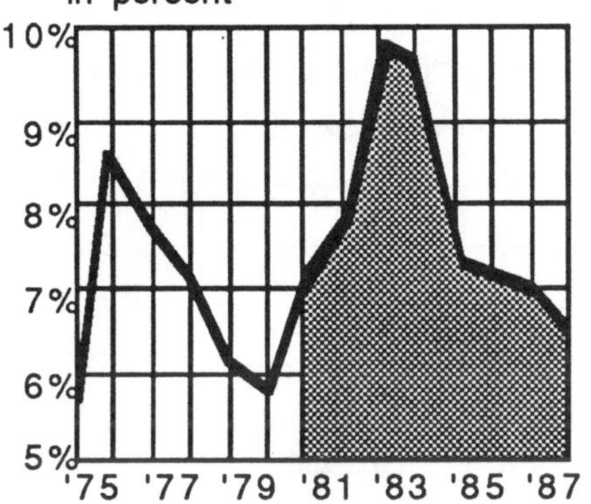

Interest Rates Declined

Annual average yield on 30-year Treasury bonds, in percent

14%
12%
10%
8%
6%
4%
'75 '77 '79 '81 '83 '85 '87

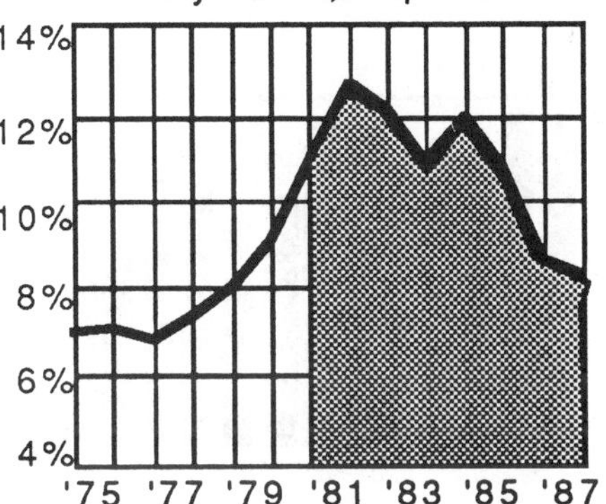

Many Had More to Spend

Real per capita disposable personal income, in thousands of dollars

$2800
2,400
2,000
1,600
1,200
800
400
0
'75 '77 '79 '81 '83 '85 '87

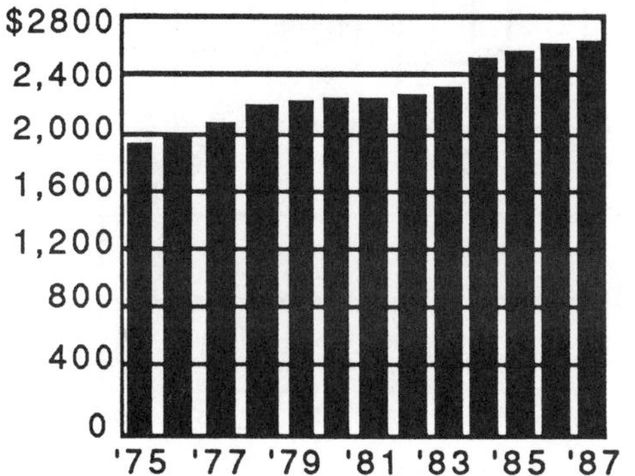

Stocks Up, Despite Crash

Wilshire 5000 equity index at year end

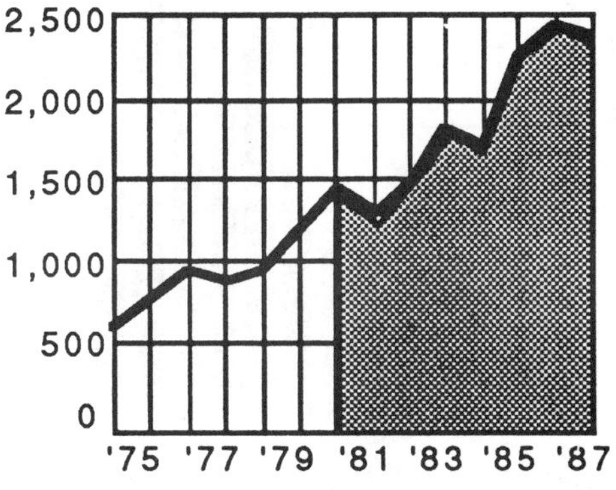

2,500
2,000
1,500
1,000
500
0
'75 '77 '79 '81 '83 '85 '87

... But in Some Key Areas the President's Policies Failed

More Family Poverty

Percentage of all families living below the poverty level

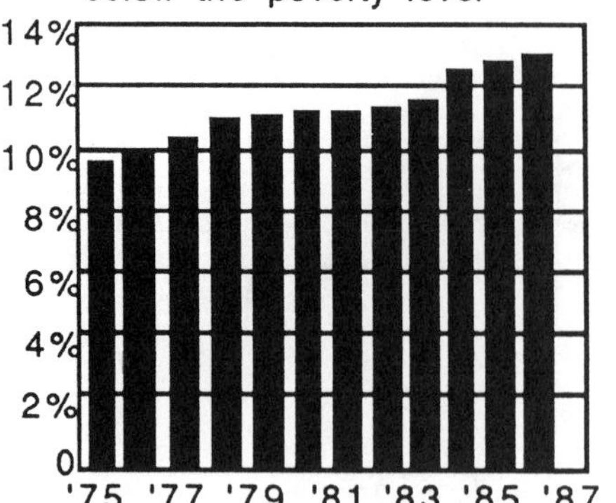

No Shift to Investment

Business investment vs. federal government as percentage of GNP

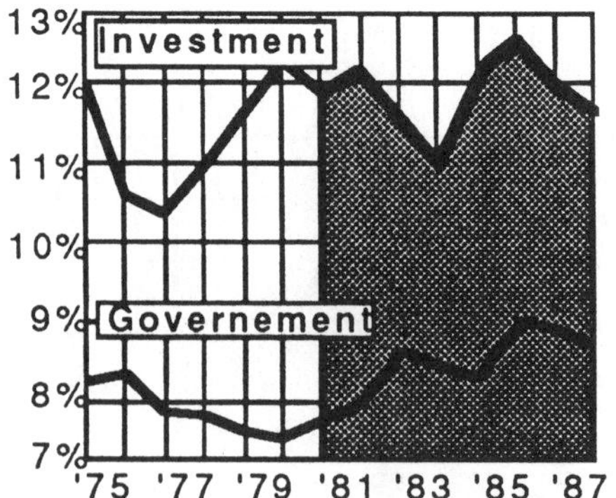

Savings Fell Sharply

Personal savings as percentage of disposable income

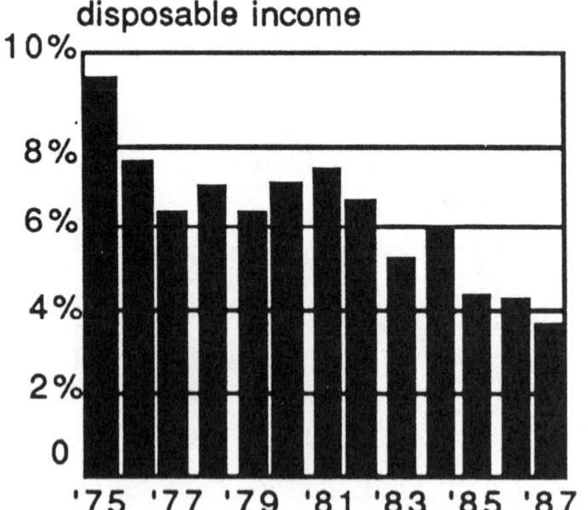

Trade Deteriorated

Merchandise trade balance, in billions of dollars

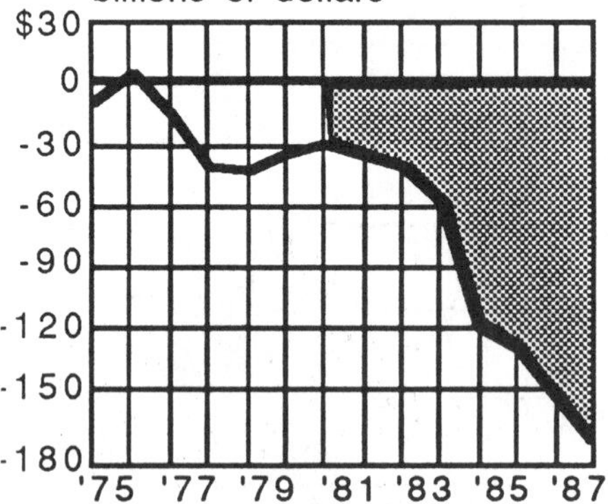

Budget Gap Ballooned

Fiscal year federal government deficit, in billions of dollars

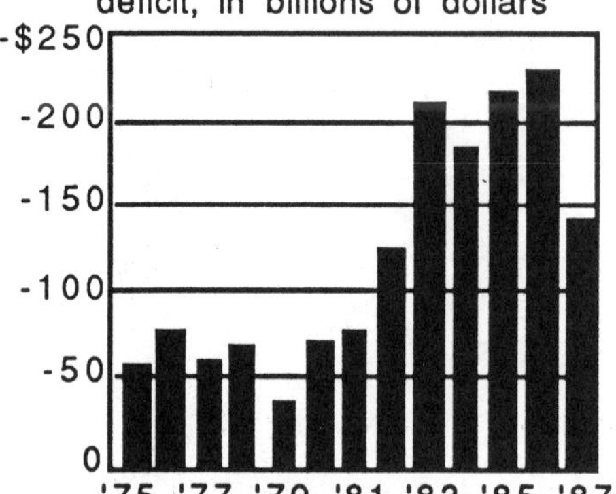

Plunge Into Debt

Net international investment position of the U.S., in billions of dollars

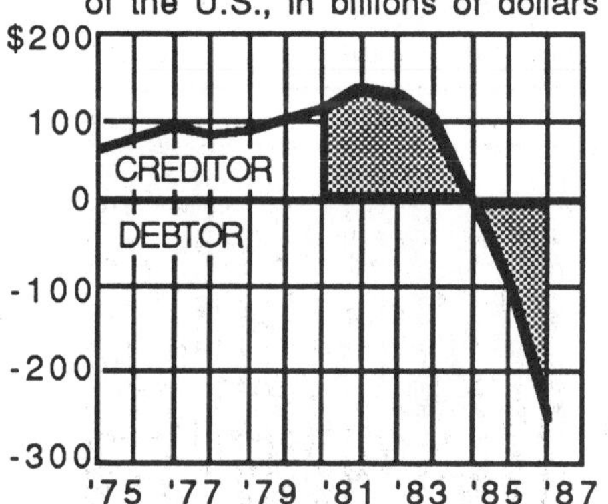

Source: Wall Street Journal - Tuesday, 17 November, 1987

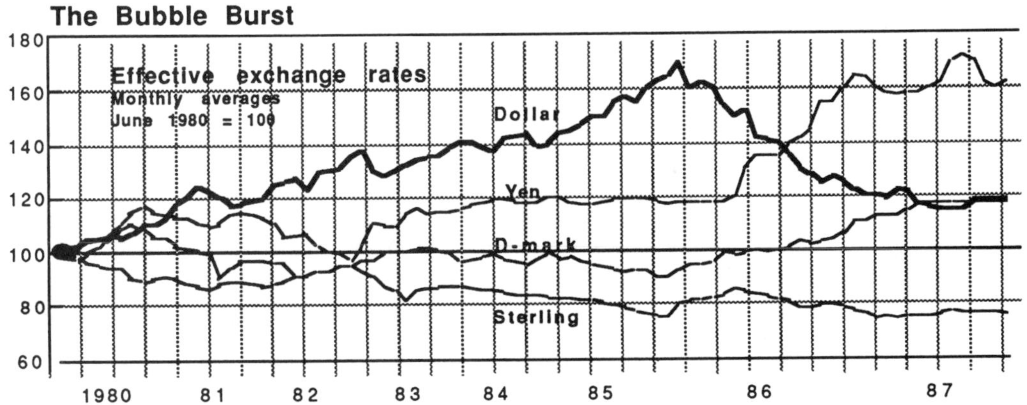
The Bubble Burst
Effective exchange rates
Monthly averages
June 1980 = 100
Dollar
Yen
D-mark
Sterling
180
160
140
120
100
80
60
1980
81
82
83
84
85
86
87

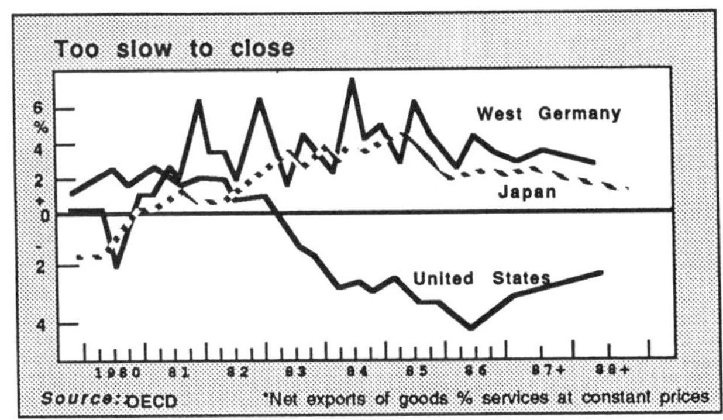
Too slow to close
West Germany
Japan
United States
6
%
4
2
+
0
-
2
4
1980
81
82
83
84
85
86
87+
88+
Source: OECD
*Net exports of goods % services at constant prices

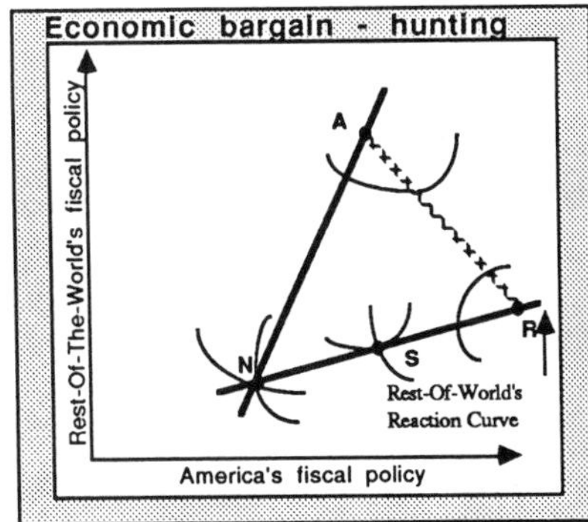
Economic bargain - hunting
Rest-Of-The-World's fiscal policy
A
N
S
R
Rest-Of-World's Reaction Curve
America's fiscal policy

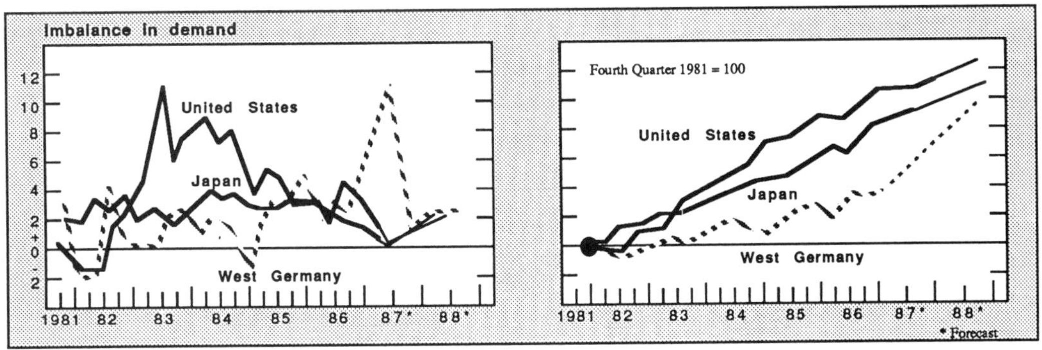
Imbalance in demand
United States
Japan
West Germany
12
10
8
6
4
2
+
0
-
2
1981
82
83
84
85
86
87*
88*
Fourth Quarter 1981 = 100
United States
Japan
West Germany
* Forecast

SOURCE: THE ECONOMIST - SEPTEMBER 26, 1987

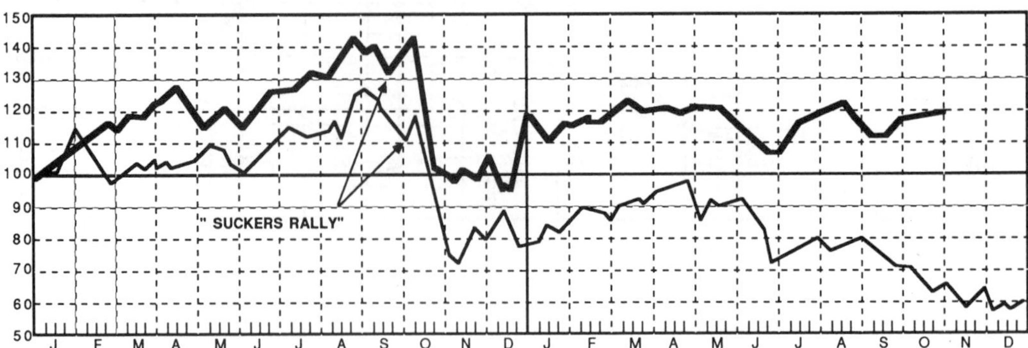

SOURCE: WALL STREET JOURNAL - OCTOBER 1987

The Crash:
How Close an Economic Parallel ?

1980-87 —— 1922-36

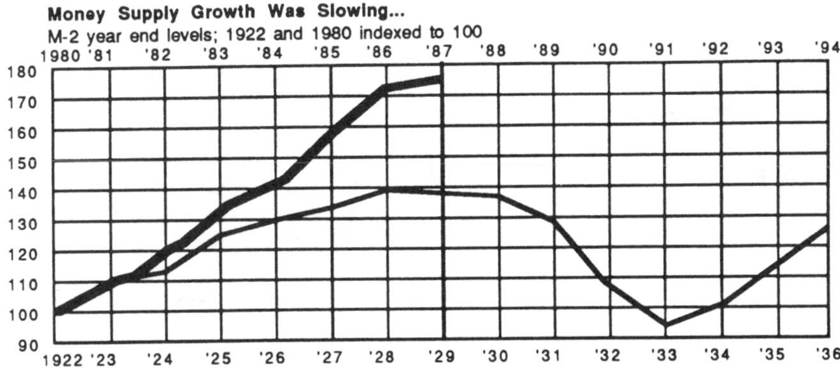

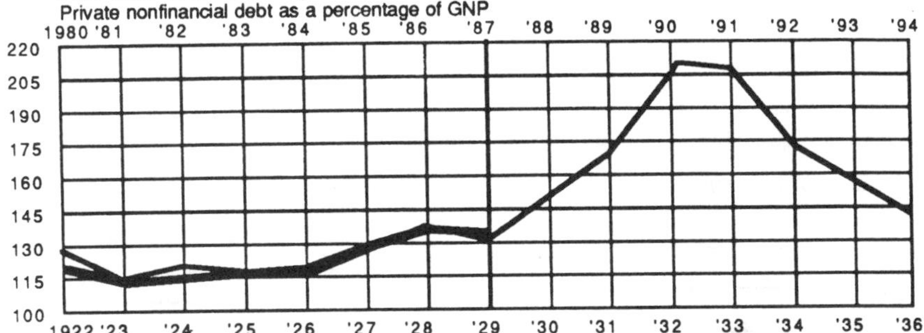

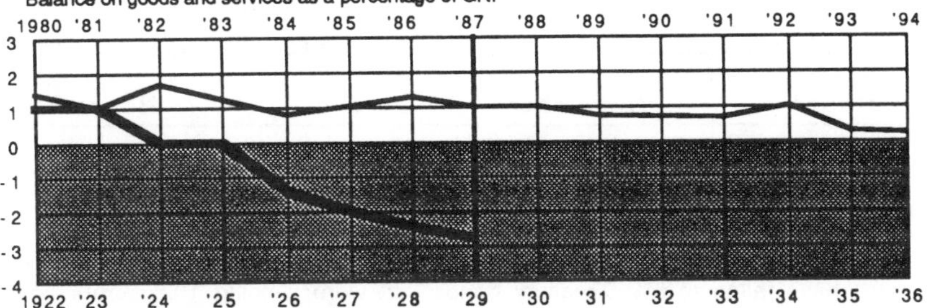

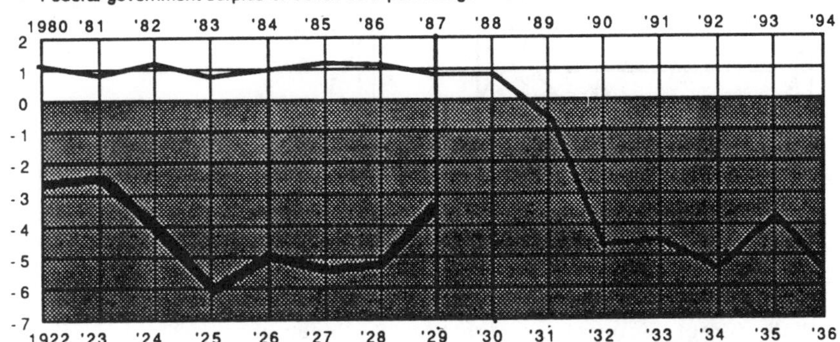

Major Market Index Cash-to-Futures Spread

In points, at 15 minute intervals

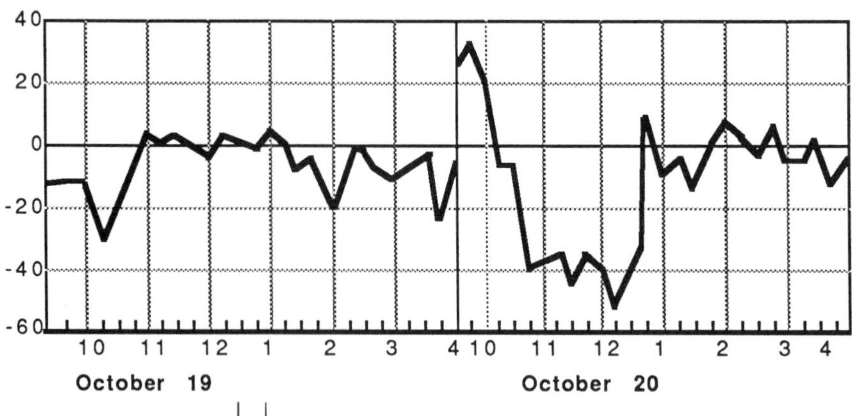

The Difference One Month Makes

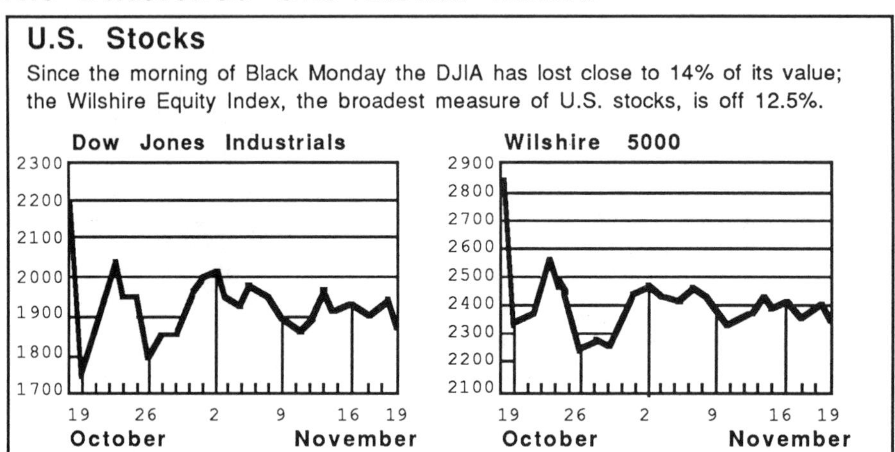

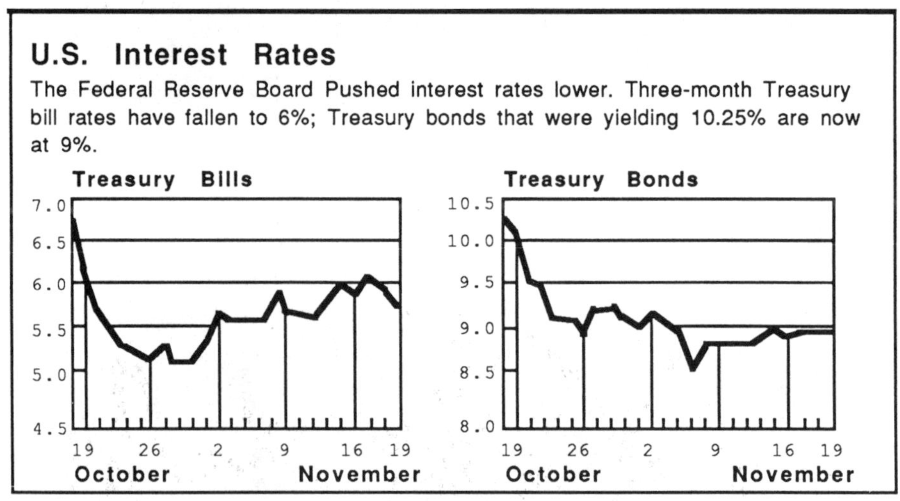

Source: Wall Street Journal - Friday, 20 November, 1987

TERRIBLE TUESDAY
HOW THE STOCK MARKET ALMOST DISINTEGRATED A DAY AFTER THE CRASH
CREDIT DRIED UP FOR BROKERS AND ESPECIALLY SPECIALISTS UNTIL FED CAME TO RESCUE
MOST PERILOUS DAY IN 50 YEARS

BY JAMES B. STEWARD AND DANIEL HERTZBERG
WALL STREET JOURNAL

NEW YORK—A month ago today, the New York Stock Exchange died. But within an hour or two, it was raised from the dead.

The previous day, Oct. 19, when the Dow Jones Industrial Average plunged 508 points in history's largest one-day loss, has been dubbed Black Monday. But it was on Tuesday, Oct. 20, that the stock market—and by extension all the world's financial markets—faced one of their gravest crises.

Full details of what happened that fateful week are only now emerging and are the subject of major inquires by a presidential commission, congressional committees and others. But minute-by-minute scrutiny of the events of that Tuesday, plus scores of interviews with key stock, commodities and futures market participants, the Federal Reserve, and investment and commercial bankers, reveals that:

- Stock, options and futures trading all but stopped during a crucial interval on Tuesday. Many major stocks, such as Internatinal Business Machines Corp. and Merck & Co., couldn't be traded. Investors large and small couldn't sell their stock; there were no buyers. The industrial average was meaningless because many of its component stocks weren't trading. The Big Board's market makers, or specialists, were overwhelmed by unfilled sell orders, and their capital was devastated.
- Many banks, frightened by the collapse in prices of stocks that were collateral for loans to securities dealers, refused to extend sorely pressed dealers any more credit. They also called in major loans, imperiling some securities firms.
- Some big investment-banking firms, facing catastrophic losses if the market panic continued, urged the New York Stock Exchange to close.
- Only the intervention of the Federal Reserve, the concerted announcement of corporate stock-buy-back programs, and the mysterious movement—and possible manipulation—of a little-used stock-index futures contract save the markets from total meltdown.

The story of that Tuesday discloses major weaknesses in the U.S. financial system and raised the specter that such a crisis could strike again. "Tuesday was the most dangerous day we had in 50 years," says Felex Rohatyn, a general partner in Lazard Freres & Co. "I think we came within an hour" of a disintegration of the stock market, he says. "The fact we didn't have a meltdown doesn't mean we didn't have a breakdown. Chernobyl didn't end the world, but it sure made a terrible mess."

Monday, Oct. 19, 11 p.m. This day was the worst in Wall Street's history—and worst of all for the Big Board's specialists. The specialists, more than 50 little-known but powerful firms, are required by Big Board rules to buy and sell assigned stocks during volatile times to keep prices as orderly as possible. They usually profit handsomely by shrewd trading—a franchise that has long been the envy of large, publicly oriented securities firms prevented by Big Board rules from becoming specialists themselves. Specialists are supposed to provide the last bastion of liquidity; in normal times, they are the reason an investor can buy or sell a stock when no other investors are in the market. On this day, at least, they were clearly not up to the task.

As the market plunged on Monday, the specialists bore the brunt of the fall. ''From 2 p.m. on, there was total despair,'' says James Maguire, the chairman of Henderson Brothers Inc., a big specialist firm that makes markets in about 70 stocks. ''The entire investment community fled the market. We were left alone on the field.'' Forced to buy stock himself when there were no other buyers, Mr. Maguire ended the day with $60 million in stock—three times his normal inventory. Like other specialists, he had to pay for this stock five business days later, the followng Monday. To do so, he would have to borrow.

Mr. Maguire phoned his bank, Bankers Trust Co., one of New York's biggest and an important lender to Wall Street. He asked for a $30 million loan, even though Henderson is one of Wall Street's best-capitalized specialist firms. He was stunned by the response. ''They stated they were in no position to make commitments,'' Mr. Maguire says.

Mr. Maguire phoned the bank five times between 11 p.m. and 12:30 a.m. It wouldn't budge.

Other specialists report similar experiences. One, A. B. Tompane & Co., similarly turned down by Bankers Trust, was hurriedly forced into the arms of well-capitalized Merrill Lynch & Co. The two firms shook hands on the merger at 3 a.m. By dawn, nevertheless, the worst was yet to come for the markets.

Tuesday, 6:30 a.m. Big Board Chairman John J. Phelan met a neighbor going down in the elevator of his Manhattan apartment building. The neighbor was concerned not about Monday's 508-point plunge but about rumors that the Big Board might close. ''He said, 'My God, if things were bad enough to close the market, things were really bad,''' Mr. Phelan recalls.

Tuesday, 8 a.m. Bank credit is the lifeline of Wall Street securities firms, and specialists weren't the only ones rushing to arrange more of it Tuesday morning. Large securities firms had swollen stock inventories, accumulated to accommodate major clients who wanted to sell, or in some cases held as part of the firms' holdings of stocks they expected to be involved in takeovers. Demand for credit was further fueled by an explosion of trading in the government-securities market. Trading by big government-securities dealers surged by $58 billion to a daily average of $173 billion that week. In addition, arbitragers, who had accumulated billions of dollars of takeover stocks, were also getting squeezed by margin calls.

The big firms fared little better. Phone calls started pouring into officials at the Big Board and the Federal Reserve Bank of New York. Angry securities dealers reported that foreign and U.S. regional banks were cutting back credit to the securities industry. Bankers Trust told Wall Street firms that it would stop extending unsecured credit—loans not collateralized by assets.

Executives at one big Wall Street securities firm were shocked when another U.S. bank Tuesday refused to deliver promptly $70 million in West German marks that it had sold to the firm in a foreign-exchange trade. Apparently, the bank feared that it might not be paid promptly—if at all—for the marks. Securities firms ''were beginning to have trouble getting extended credit,'' Big Board Chairman Phelan says. ''Japanese banks threatened to stop'' lending, adds the head of one of Wall Street's largest securities firms.

Tuesday, 9 a.m. As the credit markets came to life in the U.S., Federal Reserve officials were swinging into action. In the early-morning hours, from a hotel room in Dallas, Chairman Alan Greenspan had decided to issue a one-sentence statement that in effect would reverse the course of policies that he had set into motion upon taking office two months before. He canceled a speech and headed back to his Washington office.

Meanwhile, E. Gerald Corrigan, the beefy president of the Federal Reserve Bank of

New York and a protege of Mr. Greenspan's predecessor, Paul Volcker, was in close touch with the stock exchanges—due to open in half an hour—the banks and the bond market. As the head of the Federal Reserve's key operating unit, which daily buys or sells huge amounts of government securities and international currencies, he is the Fed official most closely in touch with Wall Street. He was to become the agency's point man in dealing with the developing crisis.

After learning of the credit squeeze facing Wall Street, Messrs. Greenspan and Corrigan feared that something far worse than a stock-market panic might be in the offing. If credit dried up, securities firms could start to collapse, much as the banks did after the 1929 crash. Fed officials saw a real threat of gridlock developing in the markets: Even the simplest financial transaction might have become impossible.

To avert that risk, Mr. Greenspan agreed to suspend, at least temporarily, the tightening grip the Fed had imposed on credit in order to head off inflation fears that he had seen building up in the economy. Signaling clearly its determination to prevent a market disaster, the Fed issued its extraordinary statement affirming its "readiness to serve as a source of liquidity to support the economic and financial system."

Even that was an understatement. Acting as the ultimate supplier of funds, the Fed flooded the banking system with dollars by buying government securities and thus quickly driving down short-term interest rates. "The Fed opened the floodgates of liquidity," says David Jones, the chief economist of Aubrey G. Lanston & Co., a major government-securities dealer.

Alerted by calls about the developing credit crisis from Mr. Phelan and others, the Fed leaned heavily on the big New York banks to meet Wall Street's soaring demand for credit. Mr. Corrigan and key aides personally telephoned top bankers to get the message across.

"Right from the beginning, Corrigan understood there was a major problem in system," says Mr. Phelan, who spoke repeatedly to the New York Fed chief. Mr. Phelan sums up the Fed's strategy as he saw it: "The banks would be kept liquid; the banks would make sure everyone else in the system would stay liquid."

The banks were told to keep an eye on the big picture—the global financial system on which all their business ultimately depends. A senior New York banker says the Fed's message was, "We're here. Whatever you need, we'll give you."

Tuesday, 9:30 a.m. The New York Stock Exchange opened. But many important sectors were at a standstill. Two-thirds of the specialists' total $3 billion of buying power had been wiped out on Monday. Some specialists refused to open trading in stocks until they had enough buy orders to enable the shares to trade at higher prices. Many stocks took more than an hour to open. When they did, they were mostly up from Monday's close. The Dow opened about 200 points higher, an extraordinary gain.

But the euphoria was short-lived. Specialists and major firms quickly unloaded some of their huge inventories, and buyers evaporated. Stock-index futures began to plunge on several exchanges. Program traders and portfolio insurers, whose computer-generated trading had accelerated Monday's fall, were largely absent from the market. Program traders switch money between stock-index futures and the underlyng stocks, depending on which is cheaper. Portfolio insurance is a method of hedging a stock portfolio, usually by selling futures contracts on stock indexes when the market falls.

Ordinarily, the huge discount of the futures contracts to the cash value of the underlying stocks would encourage selling of the stocks and buying of the futures. That, in turn, theoretically could trigger some buying of stocks at bargain prices. But as the morning continued, everything was being sold—stocks and futures alike.

Tuesday, 11:25 a.m. Of all securities linked to stock-market indexes, the Major Market Index has been the most secure, even in turbulent markets. It is pure blue chip: 17 of the 20 stocks in the index also are in the Dow Jones Industrial Average. Indeed, the MMI was created to mirror that average.

On Monday night, after the market turmoil that day, Ronald Shear, the American Stock Exchange's likable, balding senior specialist for the MMI, couldn't sleep. At 4 a.m., he gave up trying, and he went to the Brasserie, a 24-hour French restaurant in midtown Manhattan. Later, as the markets opened, he could hardly believe what he saw. One after another, major stocks broke down and couldn't be traded. By 11:30 a.m., when IBM stopped trading, the pace of closings was so fast Mr. Shear had trouble keeping track.

Big Board printouts of the morning's trading paint a harrowing picture of a market in disarray. By 11:25, even DuPont hadn't opened. Merck opened at 9:46, was overwhelmed by sell orders and closed eight minutes later. Sears closed at 11:12; Eastman Kodak at 11:28; Philip Morris at 11:30; 3M a minute later. Dow Chemical shut at 11:43; USX at 12:51. Many other major stocks also weren't trading. Those that were did so only sporadically, in small numbers of shares or on regional exchanges. Over-the-counter market makers stopped answering their phones.

Specialists didn't have any buy orders, and many simply stopped making markets. Many believed that their capital, much of it in stock that looked as though it couldn't be sold, was gone or nearly gone. The specialists had run out of buying power. "The specialist system just let (stocks) go. People just stood aside," says Leslie Quick Jr., the chairman of Quick & Reilly Group Inc., a big discount brokerage firm.

Suddenly, Mr. Shear heard rumors coursing across the Amex floor. One turned out to be true: Tompane, the USX specialist on the Big Board, was about to be taken over by Merrill Lynch. Another later proved to be false: SEC Chairman David Ruder was about to announce the closing of the exchanges.

Sensing a similar imbalance in the options trading, Mr. Shear called a floor supervisor to check the rules for index-options trading on the Amex. The supervisor confirmed that if stocks representing more than 20 percent of the underlying capitalization of the index aren't trading, then options trading should stop. From what Mr. Shear saw, well over half the stocks in the index had stopped trading.

Mr. Shear got on the loudspeaker and halted trading in the MMI options.

Tuesday, 12:15 p.m. Leo Melamed, the short, dark-haired, kinetic chairman of the Chicago Mercantile Exchange, was on the phone to Mr. Phelan in New York. The Merc trades the Standard & Poor's 500, the principal futures contract used by program traders and portfolio insurers. Mr. Melamed was alarmed by the unprecedented breakdown in trading of the stocks making up the S&P 500. The Chicago Board Options Exchange, which trades options, had already closed because so many stocks weren't trading. "I was told there were no buyers," Mr. Melamed says. Then, he received a jolt: Mr. Phelan told him that Big Board directors were convening to decide whether to close the stock exchange. Mr. Phelan told him that "a decision was close," Mr. Melamed recalls.

Mr. Melamed suddenly envisioned a selling onslaught of the futures that could exhaust every bit of liquidity on the Merc floor. "We were exposed in a very dangerous way. We couldn't bear the brunt of any panic," he says. At 12:15 p.m., the Merc ordered a halt in trading of S&P 500 futures contracts.

A few blocks away at the Chicago Board of Trade, Chairman Karsten Mahlmann, known by his nickname, "Cash," also was on the phone to the Big Board. His exchange was still trading futures contracts on the MMI. But the situation was worsening: The

MMI futures, already trading at the deepest discount to the underlying cash value of the index in its history, plunged further on the news that Mr. Shear had halted options trading on the Amex.

Mr. Mahlmann also was told that the Big Board was thinking of closing. But the Board of Trade was a little better off than the Merc. Trading of the relatively little-used MMI futures contracts had almost ground to a nervous standstill; MMI traders didn't seem to face a flood of orders.

Moreover, Mr. Mahlmann calculated that 17 of the MMI's 20 stocks still were trading, albeit sporadically, on some regional stock exchanges. Just the day before, Mr. Mahlmann had received a phone call from Beryl Sprinkel; the chairman of the President's Council of Economic Advisers urged him to keep the Board of Trade open. And there was the fierce longstanding rivalry between the Board of Trade and the New York exchange, a rivalry that has given rise to a generally defiant attitude at the Board of Trade toward any action adopted by the Big Board.

"We felt we had to stay open to do our job, to provide liquidity," Mr. Mahlmann recalls. Then he and his executives made what turned out to be one of the most critical decisions of the day: They kept the Board of Trade open and continued to trade the MMI futures contract.

Tuesday, 12:30 p.m. Mr. Phelan, Big Board President Robert Birnbaum, other top exchange officials and floor directors representing shellshocked specialists had gathered in Mr. Phelan's office to consider an extraordinary step: closing the New York Stock Exchange. The mood was grim. Mr. Phelan recalls that during the morning the market "was off 100 points and looked like it had potential to drop another 200 or 300. It looked like it would go again; it would be faster and heavier than the day before because there would be panic in the system." Exchange officials feared that selling would cascade as investors were hit with margin calls and big mutual funds dumped stock in the face of huge shareholder redemptions.

Behind the scenes, other pressures on Mr. Phelan to close the Big Board were multiplying. Several big securities firms "called the SEC and asked them to tell us to close," says Mr. Phelan (only the U.S. president and a stock exchange—but not the SEC—can order a closing). Mr. Phelan won't name the firms, but market sources say Salomon Brothers Inc. and Goldman, Sachs & Co., major firms with huge inventories of securities that were being rapidly devalued, were among those pushing to shut the exchange.

A Goldman official says the firm did discuss the possibility of a temporary closing with SEC Chairman Ruder but didn't recommend it. A Salomon spokesman didn't return a phone call.

"There were pressures from all firms that day to cut hours—to close," Mr. Phelan says. Donald Stone, a Big Board director, says there was also a discussion of a plan—broached on Black Monday—for big Wall Street firms to raise a $1 billion fund to keep specialist firms from going broke.

Mr. Phelan denies suggestions by Mr. Melamed and Mr. Mahlmann that he or other officials gave any indication the Big Board was on the brink of closing. He says he had talked during the morning to White House Chief of Staff Howard Baker. "They said if you can do it (stay open), do it," he relates.

Mr. Phelan says he shared White House fears over the impact of a Big Board closing. Shutting the biggest U.S. securities exchange not only would loudly trumpet the gravity of the stock-market crisis, "but the strain on the country . . . would be taken as an extremely bad sign," he adds. And reopening hundreds of stocks at once could later prove impossible. "If we close it, we would never open it," Mr. Phelan says bluntly.

Despite the intensifying pressures to close, the market was still officially open at 12:30.

Tuesday, 12:38 p.m. With the closing of the Big Board seemingly imminent and the market in disarray, with virtually all options and futures trading halted, something happened that some later described as a miracle: In the space of about five or six minutes, the Major Market Index futures contract, the only viable surrogate for Dow Jones Industrial Average and the only major index still trading, staged the most powerful rally in its history. The MMI rose on the Chicago Board of Trade from a discount of nearly 60 points to a premium of about 12 points. Because each point represents about five in the industrial average, the rally was the equivalent of a lightning-like 360-point rise in the Dow. Some believe that this extraordinary move set the stage for the salvation of the world's markets.

How it happened is a matter of much conjecture on Wall Street. Some attribute it to a mysterious burst of bullish sentiment that suddenly swept the markets. Some knowledgeable traders have a different interpretation: They think that the MMI futures contract was deliberately manipulated by a few major firms as part of a desperate attempt to boost the Dow and save the markets.

According to this theory, the rally in the MMI futures contract was caused by a relatively small amount of concerted buying by one or more major firms at a time when it was so thinly traded that the orders had an enormous and disproportionate upward thrust. By forcing the futures contract to a premium to the underlying cash value of the index, the buyers of futures could trigger immediate buying of the stocks in the index and selling of the futures by index arbitragers. Because so many of the MMI stocks are in the Dow, this would enable the NYSE to reopen many of these stocks at higher prices, leading to an upturn in this psychologically important index. At the very least, the buyers could flash a powerful bullish signal to the markets.

Mr. Mahlmann says he doesn't know whether this is what happened, but he says it is possible. "The market was extremely thin at that point," he recalls.

Statistics supplied by the Board of Trade lend circumstantial support to the thesis that the index was driven upward by a small number of sophisticated buyers. During the half hour—12:30 to 1 p.m. in the East, 11:30 to noon in Chicago—that encompassed the extraordinary rally, only 808 contracts traded, representing an underlying cash value of the index of about $60 million. The actual cost to someone buying those contracts can't be precisely determined, but it would have been a small fraction of the cash value.

Of the 808 contracts traded, about 70 percent were purchased at low commission rates. That indicates that the buying came from major Wall Street firms with their own traders on the floor. Only 30 percent of the buying came from so-called locals—smaller, independent traders who trade for their own and customers' accounts. The Board of Trade's statistician says this is an abnormally low percentage of local buying. Which firms were doing the buying couldn't be determined. Major firms contacted, including Morgan Stanley & Co., Kidder Peabody & Co., Paine Webber Inc., Goldman Sachs and Salomon Brothers, all either denied that they were responsible for the buying or declined comment.

As news of the rally in MMI futures reached the New York Stock Exchange (major firms maintain open lines both to their traders in Chicago and to specialists in New York), the market got another important psychological boost: The announcement of stock buybacks by major corporations. This, too, appears to have been encouraged by major invetment banks, many of which spent Tuesday morning frantically calling chief executives of major clients urging them to buy back their stock. First Boston, for example, called about 200 clients.

"It looks like there's almost a get-together on the part of corporate America to prop up the market," Stanley Abel, a consultant specializing in buybacks, observed that day. Among the companies announcing buy-backs were Shearson Lehman Brothers Holdings Inc., Merrill Lynch, Citicorp, Honeywell, ITT, Allegis, four regional Bell companies and USX.

The precise timing of those announcements and any accompanyng purchases are difficult to pinpoint, but some occurred during the crucial hour between 12:30 and 1:30. The USX specialist, for example, says trading in USX was halted at 12:43 p.m. because of a sudden influx of buy orders following the company's buyback announcement.

Floor traders at the Chicago Board of Trade say the major securities firms that maintain direct contact with specialists in New York were the first to learn of such buy orders, which in turn led to further buying by those firms of the MMI futures whenever the contract traded at a discount to the underlying cash index. (Indeed, the locals in Chicago have long complained that because the MMI consists of only 20 stocks, it can be manipulated by the major firms with access to Big Board specialists.)

A graph of Tuesday's movement in the MMI futures contract is consistent with such observations. At 12:45, the MMI contract had moved to a sharp premium to the underlying cash value of the index (so many of the stocks weren't trading that the underlying cash value was calculated using recent trades that probably overstated its true value at the time). The graph shows that the contract immediately turned downward, as traders presumably sold the futures and began to buy the underlying stocks, thereby locking in a profit.

One index arbitrager admits using such a strategy. "I did it very, very cautiously," he says. "I was terrified of the market. But it was a very profitable move."

If the goal of those buying the MMI futures beginning at 12:38 was to drive up the Dow, it succeeded brillantly.

Tuesday, 1 p.m. Like water on parched earth, buy orders began flowing into securities firms and into the stock exchange.

Banks, including the recalcitrant Bankers Trust, had finally pledged their support after receiving reassurances from the Fed, giving specialists and other firms the financial confidence to execute orders. The Fed told the banks that they were free to increase their borrowings at the Fed's discount window. New York's Chemical Bank increased its loans to securities firms for that week by $400 billion above normal, a bank official says.

All told, the 10 biggest New York banks nearly doubled their lending to securities firms that week to $12 billion, pumping in an extra $5.5 billion.

A spokesperson for Bankers Trust says, "We were able to accommodate routinely the financing requirements of our major customers in an environment characterized by great uncertainty. The requirements of most others were met after greater than usual consideration."

As the buy orders reappeared, large capitalization stocks—especially those in the MMI—began coming back to life. Merck reopened at 1:15, albeit 21 points lower, and IBM reopened at 1:26 at 112, unchanged from two hours earlier. By 2 p.m., when USX reopened, up 62 1/2 cents, all the MMI stocks were trading.

Mr. Phelan told his counterparts at the other exchanges in New York and Chicago that the day's threat of closing had passed, that the immediate crisis was over. At the Amex, Mr. Shear got on the loudspeaker to announce that MMI options would resume trading in 15 minutes. Mr. Melamed ordered the resumption of futures trading on the Merc, and the Board of Trade's Mr. Mahlmann breathed a great sigh of relief. "We were immensely pleased that the market came back and that we were the ones who stayed open," he says.

Tuesday, 4 p.m. The stock market ended it tumultuous day with a record—and psychologically crucial—gain of 102.27 points in the Dow. Volume was also a record 608,120,000 shares, a little higher than on Black Monday. On the Big Board overall, 1,398 stocks declined. Only 537 gained.

The Dow's rise partly reflected the strong performance of the stocks that make up the MMI. Throughout the afternoon, the MMI futures traded several times at a premium to the cash index, apparently triggering buying of the underlying stocks. The performance of the MMI futures diverged significantly from that of the S&P 500, which remained at a deep discount to the index even after it reopened.

Because of the Fed's aggressive move to drive down interest rates by flooding the system with liquidity, the bond market, too, rallied strongly, providing crucial support for the broader financial system. "If the bond market had been going the same direction as the stock market—down—that would have been the straw that broke the camel's back," Mr. Phelan says.

On Wednesday, Americans woke to newspaper headlines proclaiming the largest rise in the Dow's history. A wave of optimism washed over the exchanges. The stock market that day was to have a real rally—186.84 points on the Dow, with 1,749 stocks gaining.

In the end, the stock market and financial system didn't collapse on Tuesday. Although trading losses—mainly in takeover-related stocks—ran into hundreds of millions of dollars, no major securities firm defaulted on its obligations to customers or was rendered insolvent. A few specialist firms merged or were forced to find new infusions of capital; most survived. But privately, key participants say they were deeply shaken by how close to catastrophe the system came.

And the crisis in the financial system revealed glaring weaknesses that are being closely examined in Congress. The New York Stock Exchange specialist system—despite some heroic efforts—proved inadequate to meet the demands of huge international flows of capital, nearly triggering a shutdown of the exchange and a public crisis of confidence. Though there is little to suggest that program trading or portfolio insurance caused the crisis, both contributed to a degree of volatility that the system couldn't handle.

"The markets will be nothing but an open casino if you let this continue," Mr. Phelan says.

More worrisome, many officials note, is that the crisis occurred in the absence of any true calamity. What might happen to the markets in a major political or economic crisis? Could a real meltdown happen?

"I won't even get into that," the Merc's Mr. Melamed says.

Source: The Wall Street Journal, Friday, November 20, 1987.

THE TECHNOLOGY

2

Product and Process Innovation

NEW PRODUCT DEFINITION

"Nothing is so futile as to do well that which should not be done at all."

New products are the life's blood of the semiconductor industry and, while it may be true that "if a man builds a better mouse trap, even though he live in a wood, the world will beat a path to his door;" it is also true that the best manufactured widget in the world will be an exercise in futility if the customer need for such a widget has not been established. All too often, products spend months or even years in design and development, only to fail dismally in the marketplace.

At least initially then, we should confine our attention to only those parts of the new product introduction process, from the point at which a customer need is identified, up to the point at which the product to satisfy that need can be defined: in effect, the point at which the design goal can be established. Up to this point, marketing rather than manufacturing considerations will feature in this process. Execution in the factory, the mechanics of implementing the design in silicon and bringing the product into high-volume production, will be discussed in later chapters.

The process of introducing a new product is conceptually simple but practically difficult. It can be approached systematically, however, by asking the following questions:

Have all sources of new product needs and ideas been identified?
Have all potential customer product needs/available ideas been screened?
Has the nature and size of these needs been defined?
Is the product need consistent with the product portfolio strategy?
Does it fill a gap in the portfolio?
Does it overlap other existing or planned products?
Is it potentially profitable?
Is it technically feasible?
Should it be a new generic solution or variation on an existing theme?
Should it be a standard product, semicustom, or a fully customized solution?
To which strategic business unit (SBU) should it be assigned?
Can it be designed for high yield/quality, low cost manufacture?

Can it utilize already available design cells/components/methods?
How should it be sourced and marketed?
Will it fit into the customer's design window?

This approach may seem to be overly pedantic, but it is a regrettable truth that many new products fail, not because the design, development, and manufacturing tasks were executed badly, but because the products were ill conceived in the first place. They were victims of strategic misjudgment rather than tactical execution.

With a global population of 4.7 billion people, all of whom have varying needs, a company can easily stray, motivated by avarice or overzealousness, from the path of virtue and pay dearly for the excursion. These dangers can be avoided or at least minimized, if it can clearly articulate the answer to the question—What business are we in?—and focus on these distinctive competencies required to be successful in that business. Industrial history is littered with examples of companies that did not ask this question of themselves or failed to answer it properly.

Early in this century, American railroad companies would not have ignored the threat of the internal combustion engine if they had realized that they were in the transportation rather than the railroad business. This decade General Motors lost market share in deciding it was in the high-margin, large-automobile business rather than the business of satisfying individual consumer transport needs, which changed in response to escalating gasoline prices. Even more recently, the prestigious and much-admired IBM appeared to overlook the fact that they were in the data-processing business rather than simply satisfying high margin, mainframe user needs; they were caught less than well prepared by the trend towards decentralized computing, precipitated by ever increasing semiconductor chip functionality at continuously decreasing prices. Perhaps more by good luck than good judgment, they only narrowly avoided missing the rapid growth phase of the personal computer market. With several substantially different mainframe architectures to support, they are still less than well equipped to satisfy the new networking needs which the decentralization trend to distributed processing and the convergence of the data processing and telecommunication industries helped to create. To illustrate the other side of the coin however, AT&T now see themselves as being in the business of "global information management and movement" rather than as simply a telephone company.

What does all this mean with regard to integrated circuits? How do we answer the question—What business are we in? If we acknowledge that all integrated circuits are designed to fulfill a similar purpose in an almost infinite variety of applications, that of taking an input, either analog or digital, in the form of data, processing it in some fashion, and then storing or distributing the output of this process, again in the form of data, then we might conclude that we are in the electronic communications business, or at least in the business of servicing those people who are. This conclusion might be reinforced if we further acknowledge that two industries which consume a very significant portion of the semiconductor industry's output, data processing and telecommunications, which until only a few years ago were independent and unrelated, are now converging into a single industry (Data Comm). Communication needs, however, are not confined to data processing and telecommunications. Electronic engine control in the automotive industry is yet another example of integrated circuits being used to fulfill a communications need. Using analog signals as an example, they take inputs such as speed, temperature, or pressure, process these data and provide an output, again in the form of data, to some form of feedback control loop. In this instance, the human being is not included as a link in the communications chain; in an electronic dashboard application, he obviously would be.

We can envisage communications needs, which could be served by electronics in the form of integrated circuits, appearing in almost all walks of life. Being in the electronic communications business then, are we to attempt to satisfy all of these needs? Is it conceivable that we can, or is it more likely that in trying to be all things to all people, we will do everything badly? Should we specialize in satisfying only one link in everyone's communication chain, such as mass storage of data, their data processing requirement, or their data acquisition or transmission requirement, or alternatively, should we try to provide as many links as possible for fewer categories of applications? Should we try to strike some balance between those two extremes? Important questions, since they will not only determine the products we shall be required to have in our portfolio but the competencies required to provide and support them. This in turn could have a significant bearing on how we ought to organize ourselves in designing, manufacturing, and marketing these products against world-class competition. A further benefit may be in sensitizing us to trends in user needs or technology which warrant action or reaction on our part.

It would seem then, that it is not enough to know that we are in the electronics communications business, unless, of course, our size, skills, and resources allow us to participate effectively on every front. If this is not the case, it might be that we need to ask even more questions of ourselves in order to see with greater clarity those communication chains or links in the chains to which we can bring distinctive competence.

To achieve this distinctive competence, we need to develop a much better understanding of these communication needs. How they are integrated in silicon will vary by application environment, determining choices of technology, architecture, memory requirements, packaging, fixed or programmable function, cost and service requirements, and so on. Our marketing colleagues can be of great help to us here by applying the work of the economist, the psychologist, and the statistician. Our ultimate potential market of 4.7 billion people is obviously nonhomogeneous in many respects, including the needs which can be satisfied by our products. Knowing this, we could ask our marketing experts to classify our global population into categories by attribute. These attributes could be geographic, stage of industrialization, purchasing power, political system, industry, industry segment, demography, educational level, ad infinitum. We shall call these groups markets, or market segments. Obviously, the attributes selected would be those which we think best serve our purpose. The more we can refine this process, the greater will be our ability to concentrate our finite resources on specific target groups.

We already agreed it was unrealistic to try to be all things to all people, but with this approach we can be most things to some people to a more successful degree than our competition. We could further refine our market segments into niche markets, but this could easily degenerate into a discussion on semantics. What really matters is that we identify these target groups and work closely with them to develop a very comprehensive and detailed understanding of their specific needs, their buying behavior, and, if possible, the needs and behavior of their end customers, and to assess the extent to which they are being serviced by our competition. Our goal is to create a path of least resistance from their doorstep to ours, rather than to our competitors.

Despite this refinement and distillation process, this will still represent just a lot of data but that is still all that it will be, data. Only if a meaningful pattern can become apparent, if we can extract the essence from the elixer, can it be considered to be knowledge or intelligence upon which we can make decisions and take action. Even then the problem of communicating this information will remain. Both of these processes can be facilitated by the use of charts, such as histograms, pie charts, matrixes, and so on. We may then be able to identify a pattern of key competencies which would allow us to bring cohesion to an otherwise confused picture. For example, the criteria involved in a purchasing decision are common in all such decisions, and all are important, but the hierarchy of importance varies.

Criteria	Market Segment Attributes
Product function	All
Price	Cost sensitive
Quality	Military/industrial OEM
Delivery	High value/single source
Service/responsiveness	Volatile market
Track record	Repeat patronage
Risk	Politically sensitive
Policy	Corporate alliances

These are but a few of the attributes which need to be considered, but by pursuing such an approach in gathering and organizing the intelligence available to us, we can focus on these attributes considered most critical to the product definition and design goal. We can then address the equally important matter of how to bring these products to market.

NEW PRODUCT MARKETING

Not surprisingly perhaps, we find that new products, like everything else, have a life cycle, as shown in Figure 2-1. Over the course of time it has been observed that these life cycles are becoming shorter, a reflection of an ever-intensifying competitive environment as more end users, in both consumer and industrial markets, define products to provide and sustain a marketing edge in their businesses and as more suppliers enter the business of supplying these needs. In the early days of the industry, Fairchild, one of the first companies to commercially exploit semiconductors' ever-increasing pervasiveness, held an almost monopolistic position. This was almost directly analagous to the position held by Ford in the automobile industry with the Model T. Over the course of

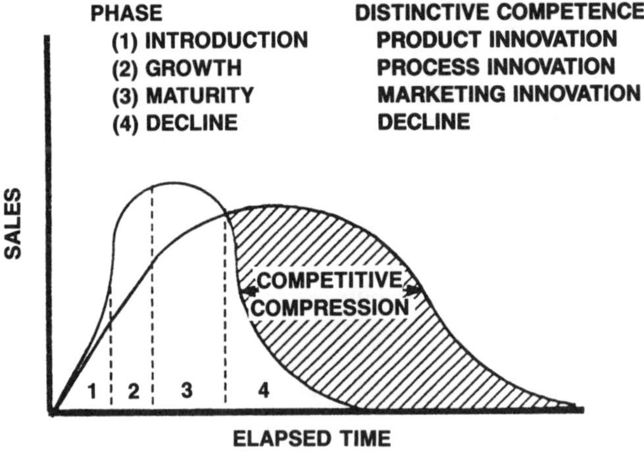

Figure 2-1 Product Life Cycle

time, however, as it became apparent that semiconductors were here to stay and the potential for growth and profit was recognized, more entrants came into the business, fueling the evolution to an oligopolistic market situation. Until the 1960s, this was almost exclusively confined to the United States with U.S. factories supplying the growing worldwide demand.

Today's environment is fast approaching one of almost perfect competition, with no supplier or consumer holding such a dominant position, at least across all product lines, that they can substantially effect supply and demand and, therefore price, in the global marketplace. Semiconductors are perceived by so many governments to be of such central importance to national sovereignty and the fundamental infrastructure of their economies that indigenous semiconductor industries are emerging in almost all corners of the world to avoid dependence on foreign suppliers. This being the case then, how do we bring our products to the international marketplace in a distinctive fashion. Being a capital-intensive industry with a high fixed cost of doing nothing, we need to win and retain world market share to be able to amortize our costs over volume.

If we study Figure 2-1 we might conclude that, in the first phase, product innovations would be the richest source of competitive advantage. New products at this stage will not have quality, reliability, and delivery track records, which can be included and measured in the prospective buyer's decision criteria, although a supplier's track record on previous products may be known. Product functionality is more likely to be the paramount criteria—the better, or perceived to be better, mouse trap. Product functionality will be judged in terms of how well it addresses the need to be satisfied. This is why a very thorough and comprehensive understanding of that need is required at the new product definition stage in order that design goals can be set which most closely conform to this requirement. It is also important at this stage not to hide our light under a bush. This will also be the period during which promotional activities, in communicating the merits and relative advantages of each competitor's particular solution to the marketplace, are most intense. At this stage these will be promises, declarations of intent. Only later will prototypes become available, giving recipients the opportunity to test these claims against reality. A vendor's past track record in this respect will therefore have a significant bearing on the credibility of these claims—the degree to which the customer assesses and is willing to accept the probability of the vendor keeping these commitments in the future. More of this in Chapter 3. For the time being let us recall that our principal task at this stage is to identify needs, define solutions, and address how we should market the solutions to these needs, assuming they exist or will exist.

These are obviously important decisions, committing significant resources to a course of action, the future outcome of which is uncertain, with the risk and cost of failure increasing with time. During the development phase, the user needs may change, a competitor may surprise us, and appear in the marketplace with a better mouse trap, a new, more appropriate technology may emerge, or we may execute badly and incur serious time delays. These risks can be minimized, but not eliminated, only by precisely understanding the end need, clearly defining the product design goals, avoiding creeping elegance, and then executing speedily and flawlessly.

There are many sources of new product ideas. Many will be generated within the enterprise itself, formally out of R&D departments, informally from almost any technical or marketing function within the factory. Perhaps the evolution of the technology will suggest ways of implementing an existing function in a better way or the creation of a new function previously not possible, but the best source of new product ideas is the market itself, the customer base. These may not be communicated in terms of a definitive product but in terms of a need—more speed, higher functionality, more integration of currently stand-alone functions, higher quality and reliability, or different packaging. There really isn't anything new in terms of human needs, only an insatiable desire to do the same things faster, cheaper, and more reliably on an ever-increasing scale. The big advantage in customer-derived new product ideas, unlike some which are suggested internally, sometimes for the wrong reason, is the probability that they will be willing to pay for the satisfaction of that need.

Migrating from phase 1 into phase 2 is where we, as a fully self-sufficient designer, developer, and manufacturer of integrated circuits, will be given the opportunity to excel—in process innovation, in on-time delivery, in cost and quality, in short—in world-class manufacturing. Bearing in mind the risks, uncertainties, and volatility of the situation however, we should not overlook ways, other than indigenous manufacturing, of satisfying the demand we have so successfully created or at least been allowed to participate in satisfying. These have been conveniently labeled for common use by Boggi as follows:

Imitate	Copy another vendor's product
Adopt	Second source another vendor's product
Adapt	Find new applications for existing products
Ignore	Continue with existing product mix
Resign	Withdraw from market
Innovate	Bring new products (and processes) to the market

(Joan Robinson, *The Economics of Imperfect Competition*; London: MacMillan, 1932. Michael J. Baker and Ronald McTavish, *Product Policy and Management*; MacMillian Studies in Marketing Management, 1976.)

To adopt a strategy of ignoring or resigning is to choose not to compete, to admit defeat. This is not a strategy a going concern is likely to choose. To imitate or adopt are potentially successful strategies, but both require that our manufacturing competence in cost, quality, and delivery are at least as good as those we imitate or from whom we adopt. These strategies improve in appeal if we also have strong marketing sales and distribution competence. We will find, however, that competition through innovation is the most enduring distinctive competence we could wish for.

Being a capital-intensive industry with very high fixed costs in the form of depreciation on facilities and capital equipment, realization of **market share** is an essential prerequisite to **profitability**. The greater the volume of product over which these costs can be absorbed, the lower the proportion which each product need carry and, therefore, **the lower the ASP at which each unit of output can be profitable**. (ASP—Average Selling Price.) There are basically two ways to increase market share:

1. By forcing existing products down the learning curve such that the reduced product cost realized permits greater penetration into existing applications and into new applications which were previously not cost effective at the higher price.

2. By **new product introduction**. In our industry, new products are the life's blood, even in the good times, and there are many examples of **distinctive competence** in this respect giving rise to **pre-eminence** in **market** share and profitability.

In times of economic recession, to be less than competent in this respect can have very grave consequences.

New product introduction is an extremely compex decision process of **selection** and **execution** which should not be left to **"seat of the pants"** flying. With regard to the selection process, it is well to remember that "**Nothing is so futile as to do well that which should not be done at all.**" With regard to the execution process, we should bear in mind "**If it's worth doing, it's worth doing well.**" It's the difference between being **effective** as opposed to being **efficient**. Because of this, defining and enforcing a **new product introdution procedure** will give rise to **best return for least effort** in use of resources consumed by the selection of which new products to pursue and which will **optimize** the **execution** phase of bringing new products into **production** and to the **market**.

In the right	**Quantity**
At the right	**Price/Cost**
At the right	**Quality/Reliability**
At the right	**Time**

The flow chart, Figure 2-2, illustrates the recommended sequence of events to be followed.

1. Compilation of "wish list"—products from **any** source which **any** individual thinks ought to be considered for introduction. There are essentially three categories of product:

a. Original designs
b. Second-source products, existing process
c. Second-source products, new process

(We are primarily concerned with original design circuits in this discussion.)

2. Completion of "new product introduction justification form" (see Table 2-1) to establish the commercial **worthwhileness** of the product and the **economic viability** of it. (These forms should be updated quarterly to accommodate any changes in **unit demand, average selling price (ASP), product cost**, and so on.)

3. Feasibility—conducted by the factory, design, and marketing to establish availability of **technology, capital equipment, human resources**, and subsequent **commitment** of same (see Figure 2-2).

4. Products successful in completing this process should then qualify for the **new product introduction plan**, and their **introduction** should be managed using the project evaluation and review technique (PERT).

5. Upon **release** to **production**, products can be controlled using the **product control** chart shown in Table 2-2, as an example.

Survival in the brutally competitive global environment will become progressively more and more dependent on superior marketing, engineering, and manufacturing. This is necessary not only to exist, but also to flourish (profitably).

PROJECT MANAGEMENT

In the present economic situation it has become increasingly important that we do an effective job in introducing new products to the market.

Our failure in the past to have a system to competently control our new product introduction prompted us to look for **a method of managing projects containing many complex activities and involving a large number of supporting groups in widely dispersed geographic locations**.

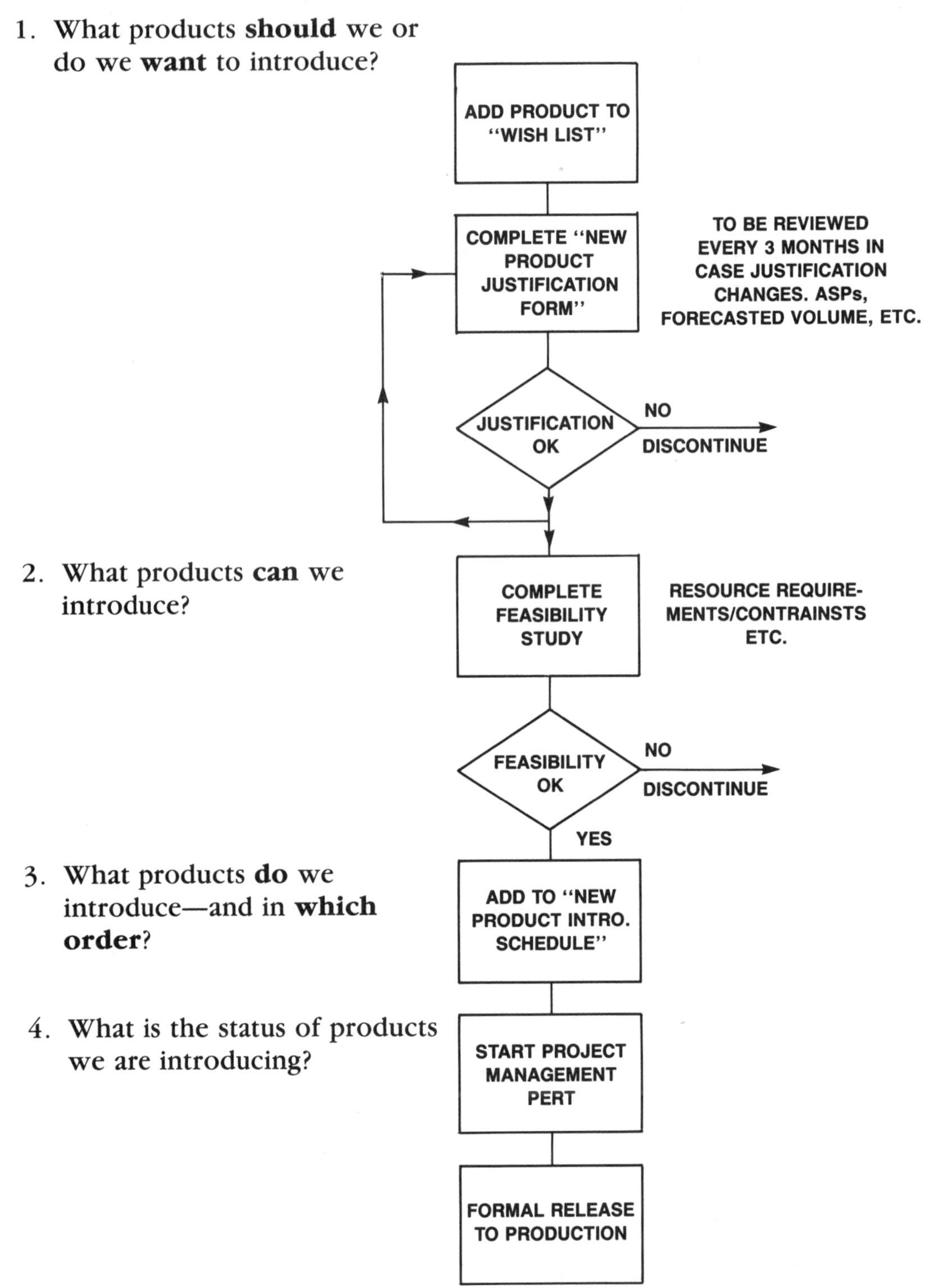
1. What products should we or do we want to introduce?
ADD PRODUCT TO "WISH LIST"
COMPLETE "NEW PRODUCT JUSTIFICATION FORM"
TO BE REVIEWED EVERY 3 MONTHS IN CASE JUSTIFICATION CHANGES. ASPs, FORECASTED VOLUME, ETC.
JUSTIFICATION OK
NO
DISCONTINUE
2. What products can we introduce?
COMPLETE FEASIBILITY STUDY
RESOURCE REQUIRE-MENTS/CONTRAINSTS ETC.
FEASIBILITY OK
NO
DISCONTINUE
YES
3. What products do we introduce—and in which order?
ADD TO "NEW PRODUCT INTRO. SCHEDULE"
4. What is the status of products we are introducing?
START PROJECT MANAGEMENT PERT
FORMAL RELEASE TO PRODUCTION

Figure 2-2 New Product Introduction Overview Flow Chart

Table 2-1 Project Management
New Product Introduction

Event		Activity	Responsibility	Scheduled Completion		Status
Start	End			Week	Date	
10	20	Identify Product Requirement	Strat./Prod. Market.			
20	30	Define Product Specification	Strat./Prod. Market.			
30	40	Define Design Goals	Strat./Prod. Market.			
40	45	Design Emulator Hardware	Design Organization			
45	50	Build and Debug Emulator	Design Organization			
40	50	Conduct Design Review	Design Organization			
50	55	Schedule Key Cust. Visit (Design)	Design Org./Mrktg.			
50	60	Complete Logic Design	Design Organization			
60	65	Prepare & Issue Product Preview	Design Org. Mrktg.			
60	70	Evaluate Logic Design	Design Organization			
70	80	Complete Logic Simulation	Design Organization			
70	90	Complete Layout	Design Organization			
80	100	Approve Simulation	Design Organization			
90	100	Approve Layout	Design Organization			
100	110	Generate Pattern Generation Tape	Design Organization			
110	120	Ship/Transmit to Mask Shop	Design Organization			
120	130	Generate Color Overlays	Mask Shop			
130	140	Ship Overlays to Design Org.	Mask Shop			
130	150	Ship Overlays to Factory	Mask Shop			
140	160	Check Overlays	Design Organization			
160	100	Possible Redesign	Product Eng./D.O.			
160	170	Gen. 1st/2nd Mask Set, Ship to W/F	Mask Shop			
170	180	Clean Mask Set	W/Fab			
180	190	Inspect Mask Set (Decide Use/Scrap)	Q.C./W. Fabrication			
190	200	Fabricate Prototype Lot No. 1	Wafer Fabrication			
200	205	Probe Prototype Lot No. 1	Probe			
205	206	Implement Yield Improvement Prog.	Probe/D.O./Wafer Fab			
200	210	Assemble Proto Lot No. 1 (Blind Assy)	Assembly			
210	220	Evaluate Samples	Design Organization			
220	100	Possible Redesign	Design Organization			
220	230	Generate 3rd/4th Generic Mask Set (With/Without Program Layer)	Mask Shop			
230	240	Fabricate Proto Lots No. 2 and 3	Wafer Fabrication			
240	250	Probe Proto Lots No. 2 and No. 3	Probe Factory			
250	255	Generate Custom Program Layer	Mask Shop			
255	270	Ship Masks to Manufacturing Plant	Mask Shop			
250	252	Carry Out Cumulative W. Mapping	Prod. Eng.			
252	260	Provide W/Maps for Evaluation	Prod. Eng.			
250	260	Assemble Proto Lots No. 2 and No. 3	Assembly			
260	270	Evaluate Samples Lots No. 2 and 3	Design Org.			

Table 2-1 (continued)

Event		Activity	Responsibility	Scheduled Completion		Status
Start	End			Week	Date	
270	275	Schedule Wafer Starts	Prod. Control			
275	277	Generate Stocking Program/Complete Inventory Profile Sheet/Genereate Run Rate Plan	Prod. Control			
270	272	Conduct Final Design Review	D.O./Prod. Eng.			
272	274	Release Device to Manufacturing	D.O./Prod. Eng.			
274	280	Fabricate Production Lots	Wafer Fabrication			
280	290	Probe Production Lots	Probe			
290	295	Evaluate Feasibility of Test on Low Cost/High Volume Tester	Manufacturing Test Area			
290	300	Assemble Production Lots	Assembly			
300	310	Final Test Production Lots	Final Test			
310	100	Possible Redesign	Prod. Eng./Design			
310	312	Generate Qual. Eval. Samples	Product Engineering			
310	320	Ship to Cus. or Stock as Required	Production Control			
10	12	Establish Potential Vol./Mkt./ASP	Strat./Prod. Market.			
30	12	Project Cost Target/Test./Account	Finance			
12	14	Conduct Cash Flow Analysis	Finance			
14	16	Generate New Product Intro./ Justification Sheet	Product Eng.			
16	60	P&L Authority to Proceed	Operations Mgnt.			
		Cost Pricing				
80	340	Establish Target Cost/Budgetary Pricing	Finance/P.E.			
330	170	Review Cost/Pricing	Finance/P.E.			
		Non-Disclosure Clause				
40	330	Decide If Non-Disclosure Clause Reqd. (Optional)	Strat. Marketing			
		Design Prototypes				
60	350	Obtain Prototypes for Design Work	Design Organization			
350	360	Generate Customer Software	Customer			
360	370	Refer to Separate ROM Customized Software				
370	100	Transfer Software to Design Organization	Customer			
		Shop Order				
100	670	Generate DHP Photograph	Prod. Eng.			
670	680	Generate Assembly Shop Order	Prod. Eng.			
680	200	Ensure S.O. and Piece Parts Available (Lot 1)	Prod. Control			

Table 2-1 (continued)

Event		Activity	Responsibility	Scheduled Completion		Status
Start	End			Week	Date	
680	250	Ensure S.O. and Piece Parts Available (Lots 2 and 3)	Prod. Control			
		Line Plots				
100	650	Generate Cell, Logic, Line Plots	Design Organization			
650	660	Ship to Product Engineering	Design Organization			
660	160	Check Cell, Logic, Line Plots	Prod. Eng.			
		Mask Purchase Order				
110	420	Request Purchase Order From Appropriate P&L Manager	Design Organization			
420	120	Raise Purchase Order	Prod. Eng.			
		Process Control Data				
100	402	Define Process Control Die	Wafer Fab Eng.			
402	404	Define Min/Max Process Parameters	Wafer/Fab Eng.			
404	170	Ensure P.C. Program Available	Prod. Eng.			
		Critical Dimensions				
100	400	Define Critical Dimensions, Threshold Targets	Prod./Wafer/Fab Eng.			
400	410	Specify V.T. Limits	Prod. Eng./Fab Eng.			
410	415	Generate Product Information Sheet/ Mask Status Chart (PIS/MSC)	Prod. Eng.			
415	170	Distribute PIS/MSC	Prod. Eng.			
		48A Spec				
170	430	Generate Provisional 48A Spec	Prod. Eng.			
430	200	Distribute 48A Spec	Prod. Eng.			
		Assembly Spec				
170	690	Generate Assy. Spec. (Shop Order)	Prod. Eng.			
690	200	Ship to Assembly Location	Prod. Eng.			
		Test Pattern				
100	380	Generate Test Patterns	Design Organization			
380	390	Transfer onto Appropriate Transmission Medium				
390	460	Encode Patterns for Test System	Design Organization			
		Promotion				
100	440	Gen. & Publish Advance Data Sheet	Design Organization			
440	470	Ship to Appropriate Product Eng.	Design Organization			
440	442	Define Promotion/Advertising Plan	Marketing			
442	444	Implement Promotion/Ad. Plan	Marketing			

Table 2-1 (continued)

Event		Activity	Responsibility	Scheduled Completion		Status
Start	End			Week	Date	
442	446	Publish Application Notes/Articles	Marketing			
446	448	Schedule Key Cust. Visit-Promotion	Marketing			
		Final Test Program				
100	450	Generate Test Information	Design Organization			
450	470	Ship to Appropriate Product Eng.	Design Organization			
100	470	Generate Design Memo	Design Organization			
460	470	Ship to Appropriate Product Eng.	Design Organization			
470	480	Generate Q.C. Test Program	Prod. Eng.			
480	490	Gen. Characterization Program	Prod. Eng.			
490	500	Arrange Devices Available for Characterization	Prod. Eng.			
200	500	Assemble Samples from Lot No. 1 for Characterization and Reliability/ Quality Evaluation	Assembly			
240	500	Assemble Samples from Lots No. 2 and 3 for Characterization and Reliability Quality	Assembly			
500	508	Provide Eng. Evaluation Samples	Prod. Eng.			
500	502	Define Reliability/Qual. Plan	Reliability Eng.			
502	510	Carry Out Reliability/Quality Eval. (Refer to Separate PERT)	Prod. Eng.			
510	260	Evaluate Reliability Qual. Results	Reliability Eng.			
500	504	Define Characterization Plan	Prod. Eng.			
504	520	Characterize Devices from Lots 1, 2, and 3	Prod. Eng.			
520	530	Generate Final Test Program	Prod. Eng.			
530	300	Debug Final Test Program	Prod. Eng.			
300	302	Publish Final Data Sheet	Design Organization			
		Probe Program				
100	155	Write Probe Program	Prod. Eng.			
200	550	Obtain Devices from Lot 1 for Debug	Prod. Eng.			
550	560	Debug Probe Program	Prod. Eng.			
560	240	Make Program Available at Probe (Procedures/Test Specs)	Prod. Eng.			
		Final Test Capacity				
100	570	Establish F/Test Capacity Avail.	Prod. Eng./Prod.			
570	575	Check Final Test Capacity Avail.	Production Control			
575	580	Decide Action Required to Increase Capacity if Needed	Manufacturing			
580	300	Take Action to Increase Capacity if Required	Manufacturing			

Table 2-1 (continued)

Event		Activity	Responsibility	Scheduled Completion		Status
Start	End			Week	Date	
		Probe Capacity				
100	590	Define Probe Capacity Required	Product. Eng./Prod.			
590	595	Check Probe Test Capacity Avail.	Production Control			
595	600	Decide Action Required to Increase Capacity if Needed	Manufacturing			
600	280	Take Action to Increase Capacity if Required	Manufacturing			
		Final Test Load Board				
100	610	Supply Final Test Load Board	Prod. Eng.			
610	620	Wire Load Board	Prod. Eng.			
620	300	Ensure Load Board Avail. for F/Test	Prod. Eng.			
		Probe Load Board				
100	630	Supply Probe Load Board	Prod. Eng.			
630	640	Wire Probe Load Board	Prod. Eng.			
640	280	Ensure Load Board Avail. For Probe	Prod. Eng.			
		Probe Card				
170	695	Supply Metal Wafer to Probe	Wafer Fab			
695	240	Build and Check Probe Card	Manufacturing			

Table 2-2 New Product Introduction/Justification Status
Program Managers

Date: ______

Priority ______ **Device Eng.:** ______

Expect Release to Prod. ______ **Product Eng.:** ______

Product Mktg.: ______

Program Slippage ______ **Design Eng.:** ______

Device XXXX

Target Cust.

No. of Pins 28

Pkg. Plastic

Die Size 180 × 180

		Target	1984 FCST	1984 ACT	1985 FCST	1985 ACT	FCST 1986	FCST 1987
Sales Projections	K Units		100		1000		1600	
	K Dlrs		240		2000		2560	
	ASP $		2.4		2.0		1.6	
					Loc Assy		Loc Assy	Loc Assy
Yield Projections	Gross DPW	494	303		20% 382		30% 494	30% 494
	Wafer Yld %	90	85		85		85	85
	Wafer Cost $	100	130		130		130	130
	Probe DPW	331	127		206		331	331
	Probe %	67	42		54		67	67
	Ft. Yield %	90	90		90		90	90
Cost Projections	M2 Die Cost $	0.369	1.13		0.714		0.465	0.465
	M2 F.G. Cost $	1.00	2.19		1.41		1.11	1.11
	Target M2 F.G. Cost $	1.00	1.00		1.00		1.00	1.00
	50% M2 ASP	2.00	4.39		2.82		2.22	2.22
	Revenue/ Wafer St. $		206.01		327.60		421.11	
	Cont./ Wafer St. $		17.51		96.64		128.96	

(a) Initial Cost Estimate ______
(b) Resource Constraints ______
(c) Equiv. Wafer Starts/Wk ______

Mask Set

Current No.	
Status	
Next No.	
Exp Date	

Wafer Fab

Process	
Shrink 20% 1985 30% 1986	
Status	
Defectivity 2/cm^2	

Product Eng

Probe Prog. Status	
F.T. Prog. Status	

1st Eng. Samples	
Qualification Samples	

Mask Shop: ______

NPIJ/6

The method chosen to manage these projects is based on **PERT**, which is based on **network analysis** and **critical path scheduling**. Basically, the PERT method of managing requires all activities, person(s) responsible, and time scales to be defined in advance of the project starting and be laid out in the form of a diagram with the activities listed on a supporting document—network. It is particularly useful in **planning, scheduling, controlling, reporting, evaluating, and documenting** of large projects with many tasks or essentially similar projects conducted frequently such as the introduction of a new product. In this way, the PERT diagram outlines every activity which needs to be completed, by whom, when, the interdependence if any, and when the event was actually completed. It does not detract from or encroach upon the prerogatives of any of the specialist functions in that it identifies **what** needs to be done, **when**, and by **whom**, and does not and cannot direct **how** those activities are to be completed.

ADVANTAGES OF PERT

- Forces people **to think a project through** from start to completion.
- Prevents activities or needs from being **overlooked**.
- Highlights **interdependence** of groups involved in the project.
- **Flags** imminent activities.
- **Focuses** attention where necessary.
- Lets people involved see not only what they have to do and when, but how their activities **relate** to the whole project.
- Provides a comprehensive **snapshot** of activities complete and incomplete.
- Forms a document which can be used for **regularly evaluating and reporting** progress of the project.
- Provides a **historical record** of all activities in the project, showing rescheduled, on-time, late, and early completion dates.

To be able to use this method, a project must have a definite beginning and end, and consist of many smaller tasks requiring performance in an orderly sequence to successfully complete the project. The network diagram principle is the breaking down of a project into **activities** and **events**, an activity being described as a time-consuming operation such as "generate mask set" or "write device specifications." An event is an instantaneous point representing the completion of one activity and the readiness to begin a new one. Activities are broken down and listed in a logical manner. Each activity is then analyzed to determine which activity immediately precedes it and which activities may follow. The time necessary to complete each activity is estimated. A network diagram can then be constructed, each event being numbered sequentially.

In this way the factory can coordinate the activities of the functions primarily involved:

- Product Marketing
- Design
- Strategic Marketing
- Product Engineering
- Test Engineering
- Assembly Engineering
- Microsystems
- Wafer Fabrication
- Device Engineering
- Production—Assembly, Probe, and Test
- Manufacturing Process Engineering
- Quality Engineering and Reliablity

The goal is to achieve **fluency, synergy**, and **security** in this most vital activity.

Author's Note: Perhaps it is a sign of the times but when first produced, this list did not include Manufacturing Process Engineering. Almost certainly, this would not have been omitted from a Japanese equivalent list.

EVENT

10 START DIFFUSION LOT #1
20 COMPLETE DIFFUSION—PROBE #1
30 COMPLETE PROBE #1
START NEXT ACTIVITY

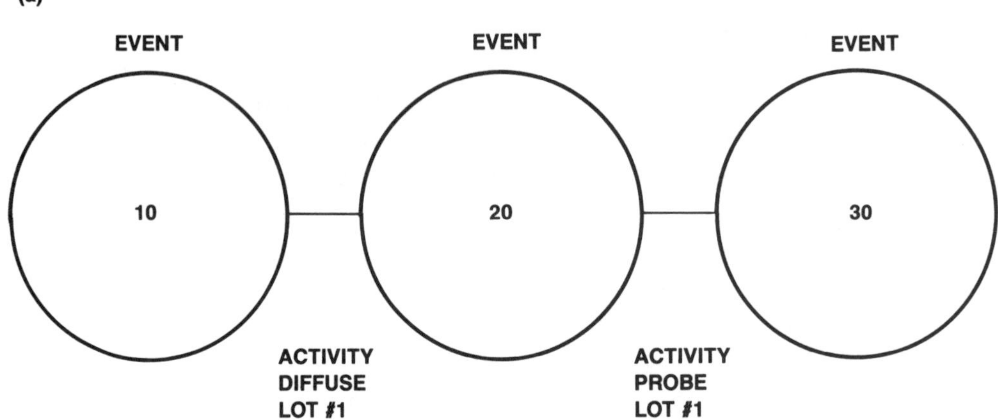

At this point, the principle has been expanded so that each event circle in Figures 2-3 and 2-4 contains four quadrants, each containing information relative to the preceding activity.

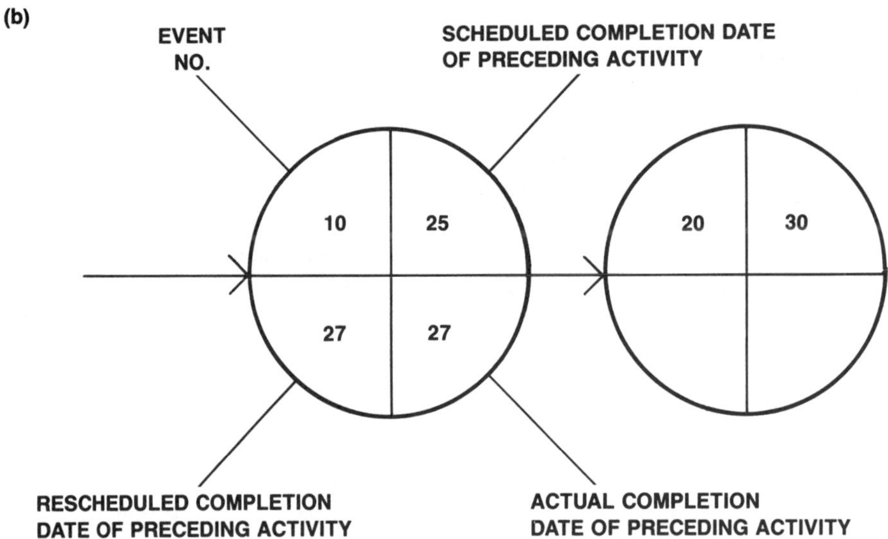

Figure 2-3 Activity Event Example

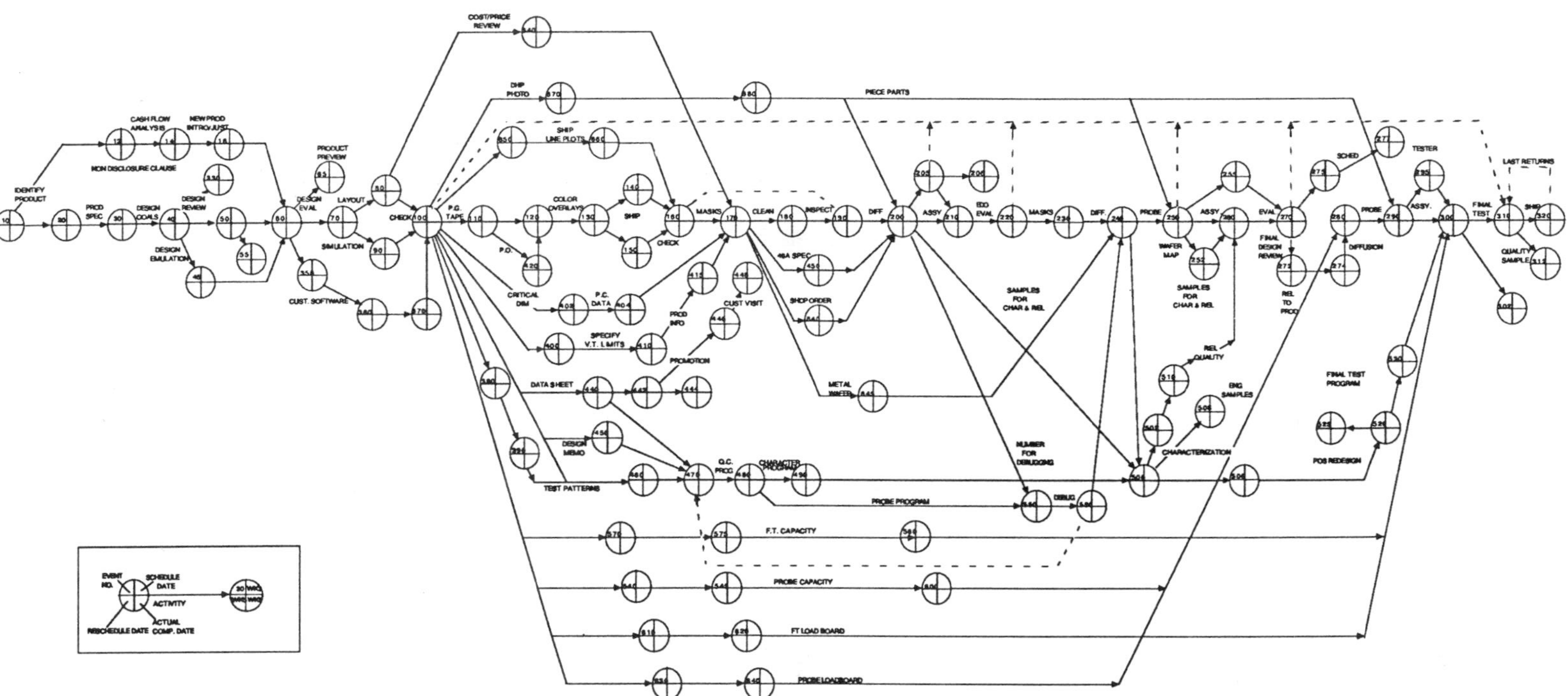

Figure 2-4 Project Management
New Product Introduction Universal PERT

NEW PRODUCT PRICING

What is new product pricing **designed to achieve**? Is the objective to:

1. Maximize short-term margins through innovative product ASP premium?
2. Maximize revenue and margin in a niche market?
3. Cover current product cost plus margin?
4. Gain market share?

It should be **designed to gain market share** through penetration and growth—**in the longer term** since **market share** is a **prerequisite** to profitability. This approach has been justified based on the work done by BCG group and others on:

1. The Learning or Experience Curve
2. Product Portfolio Analysis

The knowledge gained from this work is particularly relevant to semiconductor manufacturing, a capital-intensive industry which needs to operate at high volume to **amortize** fixed costs. There is a **high cost of doing nothing** and new products cost a great deal of money to design and develop.

Businesses or products can fall into the following categories:

1. Low Volume/Low Margin—End of Life Commodity Products
2. Low Volume/High Margin—Military Products
3. High Volume/Low Margin—Standard Product
4. High Volume/High Margin—Custom/Customized Products

A general classification analysis of such businesses was performed by BCG (Boston Consulting Group) is shown in Figure 2-5.

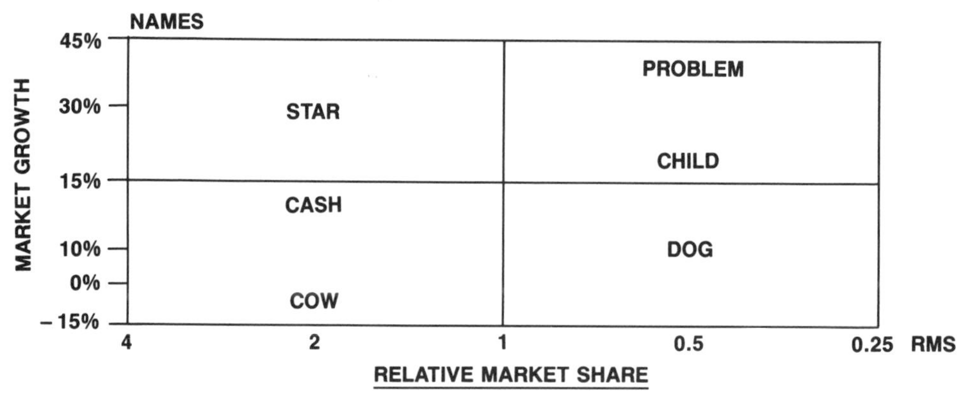

Figure 2-5

AXIS

1. **Horizontal** is **relative market share** (RMS): our market share divided by that of the biggest competition. If we are number one, this ratio will obviously be above one. Usually, to avoid confusion, by definition: high RMS is to the left. **The scale is logarithmic** (see **why later**).

2. Vertical is **market growth** either in percent (more indicative) or as an index relative to average total product market growth (the latter being around 15 percent). **The scale is linear**.

WHY RELATIVE MARKET SHARE?

The underpinnings of this BCG analysis is the experience curve effect which states that every time experience doubles, cost decreases by a constant factor found to be between 0.32 and 0.20 for semiconductors.

Thus, if product cost was $1.00 when all **accumulated** experience (since production started) was 1M units, then it should be $0.75 when **accumulated** experience reaches 2M units if the factor was 0.25. This factor is most often given as a reciprocal of 1.00; here, 0.75. In the case of competition, it is assumed that if your RMS is 0.5 and if it has been so since both you and the biggest competitor started production, then your experience is only half of his; then his cost (assuming a 75 percent experience curve) will only be 75 percent of yours, making it very tough on you to wage a successful price war. For an experience curve of 75 percent, an RMS of 0.67 (your market share 20 percent, No. 1's market share 30 percent) it yields a cost for him of 84.7 percent of your cost; still a tough fight under these conditions. All this assumes an equal degree of cleverness between each competitor.

WHICH MARKET SHARE?

The notion of experience is critical since experience is quantified in relation to cost. As such, products should not be grouped according to market statistics or internal organization, but into groups which have:

Commonality of production process, or which share experience in production.

BCG has defined an area of instability where competition is active. This is the grey area in Figure 2-6.

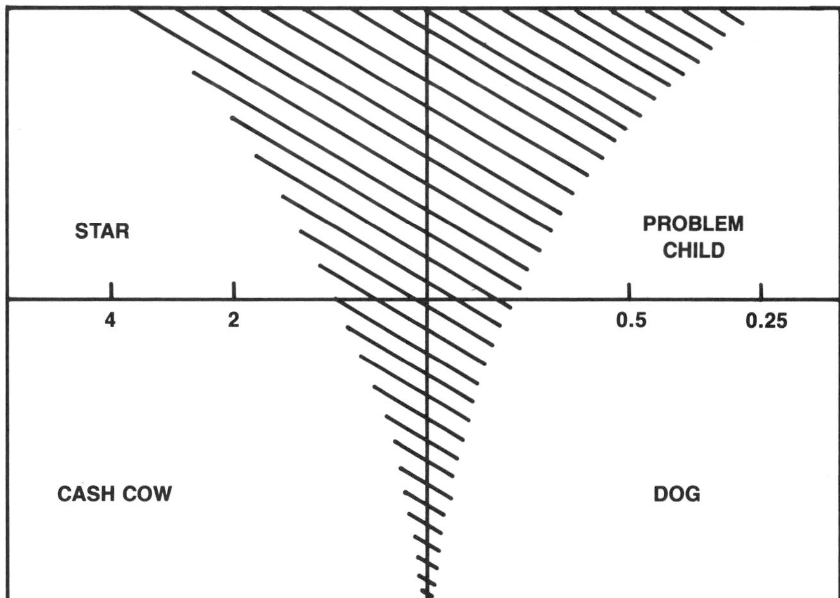

Figure 2-6 Positioning

When growth is high and the market still small, small competitors still try to get in, because if they make it the future size of their sales will largely pay their efforts. A very few years after this, the market settles because the experience accumulated by these who have held the market share since the outset puts their cost (and price) out of reach of the competition. Price aggressiveness at this stage is out of place. Good competitors have low costs, and the sales of product under attack are by then a large enough percent of their total sales that they can't afford to lose share, especially if production facilities are underutilized and can't be used readily for an alternative product. **In conclusion, aggressively trying to gain market share in products beyond the first few years is not prudent—unless the competitor under attack is willing to lose share.** This may be the case if he has a golden opportunity in a bright future product; he may withdraw by increasing prices in order to generate cash to plough into this future new product (a star or problem child).

CASH NOT PROFIT

The whole point is cash because the whole idea is to use cash generated by older products to fund newer products and hence maintain a living portfolio. As an example:

Sales	$100	
Depreciation	10	Not an expense
Other Costs	80	
PBT	$ 10	
Tax	5	
PAT	5	—Dividends 2 = Retained Earnings of $3

Cash Inflow Internal = Retained Earnings + Depreciation = 3 + 10 = 13

Say debt to equity rate is 1/1, that is, for every dollar generated internally you can raise 1 dollar externally and keep the same ratio of Debt/Equity; hence, another $13 can be generated to give a total of 26.

Now consider uses:

Say you grow at 10 percent a year—that is, your sales will grow by $10.

Say **receivable turns** and inventory turns are 6 and 7 respectively so you need:

Increased sales $10 × (1/6 + 1/7) = dollars to finance them

(Assume little payable) = $3.1.

Assume that your capital expenditures are 8 percent of next year sales = $8.8. Total uses 3.1 + 8.8 = 11.9. **Total cash generated 26 – 11.9 = 14.1 versus 5 in PAT.**

This is a typical cash cow; low profit but good cash.

The usual misconception is—"Despite what the analysis says, this product is not a cash cow because it does not make profit."

1. Figure 2-5 does not point to what this product generates, but to what it should generate given its market position. If you are positioned as a cash cow (i.e., leader with at least 50 percent or more market share than No. 2), you should make cash (not profit); but if you mismanage it, you may lose money/cash.

	Sources		Uses		
	PAT	**Depreciation**	**Plan**	**A/R = LY**	**Net**
Problem Child	LO	LO	HI	HI	NEG
Star	HI	LO	HI	HI	
Cash Cow	HI	HI	LO	LO	POS
Dog	LO	HI	LO	LO	

A dog can generate cash:

- If well managed (get out by raising prices), or
- If you can find a niche, or
- If you are the last one to get out.

Then your dog is turned into a cash cow because your RMS increased by just staying in; however, you still need to raise your prices if you want to generate this cash.

THE LEARNING OR EXPERIENCE CURVE

About 40 years ago, T.P. Wright, while doing work in the aircraft industry, observed that the trend in unit cost assumed a surprising constancy in slope if the logarithm of unit cost was plotted against the logarithm of **cumulative** production. He called this **the learning curve** (see Figure 2-7). The cause of this phenomenon was assumed to be that **skills are improved through repetition** (Adam Smith's pin maker in the "Wealth of

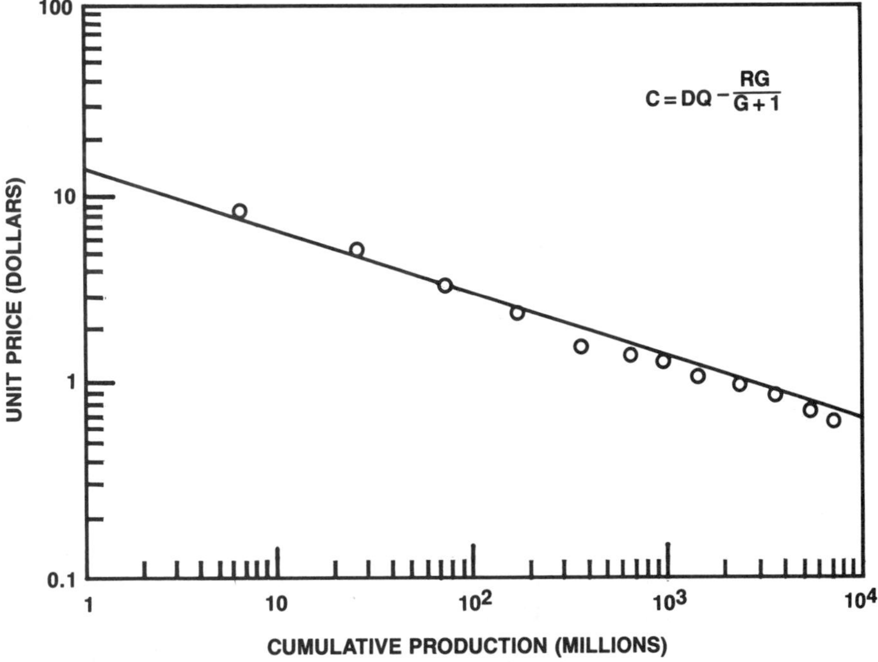

Figure 2-7 Learning Curve

Nations''). However, the trend in unit cost reduction persisted even when labor turnover was high. **''Learning''** was then **discounted** as an important contributor and the **''experience curve''** was coined. This proposed that technological change and the impact of capital investment is the cause (economics of scale).

Both the learning curve and the experience curve demonstrate the correlation between unit cost and cumulative volume but **they do not adequately explain cause and effect or allow meaningful modeling**. The possibility of **''propagation of error''** arises from the focus on **''cumulative''** volume (annual rate of production and time rate of growth) being assumed to be **a single variable**. These shortcomings gave rise to the **opportunity curve** which identifies and analyzes the correlation between a unit cost reduction trend and the **annual** rate of production. It focuses on **''future market share.''** The most articulate definition has been offered by C. T. Goddard—*IEEE Proceedings*, 1982, as follows:

> The **expanding** market warrants an increase in mechanization and in the size of batch processing facilities. The increase in annual revenue is the **source of funds** to support this **technological change**. Learning still features, but not so much from what is done in the remote past but from the growing cadre of development personnel and manufacturing engineers which the increase in revenue can support. Today's anticipation of future demand is what inspires and supports the growth and imagination of independent firms which concentrate on **innovation in mechanization**, quite apart from the firms which make the product. The driving force comes from **looking forward in time** rather than backward at cumulative production.

The **opportunity curve** then, relates **future unit costs** to the **future annual rate of production**.

OPPORTUNITY CURVE SUMMARY

- Unit costs decrease with **annual** rate of production.
- **Economies of scale** lie at the heart of **productivity improvements**.

  Productivity—Of direct/indirect human resources
  —Of capital
  —Of real estate—buildings and silicon

- **Market share** has a significant bearing on **profitability**. (Profit impact of market strategies (PIMS)—*Harvard Business Review* ten-year study involving 28 factors concluded that **''market share was dominant.''**)
- Volume provides the **opportunity and incentive** to reduce product costs. The **means** to do so must be **provided** and **applied**.
- New product pricing should be designed to achieve market share by **reconciling** the **market ASP** (maximum price it is **anticipated** the market is willing to pay)—with the minimum price the seller can/will **profitability accept.**
- **To do this we need to define:**

  1. The price/volume sensitivity curve (elasticity) (difficult—but the most important things in life are usually the most difficult).

  2. The cost/volume sensitivity curve (price is assumed to be the **independent variable—cost** is considered to be the **dependent variable**).

- Factories have **high inertia** and **momentum—a supertanker product marketing** are the **ship's pilot** and **navigator**.

PRICE VOLUME SENSITIVITY CURVE

● To construct this curve, an **understanding** of the market **future** behavior is needed.

—Market characteristics
—Competition
—Market size, share, growth rate
—Buyer behavior

Consider EPROMs, for example. EPROM MCUs were initially purchased **exclusively** to satisfy prototyping needs. Other motives have now evolved which should have a bearing on pricing strategy.

1. Prototypes—Low Volume/High Price
2. Volume Perturbations—Reasonably High Price for Flexibility
3. Fast Turnon—Cost versus Speed
4. Fast Updates—Value in Market
5. Screw Ups—Insurance Policy Premium

FURTHER THOUGHTS ON THE "LEARNING CURVE"

Nothing which we encounter in management is possibly so misunderstood, misrepresented, and misapplied as the ostensibly universal, empirical observation, that manufacturing unit costs reduce over time as volume increases as if some natural cause independent of any intention or direct intervention produces this effect. In reviewing the literature produced on this subject since the phenomena was first observed over 40 years ago, it would seem that the series of attempts to explain the underlying cause cycle through a process of first apparent enlightenment, then subsequent discreditation as each successive hypothesis, despite some awe inspiring mathematics purporting to demonstrate its legitimacy, is subsequently shown to be at best incomplete and at worst incorrect. What all of these efforts do have in common, however, is an underlying premise that the human learning process, or more fashionably, the accumulation of experience, is the primary underlying cause behind the effect. This section will attempt to show the invalidity of these premises.

As was stated earlier, this effect is based on the observation that the cost of doing a repetitive task decreases by a fixed percentage each time the total accumulated volume of production units doubles and was first observed by T. P. Wright in the manufacture of aircraft during the Second World War. Recalling Adam Smith's treatise on the Wealth of Nations, the **increased proficiency** which comes with the application of the principle of division of labor and specialization in executing manual tasks (practice makes perfect), was then believed to be the underlying case behind this effect. The fact that costs continued to decrease even during periods of high labor turnover, when improvements in the skill of those performing these repetitive tasks could be discounted, soon discredited this original explanation. In searching for a replacement, the belief that replacing the labor factor of production by **fixed function mechanization** was considered to be the causal factor and the term *experience curve* or *progress function* was substituted for *learning curve* to reflect this. This particular analysis, in an era when direct labor cost as a proportion of total product cost continued to decline, reigned supreme for the next 20 or so years. In the early 1980s, Charles T. Goddard, among others, subsequently attempted to demonstrate the incompleteness of this explanation by illustrating the inability of the mathematics developed around the experience curve, to fail to predict, or even explain, the increase in costs experienced during recessions, despite cumulative volume continuing to increase. The formula used to define this curve projected that costs, even in these circumstances, would in fact continue to decline. Goddard argued that the use of cumulative volume in the mathematics introduced a "possible propagation of error" in that "buried and inseparable in this single variable are the annual rate of production and the time rate of growth of that variable." His solution, while acknowledging the validity of the learning curve, attempted to overcome this inadequacy by **substituting cumulative volume**—in which time and volume are represented by only one variable—**by annual volume** or production. As a result, the phenomena was again renamed, the term *opportunity curve* was invoked to complement that of learning; the new belief being that **economies of scale** were in fact the underlying cause and the need to focus on future cost and price behavior rather than past history was emphasized. Each explanation has in turn been mathematically treated in an attempt to validate its integrity and support its acceptance. All of them require that prices be adjusted for inflation in order to produce smooth curves. Each also includes different constants by industry, the reason for which still has to be explained.

In reviewing the many papers produced on this subject, one is often left wondering: is the effect explained by improvements in direct labor proficiency; is it due to the substitution of fixed function mechanization or automation for direct labor; is it simply due to economics of scale; do these cost reductions, for whatever reason, occur of their own accord as if governed by some natural law—Adam Smith's "invisible hand" as it were? The truth of course is not usually so simple. While it is one thing to accept Smith's principle that specialization and division of labor will, in improving the proficiency with which manual tasks are executed, reduce costs, it is quite another to accept that (1) something as complex as the human learning process, or accumulation of experience, can be mathematically quantified in a formula and (2) that this alone can be responsible for price and cost reduction—especially in situations where direct labor is a diminishing factor. This is something intuitively rejected by people who know how marketplaces and factories really work, and suggests the need for a different explanation. The remainder of this text will attempt to place all of these factors in their proper perspective by showing that while learning and experience can, and do, indeed contribute to the end result of reduced costs, the primary underlying cause has nothing whatsoever to do with either. In fact, **the first order effect is simply due to nothing more than the effect of volume on the relationship between fixed and variable costs—and how they are managed**. See Figure 2-8. This is not to say that learning, as it relates to direct operator skill in the execution of manual tasks, and experience, as it relates to the specialist skills which constitute the manufacturing infrastructure, do not contribute to the reduction of costs; but that they are (1) **secondary, rather than first-order**, effects and (2) that they do not manifest themselves of their own accord—but **must be made to happen!**

We will begin with an analogy which will hopefully demonstrate this and which can then be related to its factory equivalent. It is fitting that this analogy be constructed in the environment in which this phenomena was first observed—the aircraft industry. Instead of dealing with the manufacturing aspect of aircraft, however, our analogy will deal with its application.

Assume we are in the commercial airline business, pursuing the profit motive by conveying people to and from various destinations. A figure of merit of our operational efficiency might be cost per passenger per mile (or cost per passenger mile). What will

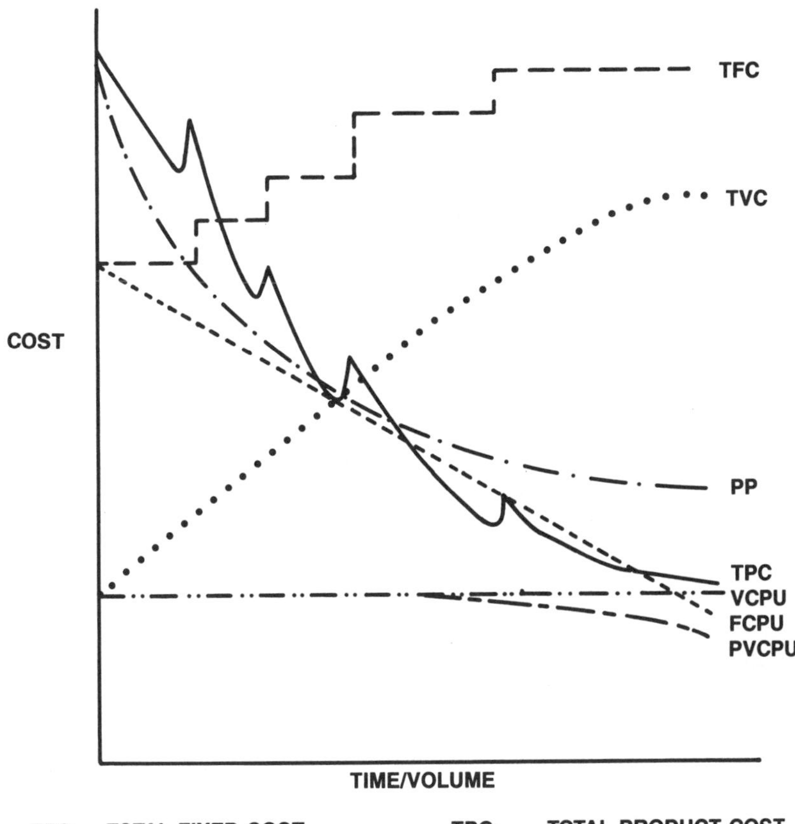

Figure 2-8 The Expanded "Learning" Curve

be the major components of these costs and what will be their behavior in relation to volume? First, in order to ply our trade, we must have at least one aircraft, with a fixed, maximum capacity of say 500 seats. Let's further assume that the purchase of this aircraft was financed by borrowing funds, the capital cost of which must be depreciated over time. This will represent a fixed cost, incurred on a periodic basis, independent of the actual time the aircraft is flying in service or the number of passengers per flight. We shall also incur operating expenses in the form of fuel and salaries, and so on. There will obviously be a relationship between these fixed and variable costs. We can accept, without even doing the arithmetic, that the less seats that are occupied on the aircraft during any flight, the greater will be the cost per passenger per mile since the denominator—the number of passengers—will be low. The lowest cost will be realized only when the aircraft is fully loaded. (This does not necessarily represent the conditions for maximum revenue or profit.) Realizing this state of affairs may have nothing to do with learning or experience, and everything to do with the price we charge. The lower the price, the greater the probability that all of the seats will be taken, the lower the proportion of fixed cost that each seat must absorb, and therefore, the lower will be the cost per passenger mile—and the higher the probability that we can be profitable **at these prices**. (A more mundane example might be an automobile conveying one person to and from work every day. If the driver is accompanied by three passengers, the cost per passenger mile will obviously be lower than that for the driver alone—but this has nothing to do with an improvement in skill of the driver.)

Now, further imagine that our pricing strategy is successful and that over a period of time, we succeed in selling most, if not all, of the seats on every flight. If we wish to gain more market share—across which to amortize our fixed costs—then the need will arise for a second aircraft, and the process of filling this new total number of available seats will continue. Our costs however will have increased due to this step function increase in capacity. But if we wish to fill the additional seats, we would be wise to try to avoid transmitting this cost increase through to our pricing. In order to avoid, or at least minimize, the erosion of our profit margin due to this increased cost, we would obviously wish to try and reduce our costs elsewhere, if at all possible. But where? We already know we can do nothing about fixed cost depreciation after the fact—**except to amortize it over increasing volume**. We can only avoid incurring these in the first place. Having committed to these costs, however, we are compelled to operate in such a fashion that the fixed cost per seat is minimized. (The importance of this is evident in the practice of overbooking the seats available by some airline companies.) This then leaves variable costs. Can we reduce these? If so, how?

Having characterized our aircraft's performance during flight trials, our supplier will be able to recommend the optimum cruising speed and altitude for lowest fuel consumption. Operating in conformance to these criteria will therefore produce fuel cost savings. Aircraft are only productive (earning revenue) when in flight—not sitting on the apron at the airport. The opportunity for further cost saving is then possible by minimizing turnaround time at each airport. Considering the prevailing winds, and so on further cost saving can be won by selecting the most efficient routes. On the revenue side of the equation, we can enhance profit with in-flight revenue by selling perfumes and refreshments, and so on. There is obviously a spectrum of such things we can do to maximize our revenue, minimize our costs, and therefore maximize our profits—or minimize our losses. The pilot in our little analogy, is the production operator, performing his repetitive task, day after day. But any reduction in cost as a result of his contribution must be miniscule in relation to other savings produced by the substantial support infrastructure behind each flight.

In many respects, it is no different with a factory! Capacity, especially in a capital intensive industry such as semiconductors, is usually (1) very expensive and (2) does not exist as a continuous variable. It occurs in step function increments (3) represents a fixed cost—**a total cost independent of volume** and (4) cannot be made available and then consumed (loaded) instantly. Regardless of the size of the opportunity available, it takes time to increase volume in any factory, or industry, especially one whose products and processes are very complex. In situ engineering is normally needed to get machines and factories to produce at any volume. There is a need to minimize initial negative cash flow with fastest possible ramp up. There are many examples of businesses which in dogmatically pursuing the learning curve, relying on nothing more than the ''natural effect'' to reduce cost who have simply pursued aggressive pricing and made their negative cash flow worse, not better. In not **forcing cost reduction**, the cost competence of these businesses can be no better than that of the rest of the pack. A typical mistake is to build big, high fixed cost factories, then avoid spending the money on indirect headcount to make it productive in the mistaken belief that these are avoidable, variable costs.

These fixed costs, by definition, are incurred whether the factory is loaded or not—**the proportion of these costs which each unit manufactured must carry however, decreases with increasing volume**. Variable costs per unit on the other hand remain constant but total variable costs increase in direct proportion to volume over time. (In reality, variable cost per unit may in fact decrease with volume due to such things as piece-part price discounts for volume, for example.)

Unlike the other ascribed causes, this explanation of the cause behind cost reduction satisfies:

1. Reduction in cost with increase in volume—and vice versa—such as might be the case during a general recession, when total volume typically falls.

2. Mathematical modeling—if accurate cost information is available. (Most cost accounting information suffers from being pooled and then apportioned or allocated, rather than specifically by product.)

3. Increases in cost with the addition of capacity. Learning and experience curves, by dwelling on price curves only, ignore this effect.

If the explanation really is so simple, why have these other red herrings been purveyed for so long? Can it be due to:

The inadequacy of most cost accounting systems and treatments?

That big, prestigious consulting companies cannot grow and flourish selling something so simple?

That academics prefer esoteric solutions, overlooking the obvious till last, are so compelled to reduce everything to an equation—even to the extent of resorting to force fitting if necessary?

That reality has been made to fit the mathematically convenient model—rather than vice versa?

GUIDELINES FOR THE PRAGMATIC PRACTITIONER

Competitive Pricing Supported by Relentless Pursuit of Cost Reduction

What conclusions can be drawn, what guidelines can be developed from our analysis of the "learning" curve phenomena which we can practically apply in real life? First, I think, we must understand not only the accounting, but the economics of our business and of the industry in which it operates. The relationship between fixed and variable costs must be very thoroughly understood. If fixed costs are high in proportion to total product cost, then high volume—apart from keeping fixed costs as low as possible—is the only way in which the per unit burden of these costs can be minimized. High volume usually means high market share—and vice versa. But how does one create this virtuous circle? Market share can only be won, and held, on product and process innovation, price, quality, on-time delivery, and service. The parameter we are most interested in, the context of this discussion, is that of price/cost. How is market share leveraged by the price/cost relationship?

With a highly innovative new product, price strategy is much more important than cost strategy. The market will be willing to pay such a high price premium that costs in such a situation will almost be academic. The monopolistic supplier can enjoy generous margins at this time by charging high prices. The risk of course is that these margins will attract competition which will, due to the subsequently improved supply and competitive situation, put downward pressure on prices. The smart supplier will anticipate this and make entry less attractive by decreasing prices voluntarily over time in the knowledge that to prevent other suppliers from getting into the market is less costly than letting them in and then subsequently trying to drive them out. The greedy or complacent monopolist will not drive his costs down aggressively and will therefore be vulnerable to attack from behind. In conditions of more equal competition however, low cost competence assumes a much more important role.

What should our pricing and cost strategy be in such circumstances? The simple lesson to be learned and applied from the study of learning curve literature is that a pricing strategy based on cost plus margin of an underloaded, and therefore high cost factory, is a self-fulfilling, self-perpetuating strategy with an **undesirable outcome**. The volume of business won at these prices will remain low and the factory costs, therefore, will remain high. This strategy **will simply perpetuate the status quo**. The other extreme is to use the anticipated product cost of a fully-loaded factory in designing our pricing strategy. This strategy will tend to win high volume (high loading), **creating the opportunity—and incentive—to drive costs down** rather than just waiting for them to do so of their own accord due to some "natural law." The result is likely to be healthy profit margins even at these lower prices. In effect, this strategy will produce a self-fulfilling, self-perpetuating, **desirable outcome**. **The focus is on the future**—demanding a strategy best designed to reconcile, in dynamic equilibrium, what Smith called the "natural" price—the product cost plus margin—with the market price determined by competition. In an expanding market, trying to win market share away from a competitor with low price, contrary to popular belief, may in fact make sense especially if the factory capacity already exists, but is unused. (The mistake might be in building such a factory in the first place. It may be that previous treatments of this topic have done nothing except perpetuate the notion, by advocating the economies of scale, that big is beautiful.)

The next step in this strategy is to then relentlessly pursue the actual realization of these cost reductions in practice upon which the whole pricing strategy was based. It is at this point that learning and experience come into play. In general, we might summarize as follows:

1. It is preposterous to define product cost, or price, only in terms of two variables—production rate and time—and believe that any meaningful conclusions can be drawn from this, far less a meaningful strategy.

2. Direct labor is a rapidly diminishing "factor of production." Any cost reduction associated with increased efficiency of this factor will encounter rapidly diminishing returns. Material and overhead are probably much larger proportions with a much higher savings potential.

3. Do not invest in fixed cost assets unless absolutely necessary. Fuel growth in market share with increased productivity first—and investment in additional capacity last. It is easier to invest in additional capacity than to make the existing capacity more productive. But with the former approach, the fixed cost will increase and diseconomies of scale may be encountered. It is imperative to know the maximum potential of the existing capacity in order to avoid buying more unnecessarily and to quantify lowest possible potential product cost associated with this capacity.

4. Add capacity in the smallest possible increments.

5. Make capital equipment as productive as possible, as soon as possible.

6. Do not pool and then allocate or apportion fixed costs. An intelligent product pricing policy cannot be developed without specific, product cost.

7. Minimize the period and maximize the frequency of the learning cycle. In the semiconductor industry, the learning cycle on a specific product is measured in mask set iterations. The length of the cycle is the time taken to analysis, identify, and correct product or process problems—in effect, the cycle-time of the complete manufacturing process. The longer this cycle-time, the fewer the opportunties to learn in a given period of time.

8. Beware economies of scale—they can be a double-edged sword. Highly specialized, capital-intensive capacity can become redundant very quickly with changes in market conditions.

9. Price, while particularly important on commodity products, is only one of the essential ingredients of total customer satisfaction.

10. Cost reduction plans based on what is theoretically possible, not history plus some small improvement, should be a way of life.

11. When diminishing returns are encountered, start a new curve.

3

New Product Design

DESIGNING FOR PERFORMANCE

Until very recently, it was common practice across much of the U.S. semiconductor industry to hold the design function primarily responsible for demonstrating only that the product specification could be successfully integrated in silicon, with design participation diminishing beyond the point where the product had been shown to be producible. The pressure to excel in product innovation made technical performance of the product the paramount consideration, compelling the design organization to focus almost exclusively on this criterion, more often than not stretching product and manufacturing process capability to the limit in support of this. It was not unusual for design practice, preceding the evolution of manufacturing capability in time, to require processes and control of tolerances, and even in some cases entire manufacturing technologies, beyond the currently prevailing "state of the art" of the day in manufacturing. (Latterday equivalents of Babbage's "analytical engines" are even now being designed.) When the point was reached where it could be demonstrated that at least some part of a lot population, no matter how small, could meet this performance criteria, the task of increasing the yield of the remainder of the product population to this specification passed to other functions.

In effect, this approach viewed design as affecting only phase 1, the innovation phase of the new product life cycle, the requirements of phase 2, the growth phase, being left essentially to the manufacturing engineering and quality control functions. (Although very active in phases 1 and 2, marketing's opportunity to really shine came in phases 3 and 4, trying to sustain a high demand for products whose novelty appeal had expired.) A generous market, simplicity of products and processes, and less than rigorous customer expectations in terms of quality, reliability, on-time delivery and cost, permitted this serial approach to be taken with no unduly serious disadvantages. If the yield of these superlative performance products was low then that was quite another matter, to be addressed by others at a later date. The design function was usually so far removed from the customer that any allegiance to his department, profession, product (or ego), was likely to exceed any felt towards the needs of the customer base at this point.

Design, like manufacturing or quality control or process and equipment engineering, tended to be regarded as an almost stand-alone, independent function, with very clear lines of demarcation, unrelated to the other functions except via a very distinct, organizational interface. Each vertically organized, highly specialized function was relied upon to perform its respective tasks in virtual organizational, and sometimes geographic, isolation. An intimate knowledge of these other functions and their requirements on the part of the designer, and vice versa, was not required, and responsibility for meeting all but product performance criteria could be delegated, in some cases abdicated, to the specialists in these other disciplines. Design was more or less considered to have fulfilled its product functionality obligations when the first die wiggled. To subsequently produce and ship high volumes of the product of high quality at low cost and on time—phase 2 of the new product life cycle—was perceived, to a large extent, to be everyone else's responsibility, usually led and coordinated by the product engineering department. At this point, the design team could then enthusiastically embark on the design of the next widget, charging their costs to a common R&D pool.

The whole process, usually proceeding at a fairly leisurely pace, was structured like a relay race, each runner passing the baton to the next, usually less than flawlessly, with ownership passing with the baton. Any race lost could easily be blamed on another runner. In a way, it was like the child's game—pass the parcel—in which the children form a circle and pass a present wrapped in paper from one to the other to music. Anyone holding the parcel when the music is stopped by someone visually isolated from the proceedings is eliminated from the game. This is not intended to cast aspersions on the good graces of the design fraternity—they simply behaved, as did the other functions, in a manner consistent with that which they were measured. Design was simply the first of many independently measured steps in what was an extremely lengthy, inefficient, and wasteful approach to satisfying customer needs.

Not so long ago, each new design was virtually hand crafted as it were, the process of integrating the system design, beginning at the individual transistor level, being designed and layed out by hand. The designer had a very high degree of freedom, from the way the function was described in logic, all the way down to the design of any individual transistor and the way it was constructed topographically, often requiring unique manufacturing processes. Almost all components could be individually prescribed, leading to a very high degree of proliferation. More often than not, the design tools to check the logic circuitry, to produce mask set data bases, and to generate the test patterns were in the form of a common resource resident on a mainframe computer, shared not only by other design users but with other functions in the organization at large. Time lost in queueing for access to this common resource frequently caused delays in project time scales.

With such a high degree of individual autonomy, there was little opportunity to develop controls to ensure the discipline required for first-time success, the skill and conscientiousness of each individual designer, or small design team, being all that could be relied upon to meet product design goals and project time scales. This, in conjunction with long manufacturing process cycle-times, even when expedited in a relatively fast prototype mode, and the burden of coordinating the project also falling on the designer at this point, missed objectives were not unusual. It was culturally acceptable for silicon not to work completely with the first mask set, but merely to show signs of life. Several design fix mask set iterations to get the product right, each consuming two to four valuable months and many tens of thousands of dollars in mask set and manufacturing costs, were par for the course. Having already spent anything from six months to three years on a project, the designer would eagerly appear with the first and subsequent iterations of the mask set data base, only to find everyone else—usually beleagured under other priorities—unwilling to give their undivided attention to expediting it through the system, much to the chagrin of the bemused and frustrated designer.

In addition to this, project planning and control was most often only rudimentary, relying on mainly manual methods, with overall ownership of the project vague and confused. With less than adequate tools to provide visibility and little executive authority to execute control, the product engineering department would usually inherit ownership by default, trying as best they could to coordinate all of the necessary tasks and players. The net result of all of this meant that more often than not, many things were done late, badly, or not at all. Processes, sometimes unavoidably unique to each product, would be lashed together in order to make up lost time and get the ''hot potato'' passed on to the next station in the chain as quickly as possible, but usually only after it had spent some considerable time in a process queue—the fast spurts and long pauses of the childrens' game. These processes, which likely as not were barely suitable even for engineering evaluation purpose, were almost invariably completely unsuitable for high volume, high quality, low cost manufacture. One of the more critical steps usually sacrificed in the interest of expediency, without which efficient manufacturing cannot be realized, was product and process characterization. Without this essential foundation, one of the main sources of manufacturing inefficiency, product and process variation, discussed later in this chapter, and to a greater extent in Chapter 14, could not begin to be controlled. Quite the contrary, the almost instinctive reaction would be to (1) increase the wafer-starts, (2) shrink an already unproduction worthy, low yielding mask set in order to increase the die per wafer—albeit reducing an already low percentage yield in order to satisfy demand. Almost invariably, the need for incremental capacity (usually in some new technology derivative in limited supply) to support the growth phase in wafer fabrication, in unit probe, in assembly, and final test, would be underestimated or even completely overlooked.

In consequence, when the need arose to ramp up production volume to satisfy the demand created by successfully marketing the product specification, the negative cash flow of phase 1 development costs was perpetuated further into phase 2 more than one would wish, due to the waste associated with the low manufacturing yields and capacity bottlenecks. The more product shipped, the greater these losses. The alternative, restraining shipments, with potentially serious customer and market share impact, was usually considered to be even less desirable. Even with the best of intentions, customer line-down situations could not always be avoided. Superimposed on all of this would be the cost of the engineering changes required to bring the product up to full production-worthy status, any such change affecting the mask set creating the prospect of work-in-process produced with the previous, now obsolete mask set, being potentially unsaleable. Only with demonstrably real demand, when overwhelmed by opportunity usually in the form of a delinquent backlog would the resources be assigned—the belated cavalry charge—to retrospectively engineer the product for manufacturability. Satisfying this demand took the form of force feeding the system with as much work-in-process as it could engorge and hoping, that after paying the usually very high waste tax, enough product would eventually emerge at the other end to take care of servicing the customers' needs.

The search for saleable product would then begin, by 100 percent test screening, lot sampling and gating, reworking or screening if necessary, and it usually was, then finally shipping the remainder of the population which conformed to specification. Since 100 percent test screening, no matter how diligently applied, cannot be entirely effective, the shipped population invariably contained some rejects, reinforcing in the customer base, already frustrated by delays in product availability, a most unfavorable first impression. Since the product was also usually probed to the lowest acceptable specification, final test yields—especially for the high performance proportion of the lot population, usually most in demand—were also low, resulting in a frantic scramble to install expensive incremental capacity to compensate for this shortfall. Such were the attributes of the new introduction process in a totally reactive, just-in-case, lot sampling quality controlled, manufacturing environment. Such "seat of the pants" flying was the then "state of the (semiconductor alchemist's) art."

SIGNS OF STRESS

With increasing complexity of products and processes affecting the design task as well as that of manufacturing, in conjunction with rapidly escalating customer expectations, shorter product life cycles and a more fiercely competitive environment, this approach, not particularly commendable to begin with, falls far short of meeting today's requirements. Increasingly manifest signs of stress mandate the need for the whole approach to be vigorously reviewed. While there is much room for improvement in the approaches taken to manufacturing and quality control in their own right, both issues being fully discussed in later chapters, it is being progressively acknowledged that at least some of the shortcomings of these functional disciplines are symptoms of a more fundamental malaise in the new product introduction process, at least some of whose original causes lie back in the design area.

In my 18 years in the industry, I have never known a new product to have been introduced on time, far less flawlessly. (There are quite possibly some Japanese exceptions.) In today's highly competitive environment, the need to do so is as great as the difficulty in being able to. On-time in this context is when the potential supplier declares, usually during product announcement, when the product will be available to the marketplace and then meeting the initial alpha and beta site delivery commitments made during the subsequent customer design-in cycles. After the projected availability date has come and gone, the apologies, explanations, excuses, specification relaxations, errata sheets, allocation exercises, and "get well plans" would follow.

Does this mean that the new product introduction cycle cannot be executed **right first time**? Is our industry condemned to operating in the mode of making and breaking the promises associated with the selling of futures which the competitive environment demands? The whole process is so dauntingly complex, especially in conjunction with our progressively increasing dependence on extremely complex and notoriously error-prone software, employed not only in the design task, but throughout the whole of the manufacturing process, that we might rather depressingly conclude that this, most regrettably, may well be the case. But even if this were so, surely that does not mean that the process cannot be substantially improved.

Of all that is wrong with our industry, this may well be an issue of pivotal importance, perhaps the single most important issue. So many of the problems which are subsequently encountered in the manufacturing process have their origins back in our approach to the new product introduction process in general and in the design process in particular, improving this will cause many of our other "problems" to disappear. Being able to introduce new products speedily and flawlessly, learning how to manufacture them with least possible waste, is the **distinctive competence par excellence without peer**—on which profitability, indeed perhaps even survival, may depend. The struggle for dominance in both phase 1 and 2 of the new product life cycle may well be the crucial battle in which the war will be won or lost. Phase 2, in which the Japanese are unquestionably dominant, with a history of several decades of manufacturing process enhancement behind them, is the beach head from which they are launching their assault back into phase 1 where we, at least in some product portfolios, are still relatively strong in our ability to define and design successful new products. This being the case, our strategy should be clear: we must consolidate, entrench, and continue to refine our distinctive competence in this area while organizing our advance back into phase 2, where we have already conceded so much ground, with renewed vigor. A very benign market tolerated our manufacturing profligacy in phase 2—a competitive one does not provide such margin for waste. If the Asian supremacy in phase 2 remains uncontested, then surely it is only a matter of time before the economic benefits accruing from this will be employed in usurping our already insecure advantage in phase 1. The remainder of this chapter addresses how we might begin to organize our campaign, not only of retaining supremacy in phase 1, but to begin the process of regaining supremacy in phase 2. Since the customer will be the final arbiter, we would be well advised to begin this process of renewal by revisiting and reviewing the criteria against which our efforts will ultimately be judged.

THE ROLE OF DESIGN IN THE NEW PRODUCT INTRODUCTION PROCESS

Setting Appropriate Objectives

In fashioning a new product introduction system, where should we begin? As in any campaign, the most appropriate strategy to employ will depend on the objectives being pursued. If these objectives are not clearly defined, if they are in any way inappropriate, vague, or incomplete, if they are not properly communicated, comprehended, and wholeheartedly embraced, then it is unlikely that any strategy to achieve these objectives will succeed. Broadly speaking, we know that the desired end result of the new product introduction process is to generate profit by satisfying customer needs. While this is generally and universally true, it still isn't much help. Perhaps our analysis should continue with an effort to develop a better understanding of these customer needs we are attempting to satisfy and how the new product introduction process in general and design practice in particular affect these needs. What are the components of the satisfaction equation, conformance to which will create a path of least resistance from the customer's doorstep to ours, rather than that of the competition? Some at least are obvious—product performance, quality, price—and based on this understanding, we might more specifically state the objectives, for the product and project respectively, as follows.

Objectives for the Product:

Meet required performance (functionality)
At the right quality/reliability
At the right price/cost
On time

Objectives for the Project:

Achieve the required: Market share, cash flow, growth, and profit margin profiles.

These, as good objectives should be, would be quantified in measureable units so that progress towards them can be reviewed on a regular basis. But is this still too general?

Are there more subtle parameters or variations on this theme? The experts have tried to help us here by offering various definitions, mainly with regard to the quality component. But at least one problem the pragmatic practitioner might have with these is that there appears to be as many definitions as there are experts. Some are so general, such as Feigenbaum's "meeting the expectations of the customer" as to be noninformative, to Taguchi's very specifically limited to product quality only "meeting conformance to target." While each in isolation might not provide us with a complete answer, taken collectively, perhaps many, if not all of the components we seek, including the more subtly elusive, are contained within them. This is especially true if we acknowledge that the customer's hierarchy of needs, the relative ranking of each component, will not be static, but will vary with circumstances and time.

In deciding to design-in a new product, for example, promised or actual product performance will be high on the customer's hierarchy; promised in the case of a product not yet available; real and measurable if the product is already available. Price will also be an important parameter, but the price/volume/time profile can be negotiated and agreed upon up front. Quality and reliability on the other hand and commitments to deliver on time, verifiable only after product shipments have actually taken place, must be accepted, at least initially, in good faith by the customer. In a choice of vendor situation, each able to offer the desired product performance, or in a repeat patronage decision, product performance and features will no longer be an issue—but quality, reliability, on-time delivery, and service will rise up the hierarchy. (This normally is the point at which a second source supplier enters the battle.) A customer's previous experience of a vendor's performance in this respect, perhaps on another product, may well prove to be a factor in this phase of the decision process.

Clearly then, there are needs to be addressed by purely product parameters, such as product performance, patently design related, and others, such as on-time delivery, price, and service, classically held to be a function of an enterprise's general overall competency other than design. If we were to classify these, the point-of-sale criteria the customer might consider to be most important in deciding between vendors might be: product performance, cost (price to the customer) features, conformance, aesthetics, perceived quality. Repeat patronage might be based on quality, reliability, on-time delivery, performance, service, and integrity. Patriotism is conspicuously absent as a parameter which can be rationally considered in the satisfaction equation.

Maximizing these will obviously depend, among other things, on the extent to which we understand design practice to affect them. The design to product performance correlation is obvious—it may not be so obvious that design also affects quality, reliability, on-time delivery, and cost. Design is in fact a common factor affecting virtually all of the parameters in the total satisfaction equation. The old way of designing, manufacturing, and testing to separate the good from the bad, rescreening, and reworking rejects, almost as independent, sequential tasks, is no longer acceptable. Functional organizations with very shallow and distinct interfaces; force feeding the system at the input with as much as it can swallow in the hope that enough specification conformant product will emerge at the other end, cannot satisfy the requirements of this equation to the degree now necessary. The contemporary approach regards design as it does manufacturing or quality control, or any other function for that matter, as a means to an end rather than as an end in its own right; as part of a system, a process, to which a total approach to quality is applied, the raison d'etre of whose existence is to create profit by satisfying customer's total needs. In an intensely competitive environment, **profit and waste are mutually exclusive**. This new approach acknowledges that customer needs are not satisfied, no matter how technically elegant the product, if the quality is bad and requires incoming inspection, the price too high, the product not delivered on time, frequent field retrofits, product updates, defective product in the form of early life (infant mortality) failures, or the invoice paper work is not correct. Achieving working silicon may well satisfy an intermediate design goal and may be usefully employed in reinforcing a customer's interest in a design specification, but complete mutual satisfaction of both supplier and customer is not assured unless, and until, the overall goals of the project, and not just those of the product, are realized in full.

Redefinition of Design Goals

Consistent with the principles of statistical process control—that of eliminating waste by controlling variability, applied at the earliest point in the process for greatest leverage, the charter of the design function is being redefined, requiring this discipline to accept the very formidable challenge of designing not only for product performance, but also for **zero defect manufacturability**. The design function, as the Japanese and some of the more enlightened manufacturers in the western hemisphere have already done, is being held accountable, at least in part, for contributing to meeting the criteria, not only of phase 1 the product innovation aspect, but also of phase 2 the project aspect of the new product life cycle. No longer are the designers off the hook when the first die wiggles in some semblance of conformance to the product performance specification. With this new level of expectation in mind, we might now attempt a redefinition of the design goals, in the form of operating principles—subordinated to and consistent with the broader goals of this overall process—requiring the design function to:

1. **Understand the effect of design practice on all parameters of the total customer satisfaction equation.**
2. **Design for performance and zero defect manufacturability.**
3. **Plan product family genealogy up front. Control self-imposed and customer-induced creeping elegance, afterthought bolt-on goodies and product or process changes after introduction. (A moving target is hard to hit.)**
4. **Contribute to the reduction of new product introduction cycle-time by developing and employing right first time methods and discipline.**
5. **Cumulatively reinforce the practice of few, fast learning cycles.**

How, in such a complex process, can these goals possibly be realized? Although easy to articulate, they are indeed extremely difficult to fulfill in practice. The trick, and it is the subject of the rest of this chapter, is in being able to put this process in practice.

ORGANIZING FOR THE TASK

While it is indeed true that the process of designing and introducing new products is already extremely complex, and becoming progressively more so, it is also repetitive. The products may differ, but the process itself, other than evolutionary refinements, does not. Where there is repetition, with study and practice, the runners in the relay race can be trained and organized, to not only run their individual laps faster, but to pass the baton much more fluently, expending the least amount of energy with least waste. Also, if the system is well structured and documented, with each step institutionalized as it were, the learning process can be cumulative, shared, and transferable. In this way, there need be less dependence on art (and good luck), and more on science, method, and discipline. Incremental improvements in the process can be pursued over time to the benefit of each subsequent project exactly as the Japanese have already done in manufacturing. Designing for state-of-the-art product performance, zero defect manufacturability, getting it right first time, in the shortest possible time—for perhaps a complete subsystem on a chip consisting of potentially more than one million transistors—is obviously an extremely formidable challenge far exceeding the capability of the individual designer's handcrafted approach of the recent past. To deal with this, the total task is split within the design community into highly specialized disciplines—system hardware design, system software, logic, circuit and layout design, mask set, and test pattern generation—supported by a complex infrastructure of workstations and mainframe computers connected to a communications network, all of which needs to be coordinated and managed. The management of this supporting infrastructure is in itself no small task. But for any project to be successful, management of the total team, of which design is but a part, presents a similar need. While the design team's goal may be working silicon, the overall team's goal is, as we already established, **to create profit by satisfying customer needs**. See Figures 3-1 through 3-3.

Success in the design phase, as for the project in total, is now much more a function of the quality of the supporting infrastructure—the tools, methods, discipline, how they are managed and coordinated, and the synergism and fluency of the total team—than of the particular skill of any individual. This is not to belittle the continuing, and indeed increasing need for creativity in design, but the design task no longer takes the form of integrating the product function in silicon transistor by transistor, but by pulling cells of complete subfunctions, previously designed, used, and in a state of continual refinement, from a software library, and connecting them together in the most space-effective manner (see note 2, page 3-20). The designer is now a member of a customer-oriented, task-focused, multidiscipline new product development and introduction team whose task is not complete until the product is being shipped in high volume, at high quality, and at low cost. To succeed in this, the players need to operate more like a rugby team and less like individual runners in a relay race. There is no place in this new regime for the immature, though gifted prima donna, whose negative effect on the total team effort exceeds any individual contributions.

One approach to organizing these activities in the most optimum manner is shown in Figure 2-4, Chapter 2, in which the necessary control is under the jurisdiction of a highly skilled and trained project leader, resourced with appropriate tools. In this way, the very substantial communications overhead burden is brought into manageable proportions. Indeed, so imperative are these competencies of designing for both performance and manufacturability that it may make sense to reflect this imperative in the organizational structure of the whole enterprise, with short- and medium-term operations and longer-term product introduction operations independently resourced, organized, and managed, but bound tightly together by a common objective and disciplined methods in the form of formally structured, new product introduction system. More on this later.

THE WAR ON WASTE

Designing for Product Performance—and Zero Defect Manufacturing

The process of being able to manufacture high performance products without waste must begin in design with a complete understanding of what, in fact, constitutes total satisfaction

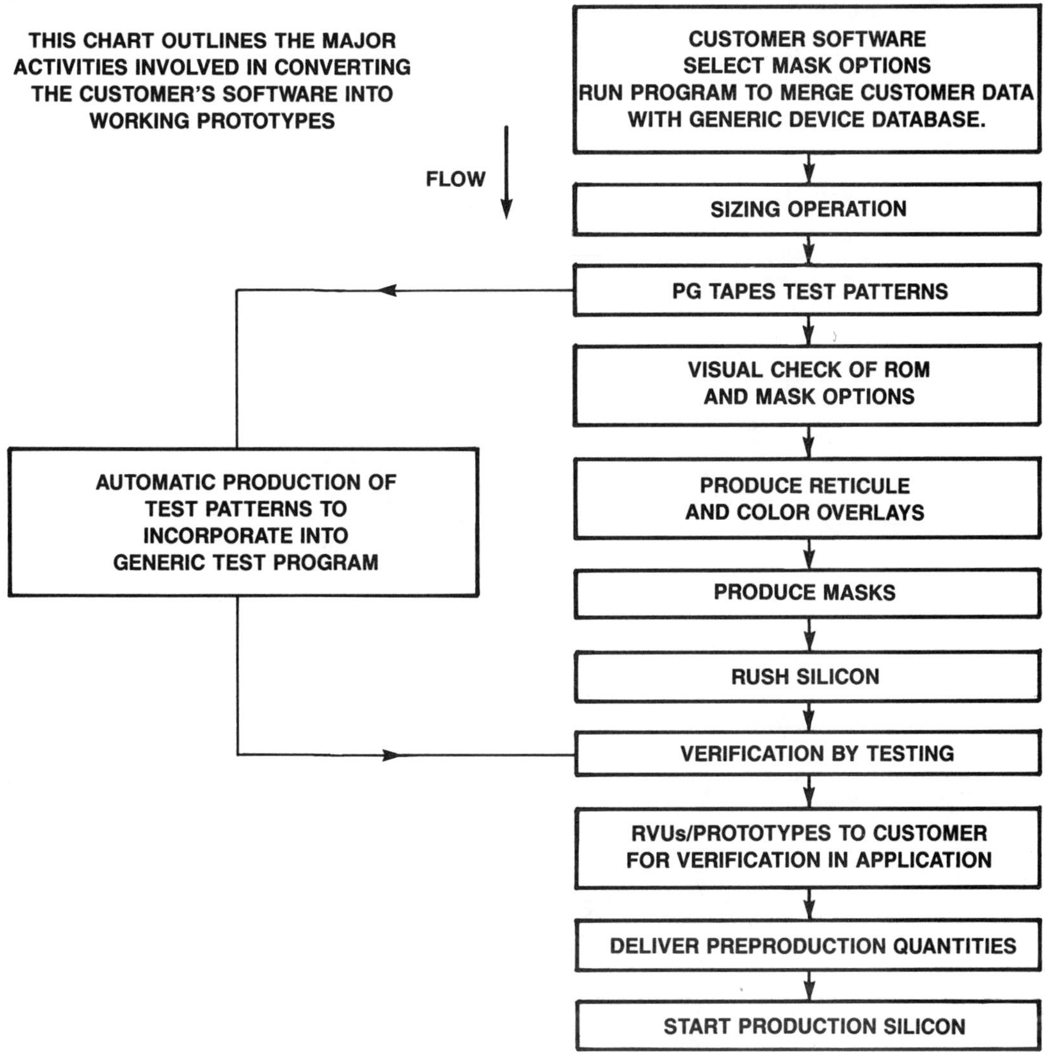

Figure 3-1 Single Chip ROM Based MCU Overview

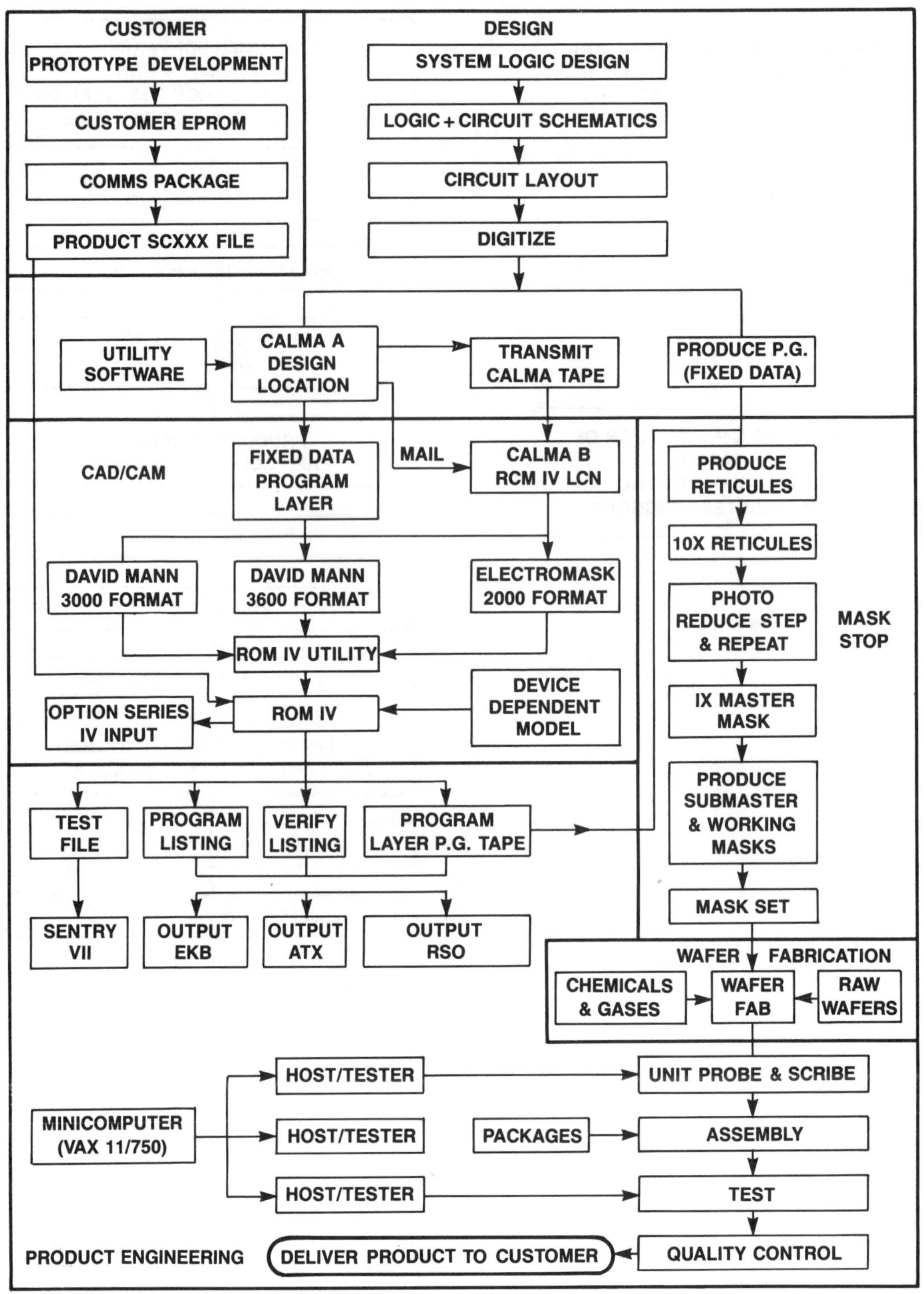

Figure 3-2 Design of Single Chip MCU and Conversion of Customer Software to Mask Program Layer

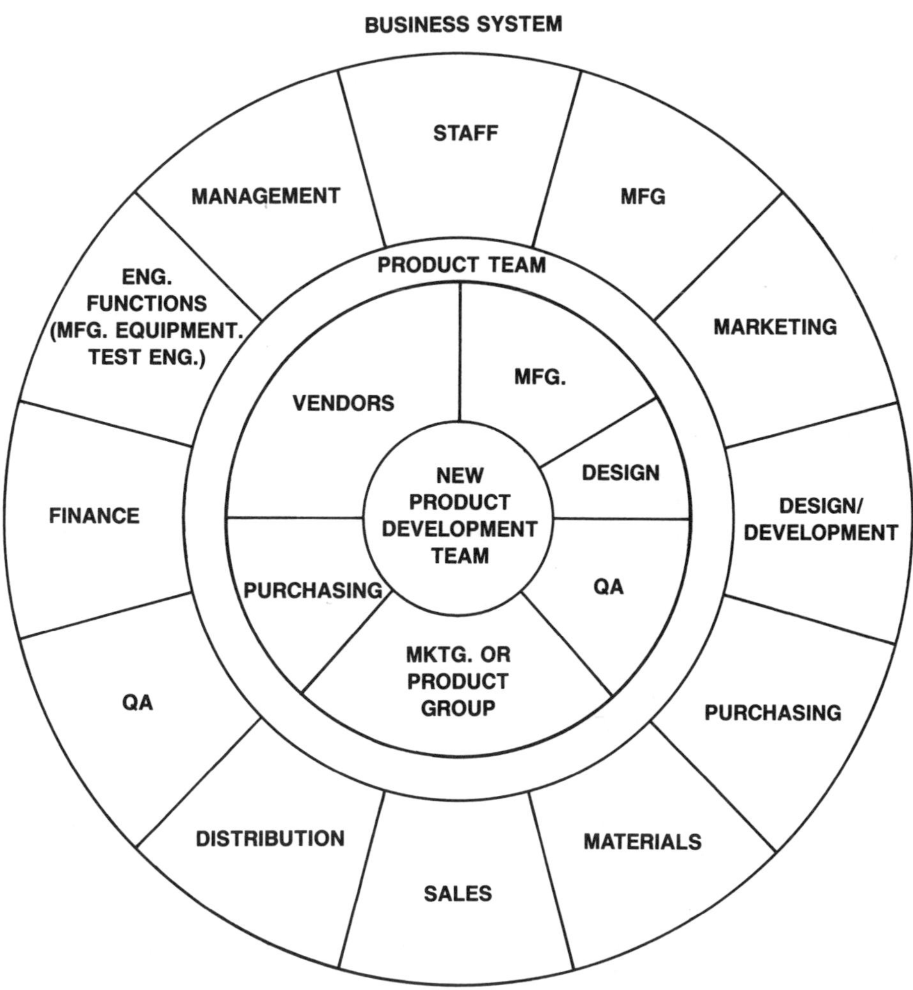

Figure 3-3 DFM—Design for Manufacturability

to the customer and how the new product introduction process, in general, and design practice in particular affects not only product performance parameters, but all of the other components of the total satisfaction equation. With regard to this broader issue of how design practice affects these overall project goals, the Taguchi definition provides us with a clue here—that product and process variation creates defects and that defects in turn create waste in time, human effort, material, and capacity—all of which may impinge on the customer in the form of measurable quality, on-time delivery, and cost penalties. As was articulated earlier, profit, the supplier's motive, and waste are mutually exclusive, so no one escapes carrying some of the cost burden of this inefficiency. How the design function can contribute to the reduction of waste by designing for manufacturability as well as product performance is now discussed.

Manufacturability is defined as **the ability to produce, within target, homogeneous populations of product which satisfy all customer requirements with respect to product and service parameters, with least possible waste**, that is, at a profit. Impeding this objective—the physical manifestation of waste—is the occurrence of defects defined as **any variation in a required characteristic of the product, or its component parts, which is far enough removed from its nominal value to prevent the product from fulfilling the physical or functional requirements of the customer**. These defects are introduced into each operation of the manufacturing system from three sources:

1. **Incoming material/preceding operation**
2. **Process variation**
3. **The environment**

In fact, it can be argued that the cause of the first category of rejects is essentially the same as the second, that of process variation, the difference being that the former describes defects imported into an operation from a preceding operation, perhaps not under statistical control, rather than naturally occurring in the recipient operation due to the intrinsic process variation of that operation. These deviations are not limited to physical, value-added manufacturing operations. Causes of nonconformant product shipments can occur as far back as the order-entry or even the order-specification stages.

A defect introduced to a die site on an SSI (small scale integration) wafer containing as many as 5,000 potentially good die sites has a barely perceptible effect on yield. With VLSI (very large scale integration) however, with perhaps only 100 potential sites, but whose proportion of active to inactive silicon area for each die site is very high, a defect will have a very significant effect on yield. The defect might take the form of a mask set defect, confined to one cell of the mask, in which case this site would be defective on every wafer. This would constitute an imported defect. (The cumulative wafer mapping technique illustrated in Chapter 8, Figure 8-6 is extremely effective in dealing with such mask set defects.) A speck of dust is typical of an environmentally induced defect encountered in a wafer fabrication area. The probability of this microscopically tiny particle falling on an active area of the silicon would be in direct proportion to the die size and the ratio of active to inactive area. Also, the longer the cycle time in the wafer fabrication area, the longer the die will be exposed to this form of environmental contamination and the greater the probability that such a defect will impact the active silicon area of the chip and cause it to completely malfunction. (With a just-in-time approach to manufacturing, this source of defects is significantly reduced.) Either of the aforementioned occurrences would result in a **functional** defect (a completely nonoperational product) one affecting the product in a uniform way; in this example, every die in a specific location, the other randomly. An example of a category 2 defect—process variation—might be the temperature of a furnace which fluctuates over time or the resolution consistency of a photomask alignment operation. As such, this variation might affect all of the product population, but not in a uniformly consistent way—any variable parameter affected in such a way as to exceed the allowable tolerance being a **parametric** defect—a product whose functionality may not be impaired but whose parametric values exceed specification.

Using the previous examples, we might now conclude that we can classify defects into two categories:

Uniform defects—Relatively easy to detect and diagnose since they occur in a regular pattern. Uniformly incident defects should never, but almost invariably do, appear at the next operation (the faulty mask set cell or process recipe). **Latent defects** are uniform or random defects which are not immediately detectable but appear later in time due to some deterioration mechanism.

Random defects—Defects whose distribution profile is not known but whose probability of occurrence can be statistically predicted using Poisson distribution theory. Such defects are difficult to detect and diagnose and are usually transmitted through to the next operation (the speck of dust, wrong recipe, process drift). Random defects are distributed according to the Poisson distribution and their occurrence in manufactured product can therefore be statistically predicted by application of the Poisson formula.

The Relationship Between Product and Process Parameters and Defects

To return to the product parameters aspect of the total satisfaction equation we are attempting to optimize, these product characteristics (parameters) fall into two categories:

Variable—A parameter whose value is a continuous variable (an analog function) within a range measured in physical units, such as volts, ohms, degrees of temperature, and so on; the variation of which, when presented as a frequency of occurrence histogram, approximates a normal distribution.

Attribute—A subjective, value judgment characteristic, measured in comparison to some standard such as marking legibility or blemishes, things which relate to cosmetic or aesthetic appearance of a product. Since the value of such a parameter is judged either good or bad relative to the standard, it can be regarded as a digital function.

Any excursion of these parameters beyond their control limits will be, by definition, a defect. Designing for zero defects then requires the design function to specify these variable parameters in terms of a nominal (target) value whose acceptable variability is limited to a tolerance, defined in terms of standard deviations, about the target. The challenge then presented to the manufacturing organization is to produce at each operation output populations of product whose mean value of this parameter is aligned to the design nominal within certain tolerances, usually ±1.5 sigma, and whose scatter, or variability, is narrowly controlled within ±3 sigma in order to prevent excursions outside the tolerance limits of the product characteristic for any shift in the location of the process mean up to ±1.5 sigma. The ideal relationship, that of 6 sigma, is shown in Figure 3-4.

An analogy might serve to illustrate this concept more clearly. Imagine the target mean value and the upper and lower design limits of a particular product parameter—the ±6 standard deviation points—to be set on the base of a slide rule with the process population mean and ±3 standard deviation points, the spread within which 99.73 percent of the population will occur, marked off on the slide. Also imagine our slide rule to have

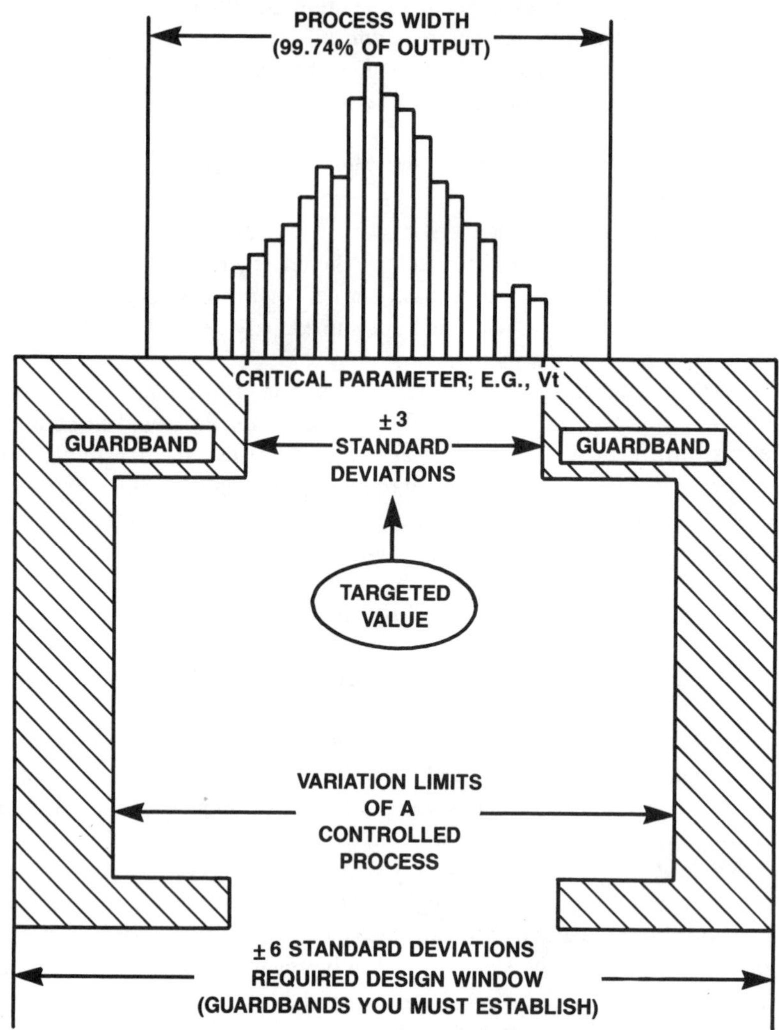

Figure 3-4 What is a Six-Sigma Design?

two cursors, each lined up at these same 6 sigma points on the base of the rule. Ideally, the mean value of the process population would exactly align with the target value set for the design. If the process mean shifts, in one direction or the other, or the shape of the distribution changes, the proportion of defects produced by this operation will not significantly increase until excursions in the process extend beyond the cursor limits. The area to the left and right of the cursors respectively will represent the proportions of defective populations.

To be successful, designing for zero defect manufacturability must be predicated on the very fundamental assumption that the manufacturing processes available to the design community are indeed truly under statistical process control, otherwise, product performance would be unacceptably compromised in optimizing these other parameters for ease of manufacturability. It is no more acceptable to achieve manufacturability at the expense of product performance, resulting perhaps in a nonmarketable product, than it is to achieve product performance at the expense of manufacturability. These can no longer be regarded as mutually exclusive objectives as was the case in the past. This aspect is more fully discussed in Chapter 14.

Designing for product performance and zero defect manufacturability must therefore be a joint effort between the design and manufacturing functions, with design specifying the widest possible design limits within which the design will still function and the manufacturing functions striving to provide the narrowest possible process distribution to allow maximum design to process drift, or variation, margin.

Controlling and Predicting Defects

Under statistical process control, it can be assumed with reasonable confidence that most operations will in fact produce output populations which are normal distributions with 99.73 percent of the output population falling within ± 3 standard deviations of the mean. The indices Cp and Cpk, as discussed at length in Chapter 14, are measures of the relationship between the product and process design correlating the relationship of the product specification to the process capability. The primary value in knowing this relationship, in addition to the consistency benefits of controlling the process, is in its property to be able to predict the probable occurrence of a random defect, since any excursion without these limits will, by definition, be a reject. Cp is used by the design community when designing in a technology which does not yet exist and cannot therefore be characterized. Cpk is substituted later. This relationship is illustrated in Figure 3-4. How these defects are treated using binominal distribution theory in the case of uniform defects and Poisson theory for random defects is discussed in Chapter 14.

Measuring Manufacturability

Historically, various definitions of yield have been used as measures of manufacturing efficiency. The use and abuse of these in the past has tended to perpetuate tolerance of waste and mediocrity in manufacturing, failing to emphasize the need for, and merits of, right first-time success. As the example presented earlier showed, these definitions also lack the sensitivity required in measuring VLSI technology. Each of these definitions is presented and discussed here in preparing for the acceptance of an approach more consistent with this new imperative, that of measuring and controlling the effectiveness and quality of processes in terms of defects per unit.

Types of Yield Calculations

$$\text{Process Yield} = \frac{\text{Number of units completed}}{\text{Number of units started}}$$

$$\text{Test/Inspect Yield} = \frac{\text{Number of units passed}}{\text{Number of units tested/inspected}}$$

$$\text{First Time Yield} = \frac{\text{Number of units passed (first time test/inspect)}}{\text{Number of units tested/inspected (first time)}}$$

$$\text{Rolled Yield} = \frac{\text{Number of units completely processed (zero defects)}}{\text{Number of units processed}}$$

For repairable product, process yield—the overall, cumulative yield of the process—is virtually 100 percent since one unit is eventually completed for every unit started. Any wasteful rework is disguised in this measurement. For nonrepairable product, however, process yield may be substantially less than 100 percent due to unredeemable defects. Rolled yield, the proportion of the product population which goes through the entire process defect free, is essentially the same as process yield for nonrepairable product. For repairable product, rolled yield may be significantly lower than process yield, reflecting the degree of rework in this number.

Measuring and Controlling Quality in Terms of Defects Per Unit

A much less ambiguous concept in measuring yields, more representative of, and sensitive to the complexities of VLSI, is in terms of defects per unit.

$$\text{Defects per unit} = \frac{\text{Number of defects found at all acceptance points}}{\text{Number of units processed}}$$

This approach can be applied to each individual operation cumulatively across all operations in the process.

Defects as a Function of Complexity

The following is a list of the more significant factors determining the probability of defects being introduced into the system:

Die area
Proportion of active to inactive area of the die
Number of layers in the mask set
Number of steps in the process
The complexity of the process equipment
Design limits/tolerances
Process capability
New materials/methods/processes
Number of pieceparts
Package pin count

Designing for product performance and zero defect manufacturability is the final and most sophisticated phase of the four phases in the evolution of quality assurance and control in manufacturing. It is confirmation for these organizations who have evolved, or are in the process of evolving to this level of competence, that the transition from the first phase of reactively inspecting out rejects through the second and third phases of process control and quality improvement respectively (quality circles), to the final phases of proactively building in quality through design and manufacture, under statistical process control, has run its course in full.

How can this level of truly world-class competence be realized? Where and how does one begin to articulate and communicate the objectives, formulate the strategies, build the organization, develop the systems, skills, methods, and discipline capable of fulfilling this? In summary, as we have hopefully already agreed, the objective of the new product introduction process including the role and contribution of the design function is to create profit by satisfying customer needs. In such a capital-intensive, high fixed cost industry as ours, with the extremely high cost associated with developing and introducing new products, winning market share—competing on product performance, quality, cost, and on-time delivery over which these high fixed costs can be absorbed—is an indispensible prerequisite to profitability. If done properly, yet another time-honored myth of our industry can be debunked—that growing market share costs money. This is only true if the pursuit of that market share is fueled first by an inefficient new product introduction process and secondly by a high waste manufacturing process. That profit and waste are mutually exclusive is a proposition that any reasonable person will readily accept. That waste can be eliminated, or at least dramatically reduced, is perhaps less acceptable but no less reasonable.

I am reminded of an anecdote, popularly quoted when the Japanese thrust for dominance in the world's ship building industry was at its height, as follows. "The British take one year to plan the building of a ship and seven years to build it. Each subsequent ship, therefore, requires seven years to build. The Japanese on the other hand, take seven years to plan the building of a ship but only one year to build it. They are then able to produce ships thereafter at the rate of one per year."

This perhaps more than anything else epitomizes the difference in our culturally biased campaign strategies in the war between the profligate occidentals and the parsimonious orientals. To us, waste, for whatever reason, is a way of life. To them, a luxury they can't afford—or will not allow themselves—which they minimize with thorough planning and meticulous execution. Our planning does not usually extend beyond those activities associated with the mad dash for first silicon—albeit not fully functional and certainly not manufacturable with least waste, our execution, casual at best-in our rush to be first to market. They are in no less of a hurry, but their preparation includes probable future market price projections, required product costs over time profile, planned product cost reductions and product family genealogy plan, and defect-free product availability up front. We deal with each of these as the need chronologically arises with the sometimes, but not always, brilliant, eleventh hour, diving catch. We love a cavalry charge, they prefer to avoid the need for one. We have creativity and skill in no small measure; it is method and discipline, in both design and manufacturing, and respect for commitments, which is lacking. We must start to see the new product introduction process as an activity whose goals extend far beyond the realization of working silicon.

Any new product introduction activity, by its very nature, will commit a significant proportion of a company's resources for significant periods of time to a plan of action whose outcome is uncertain, and therefore at risk. These risks cannot be avoided—that is the nature of opportunity. But they can be minimized with fast, flawless execution. This can only be assured by means of a formally structured, but well-oiled, system—a system designed and managed to facilitate the fast, fluent processing of information, the physical processing of the product—in design, development, and manufacturing, and the administration of the management process itself. In effect, a communications system capable of providing the visibility to, and controlling the execution of, the many functional specialists involved in the various stages of execution. To be fully effective, to achieve the highest degree of symbiotic synergism possible, each functionally specialized "brick" as it were of the structure, must be bound tightly together by the cement of formalized policies, procedures, and controls. An attempt to represent this graphically is shown in Figure 3-5.

The very considerable demands placed on this system will extend far beyond those of simply providing a communications structure, however. To serve its purpose in full, it must be so designed as to permit innovation in design without proliferation, flexible but at the same time rigid enough to allow the coexistence of creativity and discipline. It must include the facility to capture design, development, and manufacturing costs by project and product, rather than simply sinking them in a common pool. How else can the project be assessed in terms of its economic value? It must make complexity manageable by containing it within a highly structured framework. A process of such complexity requires a system capable of handling the many organizational as well as technical problems encountered. The new imperatives of competitiveness demand change in policies, practices, and procedures but perhaps even more importantly, they demand change in culture in the system of values and beliefs of an organization. In this respect, more than any other, the new product introduction system must be equal to the task of changing behavior through changed expectations.

STATISTICAL PROCESS CONTROL (SPC)—A DEFINITION

Since product quality is a function of the quality of the process (or system) by which it is designed and produced, statistical process control represents a departure from the reactive—after the event—traditional lot sampling approach with its emphasis on inspecting out rejects to the proactive approach of building quality into the product. This is done with SPC by controlling the variability of critical, input parameters of all critical operations within a process, within statistically derived and controlled, predefined alert/stop limits, correlated, and linked with process output parameters, in a real-time feedback mode. The values of mean and scatter of the output population, the distribution profile, are also controlled within predefined limits.

This is a very comprehensive, but also very cumbersome definition. A much more succinct definition is simply **to eliminate waste by controlling variability**. (A process in this context is considered to be a series of individual, but related, operations.)

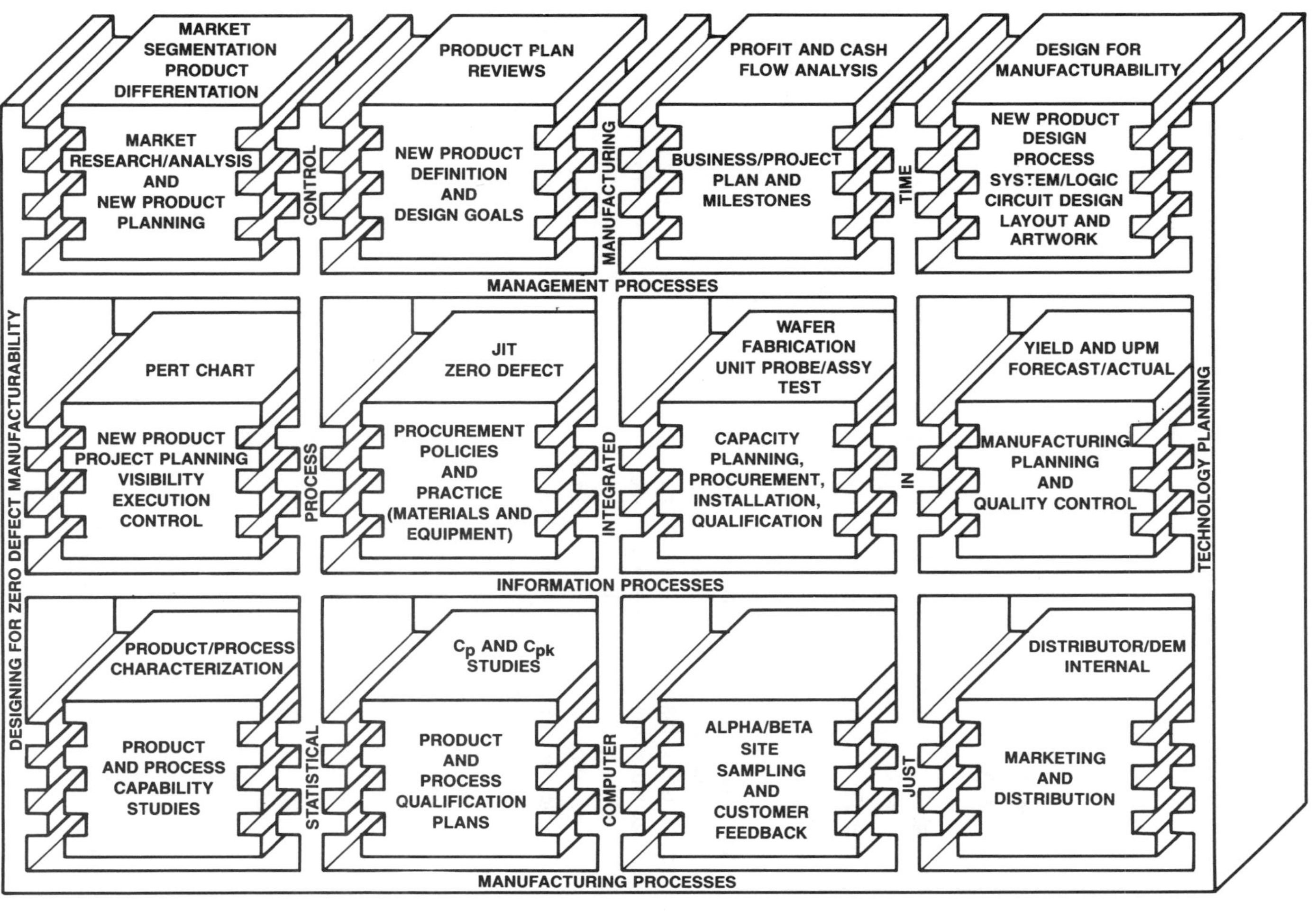

Figure 3-5 New Product Introduction System (The ''Bricks and Mortar'' of Functional Organization Integration)

OPERATING PRINCIPLES SUMMARY

1. **Setting correct objectives**
2. **Organizing for the task**
3. **Designing for product performance and zero defect manufacturing product and process characterization**
4. **Planning for profit—the coexistence of methods, discipline, and creativity**

QUALITY DEFINITIONS

- **Fitness for use—Juran**
- **Conformance to requirements—Crosby**
- **Meeting expectations of the customer—Feigenbaum**
- **Meeting conformance to target (not specification) and the reduction of variability of all key characteristics of a process or product—Taguchi**
- **Eight components of quality identified by Garvin: performance, features, reliability, conformance, durability, serviceability, aesthetics, perceived quality**

Note 1: Second sources are generally considered necessary to satisfy the customer base's understandable apprehension in being potentially dangerously dependent on a single source. (A single source may lose his manufacturing recipe, or abuse his monopoly power.) For the new product innovator, licensing a second source can be a double edged sword, unless his manufacturing and marketing competence is at least as good as that of the second source. These second sources may be internal or third party.

Note 2: Silicon compilers bring speed to the process of laying out integrated circuits, but real estate efficiency is not as great as that achieved by the slower, but more space effective, hand-drafting approach. Design of radically new architectures, the exception rather than the rule, obviously cannot benefit from the approach in the early stages.

MAJOR MILESTONES IN SEMICONDUCTORS AND COMPUTING

3000 B.C.	Abacus—invented. John Napier's Bones—Logarity—Slide Rule Blaise Pascal Pascaline—1000
1822	Charles Babbage, English mathematician, built the "difference engine" which produced the first reliable tables of life expectancy. Polynomial equations.
1833	Babbage "analytical engine" designed. Automated the whole process of calculation input, output, store, "mill," control unit.
1880	Method of storing information on punched cards (Joseph Lacquard weaving/looms) advanced by H. Hollerith, U.S. Census Bureau. Adopted and adapted by IBM.
1930's	Code breaking and ballistics led to the development of electronic computers. Alan Turing, British mathematician, and John VonNeumann laid the foundations. "War is the mother of invention."
1940's	Harvard Mark 1, Colossus, Enigma-colossus break. ENIAC, EDVAC, SEAC, UNIVAC, EDSAC built. Used electronic valves.

ENIAC		**MICROCHIP**	
Occupied	3000 cubic feet	Occupies	0.011 cubic feet
Weighed	30 tons	Weighs	2 grams
Consumed	140 kW of power	Consumes	25 watts

100,000 times more reliable

1/100,000 times the cost

1954	Transistor invented. Bell Labs, Shockley, Bardeen, Brattain received Nobel prizes.
1955	First semiconductor company formed by Shockley.
1957	Eight members of the Shockley team founded Fairchild Semiconductors (Silicon Valley) which developed the integrated circuit. Forty semiconductor companies have now been formed by scientists who onced worked at Fairchild.
1969	Dr. Ted Hoff (INTEL) proposed the architecture for the first MPU.
1971	INTEL 4004 introduced.
1974	Motorola MC6800 introduced.
1978	INTEL 8088, Motorola MC68000 introduced.
1979	Motorola 64K RAM.
1983	First 32-bit microprocessors—Motorola MC68020.
1986	1 Megabit dynamic RAMs—Japan Inc. Transputer, neural network computers artificial intelligence, and expert systems.

4

The Manufacturing Process

TECHNOLOGY OVERVIEW

MOS Technology

In the early 1970s, following in the wake of the very popular TTL (Transistor Transistor Logic) itself having toppled RTL (Resistor Transistor Logic) and DTL (Diode Transistor Logic) from a position of pre-eminence, two mainstream semiconductor technologies emerged in the form of MOS and Bipolar. It was not at all clear at that time which, if either of the technologies, would become dominant. Each had their respective relative advantages and disadvantages.

Bipolar was fast, but it was also power hungry and did not at that time lend itself very well to LSI (large-scale integration) and required more art than science to manufacture and use. MOS, on the other hand, was at that time a relatively simple process to manufacture with high tolerance to manufacturing variations, desirable electrical properties in the form of noise immunity margins, and low power consumption but was slow in terms of switching speed and consumed a lot of silicon real estate. Within each of these mainstream technologies, tributary developments continued to produce subcategories optimizing one particular parameter or another. Bipolar produced such subgroups as LSTTL (Low Power Schotky—Transistor Transistor Logic) and Linear which are still with us today in highly refined forms. Within MOS, the primary subdivisions with ardent followers in both camps were CMOS and NMOS, whose development has continued to the present day. As in Bipolar, there are many variations on the same theme within each subgroup.

By the mid 1970s, the main subgroups in MOS were complementary metal oxide silicon (CMOS) and NMOS, the N signifying that only the N-channel transistor was used in cell structures, complementary indicating the use of both P and N channel transistors. As in the Bipolar contest, CMOS and NMOS each vied for pre-eminence, with neither really succeeding. NMOS was faster, had higher density, was simpler and cheaper to manufacture because of its single-cell structure. CMOS, on the other hand, whose main disadvantage relative to NMOS was lower speed and packing density consumed much less power, had cleaner switching characteristics and better tolerance to electrically and magnetically induced extraneous noise.

Developments in both have continued unabated to the present day, with each development addressing some disadvantage relative to the other technology while attempting to preserve all other relative advantages. The final result in each case, in terms of relative advantages and disadvantages is a function of the nature of the MOS transistor—a voltage regulated device as opposed to current-operated in the case of Bipolar—the manner in which these transistors are configured to execute the switching function and the effect which both have in determining the nature of the manufacturing process. A comparison of both technologies today would probably indicate CMOS developments have been such that the only enduring advantage of NMOS is cost, and with one micron and less geometries now available in HCMOS (high-performance CMOS), even this is not likely to endure indefinitely. (For a more in-depth discussion of basic semiconductor physics see page 4-30.)

The pervasiveness of all semiconductor products, regardless of which particular branch of wafer-fabrication technology is employed in building them, is due in no small measure to the continuously improving price/performance ratio. Some of the main factors behind this improvement, common to most if not all technologies, are as follows.

Size of Wafer

By increasing the diameter of the wafer, **gross potential die per wafer** will increase as a function of the ratio of the square of the radii of the wafer, given that die size remains the same—from two to three inches will increase the gross die per wafer by 276 percent, from three to four inches by 77 percent, from four to five inches by 56 percent, and from five to six inches by 44 percent. As can be seen, diminishing returns are being encountered, each successive one-inch increment representing a smaller proportion of the diameter of the wafer.

As recently as ten years ago, two inch diameter wafers were still being used in some manufacturing processes and now there are some facilities already using six, seven, and even eight inch wafers, although it is likely we are now nearing the limits of this innovative direction. Quite apart from diminishing returns in terms of gross die per wafer, larger wafer areas make it progressively more difficult to design and equip processes which prevent warping of the wafer during the many heat treatments to which the wafers are subjected. In addition to this, the physical fragility of the wafer can result in reduced mechanical yield due to handling damage.

What really counts, however, is the number of **good die per wafer** and this is also a function of **die size**. As the die size increases, not only does the gross number of die per wafer decrease, but the die will contain proportionately more **active silicon** which can be adversely affected by any defect in either mask or environment. (See Figure 4-1.) In the future, therefore, as products become more complex, more emphasis will be placed on increasing the number of good die per wafer (yield) to counteract the effect of diminishing returns encountered in continuing to increase the size of the wafer. Some of the highly innovative techniques which are used to achieve this are described in the following.

Ion Implantation/Positive Photo Resist

Major innovations such as the substitution of diffusion by ion implantation have given rise to smaller line width geometries. Diffusion is a process by which desired impurities are forced to diffuse into the silicon by exposure to high temperatures. With ion implantation, impurities of the correct valency are bombarded into the silicon under very

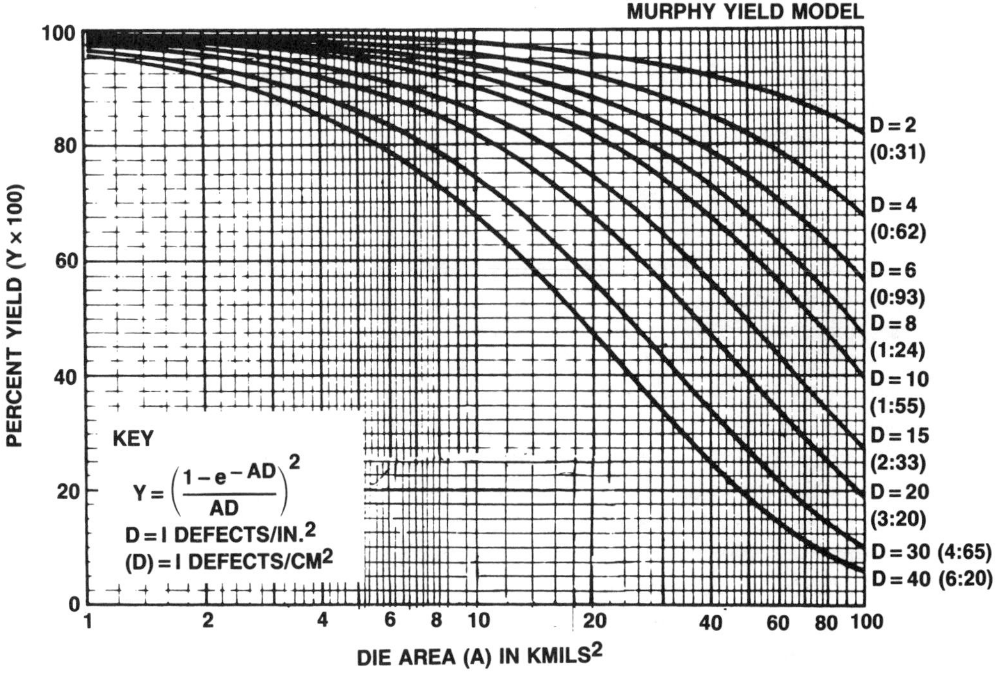

Figure 4-1 Percent Yield Versus Device Area

high energies in order to construct the desired electrical properties. Another factor has been the replacement of negative by positive resist to determine which areas of silicon are exposed and which are protected from the exposure to ultraviolet light and hence which areas of photoresist will be subsequently etched away.

Projection Printing

The replacement of contact printing by projection printing made it desirable, and indeed possible, to strive for the perfect, blemish-free mask set. Contact printing meant that each successive mask layer came in contact with the silicon and could result in tearing and lifting of the resist emulsion. Projection printing is where, in theory at least, working plates, which were consumed by wear and tear during the contact process, could be replaced by glass reticules of indefinite life which never came in contact with the wafer.

Process Base Line

The wafer base line processes themselves have changed from those, such as CMOS metal gate technology, where in the interest of ensuring adequate source/drain coverage, the gate was deliberately made to overlap the source and drain. The price paid for this insurance being higher gate to source/drain capacitance and as a direct consequence, higher switching propagation delay. Most processes now employ self-aligning source/drain to gate geometry by using the gate, constructed before the source and drain, to define the overlap and spacing such as in CMOS silicon gate technology.

Plasma Etching

There has also been a significant trend to plasma, in the form of ionized gas as opposed to wet chemical processing. Apart from the obvious environmental benefits, this has also contributed to the degree of precision and resolution attainable in defining geometries.

Sputtering/Nitride Passivation

Two other major process innovations, the replacement of aluminum evaporation by sputtering and replacement of PSG (phosphorus silicon glass) in the passivation layer of the finished wafer by nitride are also worthy of mention. These, however, have had more impact on the quality and reliability of the finished product rather than in directly reducing geometries. In the former, better coverage of steps in the topography can be realized with sputtering, in which the aluminum is driven from the source under high electrical potential than with evaporation which depends upon heating both the aluminum source from which the metal is drawn and the target. In PSG passivation materials, any phosphorus content in the glass above 10 percent can lend itself to the formation of corrosive phosphoric acid upon ingress of moisture into the package. This has traditionally restricted the performance and acceptability of plastic encapsulation. This problem is almost entirely overcome, however, by minimizing the PSG concentration or by replacing the PSG layer with one of nitride which is completely impervious to moisture.

CAD/CAM

Finally, the comparatively recent transition to extensive use of computer-aided design (CAD) and for that matter, computer-aided manufacturing (CAM), has allowed designers, product and process engineers to exploit these innovations to the full in relatively short time scales. The end result, of course, has meant more efficient use of silicon real estate and the benefits of this have been taken in different ways by different product families. In the case of the primarily small-scale, medium-scale integration products such as CMOS gates, flip-flops, and so on, the main benefit has been taken in smaller die size with the associated reduction in cost and price, although some of the benefit is now being seen to be taken in speed with the emergence of high-speed CMOS silicon gate products, using the self-aligning silicon gate technology referred to earlier.

With memories, and particularly **dynamic RAMs**, the benefits have been taken primarily in the form of larger-scale integration, i.e., more of the same in the form of larger and larger memory arrays of the same kind on the same chip. This was epitomized with the sample availability of 256K **dynamic RAMs** before the 64K had left the embryonic stage of its life cycle and with 512K, one megabit, and even four megabit products being publicly discussed. Microprocessors, however, at least 8-bit machines, have followed a third and quite distinct route by taking the payoff in being able to facilitate the convergence of previously stand-alone functions and indeed different technologies, on the same chip. Only a few short years ago it could take as many as five or six chips to implement the same function as now can be realized with one. Not only does this represent a convergence of previously stand-alone functions such as ROM, RAM, CPU, I/O, Timer, but also what were previously considered to be stand-alone process technologies such as electrically programmable read only memory (**EPROM**) and even nonvolatile technologies such as electrically erasable programmable read only memory (**EEPROM**). This has led to a transition from standard commodity-type products to more application-specific products.

In this short time, line geometries have been reduced from 6 microns to 1.5 with reductions down to the submicron regions in various stages of development and in some cases, preproduction. At the same time, new semantics were invented or applied from other disciplines such as the mini and mainframe computer fields to describe this bewildering embarrassment of riches, ranging from central processing unit (CPU), microprocessing unit (MPU), and microcomputer unit (MCU) and, of course, the terms single chip microprocessors and application specific integrated circuits (ASICs) to represent the convergence of functions in a self-contained unit. Even during the purchasing and delivery cycle, new terms emerged to cover activities which had not previously needed to be considered such as ROM verification unit **(RVU)**, **Prototypes**, **Preproduction Deliveries**, **Verification**, and so on. These will be dealt with in detail during the Manufacturing Overview part of the discussion as will more of the detail of the wafer fabrication activity. The aforementioned are only intended to highlight those developments in this area which have made such things as single chip microprocessor and ASIC technology possible.

User Benefits

Chip Count	The primary benefit must, of course, be in reduced chip count, manifesting itself in one or more of several ways.
Component Cost	The material or component cost will be significantly lower than a hard wired or multichip solution to a design problem.
PCB Layout	There will almost certainly be cost and space savings associated with a smaller and simpler printed circuit board layout.
Reliability	Reliability will be greatly enhanced due to the significant reduction in interconnections, increased immunity to crosstalk and reduced need for extensive decoupling.
Development Amortization	If the product chosen is one of a family employing a common CPU core with a wide selection of family members with different peripheral options on chip, then amortization of investment in development equipment, system design, software and software expertise can be absorbed over many projects, possibly otherwise quite unrelated.
Design Cycle	The design cycle, while it can be fairly lengthy for first-time users, for experienced users should be very short and improvements in this respect will be sustained on each subsequent design cycle.

This is the area in which benchmarking, where the number of machine cycles and read only memory (ROM) space consumed in executing the instructions in fulfilling a specific function, is quantified and compared with another machine. Caution must be exercised here, however, since the simple cost-per-bit rule-of-thumb criteria such as is applied in assessing the cost effectiveness of dynamic random access memories (RAMs), can result in an ostensibly inexpensive lower performance machine being chosen which because of its limitations may well lead to very high development costs or even severely limited product enhancement limitations. Shown in Figure 3-1 in Chapter 3 and in Figure 4-2.

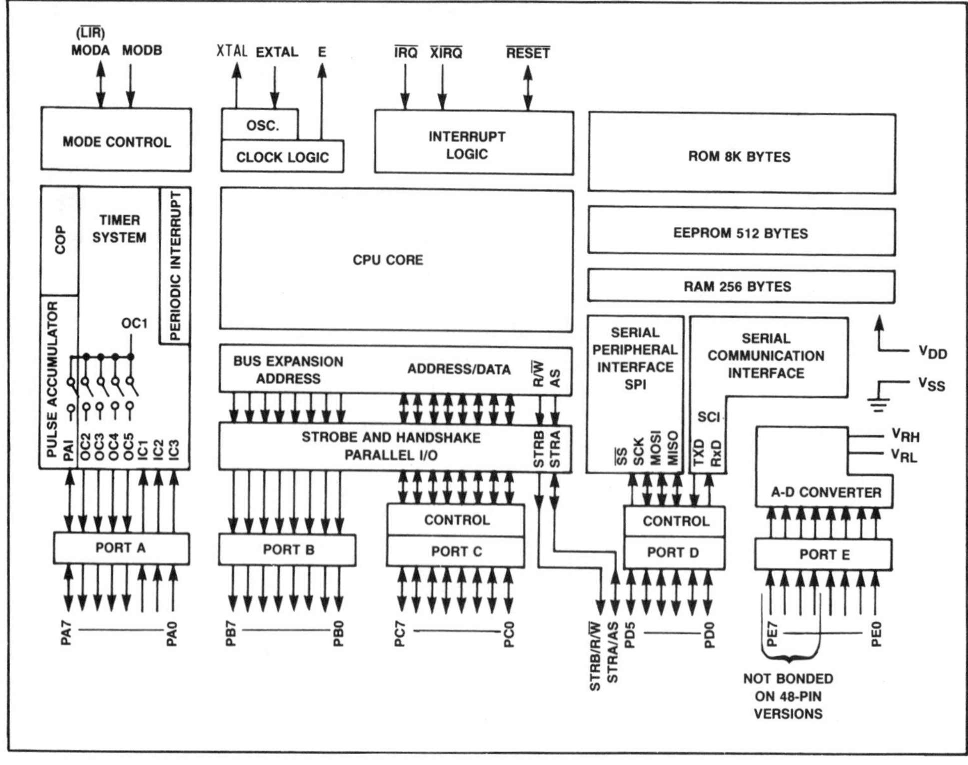

Figure 4-2 Block Diagram of Microprocessor Architecture

Peripheral Functions

In this respect there is a choice even wider than that of central processor cores but again the selection is very much a function of the application. Almost all ASIC and single chip MCU products have certain on-board functions in common such as **ROM**, **RAM**, **Timers** and **I/O** options, differences lying only in the size or quantity available, e.g., 64 or 128 bytes of RAM, 16 or 24 input/output (I/O) ports, 1 or 2K bytes of **ROM**, **Serial I/O**, number of pins, and so on. However, there are other functions which are instrumental in giving a product a more unique personality and are oriented to very specific applications. Examples of these are on-chip phase-locked loop, serial I/O, and analog and digital converters. It is in this area in which the major development thrust is likely to be concentrated, at least for the immediate future, resulting in a wide spectrum of **customized standard single-chip products** being made available. These are almost certain to include on-chip liquid crystal display driver circuitry and nonvolatile memory, since the need to display and store variable data especially during power-down situations is an integral need of many applications which lend themselves to application-specific products. This is, and will continue to be, an area where by making their needs known customers can significantly influence the semiconductor houses in the development of new products.

EPROM Versions

During the development phase of a project, while the customers' engineers are refining and optimizing the design of the system, being able to modify and execute changes in software, especially that part which will ultimately reside in the ROM of the production version, virtually dictates that an equivalent part be available in which the ROM has been substituted by EPROM. In this way, the need for flexibility during development can be accommodated using a part which forms the closest possible parallel to that which will be used in production. There need not be any apprehension about field trial or characterization data not applying to the high volume production versions as would be the case if development was conducted with external EPROM, piggyback or even Bipolar PROMs. The existence of same can also be a very expedient way of incorporating new software for any subsequently developed product enhancement feature and bringing this to the market while the semiconductor manufacturer incorporates this in new ROM versions.

From the market point of view, it is highly desirable for the EPROM version of a product be designed first. However, major longer-term considerations such as optimization of the chip layout dictate that the ROM version be designed first. This conflict of interest can only be resolved by the semiconductor vendor designing and developing both in parallel as far as is possible.

Manufacturing Overview

Figure 3-1, in Chapter 3 outlines the major activities associated with the process of converting a customer's software, made available at the end of the customer's development cycle and precipitating events leading up to prototype, preproduction and full production deliveries, of ROM customized or ASIC silicon.

The first objective is to deliver **RVUs** or **prototypes** to the customer as quickly as possible in order to verify that the **firmware** (software contained in the chip's ROM) does indeed fulfill its function in controlling the end equipment before committing large volumes of silicon to production. Since RVUs are intended to verify the customer's software only, they are usually tested at **ambient** temperatures in the interest of speed. **Prototypes**, on the other hand, are screened over the full specification to which ultimate production quantities will be delivered, including the full temperature range. **RVUs** and **prototypes** also serve to establish that no errors were introduced by the vendor during the lengthy and complex series of events, beginning with integrating the customer's software into the **generic** mask set data base in order to produce a customized mask program layer and subsequently used in fabricating the silicon. Unit quantities in both cases are usually not more than 100 devices. Since one of the goals during this phase is to achieve deliveries in the range of four weeks or less, the compression of a normal production manufacturing cycle of somewhere in the region of 12 to 16 weeks, requiring the coordination of many complex activities, frequently crossing many geographic and functional boundaries, calls for very efficient organization in order to execute in a **fluent** and **failsafe** manner.

The second objective is then to be able to deliver **preproduction** quantities shortly after confirmation of the acceptance of **prototypes**. These are usually provided within four weeks, from the balance of good die remaining from the wafers produced to service the prototype requirement, in quantities of approximately 5,000 units, depending on device type. The third **objective** is then full production quantity deliveries. Since unlike prototypes where processes are scheduled to be available upon the arrival of the product, normal production is in competition for common resources and as such, average rather than optimum process times accumulate, resulting in delivery time scales of 8 to 16 weeks, depending on process complexity and product shipping logistics. Achieving these objectives is now considered in more detail.

The customer precipitates the manufacturing cycle by contacting the appropriate sales representative in order to express an interest in a specific product. At this point the customer is primarily interested in **price** and **delivery** information, which the salesperson will obtain from the product marketing contact or customer coordinator back in the factory. Given that this information is acceptable, the customer will then place an order, probably for **RVUs** or **prototypes** only, but possibly also for production quantities and will be asked by the salesperson to provide the information necessary to completely specify the unique personality of the product. At the same time the customer will be invited to provide the salesperson with the ROM pattern, preferably in EPROM but alternatively on floppy disc, to which will be assigned a unique identifier for this pattern and for the device in which it will be contained. This will ultimately be marked on the end product to distinguish it from other customer products of the same generic device type.

Upon receipt in the factory, three things must then happen. The first is to produce a pattern generator (PG) tape which will be used by the mask shop to produce a glass reticule from which, in turn, a mask **program layer** containing at least the customer's ROM data—in some cases other options—will be produced. This will then be used by the wafer fabrication operation, in conjunction with the rest of the **generic** mask set (other nonprogramming layers), to produce prototype silicon of this device. Simultaneously, another magnetic tape is produced in a data format such that a line plot of the ROM program layer, and options if these are on a different layer, is produced on a line plotting machine such as a Xynetics plotter, for example. This is used to visually check that in the conversion from ones to zeros in the customer's EPROM to shapes corresponding to these on the mask program layer, the data have been correctly merged with the rest of the invariant generic data and that no shapes have been dropped. This data base can then be transmitted, possibly via satellite, to one of several mask shops round the world for subsequent conversion into a mask program layer, which then of course is returned to the appropriate factory for wafer processing. As a contingency back-up, the data base may also be shipped via conventional mail against the event that transmission errors are introduced in the data link, although this is also checked by handshake. Also, at this point, hard-copy verification listing is produced, to be verified by the customer that handshake is complete. This may also be output back in the regional sales office on the same network which was used to transmit customer ROM data in the first place, confirming that what was received is the same as that transmitted.

The third thing which needs to happen at this point is to produce a test program, for both unit probe and final test, in anticipation of receiving the first wafers from the wafer fabrication area. Again, this consists of merging data specific to the end customer's product with the invariant part of the test program generic data base and is accomplished in a similar way by using the same mainframe computer software package as is used to produce the PG and line plot tapes.

The following major functions will be considered in more detail:

1. PG tape generation
2. Masks
3. Wafer fabrication
4. Unit probe, assembly, and final test
5. Making and meeting delivery commitments

PG Tape Generation (Refer to Figure 3-2 in Chapter 3)

When a single-chip product is first designed, all mask layers other than the programmable layer are produced in an entirely conventional manner as would be the case for a non-customized product. Other than redesigns or yield improvements such as optical shrink of the mask set, the procedure will only be executed once. This is represented in the right-hand side of the chart.

The programmable layer, however, will change with each customer and application and as such, some means has to be provided to execute this quickly, fluently and faithfully as represented on the left-hand side of the chart. The organizational infrastructure necessary to do so pervades virtually all functional disciplines including design, mask shop, and product and systems engineering. This is one of the key areas in which distinctive competence will mean the difference between success and failure in producing prototypes quickly. The foundation upon which this infrastructure is built must be a well-equipped, resourced and effectively organized (CAD/CAM), computer-aided design and manufacturing capability with captive mask shop, assembly and test facilities. This is one of the main reasons the customer may be asked to pay a small mask charge in the range of $2,000 to $10,000.

Mask Shop/Masks

The choice of mask shop may also have a bearing on the cycle time of this sequence of events, since this function may be required to convert a pattern generator tape to mask program layer within 24 hours. The choice open to the manufacturer is a function of the extent to which the equipment he uses to support his part of the activity can be made to interface to the equipment used by the mask shop. In many cases this is a function of the pattern generator output format which the manufacturer can support on the one hand and the quality and service which can be offered by the mask shop on the other. For prototyping, where speed is relatively more important than yield or quality, it is conceivable that a program layer from one shop can be used with the rest of the generic layers produced in another. For high volume production however, where high yield and quality are important, the possible stacking incompatibilities of this shorter cycle time approach may preclude this.

Wafer Fabrication

As was stated earlier, the logistics in wafer fabrication will be managed such that processes will be made available to prototype batches, ideally as they arrive, thus minimizing the cycle-time through the wafer fabrication area (no queuing). However, other factors have an equally significant bearing on cycle time. The number of masking steps, which can vary from eight to fifteen depending on process complexity, can in turn affect the number of processes required in the manufacturing sequence. This can range from as few as 20 in relatively mature technologies such as metal gate to as many as 100 in some of the very high-density, high-performance HCMOS silicon gate processes now emerging.

There are other very compelling reasons, however, in addition to speed why prototype and production cycle-times should be minimized, perhaps more so for production. Inventory represents capital which is nonproductive and as such, work in process must be no more than the absolute minimum required to balance the wafer fabrication area at a given level of activity and to provide the level of service response required. Inventory can also have a significant bearing on quality and response time to problems in the process, perhaps hidden in nonmoving or slow-moving inventory. It can also represent a significant risk on a customized product which cannot be sold elsewhere to another customer in the event that the customer's requirements change. These all constitute reasons why the prospective user should choose to only enter into commitments with vendors who can demonstrate this level of control and expertise in running a well-managed facility, and for his part, give the supplier as much visibility as can be provided into lead times and run rates. Life is becoming too complex for arms-length relationships and a close working relationship based on mutual trust will stand both parties in good stead.

Unit Probe, Assembly, and Test

In most cases, prototype wafers will be probed within 24 hours of being delivered from wafer fabrication. Testing is usually ambient only and limited to full functionality plus some important parametrics due to the difficulty in providing a similar integrity testing environment as that which applies at final test. There are examples, where the chip is so designed, where self-testing is employed in which the chip simply need be provided with a power supply, some form of display. The CPU is then employed to execute self-check code contained in part of the chip's ROM space to test itself. If less than comprehensive, safeguards are employed in that the part will subsequently be rigorously tested at final test, and the cost of failing an expensively packaged part at this stage is an effective motivation to have satisfactory correlation between final test and unit probe results. The probed wafers will be scribed and diced and then a small quantity locally assembled in ceramic packages, usually within a few days, to be returned for final screening to the customer's RVU or prototype specification at final test. The balance of good die from the prototype wafers is at this point shipped to the high-volume assembly location in anticipation of the customer approving prototypes and then requiring pre-production quantities greater than that supplied for prototyping.

Production Control

From the point at which the customer approves verification listing, generated upon receipt of the pattern, responsibility for meeting the delivery commitment given at this time will pass to production control. In order to ensure that products are delivered on schedule for prototypes, preproduction or production qualtities, major milestones in the process will be scheduled and performance against these will be tracked. Typical monitoring points would be:

1. Verification listing approved
2. Generation of PG tape
3. Generation of mask program layer
4. Start wafers
5. Ship wafers
6. Probe
7. Assemble
8. Test
9. Ship

In this way, any deviation from the schedule can be detected early and corrective action taken. Managing these complex logistics, especially when many parts are involved, demands a computerized system which can facilitate scheduling, updating, monitoring and raising early warning flags on any product not progressing according to schedule. The data base so accumulated will also lend itself to an analysis of past performance.

HCMOS Technology

The physics of the MOS transistor, the way they are configured to execute the switching function and the characteristics of the semiconductor process with which they are implemented in silicon has given rise to the following advantages of CMOS over NMOS.

Superior Noise Immunity

Input switching thresholds are high, typically 0.7 (V_{DD}) for V_{IH} and 0.3 (V_{DD}) for V_{IL}.

Low Static Power Dissipation

Since the P and N transistors are connected in series, current flows only during a switching transition, at all other times one or other of the devices is hard off. This also contributes to the low power consumption and the linear relationship between power consumption and clock frequency.

Wide Operating Temperature Range

The junction temperature for a CMOS device will be typically 20 percent cooler than that for an NMOS device. This supports an operating temperature range of – 55 degrees Celsius to + 125 degrees without substantial yield loss.

Cleaner Switching Characteristics

An N-channel transistor, because of higher majority carrier mobility (electrons) has a shorter gate propagation delay than a CMOS transistor (due to a slower P-channel transistor). However, the NMOS switch employs a passive pull-up load transistor which limits the source current available to charge system capacitances through a highly resistive load. CMOS on the other hand exhibits both active pull-up and pull-down behavior.

Alpha Radiation Immunity

Destruction of memory cell content by alpha particle radiation is caused by electron/hole pair recombination in the transistor well. Since the P-well is shallow in an N-channel CMOS transistor configuration, the recombination is limited.

Latchup

CMOS technology is however more susceptible to a phenomenon called latchup in which the complementary cell structure goes into a self-sustaining thyristor mode of operation. This behavior is possible due to the diffused regions, as a consequence of their relative configurations, interacting with each other to form parasitic lateral bipolar transistors in the silicon substrate. Should this occur, only disconnecting the power supply will stop the action. Prevention is always better than cure, however, and this tendency can be controlled, if not eliminated, with good process design. There are many techniques to do so, such as isolating guard rings and minimizing minority carrier lifetime in the parasitic regions by increasing the impurity doping in the well. This has the effect of diverting potentially harmful currents through paths of least resistance to the substrate and away from sensitive junctions which might otherwise be forward biased. This is why power supply sequencing should be followed to ensure that the input of a CMOS device never goes more positive than V_{DD} at any time.

Nonvolatile Memory

A recent development of particular interest in computer integrated manufacturing and artificial intelligence context has been the development and integration of EEPROM memory technology on the same piece of silicon as a microprocessor. This opens up the real possibility of being able to develop systems which can "learn" from their environment, so called "self-adaptive systems." In the quest to produce a memory device with the flexibility of a dynamic RAM and the data retention capability of a ROM, nonvolatile EEPROM memory was developed. There are two major types: EPROM and EEPROM. The physics of both technologies are very similar and are based on the ability of an oxide layer to retain an electrical charge. This retained electrical charge, which is used to represent a bit of data, (charged indicating either a "1" or a "0" and uncharged representing the opposite) is stored in an "island" of polysilicon floating in a "sea" of silicon dioxide. See Figure 4-3. Silicon dioxide is an insulator and effectively isolates the polysilicon gate island. In the case of EPROMs, the control gate oxide is in the order of 1,000 angstroms thick, allowing avalanche injection to be employed as the mechanism to charge the floating gate. This charge is retained until discharged by exposure to ultraviolet light. Power-off data retention is typically "guaranteed" for ten years.

In the case of EEPROMs, the gate oxide is in the order of 50/100 angstroms thick, the charge mechanism is via a mechanism called Fowler Nordheim tunneling and the gate potential can be discharged electrically. This last characteristic gives EEPROM technology a distinct advantage over EPROM technology. EPROMs require a relatively expensive quartz lid package in order to allow the die to be erased by exposure to ultraviolet light, preventing erasure and reprogramming in situ. EEPROMs, on the other hand, can very conveniently be erased and reprogrammed electrically without being removed from the system. The quartz lid on the EPROM type device can also allow

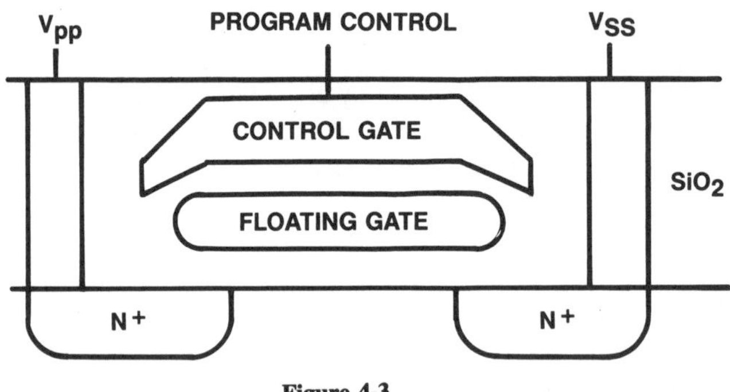

Figure 4-3

unintentional erasure due to accumulated effects, even at low dosage levels, in a natural or fluorescent light environment. Also, the EPROM can only be erased in bulk, i.e., all or nothing. EEPROMs on the other hand, can be erased in bulk by blocks of cells (pages), and even cell by cell.

Most nonvolatile memories (NVMs) produced to date have been variations on the same theme using NMOS technology as a base line. Until recently, the relatively high voltage required for programming (up to 30 volts) had to be provided by some off-chip source, necessitating at least two power supplies—five volts V_{DD} and 30 volts V_{PP}. Recent developments in charge pump technology have made it possible to produce chips requiring a single five-volt supply only. This can represent a significant saving to original equipment manufacturers since EPROMs not only require a wide range of programming voltages—5 to 30 volts—but also require very tight tolerances in the order of ± 1 volt. EEPROM devices fabricated in HCMOS technology are now available and with all the inherent advantages of this technology described earlier, it is now possible to design systems which have improved noise immunity, consume less power, even permitting battery operation, and therefore run cooler and more reliably.

EEPROMs do indeed offer the system designer many benefits, but there are still shortcomings with this technology, in varying stages of resolution. Most devices available, certainly those of any significant capacity, are byte organized. This can pose a communication problem to a processor whose input/output capability has been design restricted to serial mode only in the interest of minimizing pin count for cost and/or security reasons. Even a processor with a full complement of interfacing capability can have a problem communicating with a byte-organized stand-alone EEPROM memory device. Unless the device chosen has on-chip latches, the processor will have a ten-millisecond wait each time a byte is written to the memory (approximately 80 seconds to load a 64K byte device). Various page mode techniques have been developed which permit more than one byte to be written during a single write cycle by using on-chip latches or address and data. The disadvantage of this approach, apart from requiring greater chip area, is that even bytes whose data are the same before and after write are also erased. This can compromise the device's write endurance limit, normally specified at 10,000 cycles maximum.

Another problem which can be encountered is inadvertant write operations during voltage excursions in the system, although there are many techniques to deal with this, some of which can now be incorporated on the chip. Voltage sensing, for example, can be employed to inhibit the write line whenever V_{CC} falls below a certain level. Since EEPROMs have a limited write capability and are used in a read mainly mode, the write enable and charge pump are required infrequently and so can be inhibited for much of the time. Additionally, further protection can be had by employing similar signal gating techniques, external to the chip. Many of these problems are peculiar to stand-alone devices and do not arise where the processor and memory are integrated on the same chip.

Principle of Charge Pump Operation

At t0, node NA is at ground potential, D1 is forward biased, node NB is at V_{CC}, D2 is reversed biased and C1 charges through forward biased D1, raising N1 to ($V_{CC} - 0.7$) volts. At t1, node B is pulled to ground, C2 begins to charge through forward biased D2 at the same time that node NA rises from ground to V_{CC}, raising node N1 to ($2 \times V_{CC} - 1.4$) volts since D1 is now reversed biased. This process is repeated to as

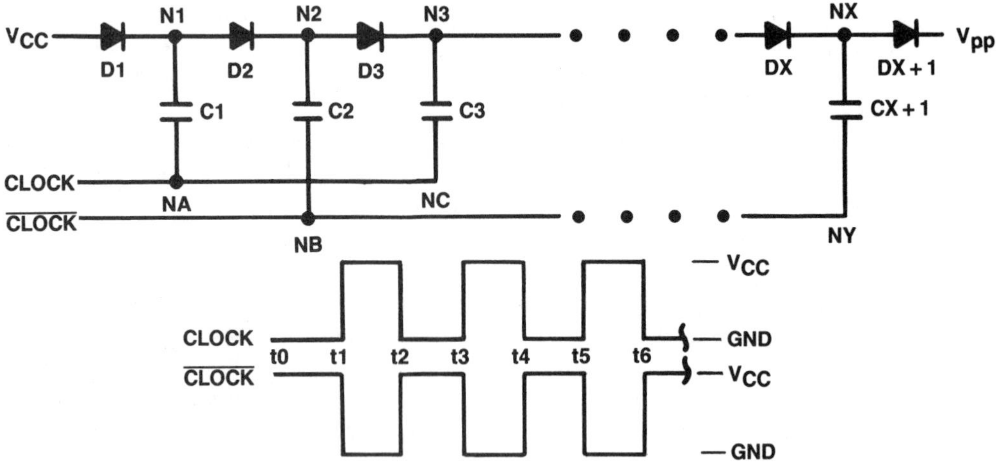

Figure 4-4 Charge Pump—Principle of Operation

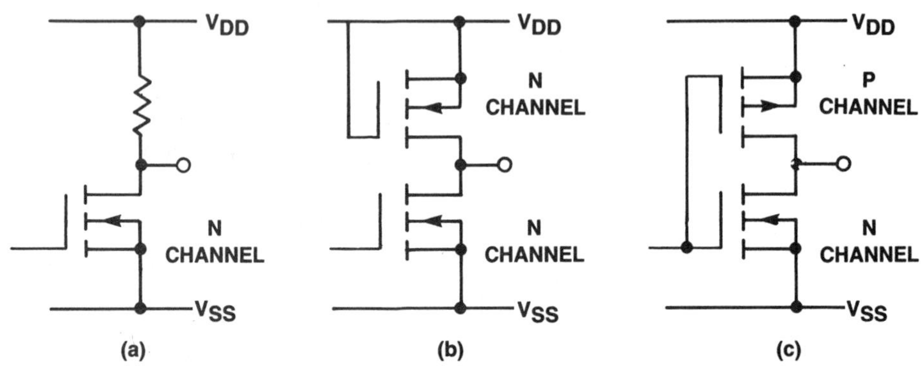

Figure 4-5 MOS Inverter Circuits

many links as there are in the chain, with each clock transition cascading the voltage of the previous stage through to the next stage, increased by (V_{CC} – 0.7) volts. In practice, diminishing returns are encountered due to imperfect coupling and bulk silicon effects, with each voltage increment slightly less than the previous one. Charge splitting across the respective capacitors also contributes to this effect. Six to eight stages may well be required to produce a 20-volt V_{pp} from a five-volt supply. (See Figure 4-4.)

MOS Transistor Switching

A voltage applied to the gate of an NMOS transistor will attract majority carriers (electrons in the case of N-channel, holes in the case of P-channel), towards the gate region, forming a conductive inversion layer between source and drain. Since the concentration of these carriers is a function of the voltage applied to the gate, the drain to source resistance will be a function of gate voltage. The pull-up load resistor function in Figure 4-5a can therefore be replaced by a transistor, as shown in Figure 4-5b. Transistors consume much less silicon real estate than do relatively high value resistors. If the load transistor is of opposite polarity to the drive transistor, i.e., complementary, then two such transistors whose gate connections are common will operate such that when one is on, the other will be off and vice versa. In this way, current only flows from source to drain during a switching transition. Power consumption is therefore very low and proportional to clock frequency.

Future Trends

There is little doubt that the technology developments which made VLSI semiconductor products possible will continue in the future. Wafer processing technologies now emerging, for example, will substantially reduce the need for power/speed/cost trade-offs, and so on, which are now so typically unavoidable. This will give both designers and users greater freedom of choice in optimizing desired features with much lower trade-off cost than has been the case in the past. Application of new photolithographic techniques in mask making and pattern definition on the silicon such as Direct Write E BEAM and X-ray lithography will sustain improvements in packing density and hopefully cost and cycle-time. The products themselves, in terms of functionality, will continue to evolve with 16- and 32-bit processor cores enhancing the 8-bit already available with the same, or at least similar, evolutionary development taking place with greater on-chip integration of peripheral functions. Many innovative adaptations will sustain the pervasiveness of single-chip, application specific, and stand-alone mass memory products. Some of these innovations could include on-chip liquid crystal display (LCD) drive, nonvolatile memory, serial I/O for telecommunications applications, fast analog to digital (A/D) resolution and accuracy at extended temperatures and speed for automotive applications, and lower price products for cost sensitive consumer white goods applications.

There will be similar improvements in the kinds of packages in which the products will be offered in order for the full benefits to be exploited. It is possible that use of the conventional dual-in-line (DIL) package will diminish as small outline DILs, quad and chip carrier packages, direct bonding of the chip to the PC board, and encapsulation in plastic cards for high volume consumer applications find ever-increasing market acceptance. The cost of entry, benefiting primarily the first-time user, will be reduced as low cost development systems are made available in conjunction with modular software and universal, or at least partially so, operating systems capable of running on any machine architecture. Application volumes which are currently beneath the benefit threshold will become economically viable in single chip as plastic encapsulated EPROM and EEPROM products are brought to the marketplace in the future. This is already technically feasible and is restricted only by the problems of dealing with the product metamorphosis aspects which arise.

A part which starts life as an EEPROM and remains so only while in die form becomes a PROM when encapsulated in an opaque package and a ROM when programmed raises problems which are even now being addressed. Testing a PROM comprehensively cannot be guaranteed but can only be assured by programming it and then testing it as a ROM. This obviously defeats the purpose of the exercise if every part were to be treated in this way. To overcome this, resort will have to be made to statistical assurance by testing a sample of the whole population as ROMS and assuring the behavior of the remainder of the population as PROMS on this evidence. The alternative to this will be factory programming and even this may become available as the disadvantage of using very high cost test systems to program PROMS is overcome by the transition to more reasonable cost, dedicated, or at least partially dedicated equipment, for testing and programming.

Factory organization will almost certainly change as a consequence of these developments in order to better support the product and hence customer requirements with product rationalization directed to "complete solutions" to customer's needs rather than simply providing the "ingredients." Memory products, for example, such as ROMS, EPROMS, and static RAMS which are a necessary part of any microprocessor application may well be included in microcomponent portfolios as an additional service to the customers in helping them find a path of least-resistance solution to their product needs.

Gate arrays, which require an essentially similar organizational infrastructure, set of skills and resources and will mainly enhance single-chip microprocessor applications by replacing the "glue" parts with a semi-customized peripheral, will almost certainly be best supported by the proficient single-chip vendor. Greatly intensified use of CAD/CAM techniques will significantly improve productivity, quality, reliability, cost, cycle-time, and service in relation to products so produced and supported. All of this will, for the user, mean significantly enhanced product performance, flexibility, reduced entry, and cost and continuation of a bright future for integrated circuit products and applications. Who will supply these is being contested now.

TYPICAL N-CHANNEL SILICON-GATE PROCESS

MOS processing is a manufacturing methodology by which the electrical properties of a single-crystal lattice semiconductor wafer are changed by chemical, physical, and thermal means; this results in the creation of field-effect transistors, resistors, capacitors, and electrical interconnections. To create the desired changes in the electrical properties in specific regions of the wafer, each wafer is processed through a series of operations in which a mask layer, superimposed over the wafer, is used to define these regions in which the structure of the underlying silicon is to be altered and those which are to remain unchanged. These regions are defined by a photosensitive chemical deposited across the wafer. Regions left exposed by the mask layer are hardened by exposure to ultraviolet light. Those unexposed and therefore unhardened regions can then be etched away chemically to leave the underlying structure open to further treatment. The physical properties of these regions are then changed by the introduction of impurities in controlled amounts, either by ion bombardment—direct injection of the impurity ions at extremely high velocities—or by chemical deposition, in which the diffusion of the impurity ions into the silicon infrastructure is accelerated under high temperature. The "hardened" emulsion is then removed prior to the next operation.

The order in which the wafers are processed through the complete sequence of operations is known as the process flow and will vary according to the technology being used and the attributes being optimized in the end product. Generally speaking, each operational cycle in the process consists of growing an oxide film, masking, exposing, etching, implanting, rinsing, buffering, drying, and baking. These steps are described in detail for a process, while still in use today in its original form, has served as a base line from which the new, higher performance technologies have evolved.

The five-volt, N-channel silicon-gate depletion-load MOS process, developed in the early 1970s, is the forerunner of the high-density MOS (HMOS) and HCMOS processes, the major changes being in the techniques developed that allow the fabrication of smaller geometric dimensions. Because of the similarities in layout rules with the original process and the modern HMOS, CMOS, and HCMOS processes, the novice mask designer will, in mastering these, find it to be an easy transition in learning the layout rules for newer processes. As such, the five-volt N-channel silicon-gate depletion load MOS manufacturing process is now described.

This process employs nine mask layers in seven separate operations, with each operation consisting of several steps. Each operation is unique and must be in proper sequence if the integrated circuit is to work properly. The integrated-circuit designer needs to understand the function of each mask layer in the process flow. It is the purpose of this chapter to illustrate, in some detail, how each of these layers is used in the manufacturing process flow. Thirty-four steps—or operations in the process—are illustrated.

01 Masking Operation

The 01 mask is used to create the pattern which defines and isolates the field regions from the electrically active regions in an integrated circuit. The steps involved in the 01 operation begin after the wafer is cleaned. The first step is to grow a thin film of thermal oxide on the surface of the wafer. This is done by heating the wafer in a sealed, oxygen rich atmosphere. This layer—called bottom oxide (Figure 4-6), protects the surface of the substrate from the nitride and provides a means to control the positioning of implanted ions in later steps.

A thin film of nitride is then deposited on top of this bottom oxide (Figure 4-7). A film of photoresist is spun on top of the nitride (Figure 4-8). This photoresist is dried; the 01 mask is aligned to the wafer; and the photoresist is then exposed and developed (Figures 4-9 and 4-10).

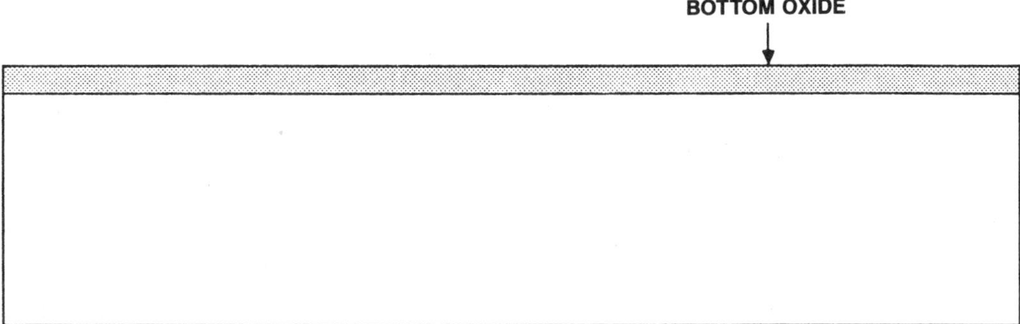

Figure 4-6 Bottom Oxide

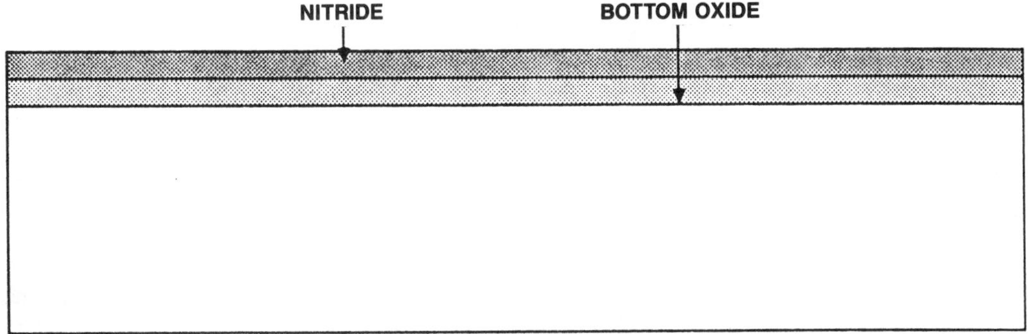

Figure 4-7 Nitride Deposition

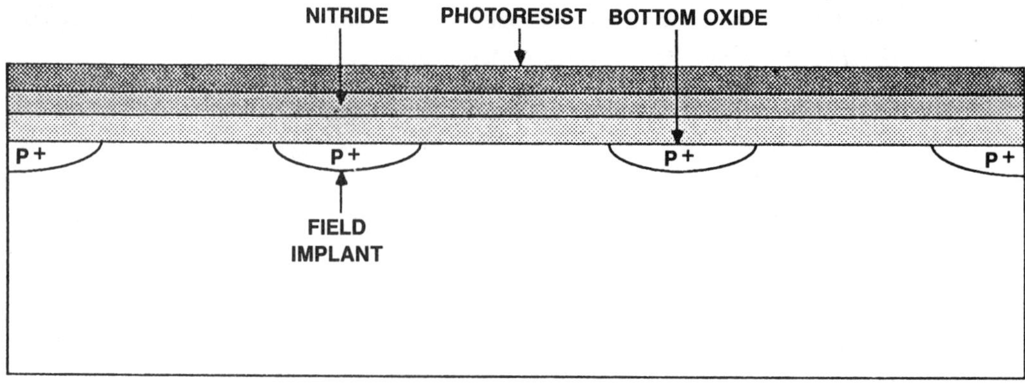

Figure 4-8 Photoresist Spin

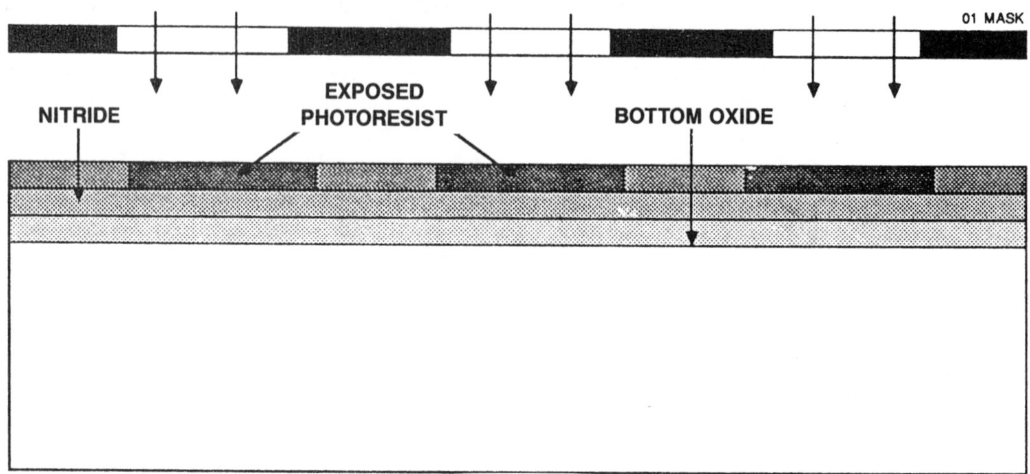

Figure 4-9 01 Align and Expose

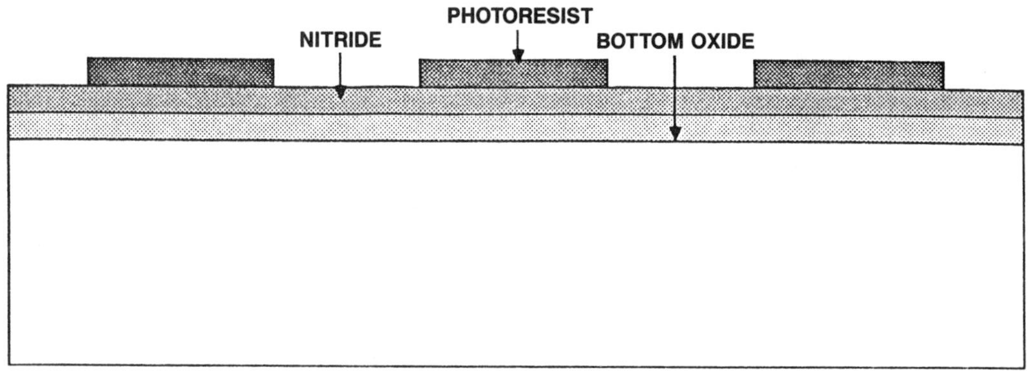

Figure 4-10 Develop and Post-Bake

Next, the surface of the wafer is implanted with boron ions (Figure 4-11). The boron ions in the substrate, deficient in donor electrons, will cause the substrate to become more heavily doped with P-type characteristics, making the surface more difficult to invert by shifting the threshold voltage.

The next step is to etch the nitride (Figure 4-12). After the 01 mask pattern is etched into the nitride layer, the photoresist is then stripped from the wafer (Figure 4-13). The next step is to grow the field oxide by exposing the wafer to oxygen (Figure 4-14). The oxygen combines with the silicon, Si, of the substrate to form silicon dioxide, SiO_2. The nitride prevents the growth of oxide in areas where it covers the wafer. Some of the silicon receiving the boron implant is converted into SiO_2. Along the edges of the nitride, the formation of the SiO_2 causes lifting of the nitride. This lifting is referred to as "bird's beaking." SiO_2 is also formed on the back of the wafer. This layer on the back is called back oxide.

Next, the nitride is removed (Figure 4-15), after which, the bottom oxide is removed (Figure 4-16).

02 Masking Operation

The purpose of the 02 mask is to define the depletion transistors. This is done by permitting implantation of phosphorus ions into regions where depletion transistors will be formed. The additional ions in the substrate will electrically change the threshold voltage of those transistors.

After stripping the bottom oxide, the gate oxide is then grown and a blanket gate ion implant is performed (Figures 4-17 and 4-18). This implant shifts all the threshold voltages of all the transistors on the wafer. After the implant photoresist is spun onto the wafer surface, the photoresist is dried. The 02 mask is aligned to the alignment keys defined by the 01 layer and the photoresist is exposed and developed (Figure 4-19). The wafers are now exposed to the depletion implant (Figure 4-20). After implantation of the depletion transistor regions, the photoresist is stripped (Figure 4-21).

03 Masking Operation

The 03 mask creates the buried contact by defining areas where gate oxide will be removed. After stripping of the photoresist with the 02 pattern, more photoresist is spun on and dried. The 03 mask is aligned to alignment keys defined by the 01 mask (Figure 4-22). The photoresist is exposed and developed. The wafer is placed into an etching solution and the exposed gate oxide is stripped (Figure 4-23). The photoresist is then removed (Figure 4-24).

04 Masking Operation

If required by the flow, an 04 mask containing the same pattern as the 03 mask may be used. In this case, the etching in the 03 masking operation is omitted and is done at the 04 masking operation. The 04 mask permits an additional photoresist layer to be used, eliminating the possibility of etchant working its way through a single oxide. The polycrystalline silicon film deposited on the surface will then come into contact with the substrate. Except for this paragraph, the 04 masking operation is not described in this text.

05 Masking Operation

A polycrystalline silicon 1 film is then deposited on the surface of the wafer (Figure 4-25), and the surface of the film is oxidized (Figure 4-26). The 05 mask defines the

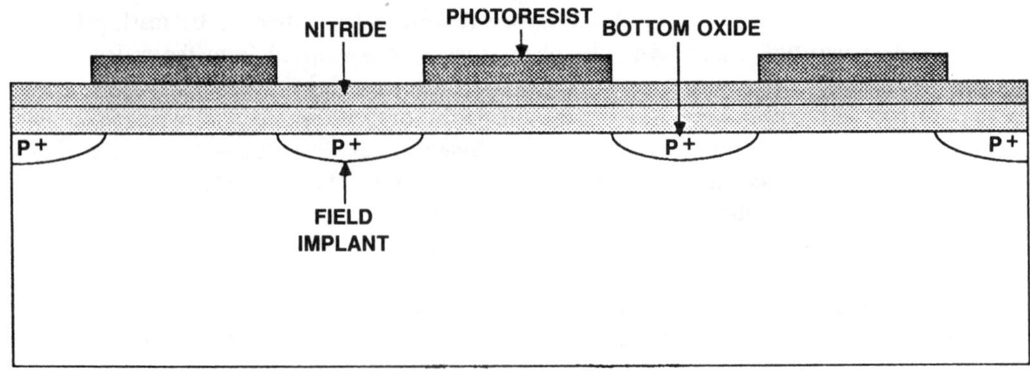

Figure 4-11 Boron Implant

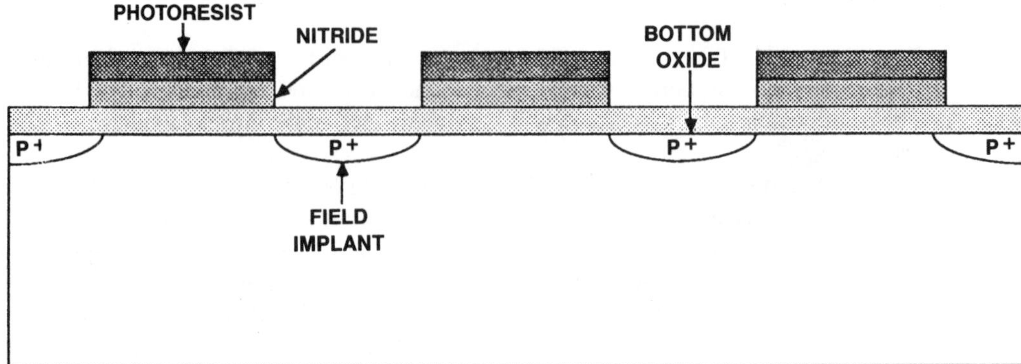

Figure 4-12 Nitride Etch

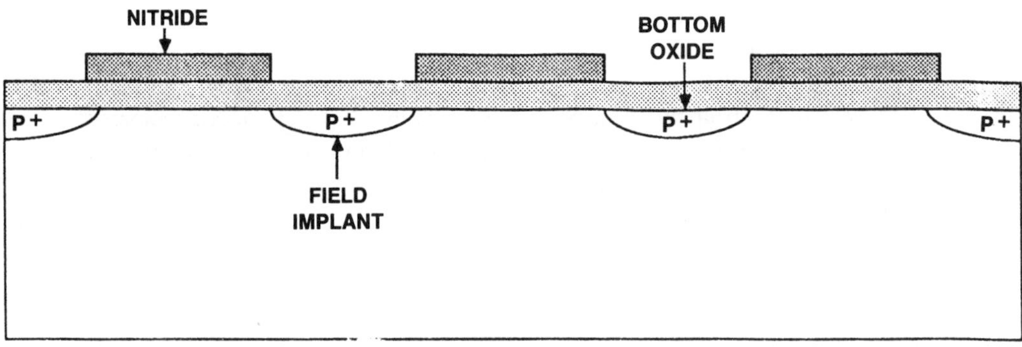

Figure 4-13 Strip Photoresist

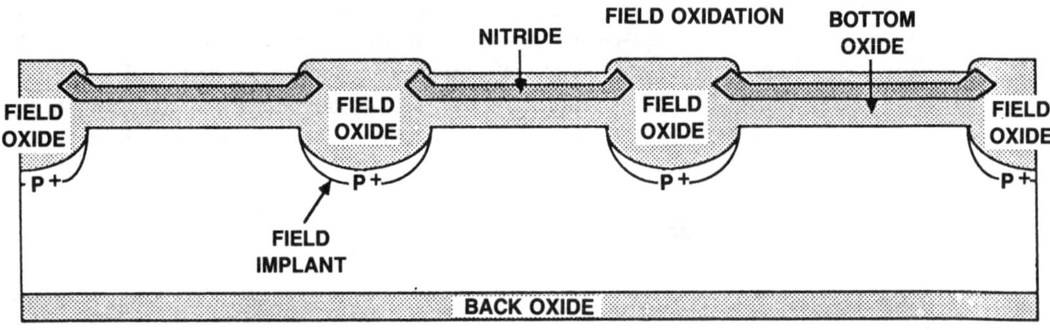

Figure 4-14 Field Oxidation

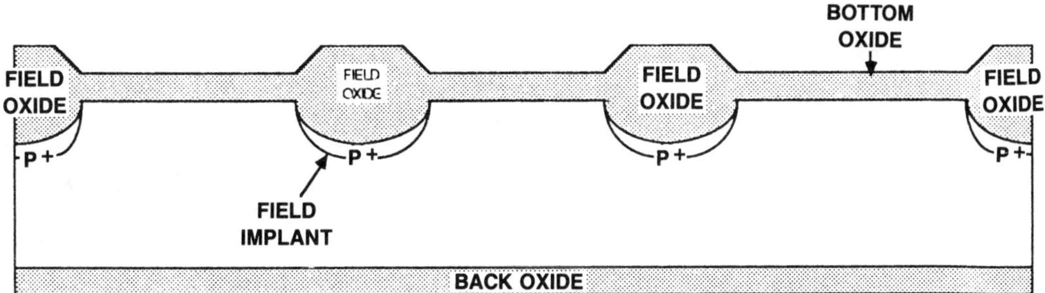

Figure 4-15 Top Oxide and Nitride Strip

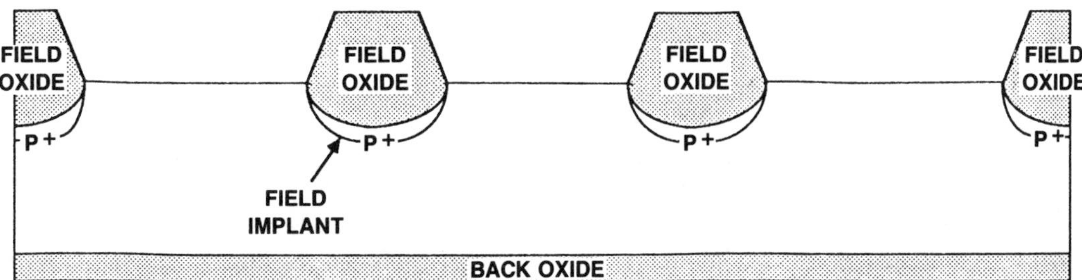

Figure 4-16 Bottom Oxide Etch

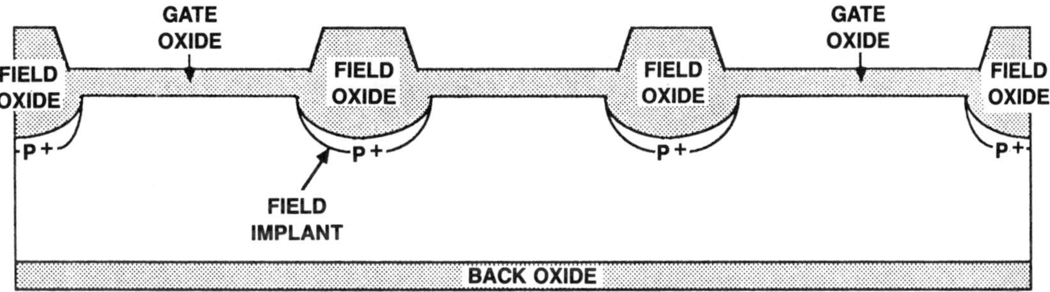

Figure 4-17 Gate Oxidation

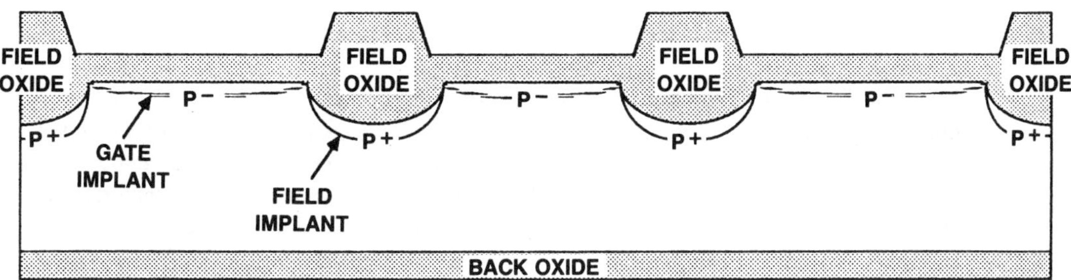

Figure 4-18 Gate Implant

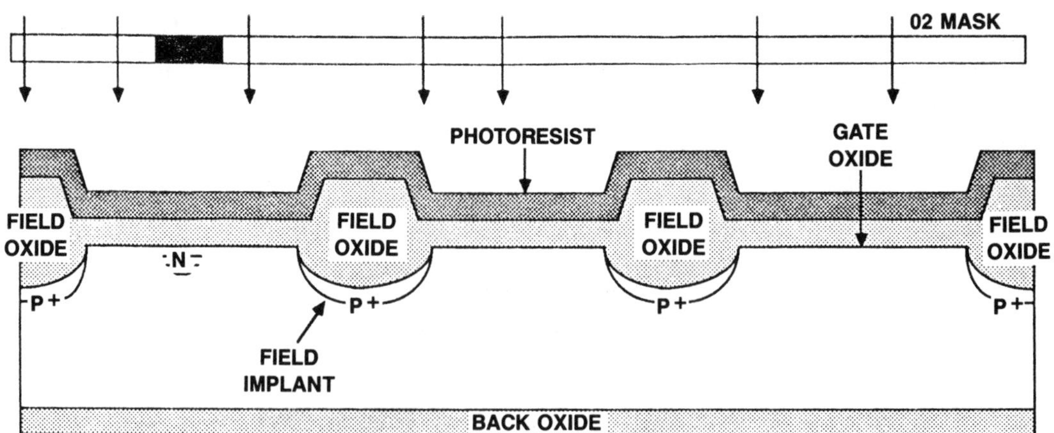

Figure 4-19 02 Align and Expose

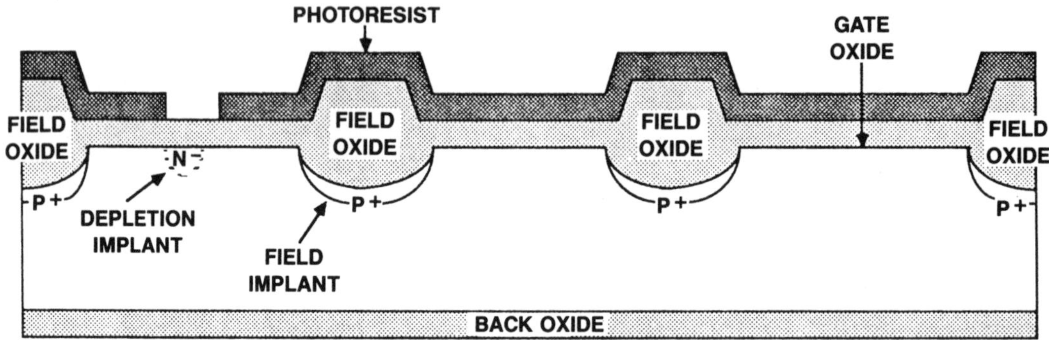

Figure 4-20 Depletion Implant

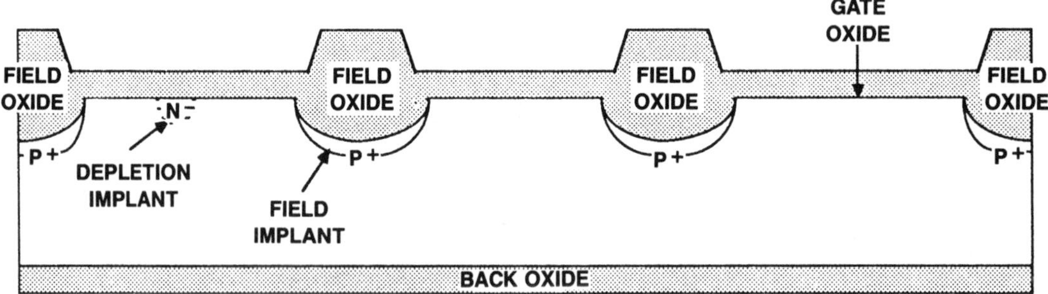

Figure 4-21 Strip PR

gates of the transistors and capacitors and the poly interconnect lines. After poly oxidation, photoresist is spun onto the surface of the wafer the 05 mask is aligned to alignment keys defined by the 01 mask and the photoresist is exposed and developed (Figure 4-27), and the 05 pattern is etched into the poly oxide (Figure 4-28). The photoresist is then removed (Figure 4-29). Using the poly oxide as a mask, the 05 pattern is etched into the poly (Figure 4-30). When the excess poly is removed, the substrate for the sources and drains and N + interconnect will then be exposed (Figure 4-31).

1. In the industry, the term ''poly'' is commonly used for ''polycrystalline silicon,'' and we will use that term extensively in the following text.

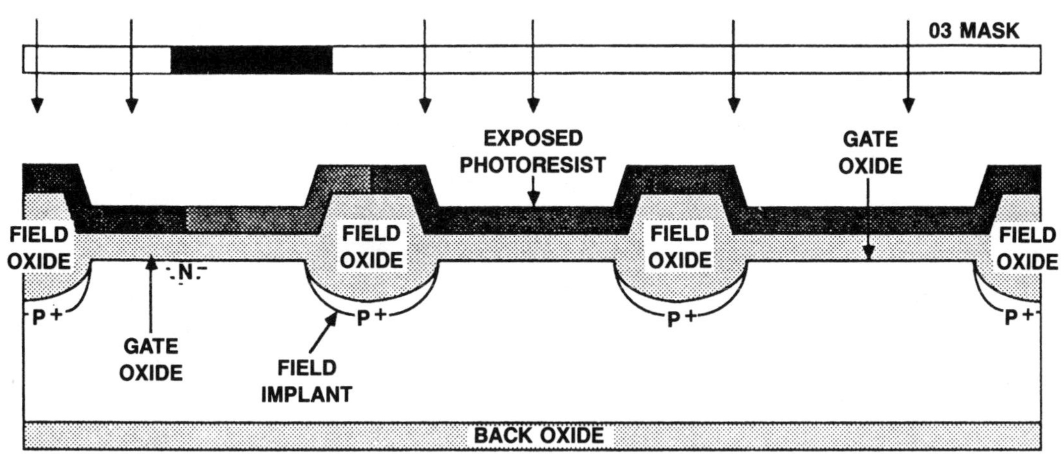

Figure 4-22 03 Align and Expose

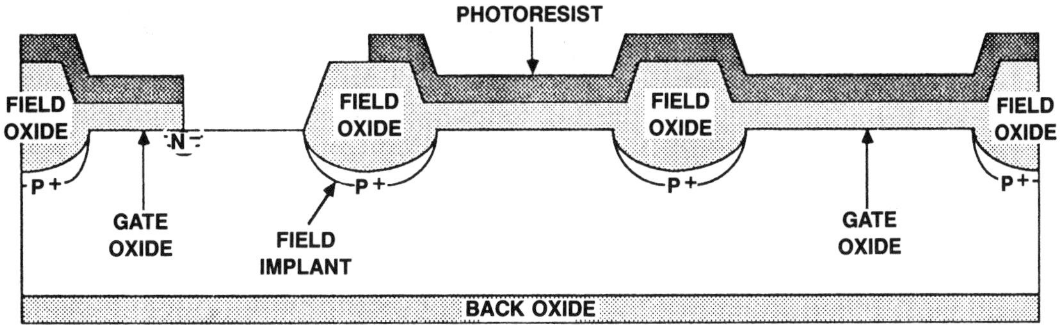

Figure 4-23 03 Gate Etch

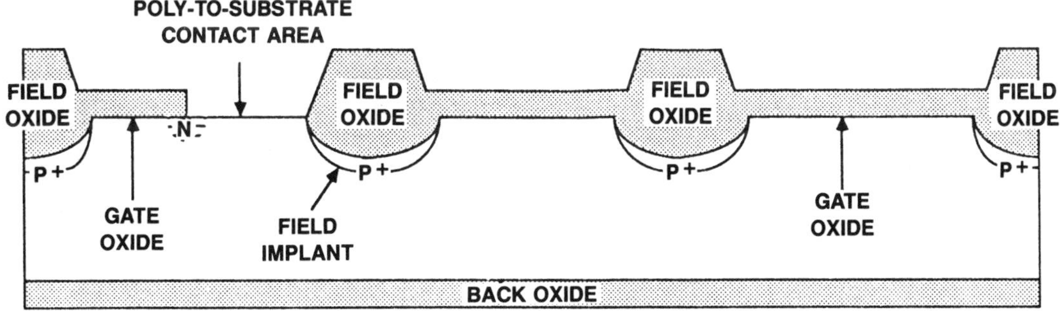

Figure 4-24 Photoresist Strip

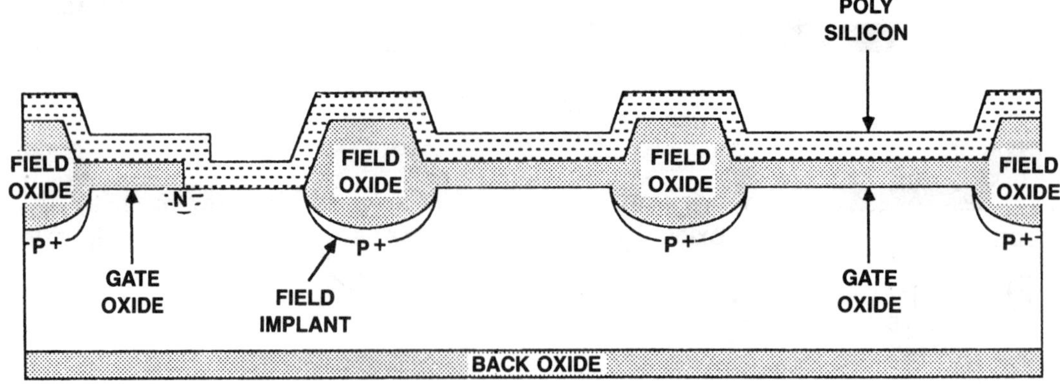

Figure 4-25 Polycrystalline Silicon

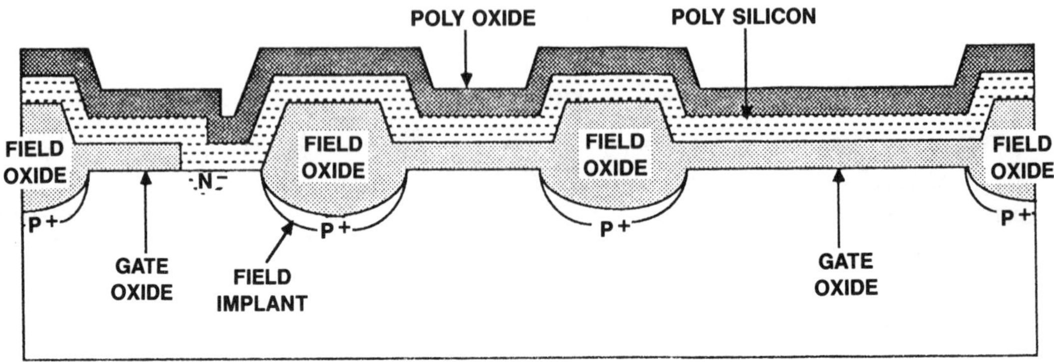

Figure 4-26 Polycrystalline Silicon Oxidation

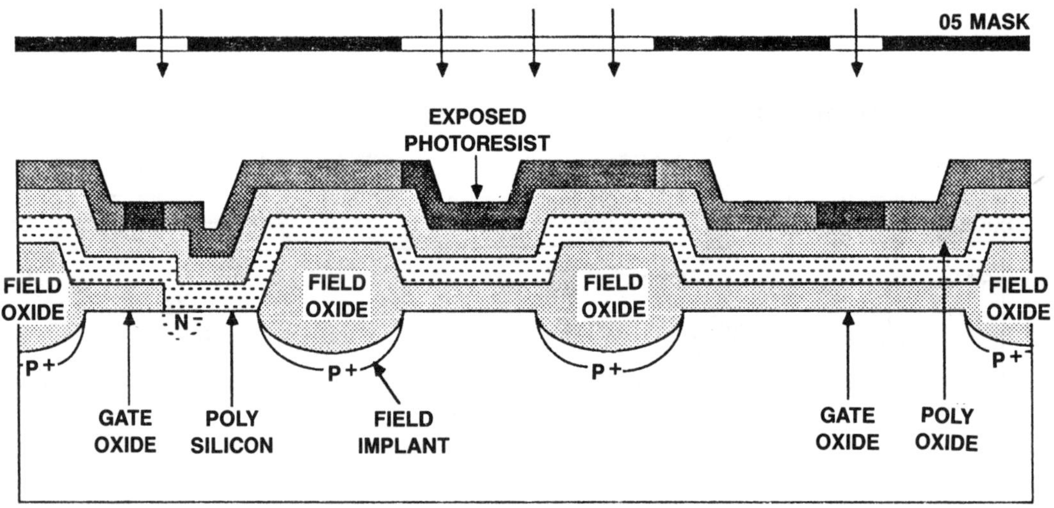

Figure 4-27 05 Align and Expose

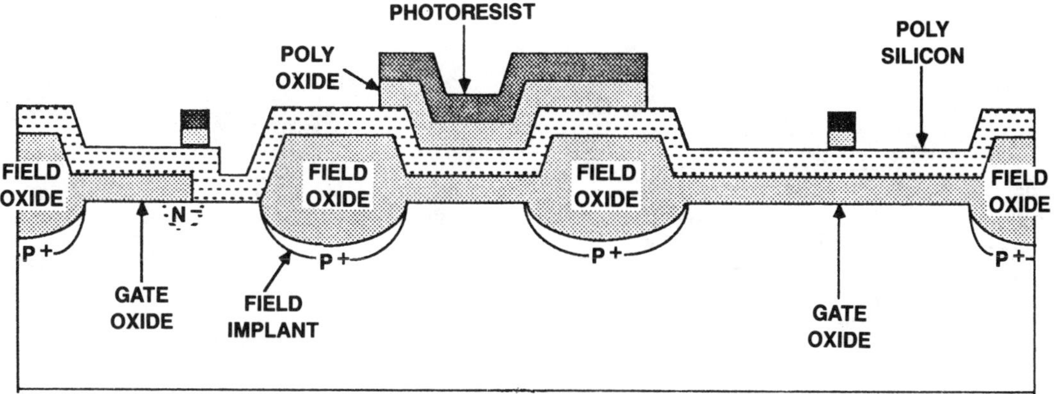

Figure 4-28 Polycrystalline Silicon Oxide Etch

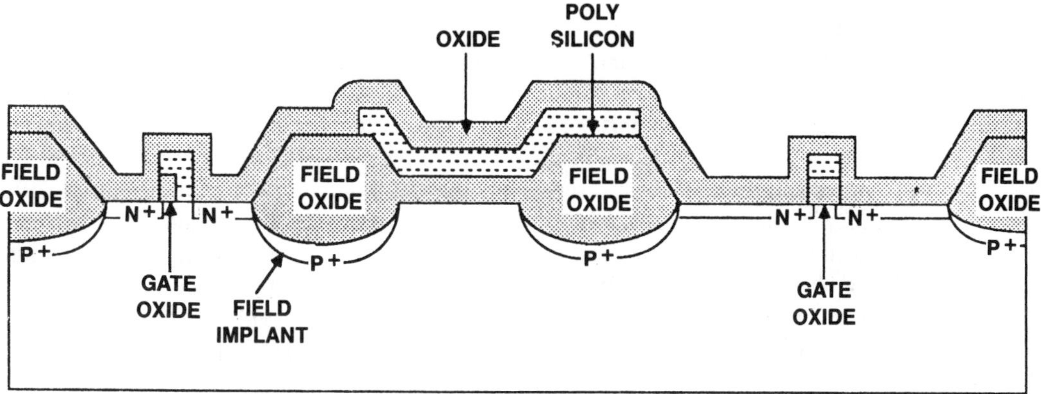

Figure 4-29 N^+ Source-Drain

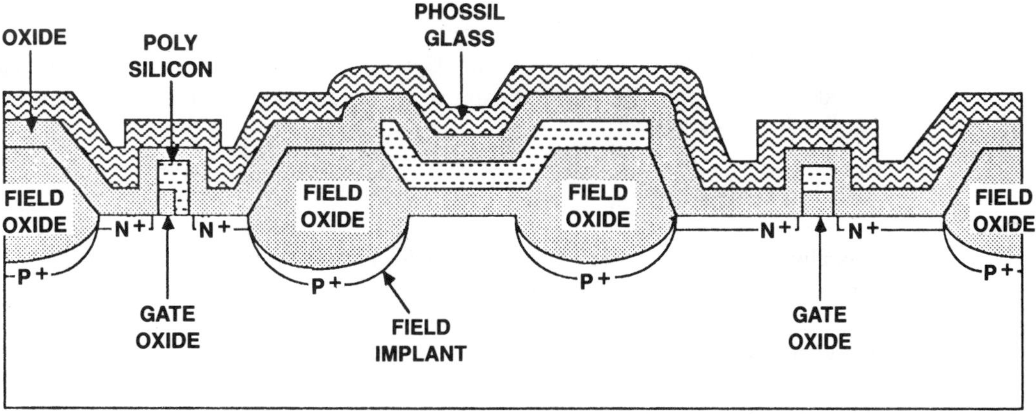

Figure 4-30 Glass Deposition

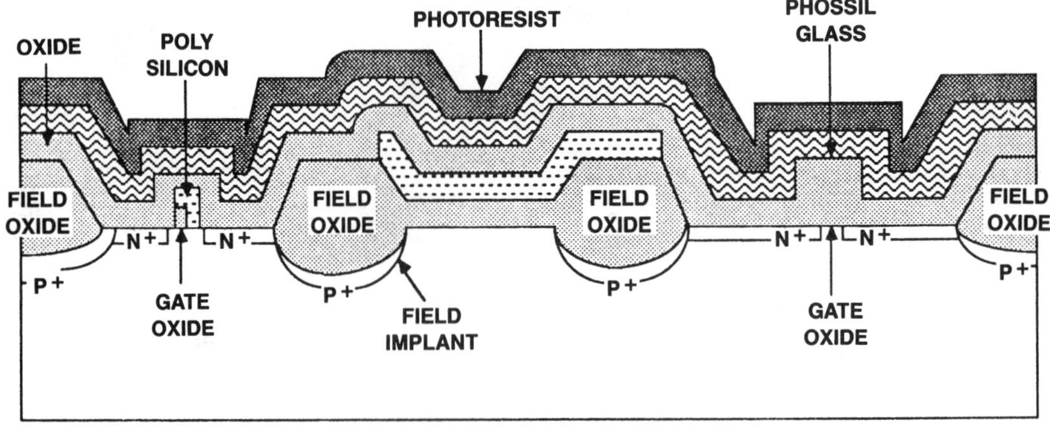

Figure 4-31 06 Align and Expose

Following the 05 masking operation is a predeposition step where the surface of the wafer is exposed to a dopant. The objective of the predeposition is to place the dopant in contact with the raw silicon surface, in these regions in which it will subsequently be diffused into the silicon. (In this particular process the dopant is phosphorus.) The dopant is used to reduce the resistance of the deposited polycrystalline silicon and to form the N+ source and drain of the transistors and the N+ interconnect regions (Figure 4-29). The wafer is subjected to heat which ''drives'' or diffuses the dopant into the silicon and forms a film of silicon and a film of silicon dioxide. After the ''drive-in'' as this step is called, a phosphorus-doped (Phossil) glass film is deposited on the wafer (Figure 4-30). The thermally grown oxide and the deposited Phossil glass form the field oxide and provide the insulation between the metal and poly layers and the N+ regions.

06 Masking Operation

The 06 mask defines the preohmic contact cuts. These contacts are formed by metal passing through the insulating layers to the poly or N+ regions. After the Phossil glass deposition, photoresist is spun onto the surface of the wafer and dried. The 06 mask is aligned to the alignment keys defined by the 05 mask and the photoresist is exposed and developed (Figure 4-31). The wafer is exposed to an etchant. The 06 contact holes are then etched (Figure 4-32).

07 Masking Operation

Occasionally, an 07 mask is used to taper the holes created by the 06 mask. The pattern is the same on the 07 as on the 06 except for the size.

08 Masking Operation

The 08 mask defines the interconnect, power buses, and the pads for the integrated circuit. Once the 06 contact holes have been cut, a metal film is deposited on the surface of the wafer (Figure 4-33). Photoresist is again deposited on the surface of the wafer. The photoresist is then dried and the 08 mask aligned to the alignment keys defined by the 06 mask (Figure 4-34). Next, the photoresist is exposed and developed, and the metal

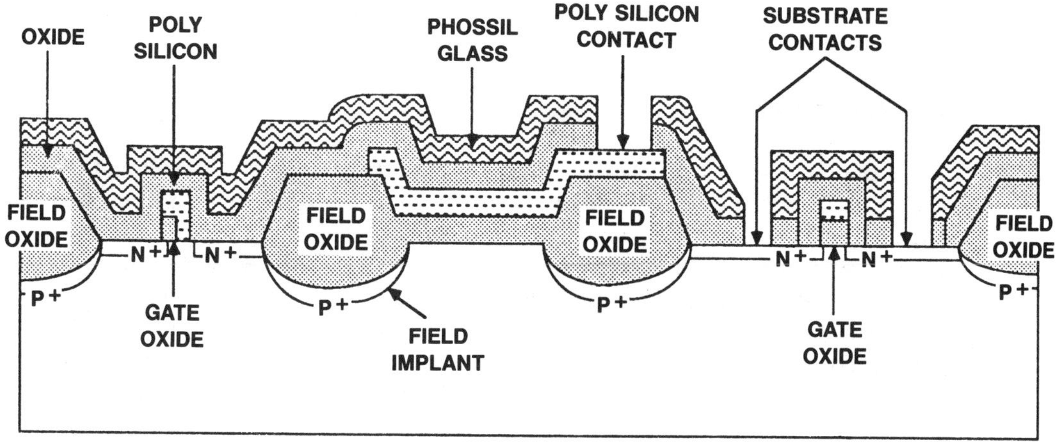

Figure 4-32 Preohmic Contact Cut and Photoresist Strip

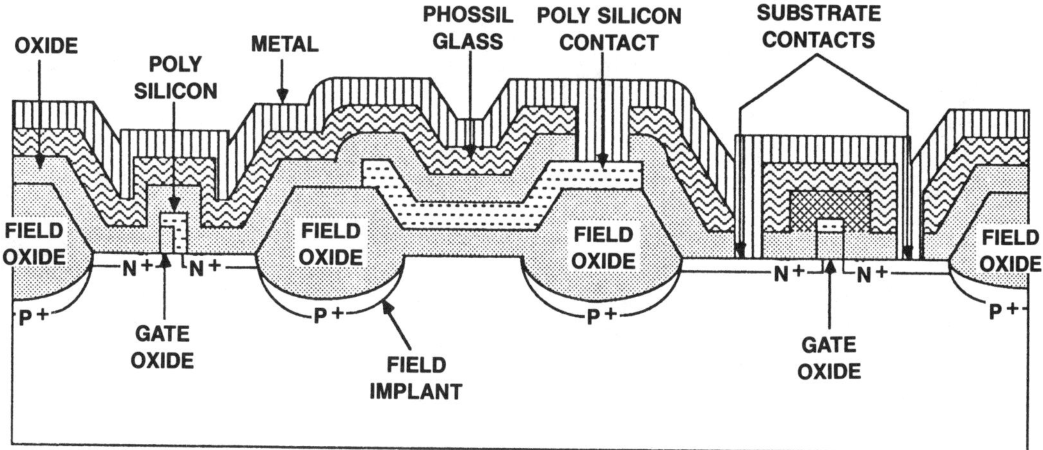

Figure 4-33 Metal

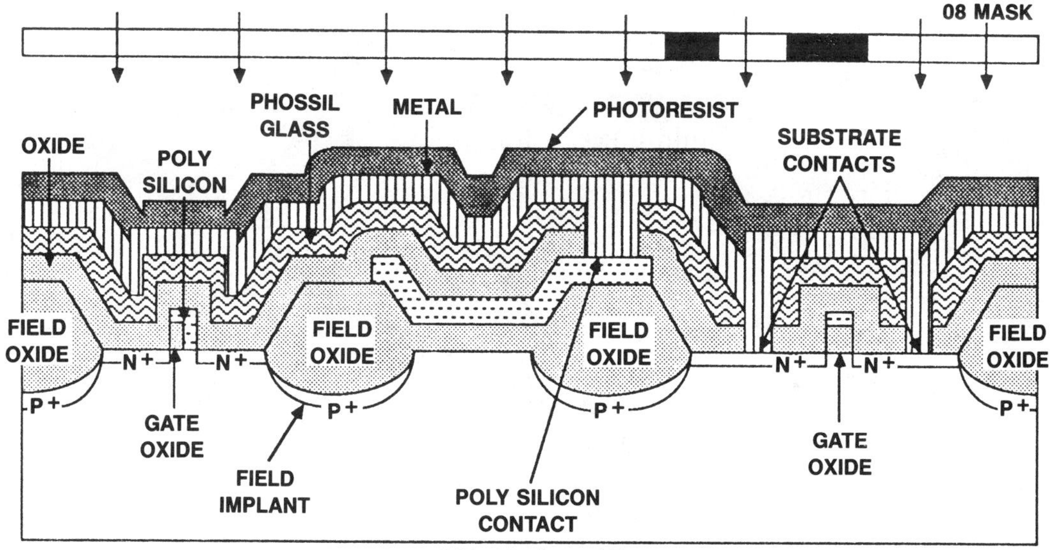

08 MASK
OXIDE
POLY SILICON
PHOSSIL GLASS
METAL
PHOTORESIST
SUBSTRATE CONTACTS
FIELD OXIDE
FIELD OXIDE
FIELD OXIDE
FIELD OXIDE
N+
N+
N+
N+
P+
P+
P+
P+
GATE OXIDE
FIELD IMPLANT
POLY SILICON CONTACT
GATE OXIDE

Figure 4-34 08 Align and Expose

pattern is etched (Figure 4-35). The metal photoresist is then removed. Passivation is deposited on the metal pattern (Figure 4-36).

09 Masking Operation

In this step, another film of photoresist is spun onto the surface of the wafer and dried. The 09 mask, which defines the openings for the pads, is aligned to the alignment keys defined by the 08 mask. The photoresist is exposed, developed, and etched. At this point the wafers are ready for back lap—where the wafer thickness is reduced from about 20 thousands of an inch to about 14—and back plating—a gold deposition process to facilitate bonding of the silicon die to the metal lead frame of the package in which it will be subsequently encapsulated. After plating, the wafers are probed and sent to the assembly area for packaging, after which they are 100 percent final tested prior to shipping.

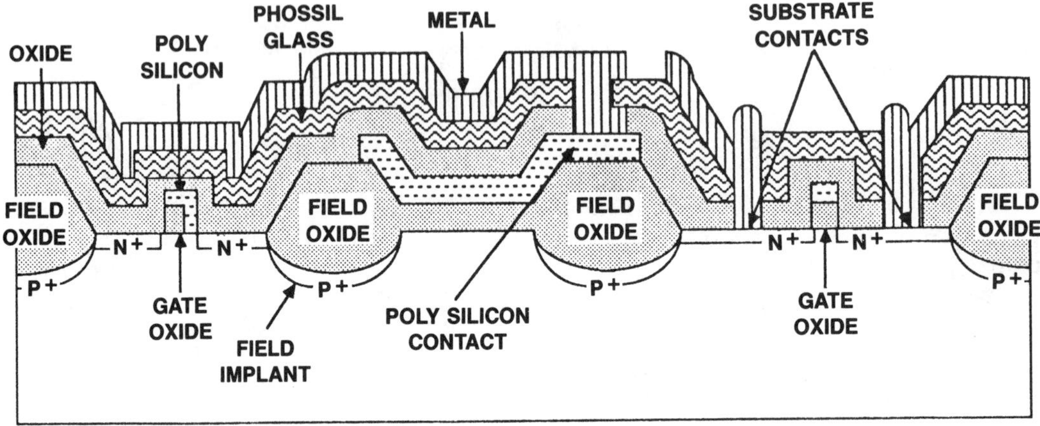

Figure 4-35 Etch and Photoresist Strip

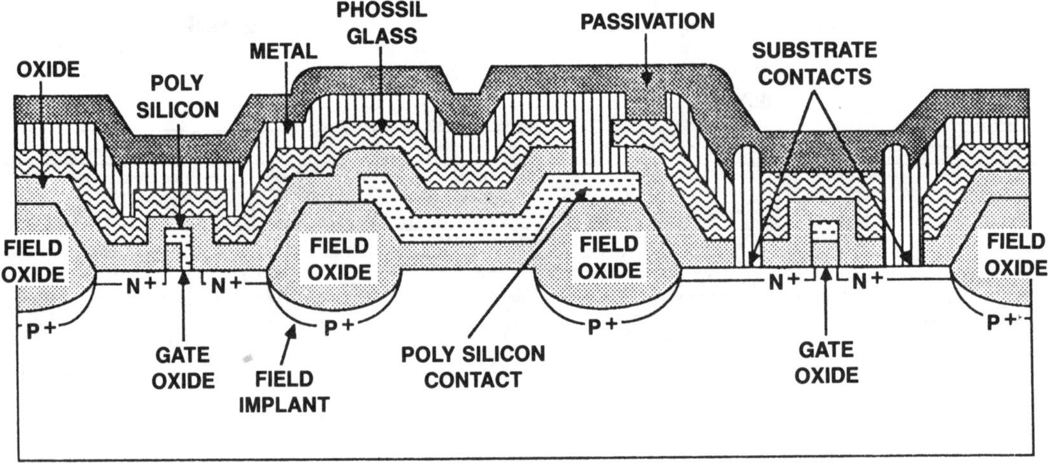

Figure 4-36 Final Passivation

LAYOUT DESIGN RULES

This section illustrates the geometrical layout rules for a typical MOSFET N-channel silicon gate process. Coding for these layout rules is illustrated in Figure 4-37.

These rules are compatible with vertical and horizontal alignment (including mask registration and etching tolerances of $\pm 2\ \mu m$). It is to be noted that simultaneous worst-case alignment in both the X and Y directions will result in a 2.8 μm-misalignment in a diagonal direction. To compensate for this 40 percent increase in alignment tolerance, a second dimension column for diagonal alignment is noted in the rules and must be strictly obeyed.

Dimensional tolerances of masks are expected to be less than $\pm 1\ \mu m$. Finished line-width dimensions will be skewed during processing.

Following are the layout design rules.

LAYER	MASK NO.	SYMBOL	DESCRIPTION
ACTIVE LAYER	01	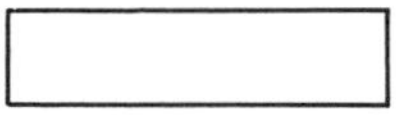	SOLID OUTLINE
DEPLETION MASK	02		OUTLINE OF SHORT DASHES
POLY TO N+	03	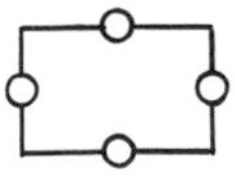	SOLID OUTLINE WITH SMALL CIRCLES
OVERSIZE 03	04		NOT NORMALLY DRAWN
POLYCRYSTALLIZED SILICON (GATE)	05	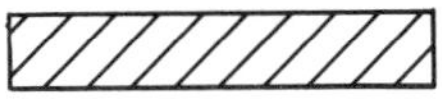	SOLID OUTLINE WITH HATCHED AREA
CONTACT HOLES (PREOHMIC)	06		SOLID OUTLINE WITH CROSS
OVERSIZE 06	07		NOT NORMALLY DRAWN
METAL	08		OUTLINE OF LONG DASHES
PASSIVATION	09		OUTLINE CONSISTING OF LONG AND SHORT LINES

Figure 4-37 Coding for Layout Rules

Bipolar and MOS Transistor Operating Characteristics

Transistors are the basic building blocks of all integrated circuits, including microprocessors and memories; such chips may contain as many as one million transistors. A transistor is essentially a switch. An input voltage applied to one element of the transistor creates or eliminates an electrical conducting channel between two other elements. When there is a channel, current can flow through the device. The forerunner of the transistor, which is a three terminal device, is the two terminal semiconductor diode.

A transistor consists of several adjacent regions of a doped silicon crystal, a crystal to which impurity atoms have been added to change its electrical properties. If the added impurity atoms have more electrons in their valence, or outer shell, than silicon atoms do, some electrons will not participate in the bonds that hold the crystal lattice together and so will be free to move about within the silicon. If an electric field (voltage) is applied to the crystal, the free electrons will move creating an electric current. Since the electrons that carry the current are negatively charged, silicon into which atoms that give up electrons have been introduced is said to be n-doped (n from donor). Conversely, impurity atoms can be added that have fewer valence electrons than silicon. Then there will be a number of "holes", vacant sites that would normally be occupied by electrons, within the crystal lattice. In a sense holes act as positively charged particles. When an electric field is applied to the crystal, holes move from atom to atom, producing an electric current. Because this current is made up of positively charged particles, silicon with an excess of holes is said to be p-doped (p from acceptor).

In one type of transistor, known as an npn bipolar transistor, a heavily n-doped region, called the collector, lies within a lightly n-doped region (see Figure 4-38). A p-doped region, called the base, also lies within the lightly n-doped region. Another heavily n-doped region, called the emitter, lies within the p-doped region and is completely

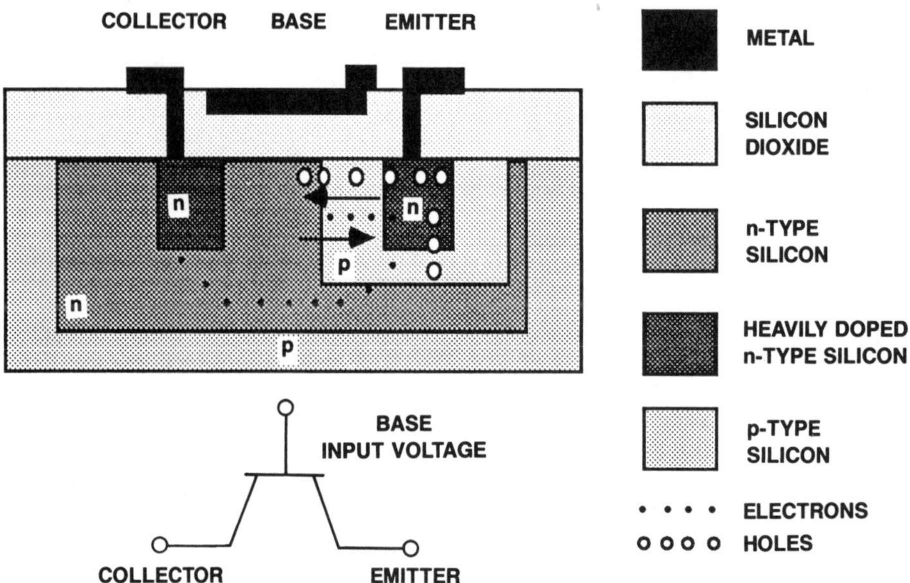

Figure 4-38 The NPN Bipolar Transistor

surrounded. Doping is the term used to define the degree of impurity donor or acceptor material which is introduced into the silicon substrate, the proportion of free electrons or holes. As a rule, electrons cannot flow from the emitter to the collector, even if a positive voltage (a voltage that attracts electrons) is applied to the collector; they cannot pass through the p-doped base. When a positive voltage is applied to the base, however, some holes pass from the base into the emitter and in exchange, some electrons from the emitter are injected into the base. Many of these electrons pass through the base and into the lightly n-doped region in which the collector, base, and emitter lie; from there they pass into the collector. In this way the positive voltage applied to the base acts as an input signal; it induces a current to flow between the emitter and the collector. This is the transistor's output signal.

Bipolar transistors are relatively inexpensive to make, and they are fast switches, that is, they respond quickly when an input voltage is applied to the base. On the other hand, they consume a relatively high amount of power: current flows from both the base and the emitter whenever the transistor is "on" (whenever a positive voltage is applied to the base). Bipolar transistors are therefore used primarily in applications in which fast-switching speed is required, even at the expense of power consumption, such as in central-host computers.

A popular alternative technology for building transistors is metal oxide silicon (MOS). There are two types of MOS transistors, known as NMOS and PMOS respectively. An NMOS transistor contains two islands of highly n-doped silicon called the source and drain; both are embedded in a substrate of p-doped material (see Figure 4-39).

A thin layer of silicon dioxide, an insulator, covers the silicon crystal, and a metal or silicon electrode, called the gate, is deposited on top of the region of silicon dioxide that is just above the p-doped silicon lying between the two n-doped regions. As in a

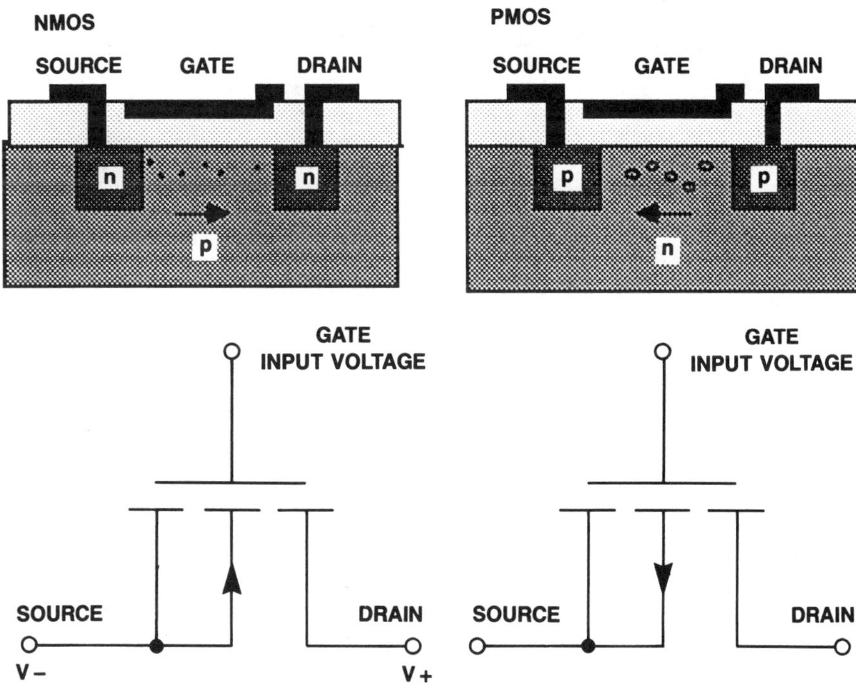

Figure 4-39 Metal-Oxide Semiconductors (MOS) Transistors

bipolar transistor, current cannot normally pass through the device; to pass from one n-doped region to the other, it would have to traverse a p-doped region. When a positive voltage is applied to the gate, however, electrons from within the p-doped substrate are pulled into the region of p-doped silicon that lies just under the silicon dioxide layer between the source and the drain. These electrons form a layer, called an inversion layer, because it is made up of charge carriers that are opposite in sign (polarity) to the holes that usually inhabit a p-doped semiconductor. The inversion layer acts as a conductive through which other electrons may flow from the source to the drain.

A PMOS transistor operates on the same principle as an NMOS transistor, but the source and drain are p-doped and lie in a substrate of n-doped material. In a PMOS transistor current is carried by holes, rather than by electrons, that pass from drain to source; a negative voltage, rather than a positive one, is needed to bring enough holes near the transistor's surface to form the inversion layer (conducting channel) between source and drain.

In a MOS circuit, as in a bipolar transistor, the voltage applied to the gate represents an input signal. Unlike the current of bipolar transistors, however, the current between the source and drain is not usually used as the output signal. In most MOS transistor circuits the drain is electrically connected, either by a resistor or by a transistor whose channel is always conductive, to a line carrying a high voltage (see Figure 4-40). The source is connected to a line carrying a low voltage. When the input voltage (the voltage

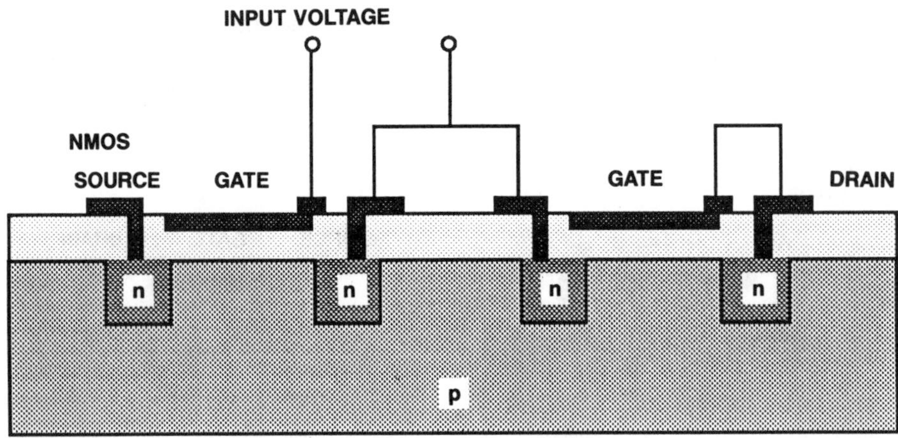

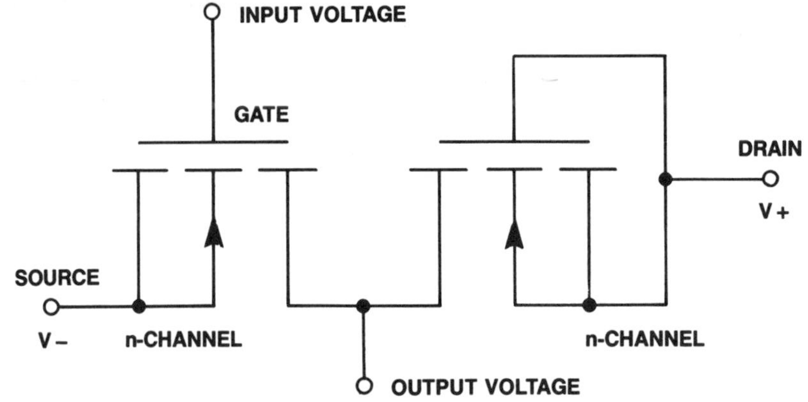

Figure 4-40 The n-Channel MOS Switching Device

applied to the transistor's gate) is low, the transistor is unable to conduct a current and the drain has no direct electrical connection to the low voltage line. The drain does, however, have a direct connection to a high voltage line. It therefore assumes a high voltage. When the input voltage is high, the transistor can carry current; the drain is then connected to the low voltage line and assumes a lower voltage. The voltage of the drain, which is low when the input voltage is high and high when the input voltage is low, is the output signal of the MOS device. In this sense, unlike a bipolar transistor, an MOS transistor is controlled by voltage on the gate rather than by current flowing into the base.

Such MOS circuits are reasonably fast, inexpensive to make and reliable. They can also be densely packed on a chip. On the other hand, they are relatively sensitive to electrical noise signals (spurious signals generated by neighboring equipment), and although they require less power to operate than bipolar transistors, they still draw a relatively large amount.

A variation on this type of MOS technology, called Complementary MOS (CMOS for short), uses nearly an order of magnitude less power and is approximately half as sensitive to noise. A CMOS circuit is a single crystal containing both an NMOS and a PMOS transistor. The gates of the two transistors are wired together (see Figure 4-40) and the voltage applied to them serves as the input signal. The responses of the two transistors to any input signal will be complementary; a signal which switches the PMOS transistor on will switch the NMOS transistor off and vice versa. The drain of the NMOS transistor is wired to the source of the PMOS transistor, so that these elements are always at the same voltage. This voltage is the output signal. The source of the NMOS transistor is connected to a line bearing a low voltage, and the drain of the PMOS transistor is connected to a high voltage line. When the input voltage is positive, the channel of the NMOS transistor is conductive and that of the PMOS transistor is not. The drain of the NMOS transistor and the source of the NMOS transistor are therefore electrically connected to the low voltage line and isolated from the high voltage line. The output voltage thus assumes the low state. Conversely, when the input voltage is negative, current can flow through the PMOS but not the NMOS transistor. The drain of the NMOS transistor and the source of the PMOS transistor are then connected to the high voltage line and isolated from the low voltage line. The output voltage thus assumes a high value. Perhaps the most significant feature of a CMOS device is that no current can pass between the high voltage line connected to the PMOS transistor's drain and the low voltage line connected to the NMOS transistor's source except during the short period when the input signal on the gate is switched between the high and low state. This characteristic means that a CMOS device will draw less current than either a bipolar device or a pair of NMOS or PMOS transistors connected in tandem (see Figure 4-41).

A CMOS device is also much less susceptible to electrical noise. To switch a standard NMOS device, say from low output state to high output state, the input voltage need only be switched from some positive value, at which the conductive channel between source and drain is open, to zero voltage when the gate is at zero volts, no electrons are attracted to the surface of the device and therefore, there is no conductive channel. To switch a CMOS device the input voltage must be switched from a positive value, at which the PMOS transistor is conducting, to a negative value at which the PMOS transistor switches off and the NMOS transistor conducts. The difference between the new input voltage and the old is twice as high for a CMOS device as for either PMOS or NMOS circuitry and so a spurious noise signal is less likely to flip the "switch" to an undesired state. CMOS devices are currently slightly more expensive to produce than either NMOS

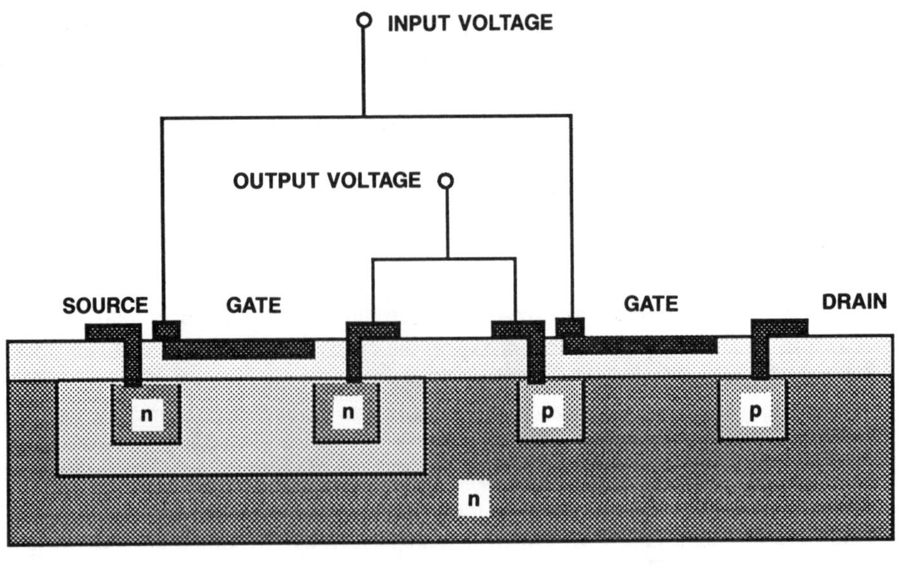

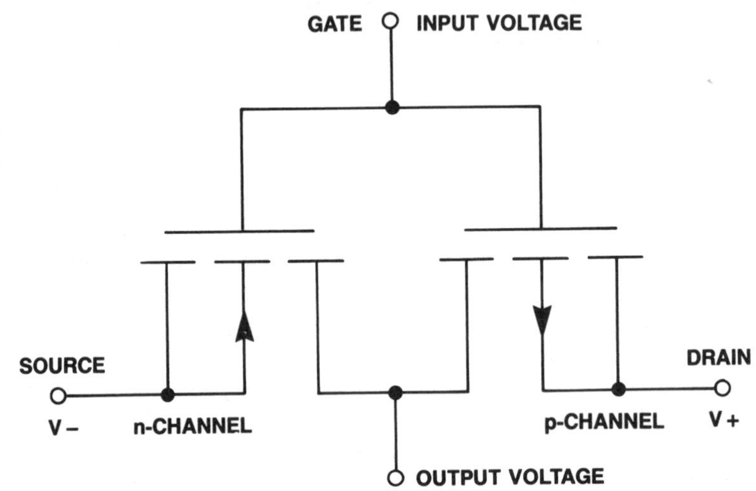

Figure 4-41 The Complementary MOS (CMOS) Switching Device

or PMOS devices exclusively and are less efficient in their use of silicon "real estate" because of larger device geometries. The reason, at least in part, is that CMOS is a relatively new technology and the traditional semiconductor industry improvement treatment has not yet run its full course. Within a few years it will be possible to produce CMOS devices that are as small and inexpensive as even NMOS devices, which because of the higher mobility of electrons than "holes" in PMOS devices, consume the least amount of silicon for a given function.

The most advanced variation on this theme is a technology called HCMOS (the H meaning high performance). HCMOS technology is essentially the same as CMOS, the differences being primarily ones of scale. For example, the space between the source and drain of a CMOS device is typically in the order of two to three microns (micrometer) while that of an HCMOS device is one micron and less. This results in distinct performance advantages in speed and power consumption, etc. but requires much more "state of the art" equipment to achieve the degree of precision necessary in the manufacturing process.

The P-N Junction (Diode)

A semiconductor material is one whose ability to conduct an electrical current can be altered by the addition of specific impurities (doping). Silicon in its intrinsically pure state is an electrical insulator. It is a semiconductor in that its conductance (reciprocal of resistance) can be increased in a very controllable manner by the addition of these impurities, to the extent that it can be made to switch quickly between a highly insulative (**open switch**) state to a highly conductive (**closed switch**) state. The current which flows during the conductive state can consist of electrons of ''holes'' as the majority carriers, depending on the atomic structure (number of electrons in the atom's valency band) of the impurity dopant used. Adding boron to intrinsically pure silicon results in a surplus of electrons being available in the bulk substrate to satisfy the atomic bonding requirements in the crystal lattice. (Nature abhors a vacuum.) These electrons are thus available to be used as majority carriers in forming the flow of an electric current in the material. Silicon so doped is described as **N-type** or **N +** silicon (N from donor boron). Adding phosphorous results in a surplus of ''holes'', sites in the crystal lattice with unsatisfied bonding requirements due to an overall electron deficiency. This is described as **P-type** or **P +** silicon (P from acceptor phosphorous). A piece of silicon to which both boron and phosphorous have been added to adjacent regions results in the formation of a **P-N** junction at the interface. (See Figure 4-42.)

With no external voltage bias applied across the material, the force of attraction between the surplus of electron in the **N-type** silicon and the surplus of holes in the **P-type** silicon will be too weak to allow electrons and holes to move and recombine, the material will thus be electrically neutral. If, however, we connect the positive and negative terminals of a battery to the P and N regions, the behavior of the silicon will change, depending on the polarity of the connections. If the battery is connected as shown in Figure 4-42 operating characteristics, the surplus of holes in the P-type material (the **anode**), will be attracted to the positive (+ ve) voltage battery terminal. Likewise, the surplus electrons in the N-type silicon material, (the **cathode**) will be attracted to the negative (– ve) terminal. No holes or electrons will flow across the P-N junction. In other words, since no current is flowing, we have an **open switch** condition or state. If the polarity of the battery connections is now reversed, both elecrons and holes, repelled by their respective battery terminal potentials, will now flow across the junction. In effect, a current now flows and this then constitutes the desired **on switch** condition or state. Since we hve now satisfied one of the major requirements of a switch-two, well defined, stable states—**on** and **off**, it simply remains to replace the contribution made by the human hand in controlling the transition between these two states, in being able to completely replace the electromechanical switch in our example. This is fulfilled by the **transistor**—a three element enhancement of the two element, one P-N junction, diode, the third element being the **on-off** control terminal.

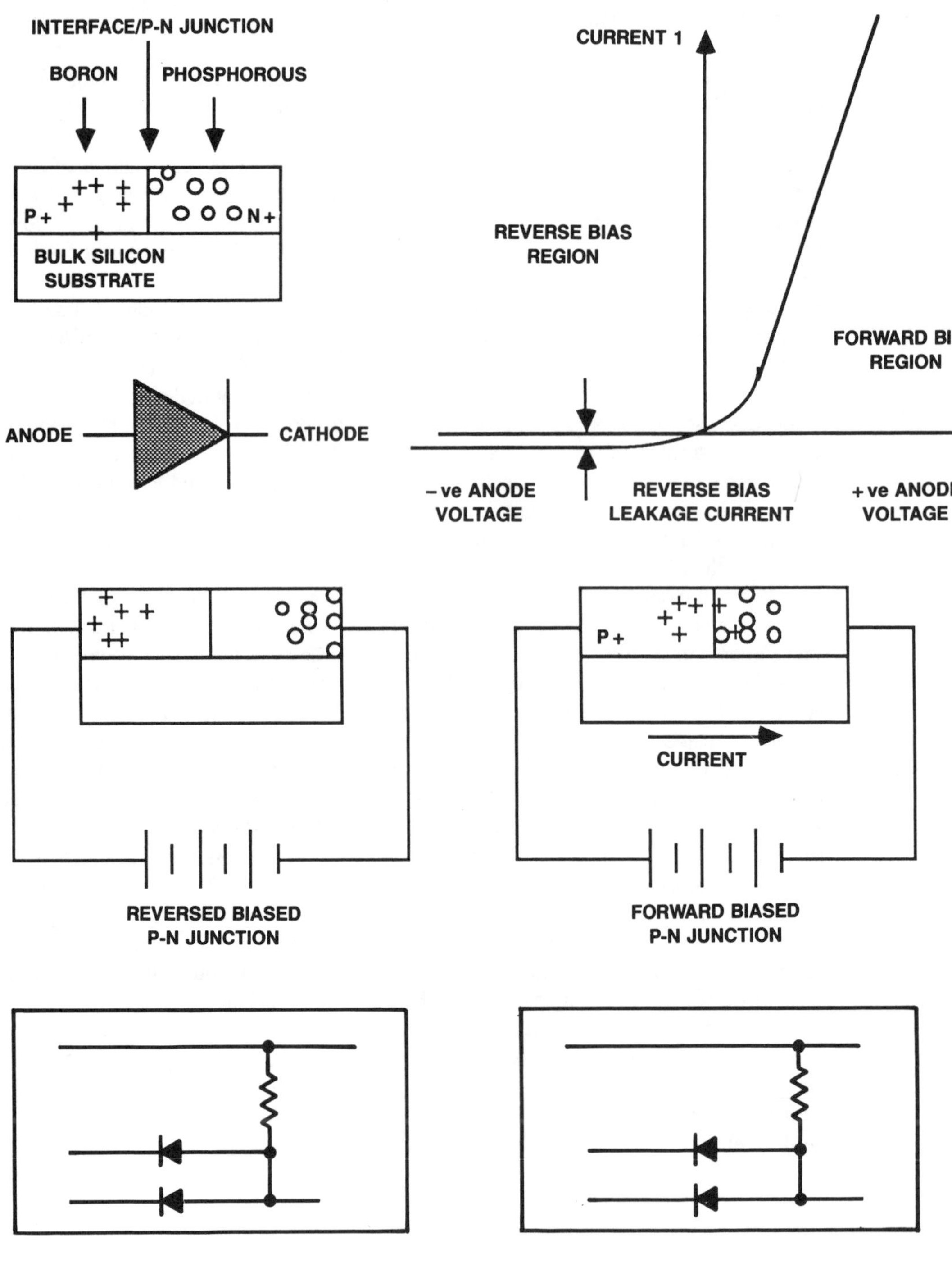

Figure 4-42 The P-N Junction Diode

MANUFACTURING PROCESS BASE LINE

Spec. no.: 70MSE00104W, rev. 0
Product group: MPG
Title: **Military Screened Product (DESC Drawing) Flow Chart**

1.0 **Purpose**

This specification establishes the overall general processing flow chart for high reliability MOS integrated circuits tested by the Motorola HI-END Mircoprocessor Group, Austin, TX.

This document is applicable to all devices manufactured in accordance with MIL-STD-883 (latest revision) and subject to qualification or Quality Conformance Inspection (QCI).

2.0 **Referenced Documents**

2.1 GOVERNMENT DOCUMENTS (Latest Revision)

2.1.1	MIL-M-38510:	General Specification for MILITARY Circuits
2.1.2	MIL-STD-883:	Test Methods and Procedures for Microcircuits.
2.1.3	DESC Drawing:	Applicable device specification

2.2 MOTOROLA DOCUMENTS (Latest Revision)

2.2.1	SOP 3-41:	Purchase Order Procedure.
2.2.2	12MRB05532A:	MOS Class B Internal Inspection Criteria.
2.2.3	12MRD03582W:	Preferred Burn-In Schematics, N-channel.
2.2.4	12MRD08115W:	Salt Atmosphere.
2.2.5	12MRD08120W:	Solderability Test.
2.2.6	12MRD08121W:	Mechanical Shock.
2.2.7	12MRD08122W:	Vibration: Variable Frequency Test.
2.2.8	12MRD08125W:	Thermal Shock.
2.2.9	12MRD08126W:	Constant Acceleration.
2.2.10	12MRD08127W:	Moisture Resistance Test.
2.2.11	12MRD08128W:	Temperature Cycling.
2.2.12	12MRD08129W:	Resistance to Solvent.
2.2.13	12MRD09009W:	MOS Finished Product Label Requirements.
2.2.14	12MRD12700W:	Q.A. Specification.
2.2.15	12MRD12881W:	Internal Visual/Mechanical: JAN, Hi-Rel.
2.2.16	12MRD12882W:	Physical Dimension Method.
2.2.17	12MRD12883W:	Bond Strength Method.
2.2.18	12MRD13302W:	Lead Finish.
2.2.19	12MRD13701W:	R. and Q.A. Environmental Lab.
2.2.20	12MRD20705W:	General Specification for MIL-STD-883.
2.2.21	12MRD20786W:	MPU-QC Lot Gate Sampling.
2.2.22	12MRD21533W:	Incoming Procedures.
2.2.23	12MRD21538W:	Shipping Final Test.
2.2.24	12MRD21541W:	Test Sampling Procedure.
2.2.25	12MRD21572W:	ADCOTECH Automatic Marking Procedure.
2.2.26	12MRD21577W:	Microprocessor Pack and Label Procedure.
2.2.27	12MRE00145W:	Completing the MPG HI-END Hi-Rel Shop Order.
2.2.28	12MRE20683W:	Proposed In-Line Q.A. Gate.

2.2.29 12MRM09115W: Wire Pull Monitor.
2.2.30 12MRM09116A: Final Inspection Criteria for I/C Products.
2.2.31 12MSB05204W: Seal Procedure: Ceramic Packages.
2.2.32 12MSB05207W: Die Bond Inpsection, Cer-DIP and Solder Seal.
2.2.33 12MSB05208W: Ultrasonic Wire Bond, Manual, MECH-EL.
2.2.34 12MSB05211W: Aging.
2.2.35 12MSB05212W: Die High Power Inspection.
2.2.36 12MSB05213W: Solder Seal—Sealing Inspection.
2.2.37 12MSB05217W: Centrifuge.
2.2.38 12MSB05222W: Lead Clipping, Cer-DIP & Solder Seal.
2.2.39 12MSB05223W: Fluorocarbon Gross Leak, Manual (Bubble Test).
2.2.40 12MSB05225W: Wire Bond Inspection: Standard/Hi-Rel.
2.2.41 12MSB05227W: Pre-Cap Inspection, Cer-DIP & Solder Seal.
2.2.42 12MSB05254W: Fluorocarbon 2-Step Gross Leak Test, Automatic.
2.2.43 12MSB05259W: Wafer Break and Die Load.
2.2.44 12MSB05271W: Furnace Die Bond.
2.2.45 12MSB05275W: Branson Ultrasonic Cleaner, Piece Parts.
2.2.46 12MSB05280W: Radioisotope Fine/Gross Leak Test.
2.2.47 12MSB05285W: Wire Pull Monitor, Cer-DIP & Solder Seal.
2.2.48 12MSD05251W: Preshipment Visual Inspection for MOS Solder Seal.
2.2.49 12MSD08603W: MICROANIMATION Wafer Saw.
2.2.50 12MSD11678W: Shipping Rail Loading/Packing Procedure.
2.2.51 12MSD21580W: MARKEM Manual Marker Operation Procedure.

3.0 **DEFINITIONS**

3.1 FLOW CHART LEGEND, see Figure 4-43.

3.2 DEVICE NOMENCLATURE, see Figure 4-44.

3.3 DATE CODE NOMENCLATURE, see Figure 4-45.

4.0 **FLOW CHART**

See Figure 4-46.

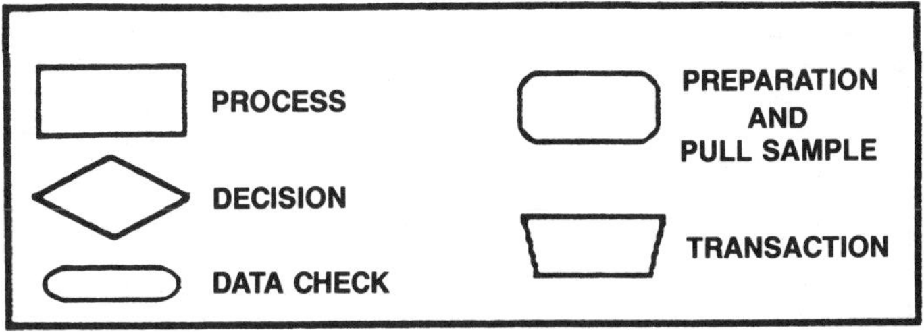

Figure 4-43 Flow Chart Legend

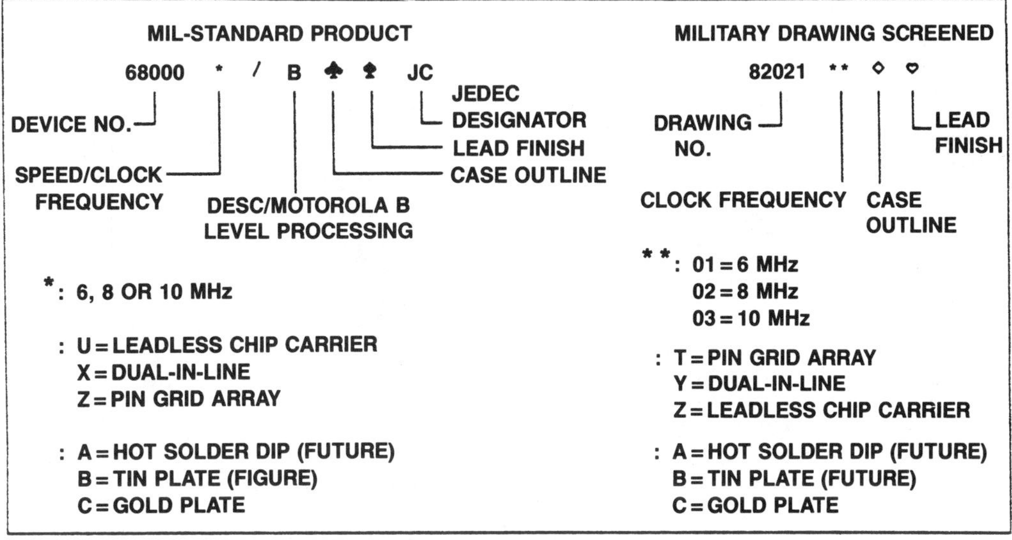

Figure 4-44 Device Part Number Nomenclature

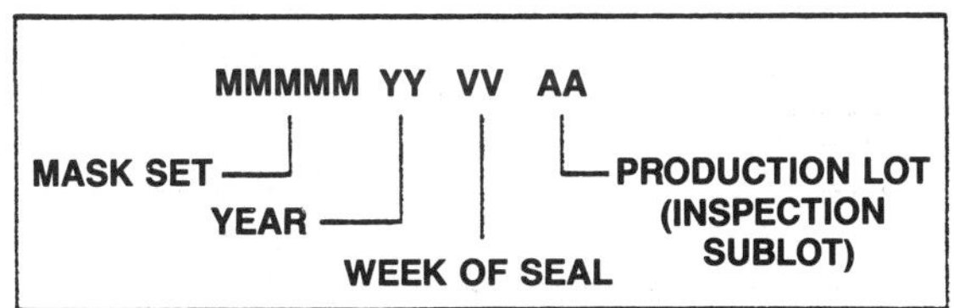

Figure 4-45 Mask Set/Production Lot/Inspection Lot Suffix Letters

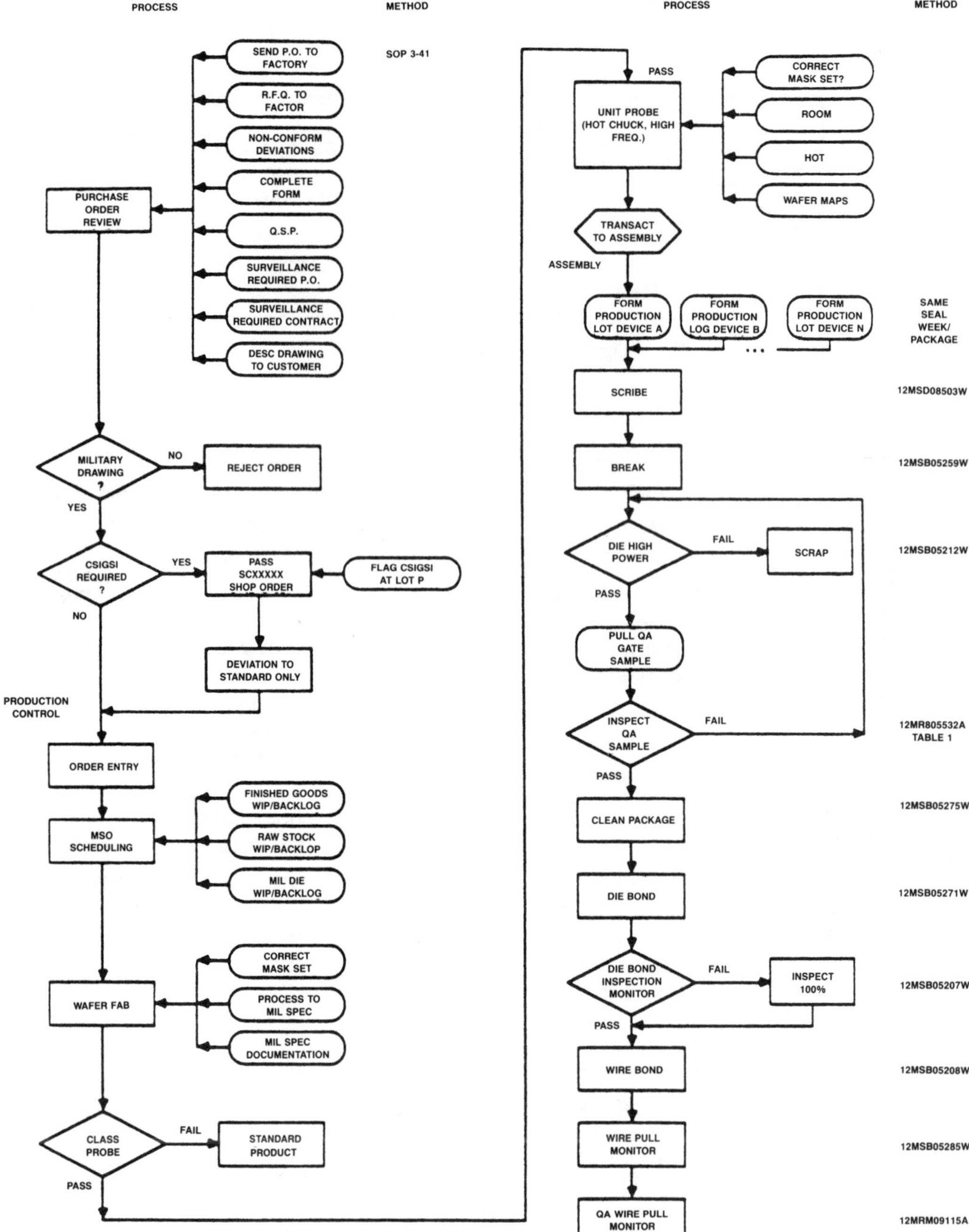
PROCESS
METHOD
PROCESS
METHOD
SEND P.O. TO FACTORY
SOP 3-41
R.F.Q. TO FACTOR
NON-CONFORM DEVIATIONS
COMPLETE FORM
PURCHASE ORDER REVIEW
Q.S.P.
SURVEILLANCE REQUIRED P.O.
SURVEILLANCE REQUIRED CONTRACT
DESC DRAWING TO CUSTOMER
MILITARY DRAWING ?
NO
REJECT ORDER
YES
CSIGSI REQUIRED ?
YES
PASS SCXXXXX SHOP ORDER
FLAG CSIGSI AT LOT P
NO
DEVIATION TO STANDARD ONLY
PRODUCTION CONTROL
ORDER ENTRY
FINISHED GOODS WIP/BACKLOG
MSO SCHEDULING
RAW STOCK WIP/BACKLOP
MIL DIE WIP/BACKLOG
CORRECT MASK SET
WAFER FAB
PROCESS TO MIL SPEC
MIL SPEC DOCUMENTATION
CLASS PROBE
FAIL
STANDARD PRODUCT
PASS
PASS
UNIT PROBE (HOT CHUCK, HIGH FREQ.)
CORRECT MASK SET?
ROOM
HOT
WAFER MAPS
TRANSACT TO ASSEMBLY
ASSEMBLY
FORM PRODUCTION LOT DEVICE A
FORM PRODUCTION LOG DEVICE B
FORM PRODUCTION LOT DEVICE N
SAME SEAL WEEK/ PACKAGE
SCRIBE
12MSD08503W
BREAK
12MSB05259W
DIE HIGH POWER
FAIL
SCRAP
12MSB05212W
PASS
PULL QA GATE SAMPLE
INSPECT QA SAMPLE
FAIL
12MR805532A TABLE 1
PASS
CLEAN PACKAGE
12MSB05275W
DIE BOND
12MSB05271W
DIE BOND INSPECTION MONITOR
FAIL
INSPECT 100%
12MSB05207W
PASS
WIRE BOND
12MSB05208W
WIRE PULL MONITOR
12MSB05285W
QA WIRE PULL MONITOR
12MRM09115A

Figure 4-46 Military Screened Product (DESC Drawing) Flow Chart

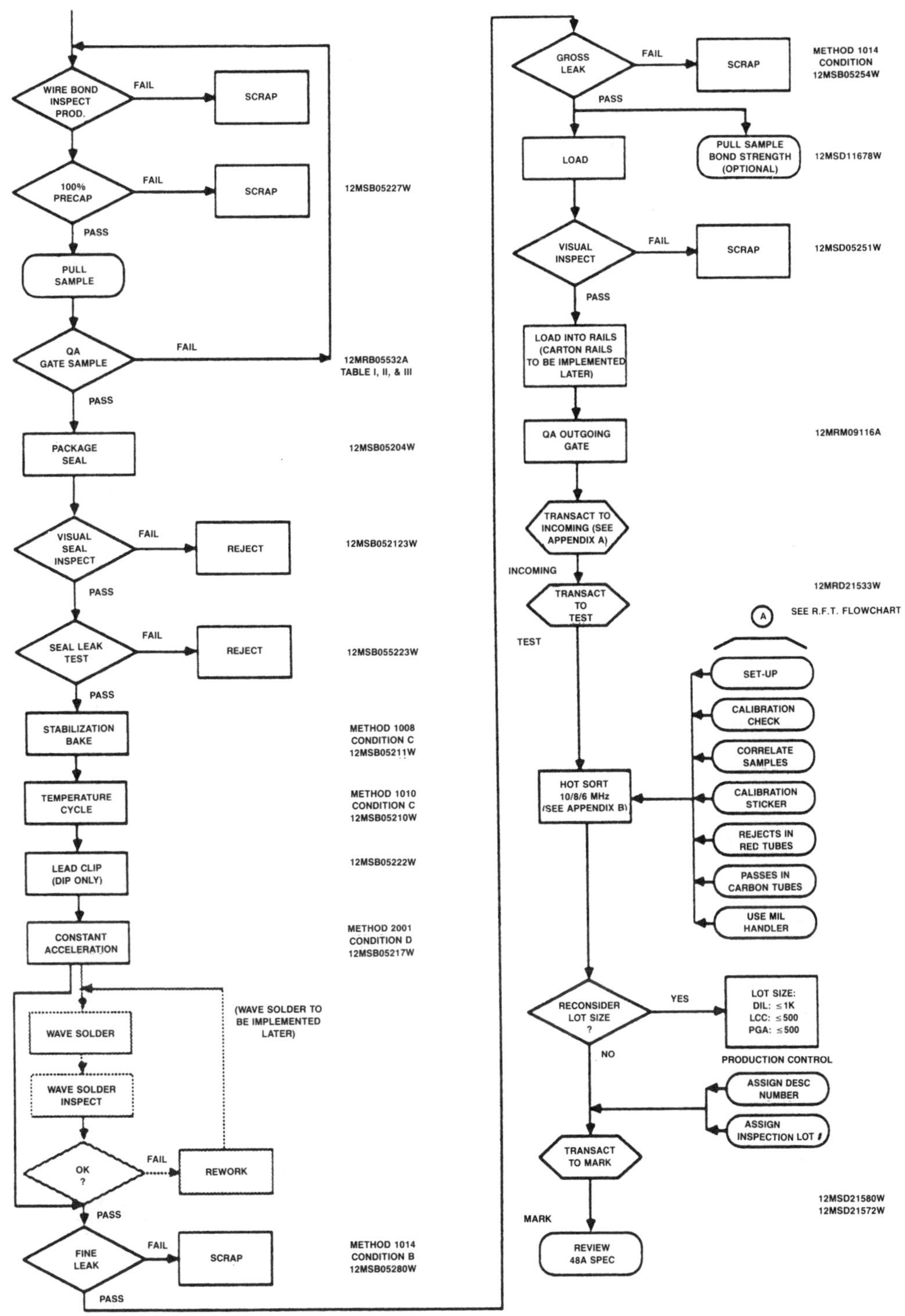

Figure 4-46 (continued)

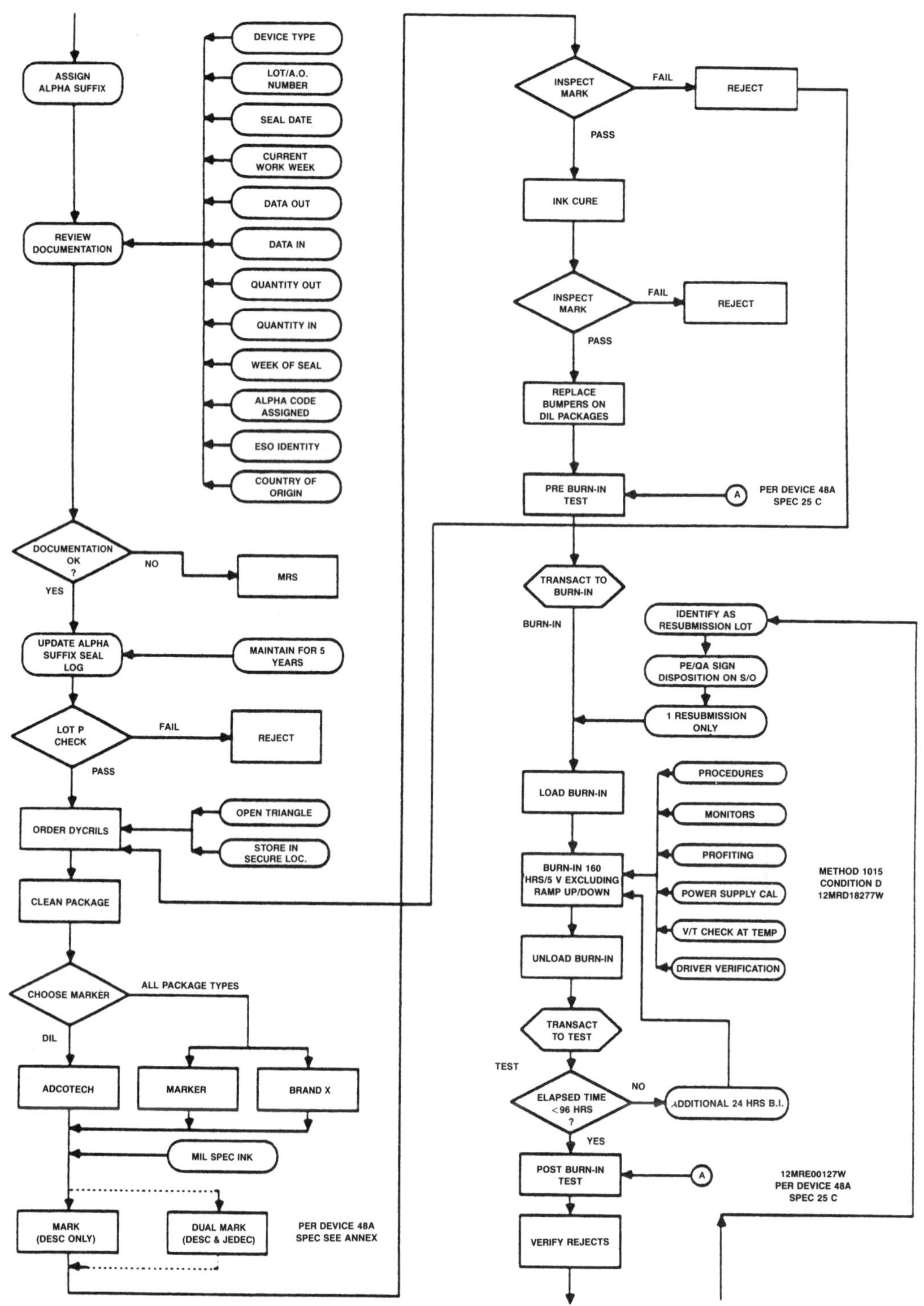

Figure 4-46 (continued)

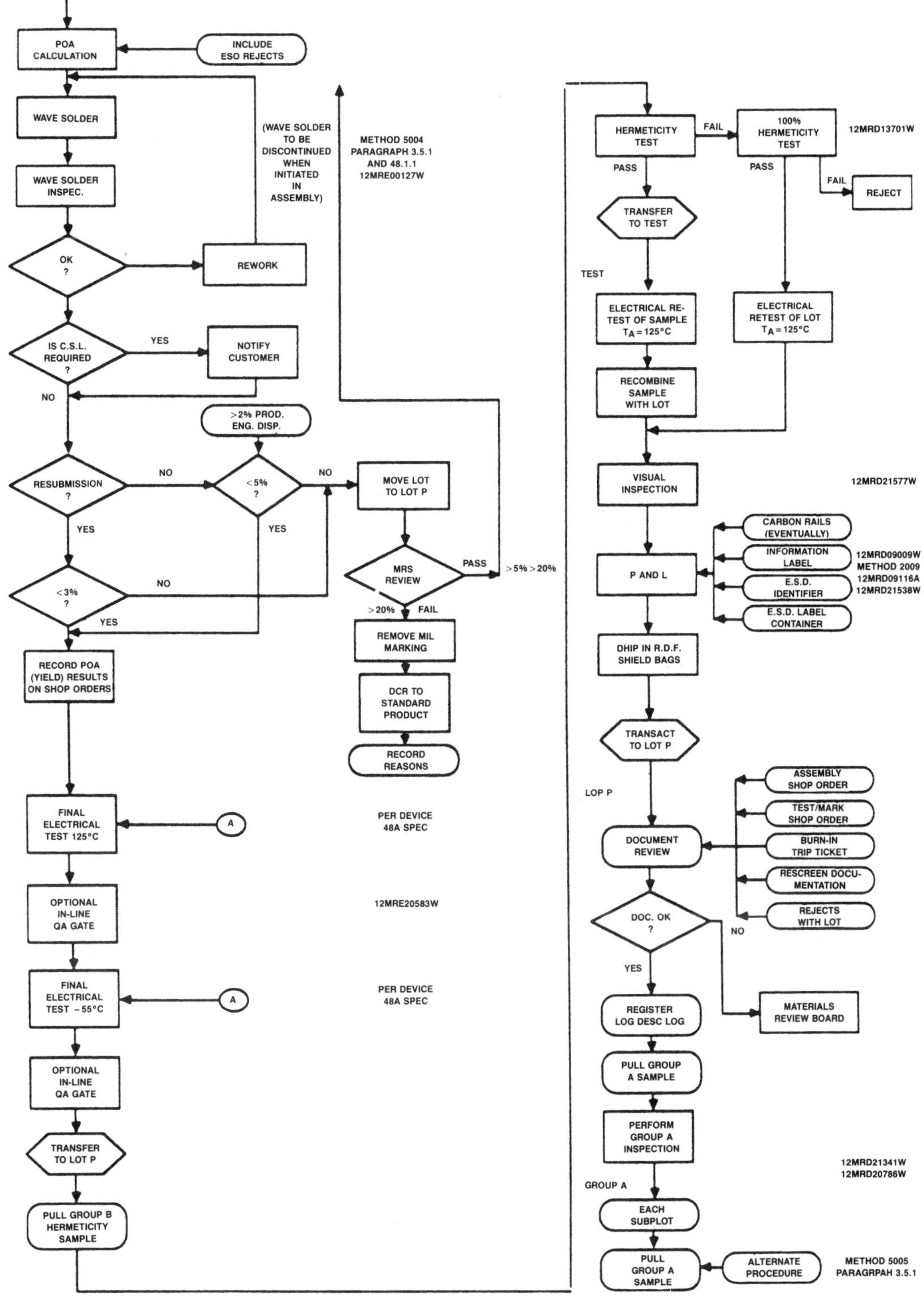

Figure 4-46 (continued)

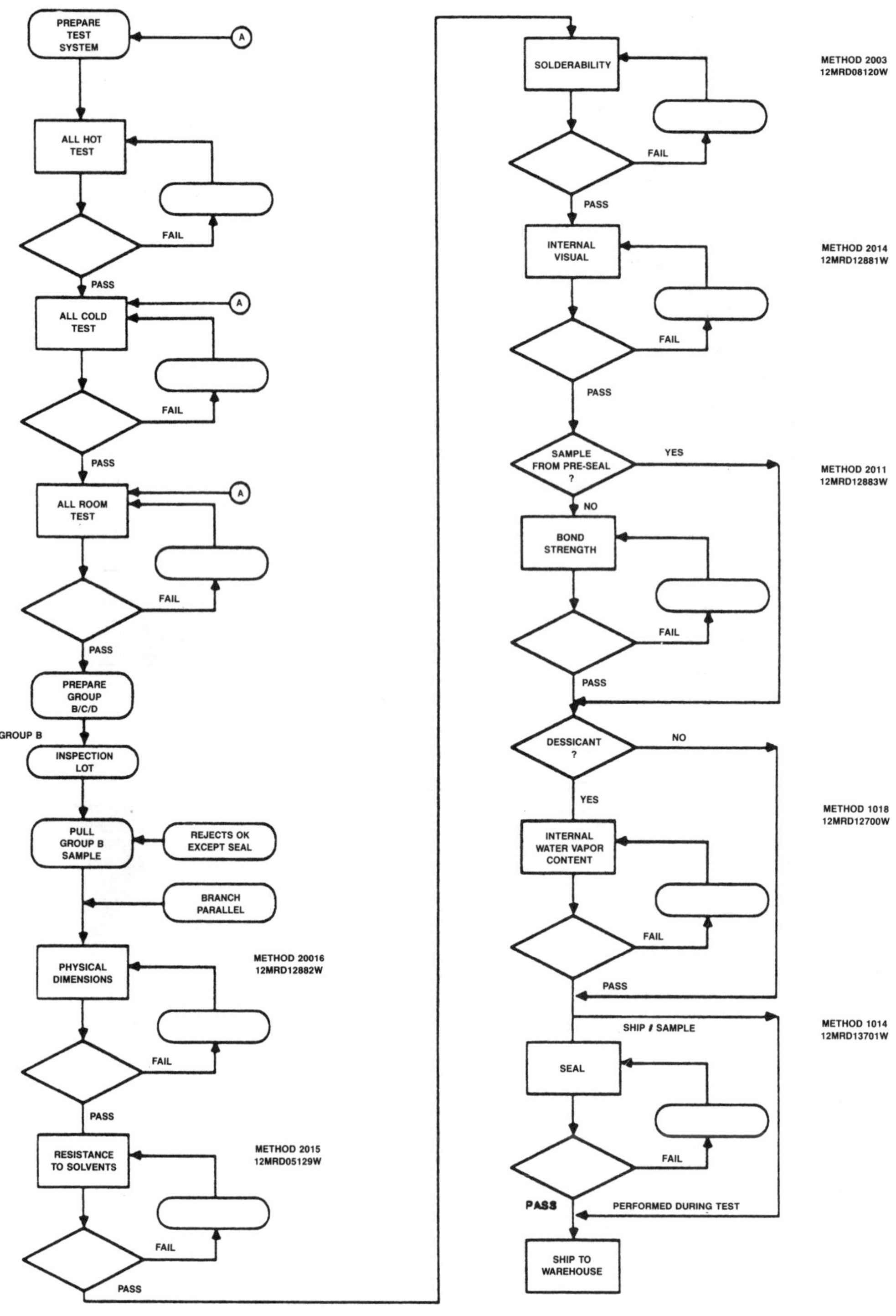

Figure 4-46 (continued)

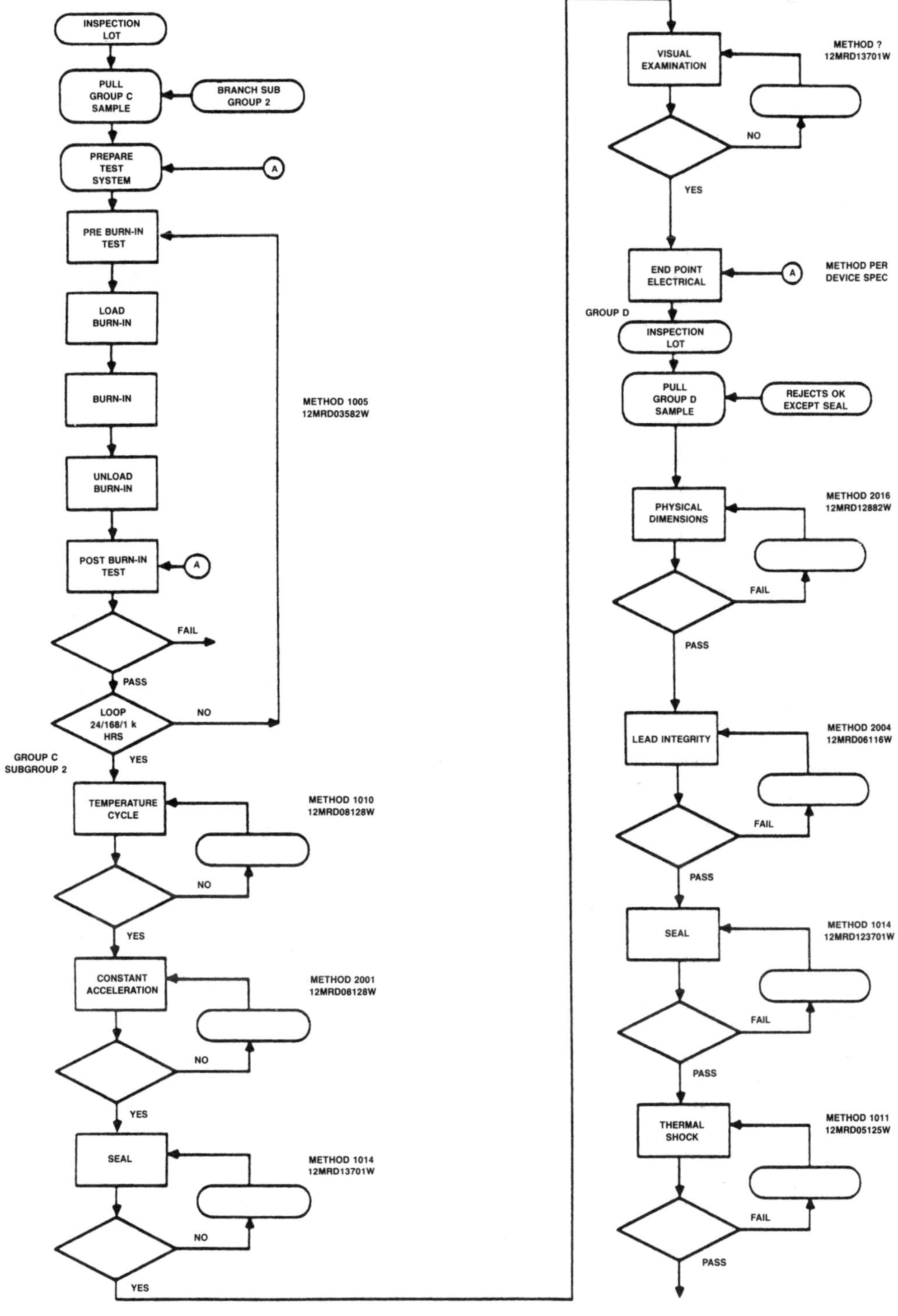

Figure 4-46 (continued)

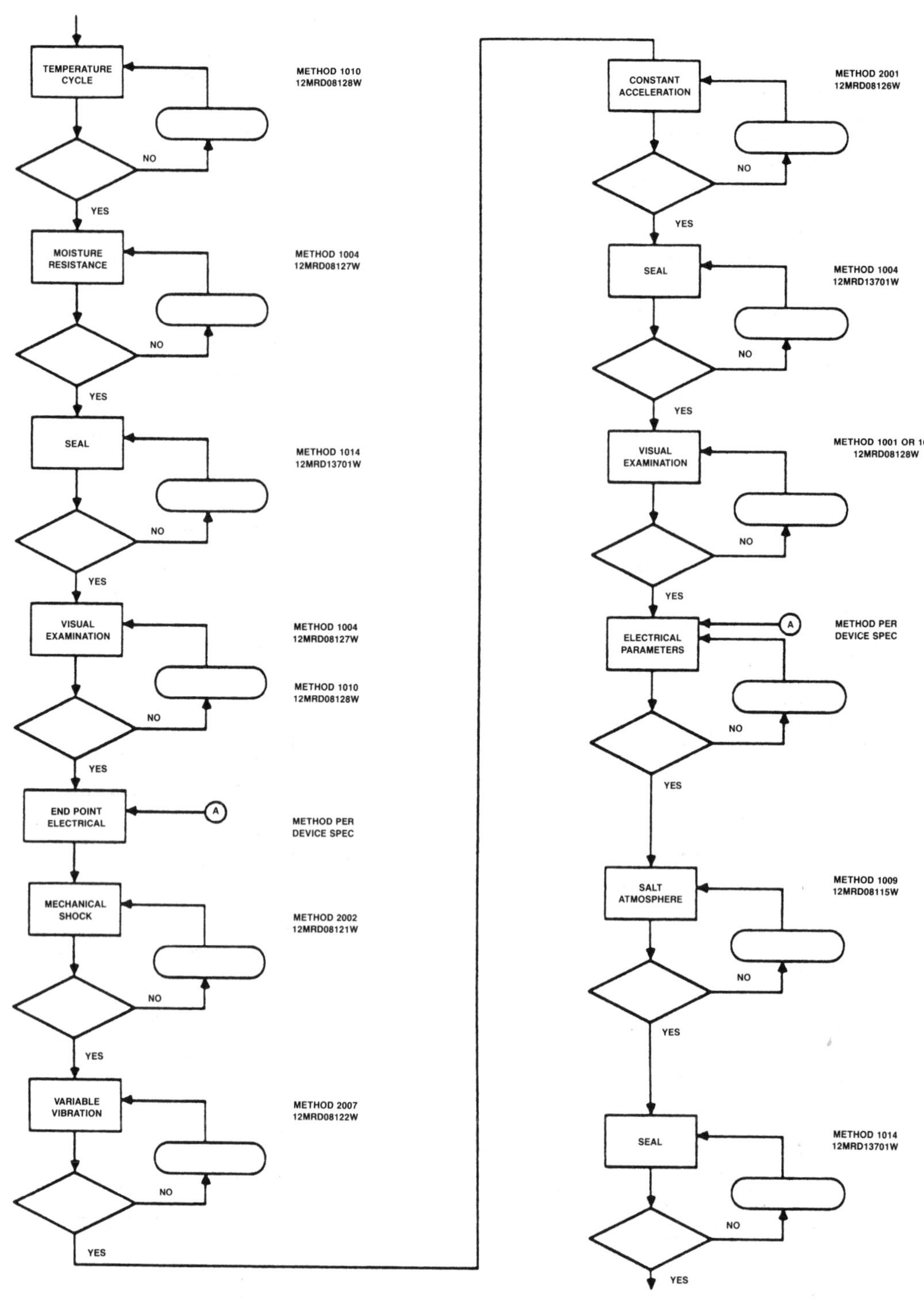

Figure 4-46 (continued)

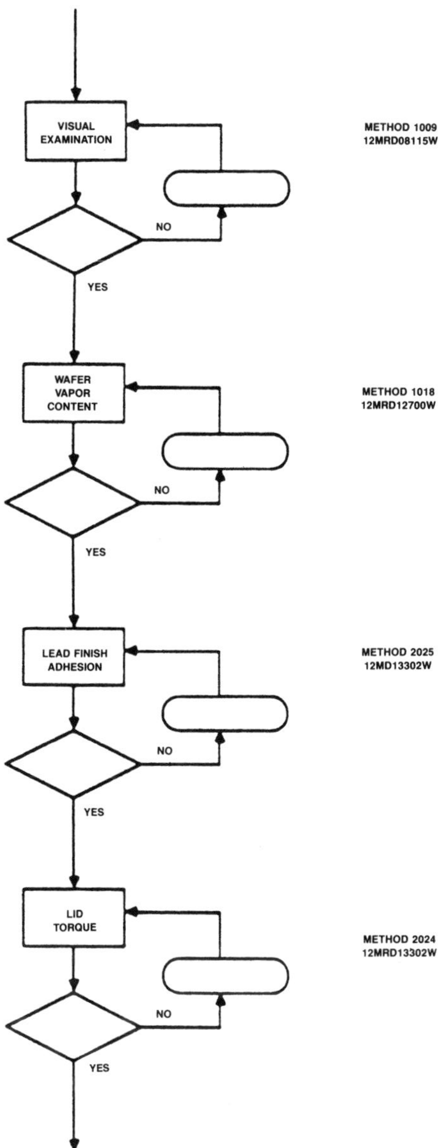

Figure 4-41 (continued)

5

Production Systems

JUST IN CASE (JIC)—PUSH SYSTEM VERSUS JUST IN TIME (JIT)—PULL SYSTEM

The "Window of Uncertainty"

In the traditional functional push system of manufacturing, "uncertainty" is dealt with by holding inventory at various stages of completion up to and including finished goods. This uncertainty takes many guises. The uncertainty of demand: which products will our customers require, when and in what quantity, when will they place their orders, and how much lead time will they provide us with from the time they place their order to the time they ask for delivery? The uncertainty of supply: will our piecepart vendors deliver what we require, when we require it; will the quality of the material be acceptable; will we encounter unforeseen capacity bottlenecks in our manufacturing process; will there be product or process engineering problems? Because we cannot look into the future and see the answer to these questions, we take out an insurance policy in the form of inventory. The more inventory we have, the less insecure we feel in the face of these anxieties.

The duration of the period of uncertainty is a function of cycle-time. If it takes four months to build product, for example, then we need to anticipate (forecast) what we think our customers will require of us four months from now and start building it, in our case by forcing wafer starts into the system. Apart from the cost of holding inventory, this is an adequate solution for standard products, of ensuring that there is always product instantaneously available when the customer needs it. Since it takes four months to replenish finished goods inventory, that is the minimum amount the system needs to contain, properly profiled, by stage of completion. On "build to order" semi-custom or full-custom products, however, the four-month cycle time cannot be made to appear invisible to the customer by holding finished goods inventory. This may or may not be acceptable. If this were the only adverse effect of inventory in this system of manufacturing this would be bad enough—but it's not. Since supply and demand are never exactly balanced, and certainly not by stage of completion in the process, we also find inventory queuing pending further processing. A third category of inventory in the system is due to geographic separation of the processes. This we can describe as pipeline inventory. The fourth category of inventory, arguably the only desirable form, is that inventory actually undergoing a value-adding operation. This is truly work in process

(WIP). Even this contributes to our cost of inventory problem since each unit's value increases by stage of completion as it proceeds through the process and because unavoidable proliferation increases as die are encapsulated in a range of packages and these packaged devices in turn become an even larger range of speed, temperature, and other special specification product.

To summarize then, inventory exists to deal with uncertainty in many guises and is held in several forms:

Finished goods inventory
Pipeline inventory
Queuing inventory
True WIP inventory (work in process actually having value)

The total amount of inventory in the system is obviously a function of many interdependent variables, the main ones being:

Uncertainty of customer demand
Uncertainty of vendor supply
Number of operations in the manufacturing process
The cycle time of each operation
The production worthiness of the process
The production worthiness of the product
The geographic proximity of manufacturing locations
The degree of product and product portfolio proliferation

Because of these interdependencies, inventory in the functional or push type of system tends to propagate itself to ever increasing levels. Long manufacturing cycle-times, for example, give rise to lot queuing which in turn leads to longer overall cycle-times. Engineering problems, with either product or process, also contribute to longer cycle-times and lead to accumulation of product as problems get circumvented rather than fixed.

Inventory—Asset or Liability?

In attempting to answer this, it would help to summarize what we know about inventory.

Costs money to hold (inventory is money in a nonproductive form)
Delays response in being made aware of and in fixing problems
Permits WIP zig/zag to take place (if this lot does not work, try another)
Needs sophisticated bank network and accounting system
Can camouflage real product or process problems
Creates inertia
Provides manufacturing with opportunity to work on what is available or easy, rather than what is needed
Write-off jeopardy increases with quantity (is material good or saleable)

Ideally then, we would prefer to have a manufacturing system whose appetite for inventory was limited only to that material actually having value added to it. This is the condition which just-in-time materials management (JIT) and short cycle-time manufacturing (SCM) attempt to satisfy. By reducing cycle-time and ensuring that material is released to a subsequent operation only when that operation has the capacity to deal with it, uncertainty is dealt with by faster responsiveness rather than by inventory insurance. The most fundamental premise in this approach to manufacturing is that problems with product or process or both must be fixed rather than compensated for with more inventory and that material is pulled out of the system rather than pushed into it.

Let's consider an example. In order not to forego an unforeseen sales opportunity, we can hold finished goods inventory in our warehouse. What is the minimum quantity we need to hold? If it takes four weeks to process product through final test, this is how long it would take to replenish our finished goods stock in the warehouse if it were suddenly consumed. So we need to hold four weeks of finished goods at our weekly consumption run rate. Alternatively, if cycle-time through final test can be reduced to only two days, the theoretical cycle-time, then we need only hold two days of inventory in finished goods. As this principle is extended back into the manufacturing process, the amount of inventory required in the system can be significantly reduced without jeopardizing service to the customer. Responsiveness is substituted for inventory.

PREFERRED INVENTORY PROFILE

The Notion of Value

In an inventory profligate system, since inventory, at least by accounting convention, is considered to be an asset, it must be valued and accounted for (see Figure 5-1). In a standard cost accounting system, this is accomplished by applying the concept of "value added at standard cost." (It would appear that the Marxists are not alone in considering value to be a function of labor expended.) This approach presumes, not unreasonably one would think, that the material will eventually be sold. For a variety of reasons, this can occasionally turn out to be a false assumption. With very long manufacturing cycle times, material built to forecast may not encounter the demand anticipated and remain in finished goods inventory until scrapped and written off financially. Even material built

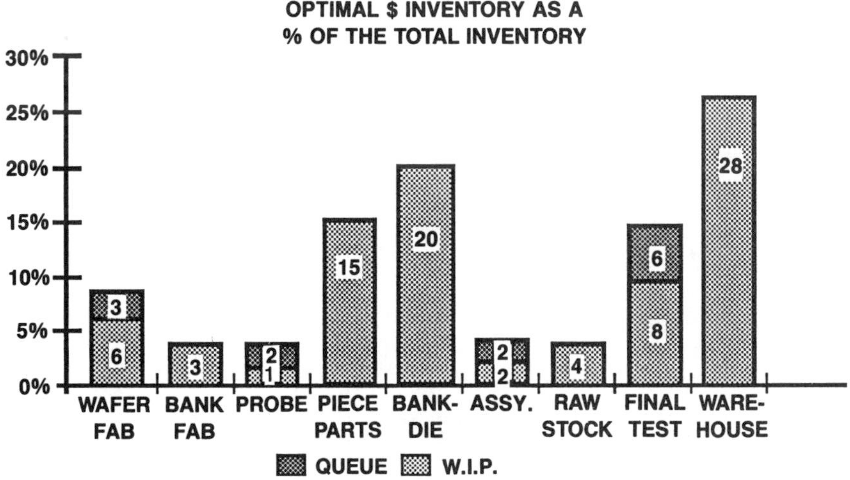

Figure 5-1 Preferred Inventory Profile

to order can sometimes find the orders against which the material was committed to manufacture being cancelled. The longer the manufacturing cycle, the greater is the probability of this happening, especially during business downturns. The delayed feedback inherent in a lot sampling approach to quality control may subsequently indicate that the material is defective, again resulting in an expensive write-off. The selling decision itself may be taken on the basis of hypothetical standard cost—the cost which should have been, but was not necessarily incurred, in manufacturing the product. In addition to this, there will be a time phase problem between time of manufacture and time of sale. Actual costs incurred may not be fully comprehended, giving rise to margin misconceptions. This approach, in addition to the cost of carrying the inventory, is obviously then, not without risk. The material, valued as an asset, may in fact turn out to be a liability.

In a JIT/SPC system, much if not all of these risks are avoided. (The die hards would no doubt counter with the increased risk of being caught without inventory in the event of some unforeseen windfall opportunity.) But more importantly, the notion of true economic value, consistent with the principles of the free market and laissez-faire economics—that value is what someone is willing to pay, rather than in terms of "value added"—is more readily applied. This is not entirely a philosophical issue with no practical ramifications. The shorter the time between build and sell, the greater the degree to which the system contains only sellable work—in process, the more appropriately can this approach to value be applied. "It is not that pearls are valuable because men dive for them. It is because they are valuable that they dive for them."

COMPARISON OF TRADITIONAL VERSUS MODERN MANUFACTURING METHODS

JIC Just in Case—Push System	JIT Just in Time—Pull System
• Long cycle times	• Short cycle times
• Build big factories to hold WIP	• No WIP—highly efficient use of space
• Circumvent problems (change WIP/increase inspection)	• Enforced problem solving eliminate cause (rocks in the river)
• Paper moves/product doesn't	• Product moves/paper doesn't
• Product/process problems invisible	• Product/process problems visible
• Decision based on direct labor, loaded burden and overhead	• Decisions based on material/process loaded B and O
• Functional organization—People Equipment Product	• Modular organization—People Equipment Product
• Many suppliers—win/lose relationship	• One supplier—win/win relationship
• Maximize RIP/WIP	• Minimize RIP/WIP
• Focus on direct labor/stability	• Focus on minimum setup time/flexibility
• Process sporadic, asynchronous lumps	• Continuous flow
• Semimanual order processing	• Online order entry
• Count/recount WIP	• No WIP to count
• EOQ supply	• Kan ban supply
• Potentially many accounting transactions	• Few accounting transactions
• Erratic (batch) run rate	• Steady (linear) run rate
• Division of labor/specialization	• Multiskill direct operators
• Focus on direct operator productivity	• Focus on process productivity
• Keep equipment running/operators working (build unsaleable WIP)	• Run only if sellable material available
• Uncoordinated chaotic proliferation	• Group technology/focused factories
• Focus on product AOQs at gate	• TQS—total quality system
• Treat quality symptoms/not causes (inspect out rejects/replace WIP)	• SPC—statistical process control (build in quality/address causes)
• All stages nonlinear	• Uniform balanced line linearity
• Labor intensive	• Automation intensive
• AOQ/LTPD	• 0 or 100 percent incoming inspect
• Inventory is good	• Inventory is evil

A COMPARISON OF FUNCTIONAL, MODULAR, AND IMC (INTEGRATED MANUFACTURING CELL) SYSTEMS

Functional System

In the functional system of manufacturing, consistent with the principle of the division of labor and specialization, people and equipment are assigned on a dedicated basis, to a very narrowly defined task in the whole sequence of tasks. With such an intensity of focus, this approach is most conducive to maximizing the output of each operation across the complete sequence of operations, producing high overhead recovery, or absorption, as its most redeeming figure of merit. The rationale behind this approach is that with repetition, the learning cycle will be short and the frequency of learning, the number of cycles in a given period, will be high, leading to high levels of output in the shortest possible time. This indeed is the case, but not surprisingly, there are also shortcomings, costs if you will, with this approach.

Not only will work in process at each operation be high, due to the high throughput and specialization mentioned earlier, but the reserves of inventory held prior to each operation will also need to be high. Since material is transported and transacted to and from each operation and inventory staging banks, rather than from each operation to the next in direct succession, the amount of material movement and clerical transactions to log the material in and out of these banks will also be high. There is no mandate or requirement under this system for all operations to be processing the same product lot, or even the same product type from different lots. This gives rise to the need for accounting systems and clerical resources to keep track of the many lots in varying stages of completion. Since each operation functions independently of all others, there is no compulsion, or even requirement, to balance capacity by stage of completion—each operation is buffered from its immediate neighbors by inventory.

Since overhead recovery is held to be the primary figure of merit in this system, there is a propensity for material which is easy to process, rather than that which is needed but may be more difficult to process, to be favored. In addition to this, the need for changeovers will be fulfilled only reluctantly. In the extreme, since many cost blocks are likely to be required to support this inventory profligate system, it is possible to maximize overhead recovery without shipping any product out of the factory to the finished goods warehouse or if so, that which is not immediately sellable. The considerable amount of handling of product in this system, in loading and unloading to and from each operation and the staging banks, also has an adverse effect on both quality and productivity. Also, these inventory buffers may not only delay the detection, and therefore correction of a quality problem imported from some upstream operation, but the inventory in jeopardy which at best might have to be reworked and at worst may have to be scrapped, will be high.

Perhaps this system's greatest shortcoming is its propensity to lead to overstaffing simply to build inventory. In the preoccupation with keeping each piece of equipment running, almost at any cost, material will be processed simply because it is available and equipment will be staffed accordingly, whether the product processed is immediately sellable or not.

Modular System

The essence of the modular system of manufacturing is to process only product which is immediately required in such a way as to avoid work in process zig/zag to and from operations and inventory banks, by pulling the material from inventory staging, processing it through a series of related operations in a sequential fashion, and then shipping the finished product. An additional major benefit in pursuing a modular approach to processing product is in being able to escape the historical constraint that quality, cost, and on-time delivery must be held to be mutually exclusive—that no manufacturing system is capable of optimizing all of these simultaneously. Understandably, for such a significant benefit, the investment in time and effort to create a manufacturing operation capable of avoiding this misconception is high, but there is no question that not only is it possible, it is also necessary. To operate successfully, it means that problems associated with processing the product, either in the design of the products themselves or out of tolerance excursions in the raw materials, or the equipment, or processes and methods employed, must be fixed rather than circumvented. What manufacturing organization would not benefit from such enforced discipline?

Despite its many benefits, the modular approach, like that of the functional, suffers from the disadvantage of having to load and unload the product to and from each individual operation (see Figure 5-2). To eliminate or at least minimize this unnecessary handling is the primary objective of the integrated manufacturing cell (IMC) approach. (The modular approach is fully discussed in Chapter 6.)

IMC

This approach has been designed to be least labor intensive by employing the most reliable, automatic processing techniques now available. All intermediate material movements between operations are automated, not by overly sophisticated robots but by means of moving tracks and pick and place mechanisms. As can be seen from Figure 5-3, there is only one manual loading and unloading operation, for each series of operations, within a cell.

Implications of Automation

Increasing automation brings with it implications, not only for the manufacturing organization, but also for other functions such as personnel, accounting, process and equipment engineering, materials control, and the quality organization.

Personnel. Fewer people are required in the classically defined ''direct labor'' category, directly adding value to the product for the same level of output, but require a different, usually higher level of skills. In an automated operation or series of operations, it is the equipment, not people, which adds value to the product. The human contribution changes from primarily physical effort and dexterity of hand, to one of:

1. **Loading and unloading the equipment with raw material.**
2. **Monitoring the operation of the equipment.**
3. **Executing equipment configuration changeovers.**

In a semiconductor environment, this is true of all manufacturing functions: wafer fabrication (loading wafers and mask layers), unit probe (loading wafers to probe machine), assembly (loading pieceparts to wire and die bond, and so on), final test (loading raw stock to test handlers).

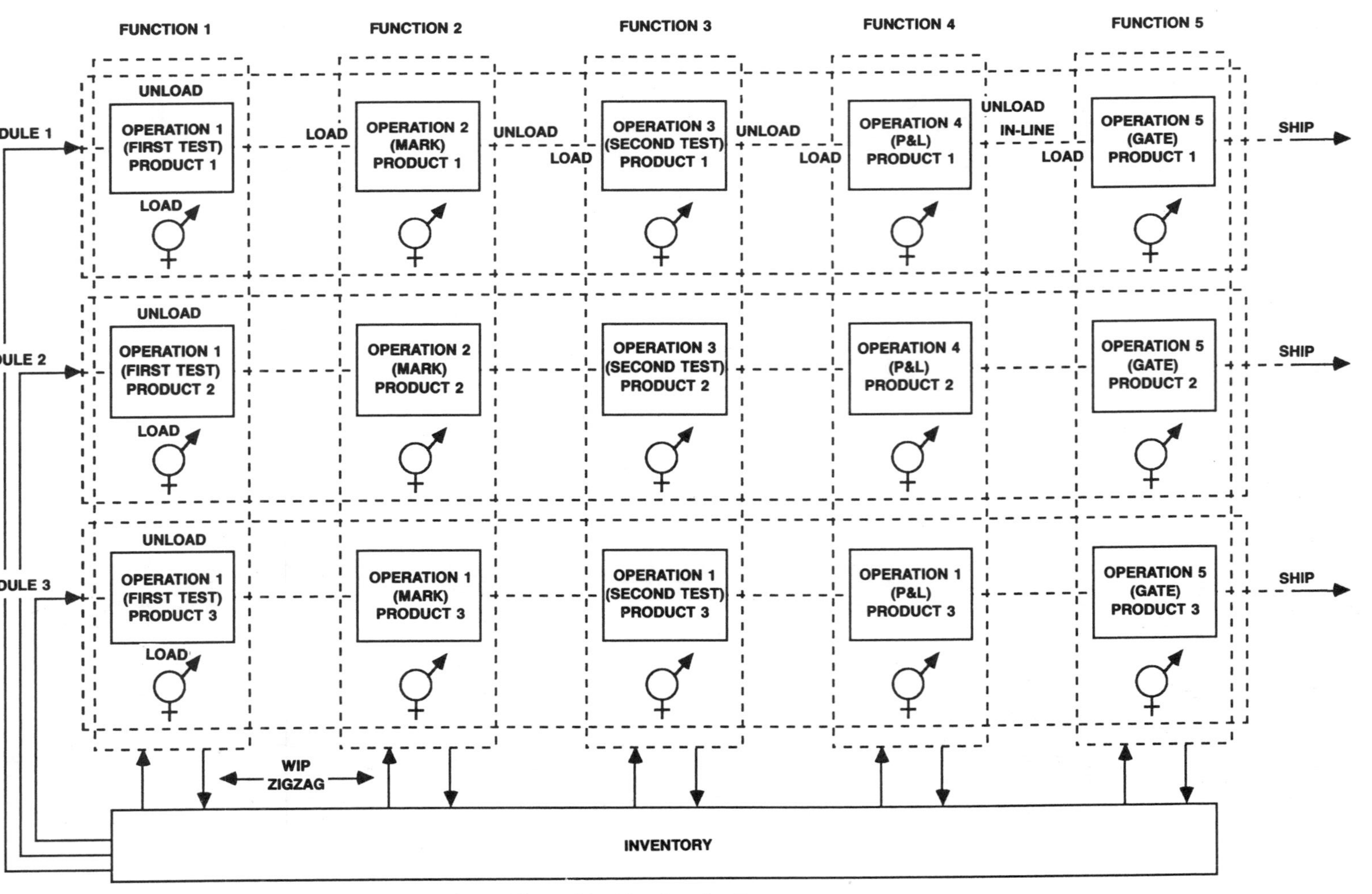

Figure 5-2 Manufacturing Systems
The Transition from Function to Modular

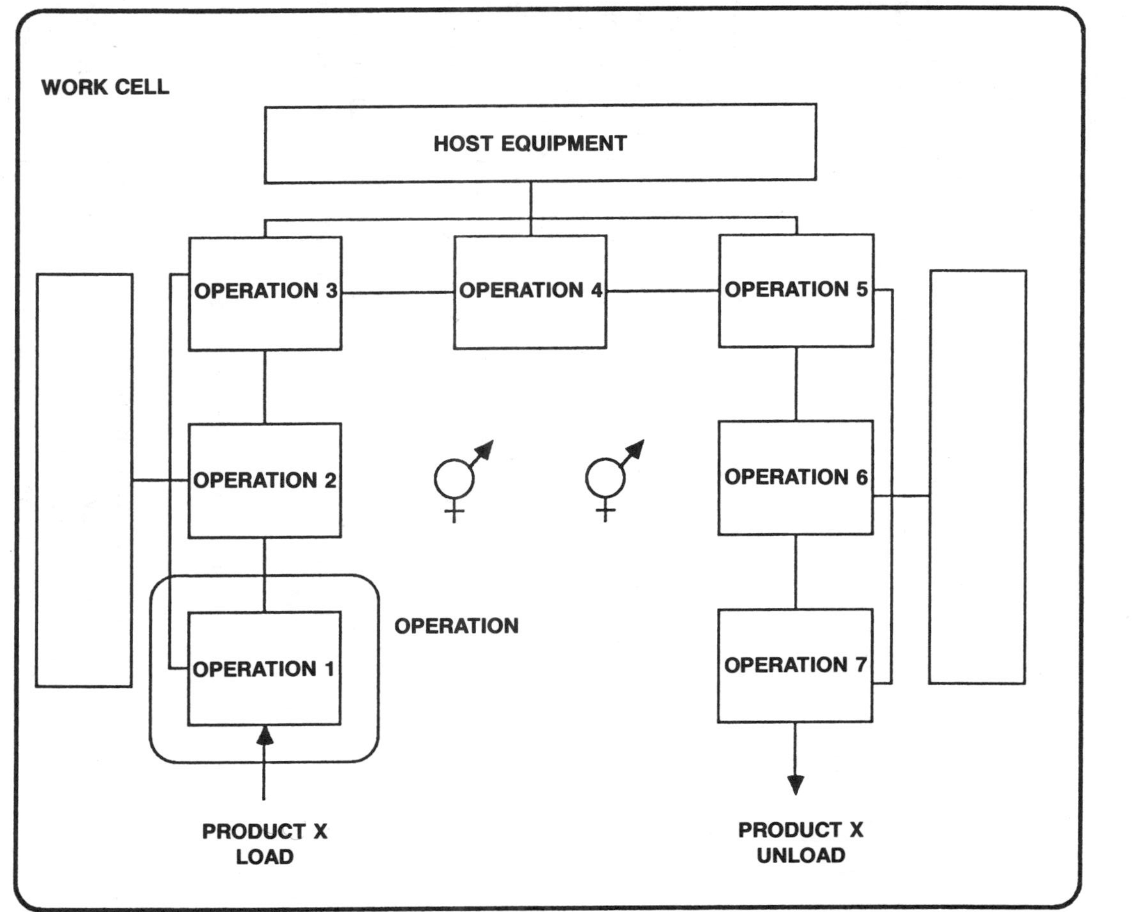

PHASE 1: TEST
MARK
VISUAL INSPECTION
LEAD STRAIGHTEN
GATE

PHASE 2: PHASE 1
+SPC
+ES

PHASE 3: ASSEMBLY/TEST

PHASE 4: PROBE
ASSEMBLY
TEST

Figure 5-3 Manufacturing Systems
Integrated Manufacturing Cell

With IMC, the loading and unloading requirement diminishes the more each individual and independent operation is included in a series of operations (see Figure 5-4). By employing statistical process control, the quality monitoring requirement also diminishes, with implications for the quality control and assurance organization. All of this brings with it implications for the personnel function in terms of recruitment, training, retraining, redeployment, job classification and remuneration administration.

Accounting Function. Direct-labor cost becomes a diminishing proportion of both operating and product costs, with material and overhead increasing. With much accounting practice methods, procedures, measurement systems, and "figures of merit" based upon and oriented towards direct labor, the need to review, almost certainly to revise and in some cases to discard these as a consequence of direct labor's diminishing role would seem to be apparent. Accounting for overhead recovery using direct labor as the denominator of the measurement equation may require examination, for example. With a diminishing value of denominator, overheads can be duly accounted for by increasing the overhead absorption rate percentage multiplier but is this really meaningful and informative, or should overhead recovery be measured in terms of material costs instead? As capital equipment assumes more dominance as a factor of production, should we consider classifying capital as we did labor, into direct and indirect, those directly involved in adding value to the product as distinct from those supporting engineering development, or management information systems, or utilities, for example? As material and capital equipment assume greater significance, should our focus in controlling costs shift more towards these, with the same emphasis as was accorded direct labor in the labor-intensive system?

Manufacturing. Since value added is progressively more and more a function of capital equipment, then quality, productivity, manufacturing cycle-time, and cost become more a function of that factor of production. These things are then in turn more a function of how well this equipment is designed, developed, maintained, and operated by resources classically defined as "indirect" or exempt, rather than direct. Equipment utilization, efficiency, and effectiveness become more a function of the supporting infrastructure—how the machines are scheduled, loaded, how quickly they can be reconfigured, and so on—than the degree of direct labor effort or manual dexterity applied. Networking and statistical process control become much more meaningful and feasible in an automated environment than one in which operations are independent and labor intensive.

Materials Control. Making most productive use of expensive capital equipment and materials requires different skills of a material control function than those required to support a labor-intensive one.

Cycle-Time—The All-Encompassing, Superordinate Measurement Parameter

The benefits of reducing cycle-time as an alternative to building inventory in dealing with the "window of uncertainty" have already been discussed. As we have seen, total cycle-time for a manufacturing operation is the sum of (1) queuing cycle-time; (2) coupling cycle-time if, as is so often the case, operations in the process are geographically dispersed; and (3) the intrinsic cycle-time of each operation. Most cycle-time reduction programs

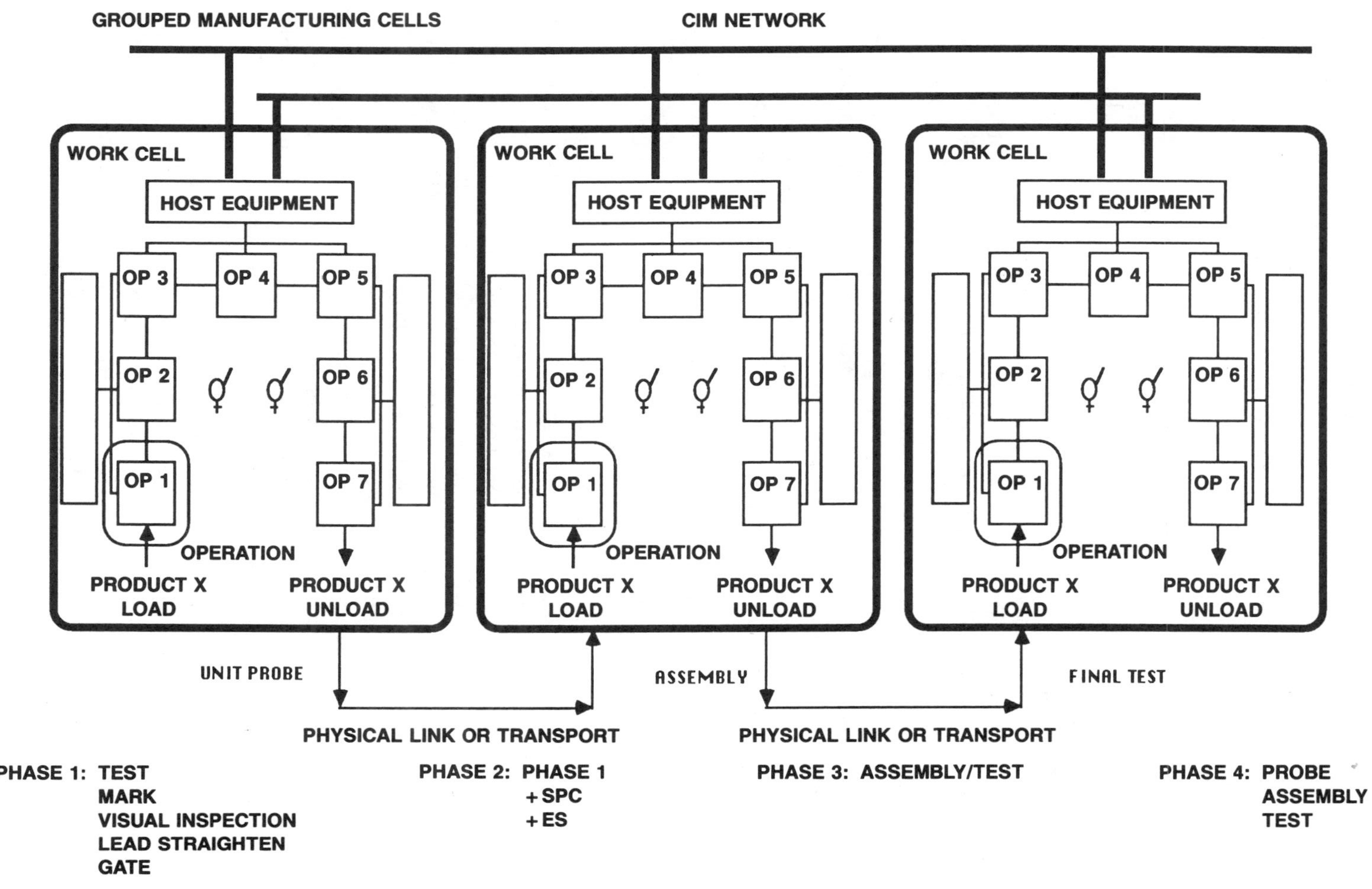

Figure 5-4 Manufacturing Systems
Grouped Integrated Manufacturing Cells

consist only of bleeding off the queuing inventory by reducing the amount of material flowing into the start of the process. As this queuing inventory diminishes, cycle-time does indeed decrease, usually by a fairly significant amount. All too often, however, in thinking that the full potential reduction has been realized, people take these cycle-time reduction gains and then divert their thrust elsewhere, perhaps to some other equally topical management hula hoop program of the year or month, such as quality improvement or increased productivity. Little do they realize that not only is there still unrealized cycle-time reduction potential but that these other parameters would improve if they continued to attack cycle-time. Also, because of our predisposition to functionally specialized organizations, the so called "white space" cycle-time—the cycle-time incurred in the no man's land at every functional interface—goes unaddressed for lack of or disputed ownership.

A truly sound cycle-time reduction program must begin by quantifying the "theoretical cycle-time" of the total sequence of value-adding operations, ignoring the white space and queuing time. This is then the true, ultimate potential. Ratios of ten, twenty, even fifty to one of actual to theoretical cycle-time are not at all untypical. The degree to which this is not realized is waste. The thrust then must be on reducing or eliminating this waste by identifying the causes. In reaping the full potential of this, however, an enterprise may have to reorganize, or change the physical relationship of the operations to reduce this ratio. Having dealt with the queuing and white space cycle-time, the intrinsic cycle-time in each operation in the complete sequence of operations can then be addressed. This is one of the reasons why detailed flow charting is so important. Redundant, non-value adding but time-stealing operations can be identified in this way. The biggest elements can be ranked by greatest time and attacked accordingly.

So encompassing is the cycle-time measurement, there is little if anything in the way of excursions in all other parameters which escape its grasp. To demonstrate this, consider a process consisting of say ten operations, each of which has queuing inventory due to some demand capacity mismatch, and each of which is coupled to the next via white space. Further assume that we have measured the overall cycle-time, from start of operation one to the completion of operation ten and found it to be 20 days. Also assume that the theoretical cycle-time has been computed and found to be one day. Almost anything which varies within any one operation, or in the white spaces within this sequence of operations, will be captured in the actual cycle-time measurement. If inventory increases or decreases, if there is a quality problem on the line, if there is machine down-time, if there is an absenteeism problem, if productivity declines, if there is an engineering problem, if there is a faulty hand-over of the baton across a functional interface, all will result in an increase in the cycle-time measurement. Measuring the overall cycle-time will not of course, indicate what is wrong but simply that there is something wrong. So powerful is this concept, it may in fact be the way to measure indirect productivity which has escaped the grasp of academics, consultants, and practitioners for so long. If the cycle-time measurement is applied to all functions in an organization, from designing new products to shipping to the customer, then every variable will be captured. While the correlation may not be exactly quantifiable, it would be safe to assume that any reduction in cycle-time was due to a productivity improvement in some form, either direct or indirect. Since improvements in direct operator functions can be measured, any improvement in the absence of this could be safely assumed to be due to an improvement in indirect productivity.

6

Manufacturing's Role in Providing Total Customer Satisfaction

THE INGREDIENTS OF TOTAL CUSTOMER SATISFACTION

Easy to articulate, but difficult to realize in practice, these ingredients are as follows:

1. Product Functionality: to offer by means of the new product introduction process a portfolio of products which includes functions matching the application needs of the customer, to the closest possible degree. (This is the primary need. If not satisfied, any distinctive competence in satisfying the other ingredients is academic.)

2. High Quality/Reliability: to provide the customer with sufficient confidence to dispense with the need for costly incoming inspection, allowing product to proceed directly to the customer's manufacturing process; to provide the assurance of quality over time.

3. Low Cost (Price): to support the customer's competitive need to be cost effective in the marketplace.

4. 100 Percent On-Time Delivery: to avoid the need for the customer to fund inventory carrying costs and to avoid work in process jeopardy in the event of demand fluctuations or quality problems which only become apparent on absorption of the material into the customer's manufacturing process.

5. Total Service: to service customer's needs, other than those specifically previously defined, which create a "path of least resistance" from the customer's doorstep to ours, rather than that of the competition.

While virtually all of the specialist functions within an organization contribute, to some degree, in providing all of these ingredients, some of the ingredients are more specifically dependent on the contribution of some functions than others.

The product marketing and design functions, for example, have the primary responsibility for product functionality in defining and designing the product portfolio. Likewise, but by no means exclusively, manufacturing has the primary obligation to accept ownership—to belly up to the bar—in satisfying the needs of **high quality, low**

cost, and **100 percent on-time delivery**. (The temptation to use the principle of nonexclusive control or lack of total ownership of the events affecting on-time delivery—or any other parameter for that matter—should not be allowed to be invoked.) This is represented graphically in Figure 6-1.

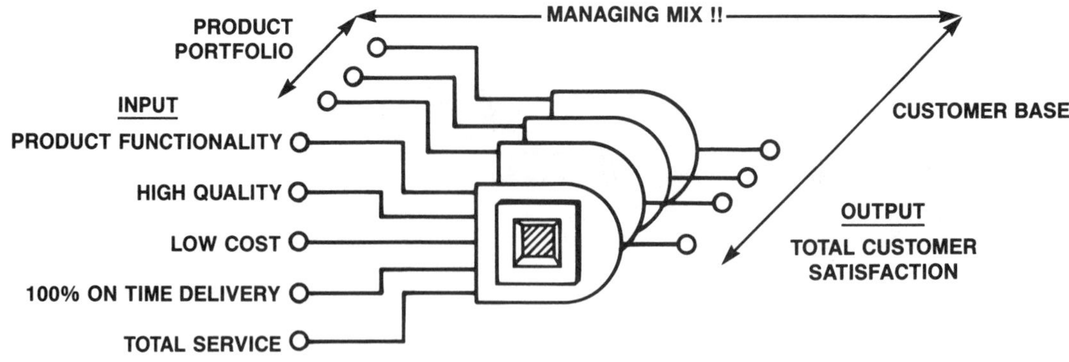

Figure 6-1 The Complexity Matrix

In summary then, manufacturing's role in providing total customer satisfaction is to ship:

High quality product
On-time
At low cost
Across a wide portfolio of products
To a wide customer base

THE OBSTACLES IN ACHIEVING TOTAL CUSTOMER SATISFACTION

Being able to offer a wide portfolio of products, especially if they are leading edge in terms of state of the art, is most certainly a marketing strength. Overall bookings vigor and magnitude is a function of choice. To be able to offer this choice in the form of a rich product portfolio to a wide customer base is in minimizing vulnerability an added business strength. Not to have all of one's eggs in only one basket but in many is to be resilient to individual product or customer perturbations. But historically, this is not the kind of overall scenario—to deliver high quality products, at low cost, on time, across a wide product portfolio, to a wide base of customers—in which factories have been distinctively competent. Traditionally these competencies were considered to be mutually exclusive. You could have distinctive competence in one, possibly even two, seldom three—but certainly not all. This in the past led to strategies of marketing what factories could build rather than learning to build, more competently than anyone else, what the market really wanted. At least part of the challenge then is in **managing mix!** All of this in the face of uncertainty. The uncertainty of customer demand—who will place orders, when, for what product, in what quantity, for what delivery profile? The uncertainty of supply—will our raw material supplier (or preceding operation) deliver on time; will the quality be acceptable; can we process the material through the factory in a predictable and controllable fashion? Again for historical rather than good operational reasons, we learned to deal with uncertainty by building inventory—the JIC—just-in-case approach to manufacturing. In the semiconductor environment, this is depicted in Figure 6-2.

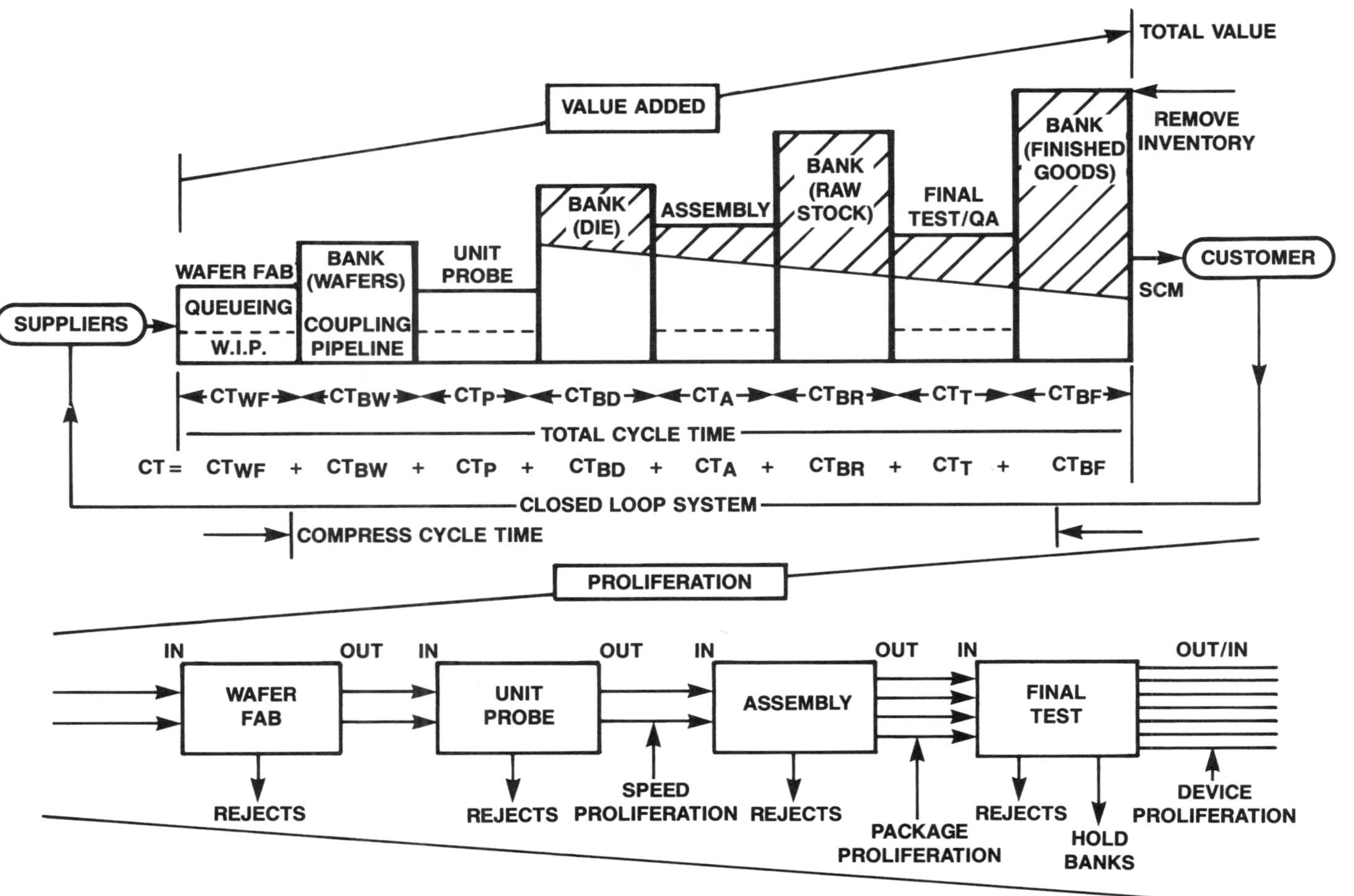

REDUCING CYCLE TIME AT FINAL TEST/LOT PROCESSING, WHERE UNIT VALUE/TOTAL VALUE OF WIP AND PROLIFERATION IS GREATEST ALLOWS THE FINISHED GOODS BANK AND THE RAW STOCK BANK TO BE REDUCED. QUEUE WIP + BANK WIP = ASSET OR LIABILITY COUPLING PIPELINE WIP = SHIP DOCK + TRUCKS + AIRPLANES + CUSTOMS + TRUCKS + INCOMING DOCKS + STAGING.

Figure 6-2 Inventory Philosophy Traditional ''Push'' System

In this approach, sufficient product is "forced" into the start of the line in the hope that enough will eventually emerge—having paid a substantial **waste tax**—to satisfy the aggregate customer demand. Almost invariably, due to demand/capacity mismatches, product, equipment, process and miscommunication problems, at least some of the energy injected into the system results only in building an inventory work-in-process bubble. (The only true work-in-process is that actually having value added to it. All else, for whatever reason, is waste—either of material, money, space, or capacity.)

Much of this effect is a result of cycle-time. If, for example, it takes four weeks to process product through the final test area, then by definition, the finished goods warehouse must contain at least four weeks of inventory, since this is how long it will take to replenish this inventory in the event that it is totally consumed in servicing an unforeseen windfall opportunity. If however, the final test cycle time is reduced to say four days, then this greatly reduces the amount of inventory which needs to be held in this form. Obviously, the further back in the process which this reduced cycle-time extends, the greater the benefits. Our particular success in applying a radically different approach, described later, is shown in Figures 6-3 through 6-14.

HOW THESE RESULTS WERE ACHIEVED

FOCUSING ON THE CUSTOMER

Quality, On-Time Delivery, Cost, and Modules

Quality, on-time delivery, and cost have historically been regarded as mutually exclusive by manufacturing people. You could legitimately ask a manufacturing operation to execute with distinctive competence in any one of these, possibly two—but no way were all three considered to be simultaneously attainable, especially if mix management problems due to product portfolio proliferation, small lot sizes, and product or process engineering problems could be used as an excuse. Volume (units shipped) was usually considered to be the sacrosanct, paramount criteria. Among the main reasons that this position was held, and vigorously defended, was the fact that the **functional** push system of manufacturing—where each person specializes in one very narrowly defined specific task, such as unit probe, wire bond, final test, P&L, or mark—is not consistent, due to its inherent inflexibility, with the need to manage increasing proliferation of mix and smaller lot sizes. In today's fiercely competitive global environment, these attitudes and this level of performance are obviously no longer acceptable. Ways have to be found to deal with these parameters inclusively rather than exclusively.

In our particular case, in any given month we face the challenge of delivering, on-time, at the right quality and cost, up to 4,000 different device types or variations in the form of package, speed, temperature, marking, or other special process flows in individual lot quantities varying from 25 units to 50,000 units. While this represents an opportunity to maximize revenue, the challenge is in being able to do so without increasing costs commensurately. These products tend to be processed in nonuniform ways on a wide proliferation of equipment. The propensity in the past was to focus on the high volume, mature products in order to maximize overhead recovery, whether or not these particular products were needed, often using capacity at the expense of products which were needed. All the while hoping that the need for the more difficult to process products would "go away."

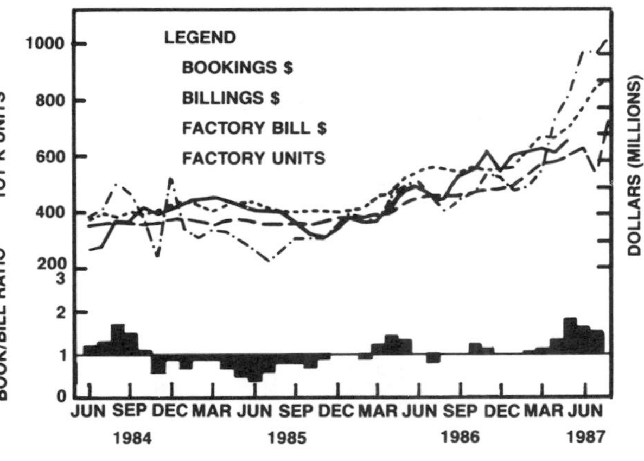

Figure 6-3 Domestic Bookings/Billings
Three Month Moving Average

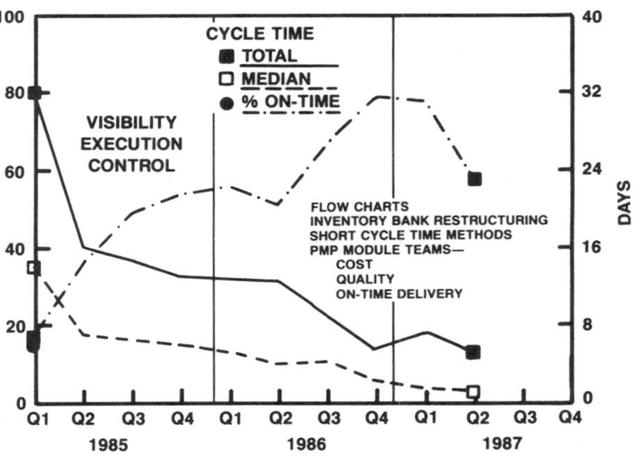

Figure 6-4 On-Time Delivery to MSD/Cycle Time

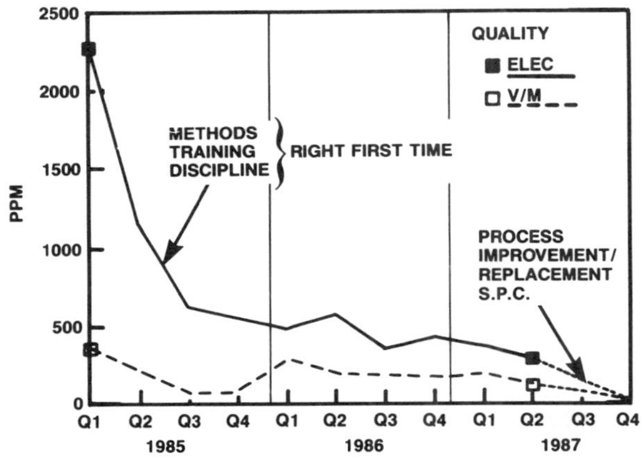

Figure 6-5 Quality

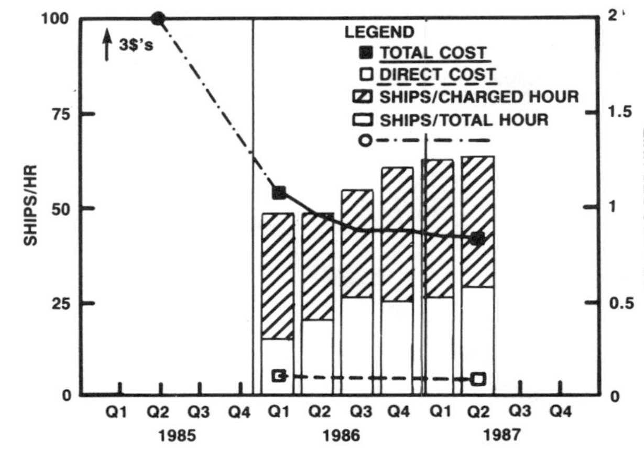

Figure 6-6 Productivity/Test Cost

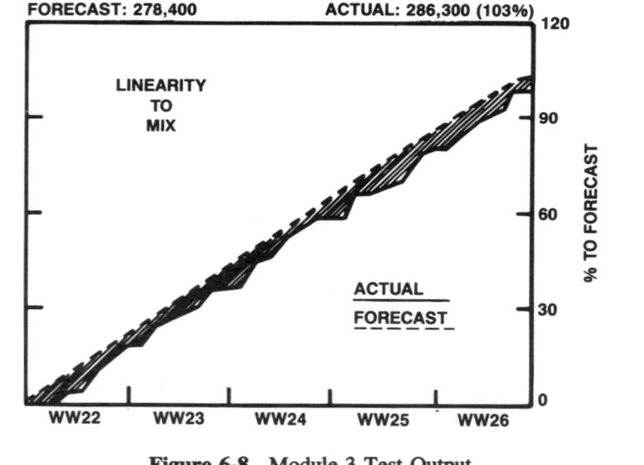

Figure 6-7 Total Test Output

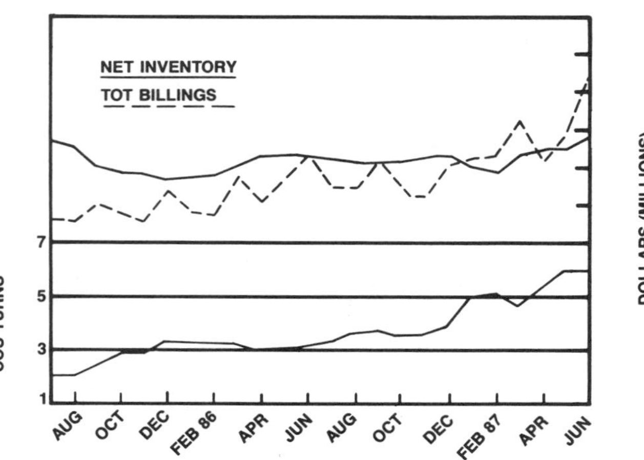

Figure 6-8 Module 3 Test Output

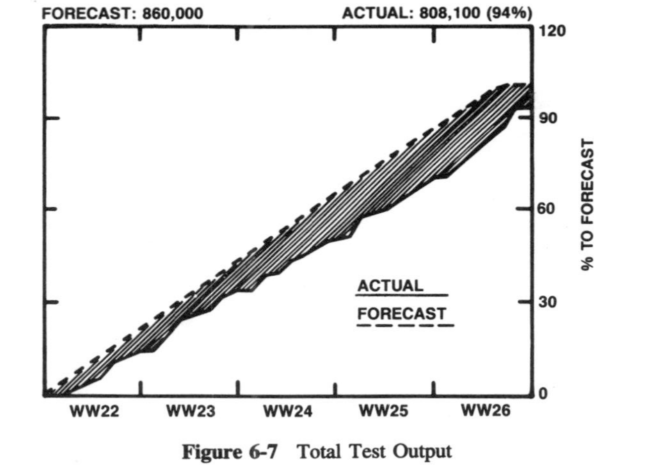

Figure 6-9 Net Inventory/Total Billings/COS Turns

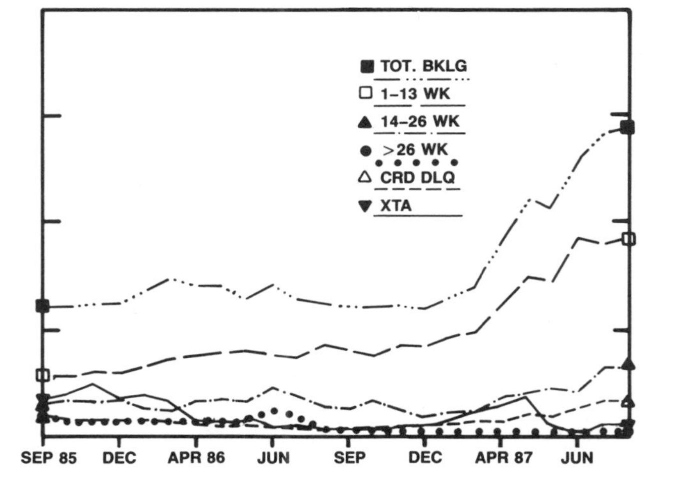

Figure 6-10 Factory Backlog

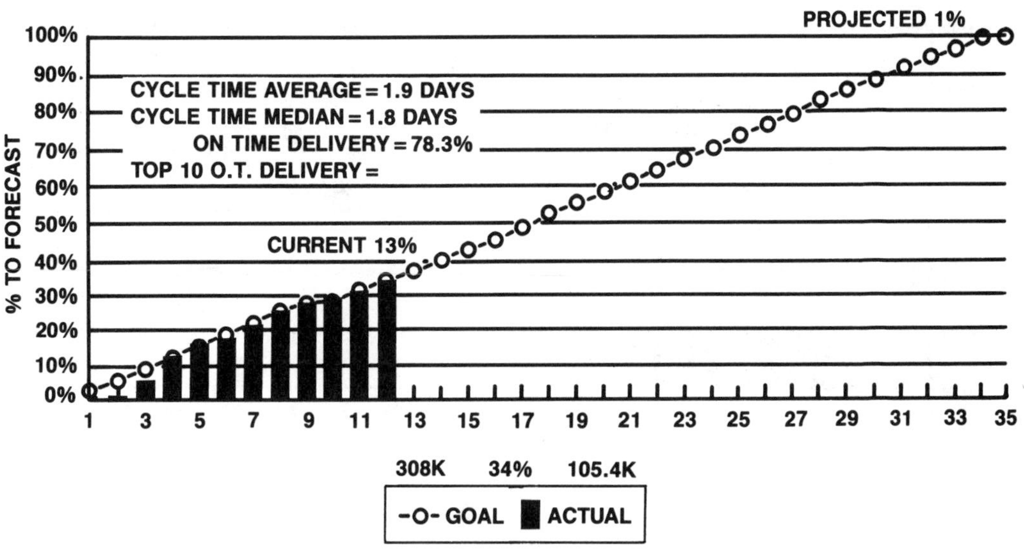

Figure 6-11 Module 3 Non-Speed Shipments for SEPT

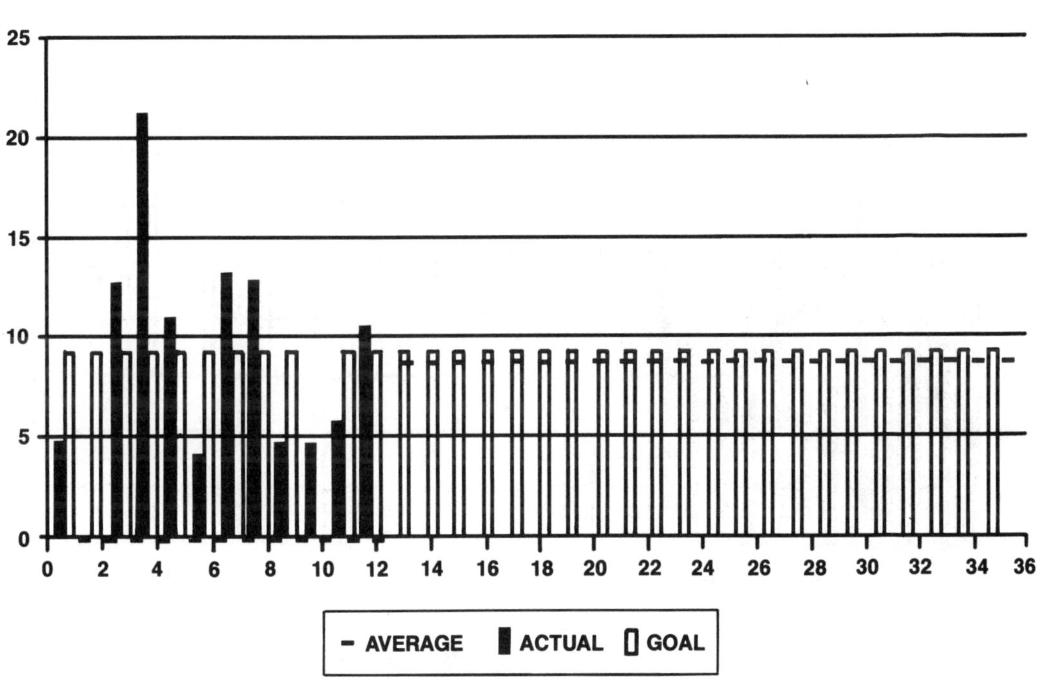

Figure 6-12 Non-Speed, Module 3 Daily Performance to Shipping Goal

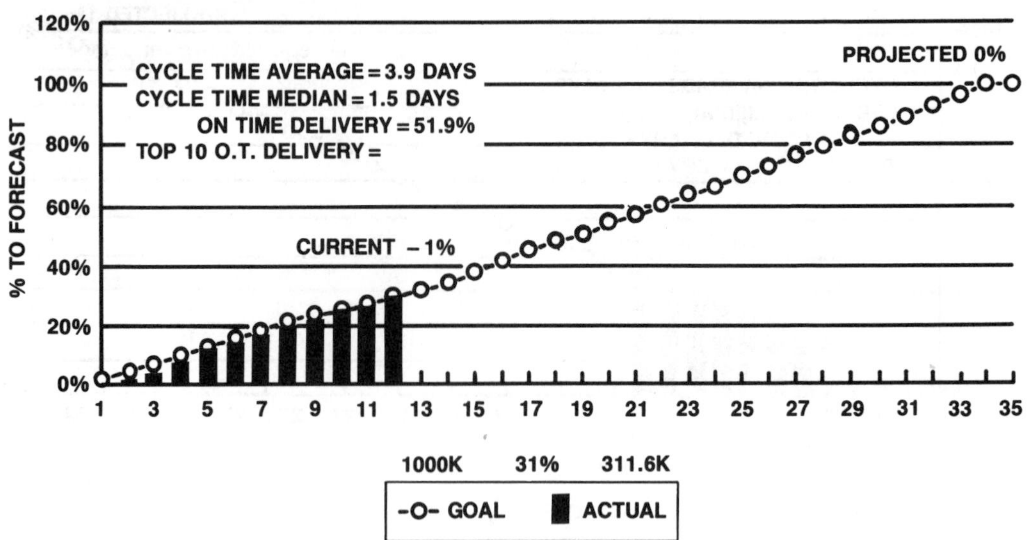

Figure 6-13 Cumulative Shipments: Shipments for SEPT

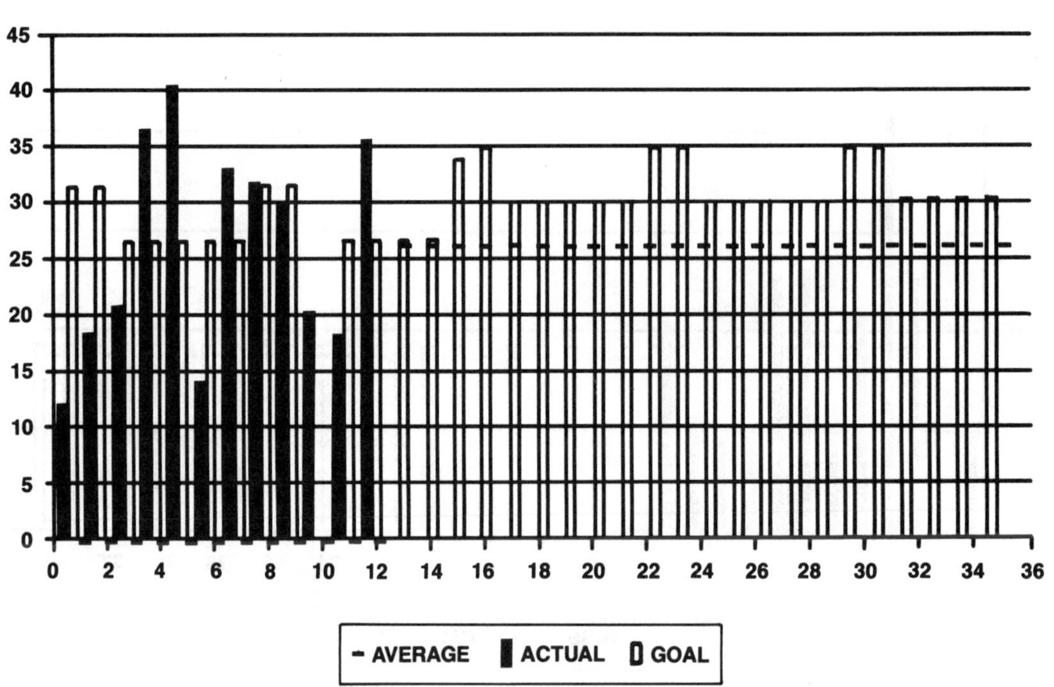

Figure 6-14 Cumulative, Total Module High-End's Daily Performance to Shipping Goal

After much soul searching we ultimately concluded that, with such a complex matrix of variables, we could not achieve this escalating required level of competence using a functional manufacturing system. (Under a functional system, groups of specialized people focus on moving units through a specific operation, regardless of whether any subsequent operation is backlogged with WIP. This is called "busy work.") This approach to processing product both encourages and depends on having lots of WIP on the factory floor. If problems are encountered with a specific product lot, the time honored response was to put it on engineering hold, return it to some inventory bank and then pull another lot to see if we would have any "better luck" with that one. This creates WIP zig/zag to and from shelves and workstations, the need for more space to store product, inventory control systems to account for it, but more importantly—it encourages us to circumvent or learn to live with problems rather than fix them—all of which add up to missing all objectives—quality, on-time delivery, cost, and volume.

In October 1985, we committed ourselves to a different approach called Modules, in effect small focused factories within a factory. It was the only alternative which we could see which at least had the potential to allow us to achieve our collective objectives on a mutually inclusive rather than exclusive basis.

The Modular System approach is predicated on working on one product lot, and **only** one product lot, until that lot ships from QA gate to the finished goods warehouse.

A Module consists of:

1. A groups of products with similar characteristics from the test area point of view—e.g., use the same final test machine/test flow, package, and so on (group technology).

2. An arrangement of equipment (a work cell) to support processing this group of products—from incoming to ship from QA gate.

3. A group of people participative management culture (PCM) improvement team assigned ownership of this group of products—from incoming to shipping from quality control gate. (We have since expanded this to formally include product, equipment, and quality engineering, etc. See Module Organization—Figures 6-22 and 6-23.)

A major reason behind our difficulty in continuing to improve quality, on-time delivery, volume shipped, and cost reduction to world class standard was **mix management**. See Figure 6-15.

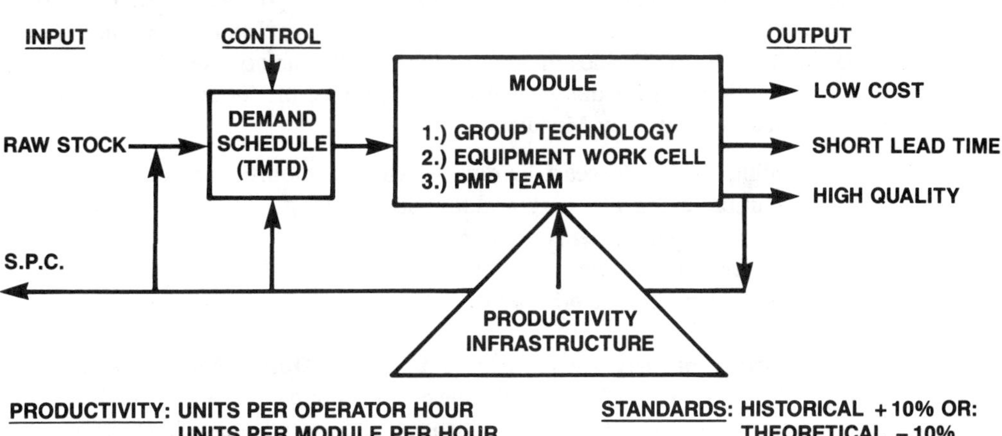

Figure 6-15 Mix Management and Modules

Our mix of products with all of their unique variables was too big a problem to deal with as a single set of variables, so by adopting a Module approach we were able to divide it into several, smaller sets of variables, unique to each module. In addition to this, the manufacturing strategy we developed and applied embraced three broad themes: **visibility, control, and execution**.

As in any other business, manufacturing's task is to support the existing backlog of orders, turns bookings, forecasted or otherwise, and the aged bookings forecast by device, if available. This is obviously a dynamically moving target as the existing orders are fulfilled by delivering product against them, as new orders are added, usually in an unpredictable manner, and as the aged bookings forecast rolls forward. Historically, this "window of uncertainty," of both supply and demand, was accommodated by holding large quantities of finished goods inventory and WIP at various stage of completion. Apart from being costly, this solution, although adequate from a service point of view for standard commodity products, was in no way an adequate solution in responding competitively to the short lead times normally required by customers for customized standard and fully customized products. The alternative, in conjunction with the modular approach to organizing our factory, was to attack manufacturing cycle-times and thereby reduce our response time from order entry to delivery. Shorter cycle-times in final test, assembly, unit probe, and wafer fabrication, using various JIT and SCM techniques and focused factories (modules) described earlier, made it possible to remain and even improve responsiveness to order entry at much reduced inventory levels while significantly reducing the window of uncertainty referred to earlier.

The task of restructuring our organization addressed the visibility issue first, back in production control—what to build, when, and how much, with objectives for sales volume (billings), inventory, quality, on-time delivery, cost, and cycle-time being established in terms of world class standards (benchmarks).

The visibility issue was addressed by restructuring production control along group technology lines and by developing powerful new tools using Nomad, to allow us to capture, process, and communicate the effects of changes in the many variables in our highly volatile, dynamically changing environment, in a one-day to five-year horizon. The business needs in total, rather than just the narrowly defined needs of a single specialist department such as production control or product marketing, for example, were addressed within a structured, universal, electronic data base framework we called integrated business information system (IBIS). Examples of reports produced by this system are shown in Figure 6-16. (Solving the problem of "Islands of Information" must precede solving the problem of "Islands of Automation" on the factory floor.)

Our specific goals for this system were to provide the following, speedily, accurately, and automatically—by Module:

Billings (sales) forecast by device—current month and beyond
Manufacturing planning and machine loading
Capacity requirements analysis
Margins forecasting
Work-in-process profile by device

Measuring Factory Performance to Plan—Daily, Weekly, and Cumulatively. On the execution side, despite the better visiblity afforded by the IBIS reports, the manufacturing area still faced a formidable challenge in being able to support a mix of product which ranged from reasonably high volume, low ASP mature standard product,

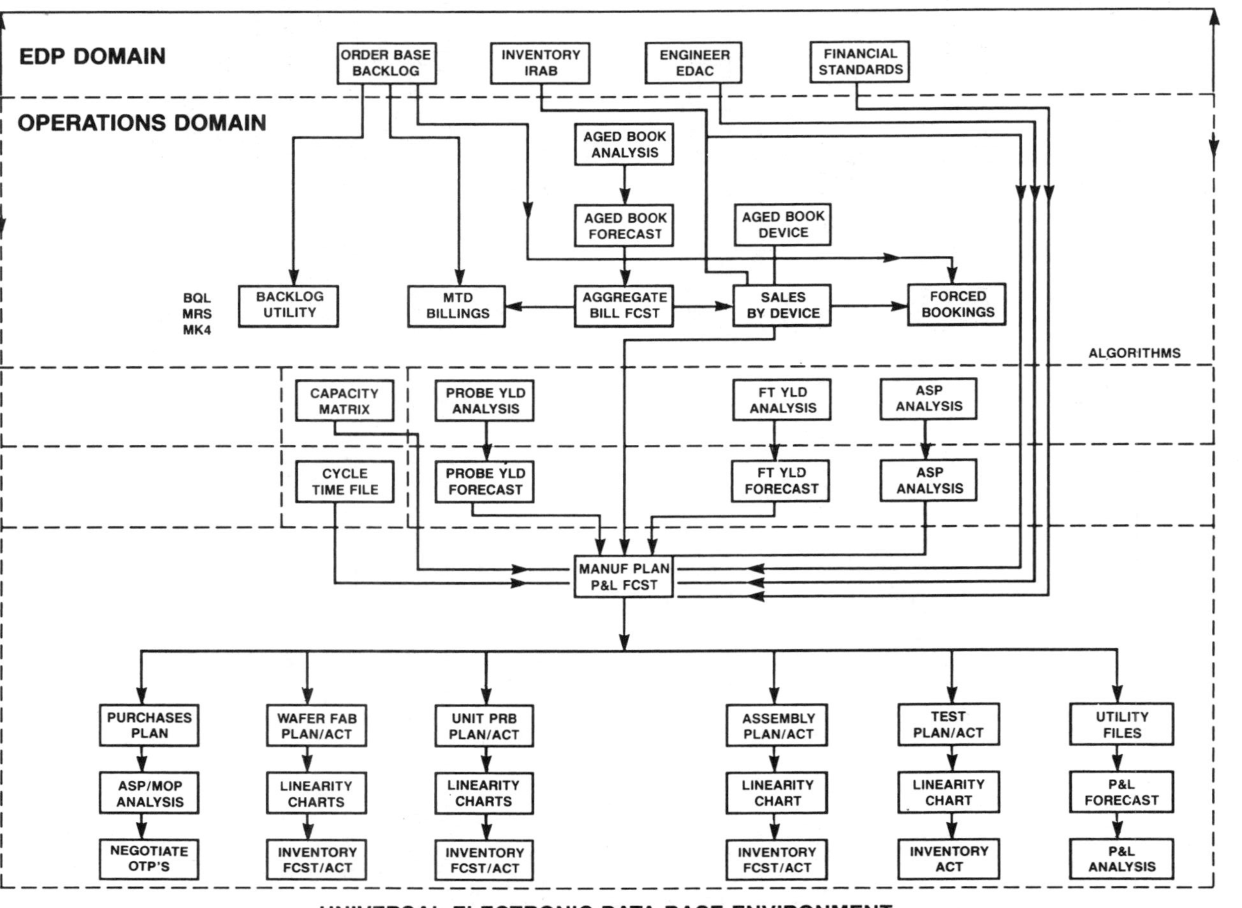

Figure 6-16 IBIS—Integrated Business Information System

to very low volume, extremely difficult to manufacture and test, high ASP product such as Military Standard 883-C microprocessors and peripherals.

The essence of our manufacturing strategy was to:

1. Make the mix problem more manageable on the factory floor.

2. Inculcate a strong sense of ownership and accountability at the individual level by creating an organizational environment in which a participative management culture could be created and applied as intended, in the most practically meaningful way.

3. Create an operating environment in which manufacturing could focus exclusively on execution, by relieving them of the need to address more mundane, but very time consuming housekeeping issues such as materials availability and clerical work, and so on.

To do so, having decided for various reasons that our complete product portfolio would best be supported across six modules, we then established several task forces to focus on realizing these objectives for each module, with each individual task force subordinated to an overall coordinating task force.

In the test environment, our modular concept is predicated on the rationale that raw stock, control, and productivity are inputs to the system and that quality, on-time delivery, and low cost are the end products of the process within each modular system, each output parameter being maximized with the least possible impact on any other—and that product quality is a function of the quality of the process to which it is subjected.

Efforts to improve the values of the output parameters have been focused on the three input elements as follows.

Raw Stock

Historically we have probed wafers to a specification which maximized yield of our lowest specification product at final test. With relatively high cost LSI and VLSI die, expensive packages and extensive proliferation in the form of packages, speed, and temperature sorts, apart from being economically wasteful, this approach frequently resulted in very serious backlog distribution profile to product available mismatches. On the one hand, sales opportunties were often not realized due to nonavailability of product while on the other, inventory was being accumulated on products for which there was little or no demand. A technically feasible and economically viable solution to this problem is to create, as far as possible, the same electrical test environment at unit probe as the device encounters at final test. By implementing hot chuck, high frequency, inkless probing, the unit probe conditions can be selected at run-time, consistent with the least to most demanding product specification as required. Input to assembly can thus be controlled to optimize use of capacity and piecepart availability in servicing the backlog in the most cost-effective manner.

Control

On-Time Delivery

Visibility of what is required to be done, which product, how many, and when, is provided to each module using **Nomad** and **Tandem** reports, unique to each module. The Nomad report provides an overview status, the Tandem report shows both active and inactive

WIP by lot and by stage of completion. Status to plan is measured automatically using the same charts, generated once per day on Nomad and real-time via Tandem. Each module is measured independently on quality, on-time delivery, cycle time, unit shipments, linearity, cost, and inventory as shown in Figures 6-3 through 6-14. The standards are set independently for each module to comprehend differences in test flows, degrees of difficulty, and so on.

Test Cost

Until recently, test cost had been available at the product line level only. The usefulness of this was limited due to inaccuracies and the use of averages. (With a product portfolio in which ASPs range from $2 to $2,000, and product costs from $0.50 to $50—use of averages is not only meaningless—it can be dangerous.) Since October 1986, the beginning of our standards period, both standard and actual test cost by device are now generated by reconciling the financial standards and the direct-labor tracking systems inputs in a common electronic data base environment. This is now included as a performance measurement in each module composite chart. (The very wasteful, paper based direct labor tracking (DLT) system, has also been transferred to the same electronic data base.)

Productivity

In the belief that quality, on-time delivery, and cost are all end effects of a common input cause—productivity—this topic, needless to say, is receiving much attention. Figure 6-17 depicts the guide we are using to focus our thrust in a structured and controlled fashion, with ownership of each box on the chart assigned to the appropriate functionally specialized department. While we continue our efforts to make best use of what we have, we have also begun to lay the foundation for the future in the form of CIM. An outline showing our program of systematically building "Layers of Competence," is shown in Figure 6-18.

Short Cycle-Time Manufacturing

1. **Raw stock transfer.** Until recently, the time required to transfer raw stock to the test floor averaged five days. This process has been completely overhauled, resulting in far fewer product movements and storage transactions and consequently, far fewer clerical transactions. The average transfer time is now four hours with 30 minutes on expedite. Part of this overhead involved completely restructuring our inventory bank network. The old and new networks are shown in Figures 6-19 and 6-20.

2. **Actual processing of product on the test floor.** This is the function of the modules themselves.

3. **Changeovers.** Depending on test set-up configuration—test system, handler, product, and so on, this could take up to four hours, our average being 45 minutes. A universal electromechanical interface adapter designed to allow the docking of any type of prober or test handler to any type of test system is at an advanced stage of development and will allow any configuration to be set up in less than 10 minutes.

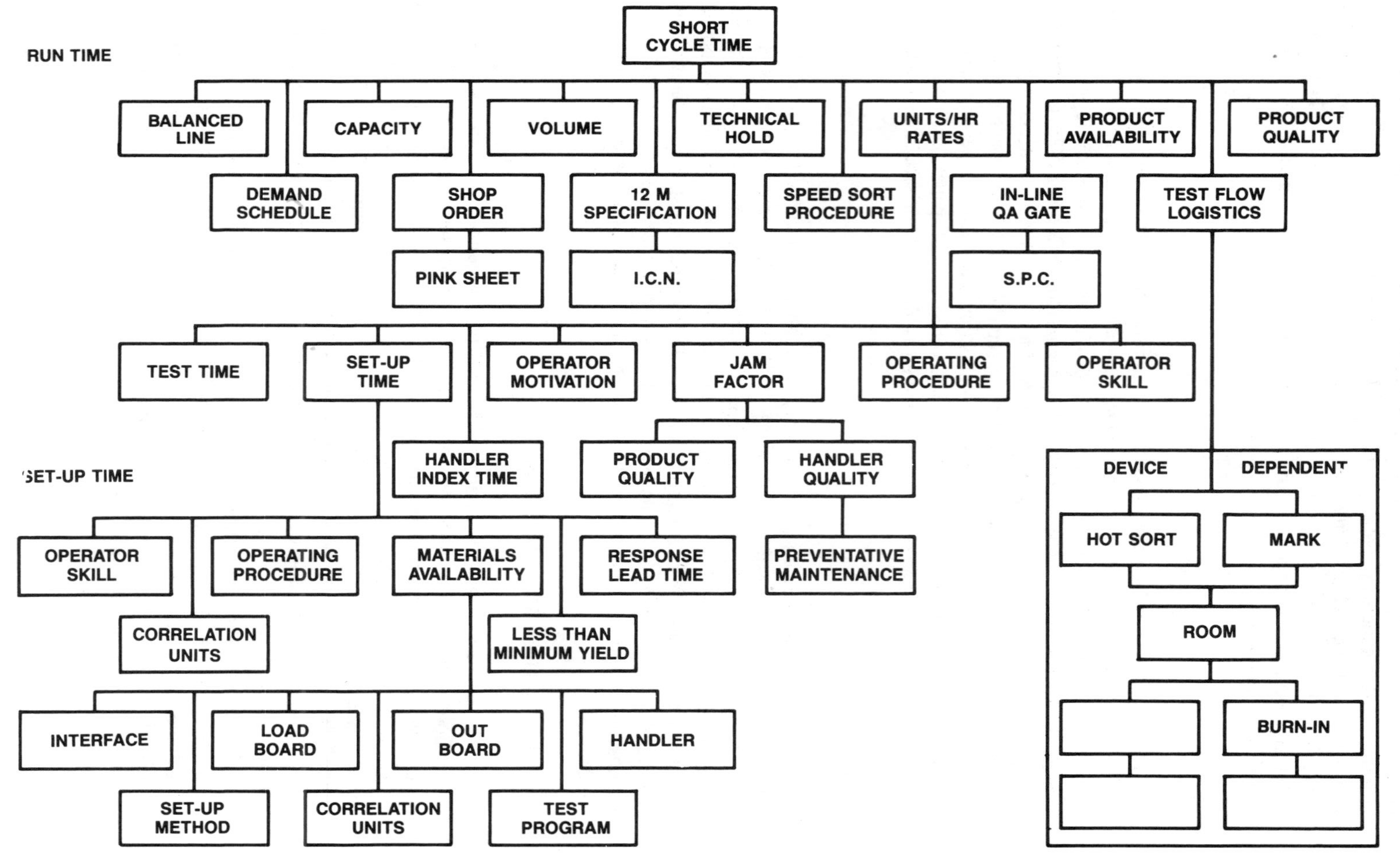

Figure 6-17 Productivity and Short Cycle Time Manufacturing

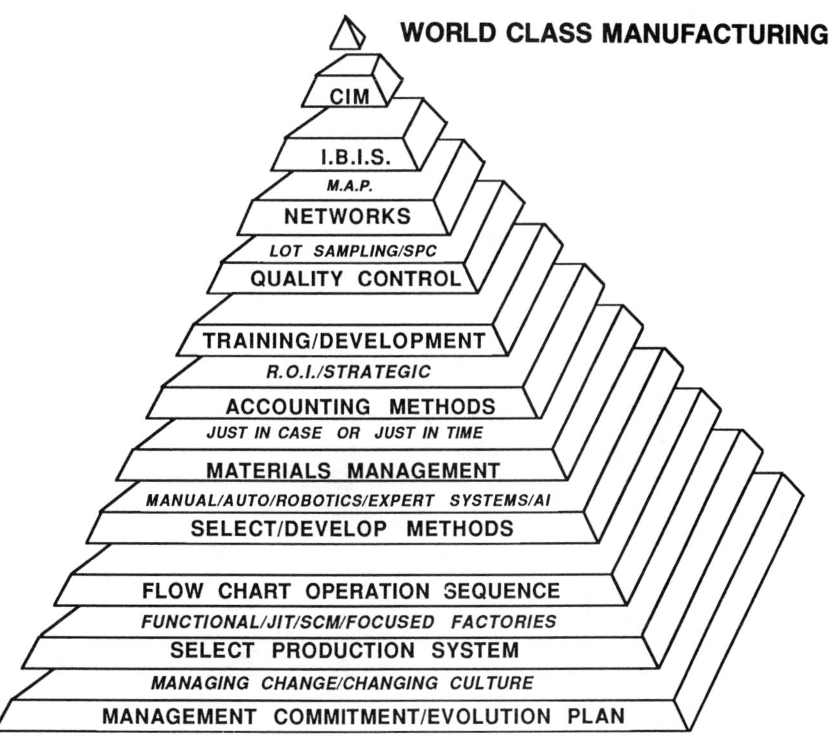

Figure 6-18 Building Layers of Competence

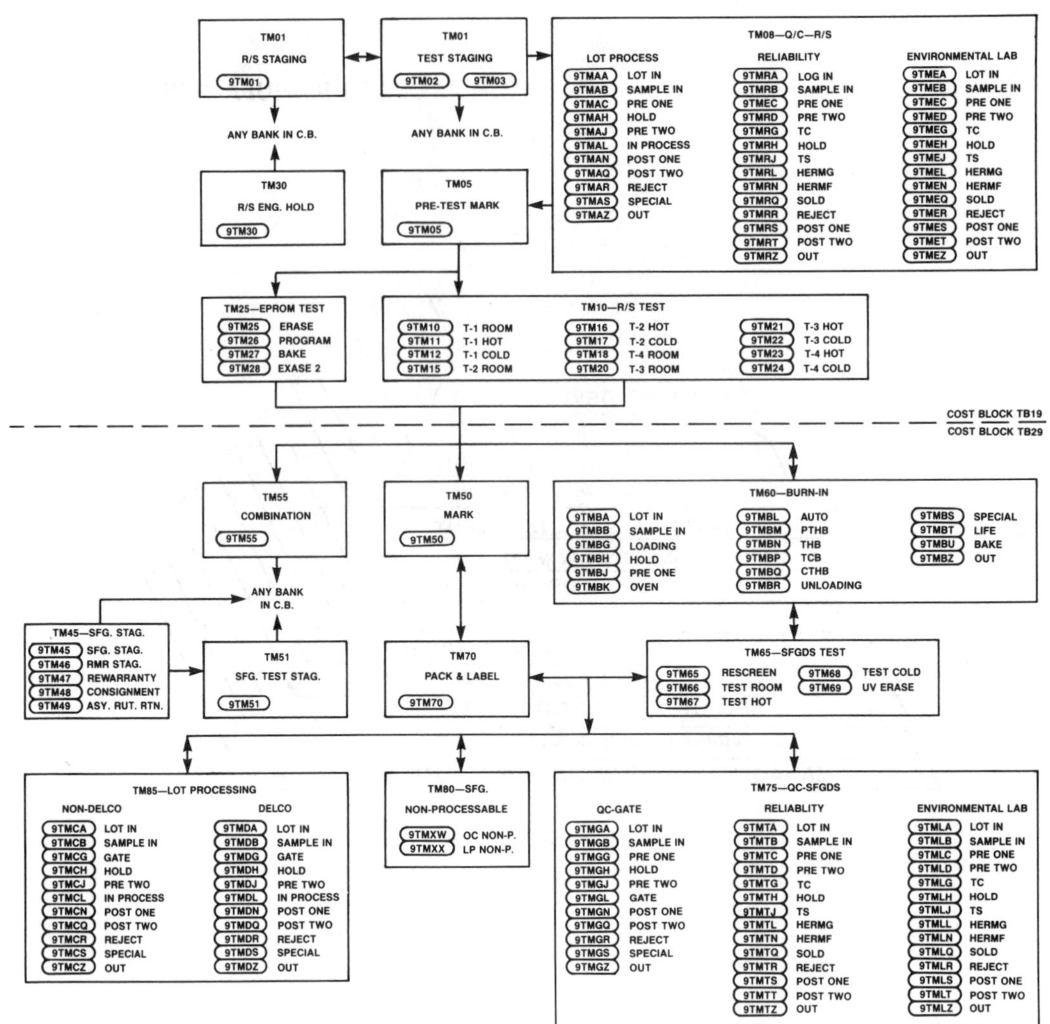

Figure 6-19 Accounting Bank Transaction Network—Old

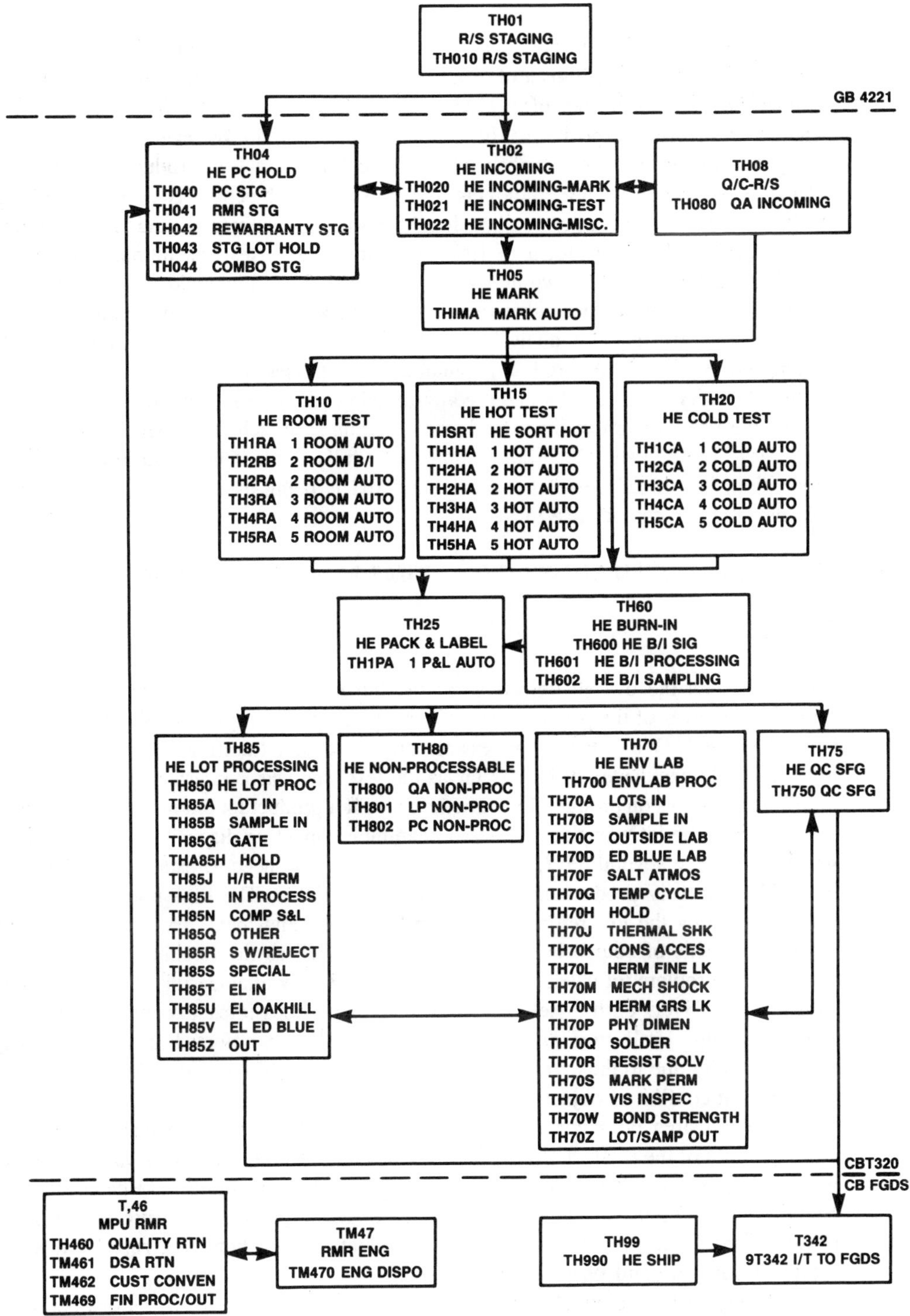

Figure 6-20 Accounting Bank Transaction Network—January 1988

Quality

Our short-term goal was to eliminate the need for rescreen by reducing gate failures to zero and to eliminate the impact of product yield uncertainty by lot on on-time delivery. Historically, if a lot did not meet predefined yield criteria, the lot was placed on hold pending engineering disposition. This process, which could take several days, was necessary due to the need to establish whether the low yield was product or test set-up related. The strategy we are employing to achieve these objectives is expressed conceptually as "building in quality" rather than "inspecting our rejects" and is being implemented practically in the form of right first time (RFT) test discipline. How this is structured and applied is shown in Figure 6-21. With RFT, low yield can confidently be assumed to be truly product rather than test system set-up related and therefore, as long as test rejects are held for analysis by engineering, there is nothing to be gained by holding the portion of the product populaton which passes. In this way, least impact to on-time delivery is achieved without compromising either yield, quality, or throughput. When gate results confirm the effectiveness of this approach, each Module then earns the right to in-line gate. Our pilot module, now fully implemented and in high volume production, has already earned this privilege and is being used as a pilot yet again to help develop our competence in SPC.

ENGINEERING HOLD AND SHORT CYCLE TIME MANUFACTURING

RFT Testing

Consistent with the overall objectives of the business operation, the test area is also measured in terms of the primary performance parameters of **quality, on-time deivery,** and **price (cost)**. One of the major reasons why these have traditionally been considered to be mutually exclusive, at least as far as the test area was concerned, was the impact of low yielding lots on product flow. Historically, if a product lot did not meet predefined yield criteria, the lot was placed on hold pending engineering disposition. This process, which could take several days, was necessary due to the need to establish whether the low yield was truly product or test system set-up related. The time honored response was to withdraw the lot, return it to an on hold shelf and then "try your luck" with another lot. This of course led to WIP zig/zag as well as the likelihood of having to rescreen the problem lot when eventually dispositioned by engineering. This procedure, focusing exclusively on the yield objective, had an obvious impact on on-time delivery and cost in that cycle time and throughput were adversly affected. It also adversely affected quality due to the extra handling of the product. RFT was developed to resolve this apparent conflict of objectives.

The test area does not add value to the product in the sense that the physical characteristics of the product are changed. This being the case, ideally its purpose should be to simply confirm that all other preceding value added operations have been executed within control. Until we reach that idyllic state, its purpose is to ensure with highest possible confidence, in conformance to the product specification, that **reject parts are screened out** and **good parts are not rejected**.

Quality problems which may be induced in the test area itself, as distinct from those imported from upstream operations, can occur either at set-up time or during run-time. (Sources of these problems are specifically identified on the following page.) If a product fails QA gate, the probability is high that such a problem occurred, or could

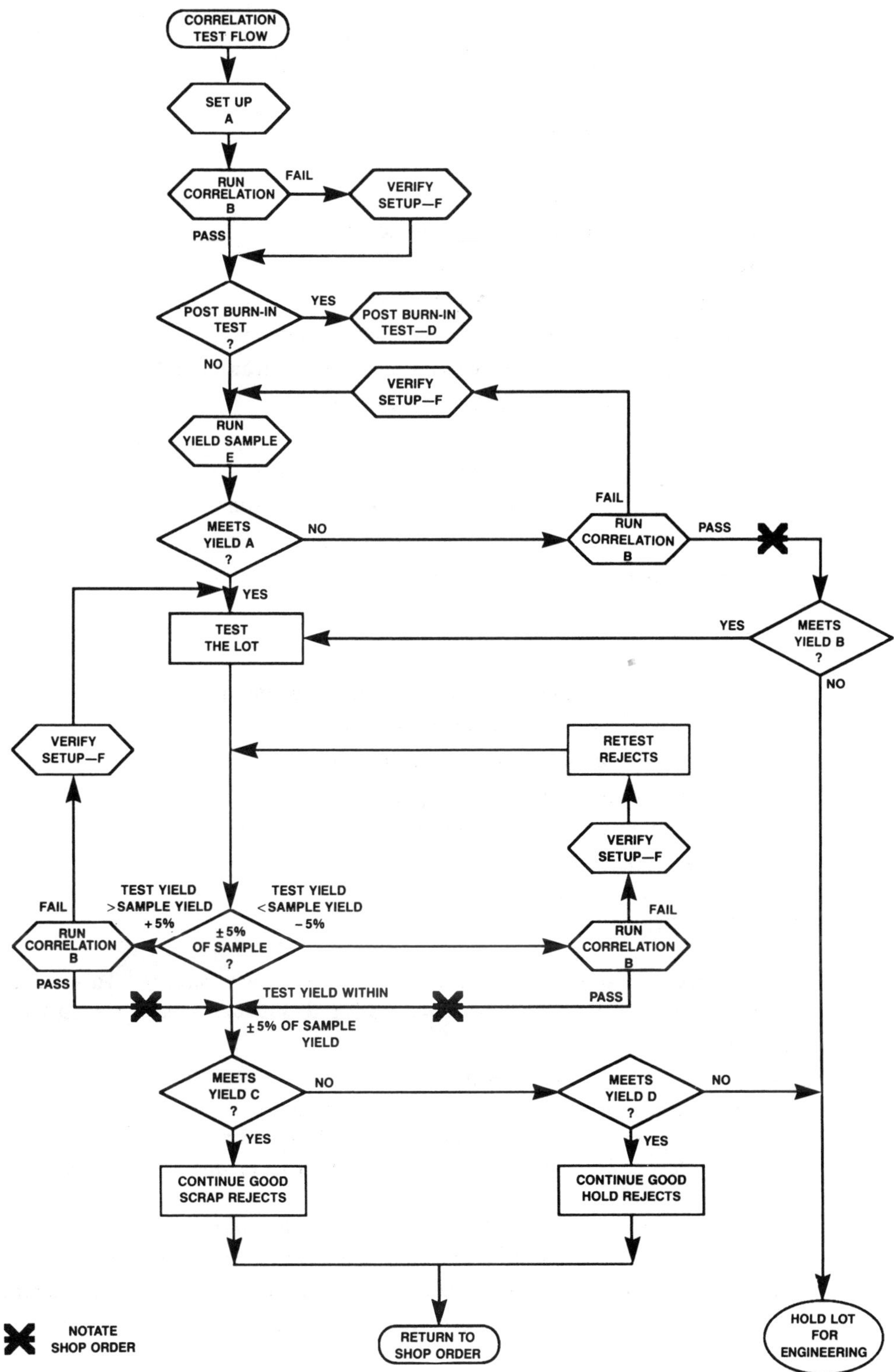

Figure 6-21 RFT Test Flow
I. Correlation

have been detected during or immediately after test system set-up, rather than during run-time. Test set-ups, which are frequently reconfigured to accommodate device lot or shift changes are the primary focus of the RFT discipline.

Time Zero Set-Up Problems

Unapparent system problem

Faulty loadboard/test socket/interface/handler
Incorrect test program selected
Test program software problem
Inadequacy, misapplication of methods/procedures
Test program/shop order/device specification incompatibility
Shop order complexity/ambiguity/inaccuracy
Electrostatic damage
Communications delay/distortion/misinterpretation
Incorrect set-up conditions, e.g., wrong temperature
Real product problems (imported from upstream operations)
Proliferation problems/instability

Run-Time Problems

Hardware failure-system/handler/interface/loadboard
Shift change discontinuity/misunderstanding
Inadequate level of operator skill/commitment
Power transients in electrical supply
Real product problems (population or lot by lot dependent)
Damage induced by handling methods

The Main Theme of RFT

1. **Ensure that test system set-up configurations are correct.** (This provides confidence that any low yielding lot encountered is truly product, rather than test system set-up related.)
2. **Provide predefined lot disposition criteria with respect to yield.**
   A. Category 1—Complete testing the lot, ship good parts, scrap rejects.
   B. Category 2—Complete testing the lot, ship good parts, hold rejects.
   C. Category 3—Complete testing the lot, place all product on hold immediately after P&L.
   D. Category 4—If lot fails to meet yield B criteria—place lot on hold immediately (to help compensate for reduced engineering cover on off-shifts.)
3. **Ensure short cycle-time** (predefined action sequence if problem encountered).
4. **Conform system integrity over the lot test time** (system performance same at end of lot as at beginning).
5. **Satisfy prerequisite conditions for in-line QA gate** (minimize system change-overs and reconfirms that the test set-up is still OK immediately prior to in-line gate).

6. Satisfy prerequisite conditions for SPC (product quality is a function of the quality of the process).

While the RFT flow is universally constant across all modules, the four yield limits, A, B, C, and D (as shown in Figure 6-21) may be unique to each product within any Module. The logic of the flow chart and these yield limits, determined by the appropriate product engineer, are chosen such that a significant percentage of lots (eventually 95 percent) will be dispositioned in categories one, two, and three with only 5 percent falling into the "**hold all immediately**" category four. With RFT, low yield can confidently be assumed to be truly product related and therefore, as long as test rejects are held for engineering analysis, there is nothing to be gained by holding product which passes. In this way, quality criteria can be met with least impact to on-time delivery and price (cost). When QA gate results confirmed the effectiveness of this approach, i.e., a history of zero gate failures, each module then earned the privilege of converting to in-line gate, prior to implementing SPC. (RFT and in-line gate must precede SPC.) In the interest of shortest possible cycle time, set-up time needs to be minimized but this does not detract from the need for a set-up check list to be rigorously adhered to.

In addition to locally introduced quality problems, much of the quality problems encountered in the test area are imported from upstream sources—incorrectly fabricated or inadequately probed die, poor quality raw stock from assembly subs for example. As such, no matter how elaborate the safeguards taken in the test area, quality, on-time delivery, and cost objectives cannot be met unless these sources are incorporated in the RFT program as well. To this end, RFT is being introduced at unit probe in conjunction with efforts to create the same test environment here as is encountered at final test. These efforts take the form of: **hot chuck/high frequency/inkless probe**. We cannot prevent the wafer fabrication areas from shipping "out of spec" die but we can prevent those die from consuming assembly capacity, expensive package pieceparts, and test resources.

Summary On Modules

When we embarked on the module path, we could not be sure that we were going in the right direction to reach our goals, but we were fairly convinced that the other direction, the "more of the same" functional path would absolutely not take us there. We now have sufficient empirical data, over a meaningful enough period of time, to have no reservations whatsoever about modules being the right approach. While our sales revenue continue to grow and volume and product proliferation continue to increase; as ASPs decline and new products are added to our portfolio, we are continuing to see significant improvements in inventory levels, direct labor force requirements, cycle time, quality, on-time delivery, and costs, and so on. (Incidentally, we are also profitable.) These kinds of improvements are relatively easy to achieve in a business downturn, with excess capacity available. In a rapid growth environment such as ours, the results are all the more encouraging. The performance of Module III, our most mature configuration and that which we used to develop this new approach, is indicative of the improvements we could confidently anticipate and have since realized from our other modules. In 1985 we had 37 lots fail QA Gate in this product group. Since October 1986 we have had zero. Our units per hour has increased from 145 to 465 at the same time that the median cycle-time came down from 28 days to 2 and on-time delivery improved from 10 percent to 96 percent.

Needless to say, there were problems impeding this approach to world-class performance, but we chose to attack them rather than use them as excuses to hide behind, to defend perpetuating status quo. The results we are seeing are well worth the effort. All six modules are now fully established and producing results exactly similar to those we enjoyed in Module III. In fact, on our 32-bit family, our most strategically important products, we have reduced cycle time, with the help of our colleagues in our assembly factory, from unprobed wafers to shipping to the end customer, to three days.

Implementing the Module Strategy

A main task force, consisting of the production manager, the equipment engineering manager, and the manufacturing control manager was formed, with each of the individuals on the main task force then in turn forming and leading a subordinate task force with responsibilities as follows:

I. **System Utilization**—Manufacturing Control Team
   1. **Evaluate Process Flows**
      a) Three standard product flows maximum
      b) Review/standardize all shop orders
   2. **Scheduling of Equipment**
      a) Engineering time
      b) Production/QC time
   3. **Schedule Product**
      a) Machine loading
      b) Materials supply control

II. **Equipment Utilization**—Equipment Engineering Team
   1. a) Reconfigure equipment into work cells
      b) Revise UPH standards for line balancing
      c) Review/modify all process specs
   2. **Process Control**
      a) Establish/monitor/flag minimum yields
      b) Quantify/control defects as test/mark/P&L
      c) Setup/sustain statistical process control
   3. **Methods Analysis/Improvement**
      a) Minimize set-ups/change over cycle time
      b) Establish down time/change over measurement
      c) Establish preventative maintenance program
   4. **Automation Program**
      a) Establish foundation for computer integrated manufacturing (CIM)

III. **Human Resources**—Production Team
   1. **Organize Modules**
      a) Systems
      b) People
      c) Products

2. **Establish Training Program**
    a) People
    b) Methods
    c) Documentation
3. **Address Line Balancing Requirement**
    a) UPH standards interdependence
    b) Short cycle manufacturing
    c) On-time delivery
4. **Participative Management Program**
    a) Standards
    b) "I Recommend" communication
5. **Quality**
    a) In-line QC gates
    b) Quality improvement
    c) Develop/implement SPC
6. **Productivity/Cost Reduction**
    a) Methods improvement
    b) Evaluations
    c) Cost accounting measurement changes
7. **Build Team Concept**

Operating Principles

- Retain close working relationship with production control/product engineering. **(Task oriented transfunctional project organization)**
- PMC module teams responsible from incoming to ship—create **"ownership"** of "factories" within a factory.
- Apply **total system productivity** approach—**infrastructure**—not just direct operators.
- Focus thrust on **engineering the process—product quality is a function of process quality.** (Build in quality rather than inspect out rejects)
- Streamline/**rationalize** product process flow **logistics**.
- **Balance** mechanization/automation and people—build foundation for CIM (computer-integrated manufacturing).—**Retain flexibility**.
- Optimize individual/group/task goals:—**"Concentric circles"**
- Encourage **identification**/adaptation to module goals.
- Employ our **people's knowledge**—not just their manual dexterity.
- Operate **pull rather than push** system—continue to force trend to zero inventory.
- Participate more fully in **new product introduction process.**
- Support **training/education/certification** in best methods (military products).
- **Attack material and overhead costs/productivity**—not just direct labor.
- Overhaul and **simplify inventory bank network** and **accounting system**.
- Avoid **hiding behind excuses**/creeping **complacency**.
- Special **focus** on **top 20 OEM** list.

- Develop/enforce comprehensive **equipment set up** and **check off procedure**.
- Develop/implement **short cycle-time methods.** (Particularly major equipment set-up/changeover—**reduce frequency, minimize duration**).
- **Take ownership/develop self sufficiency in**: Unit probe/incoming materials/ test/process engineering.
- Achieve excellence in **commodity and niche** markets. (High volume/low ASP **and** low volume/high ASP).
- Work to **improve** real/perceived **status** of **equipment/process and test engineering** and **manufacturing management and supervision.**
- Fuel continued **growth through productivity** improvements.
- Continue to change **balance of skills mix** in order to execute **productively** and **predictably.**
- Implement in-line QA gate as prerequisite to developing/applying **statistical process control.**
- Maintain **balance of effort** (A) short (B) medium and (C) long term.
- Enhance QOWL—**Quality of working life**.
- Set performance standards based on what is **theoretically possible**—not history + 10 percent.
- **Quality, on-time delivery, and cost** will be the **primary measurement parameters.**
- Work towards **"zero defect"** incoming material: **internal** as well as **external** suppliers.
- **Ship to OEMs from test**—not warehouse.
- Implement **hot chuck/high frequency/inkless probe**.

The Mind to Imagine, the Skill to Do.

The **Determination**, to **Follow Through!**

Organizational Structure and Change

How we reorganized the "cutting edge" of our manufacturing operation on the factory floor—phase one in our journey towards world-class competence—has already been described in "focusing on the customer." The following section describes our research prior to phase 2—the much more difficult task of reaching even deeper into the supporting infrastructure of the organization in order to begin the process of realigning those functions other than manufacturing on the new realities—these imperatives expressed earlier in a collective form in terms of the superordinate goal of total customer satisfaction. The desired end result of this process in the formation of self-sufficient, self managing module groups as the vehicle to facilitate the practical realization of this common goal is also described.

Cognizant of the fact that there is almost always institutionalized resistance to change, we began by reviewing the model most widely used, in both industry and business schools, to represent a typical organizational structure. In attempting to understand the nature and scope of this phenomena, we quite simply set ourselves the task of trying to answer the question of why is it, in a time when the need for change is so apparent, that some organizations find it so difficult to change.

It would seem that organizations fall into several categories in this respect. There are those impervious to the need for change. There are those who consider the need to but then conclude that it is not necessary—or cannot muster the courage, enthusiasm, and determination to execute. These are not the categories of interest to us. The category we were interested in was that which includes those organizations which recognize and accept the need for internal change in response to external factors and begin the process of doing so but then encounter difficulties in the mechanics of implementation, even when this new direction is mandated by senior management. Why is change, even after the need for it is fully accepted at least by management, so difficult to deal with? Can there be structural as well as the individual human factors which present resistance to the process?

Classical Organizational Structure

In reviewing the model, our first observations in trying to identify its attributes were that:

1. It is constructed from very simple components—boxes—containing descriptive labels (titles) **and names—joined by horizontal and vertical lines.** (The thought crossed our minds at this point that surely something so complex as an organization—with all of its dynamic interaction and heavy communication traffic—cannot be adequately represented by something so simple. Nothing like this occurs in nature, where all structures are composed of atoms. This clue to a potentially enlightening path of enquiry, will be pursued later.)

2. The structure is hierarchical and pyramidic, with many plain little bricks supporting not a few ornate ones. It consists of several layers, with span increasing towards the base. There is a suggestion of vertical columns in the form of the substructure of the specialist departments.

3. It represents the formal organization only. It does not define the informal organizational structure and communications network which exists in every organization.

4. Communication channels are vertical and horizontal.

5. There is a well defined pecking order and chain of command. This much is factual, established by observation alone. To proceed further, we resorted to conjecture.

6. The structure is designed to ensure stability and continuity to perpetuate status quo. In this it has much momentum in proceeding along a set course but any change of direction, no matter how slight, is resisted by the inertia associated with the rigid structure, institutionalized policy, and procedures. In today's competitive world, change must be embraced—not resisted.

7. It preserves each functionally specialized discipline in its purest (but limited perspective) **form.** There is always the possibility that a function will see itself as an end in its own right—rather than as a means to an end.

8. Decisions affecting more than one function will tend to rise up the hierarchy to a point of convergence. (The decision making cycle-time will not be optimized.)

9. Allegiance will tend to be focused towards department or profession—not necessarily the customer.

10. Behavior will be supervisor oriented—the most immediate source of pain and pleasure.

11. Territorial parochialism and empire building will be a natural propensity. The instincts of self-preservation and territorial expansion are strong.

12. Direct line of sight to the customer is not immediately obvious. How customer needs are comprehended in setting priorities internal to these specialized functions may not be readily apparent.

13. The organization will tend to cope with growth—usually after the fact—by adding additional layers. Increased control is gained at the expense of reduced responsiveness.

14. Us and them attitudes—not just vertically, but across functional interfaces—are entirely typical, with the production supervisor often excluded from both camps and forced to "sit on the fence."

15. Preoccupation may be on power, status, prestige—associated with level in the hierarchy and span of control—not necessarily on the customer. (The fortress of the "old brigade"—unwilling or unable to adjust to a new regime. Pyramids are mausoleums.)

16. In times of economic adversity, efforts to reduce the number of layers usually begins at the bottom—and usually does not rise very far.

17. "Ownership" of a problem or situation can be refuted/disputed. (That's not my job! It's someone else's fault! It's not on my priority list!)

There is something incomplete and unsatisfying in this approach. It is a legacy from the past when products and processes were much simpler, when customer expectations were moderate, when competition was much less intense, when change occurred slowly and moderately.

Task Force Structure

1. As the name implies, it is task specific.

2. Members are usually drawn from a cross section of disciplines appropriate to the task.

3. Is usually created to address project type activities—reactive in the case of a crisis, and proactive, at least in intent, in dealing with a distinct project such as new product introduction, for example.

4. Exists as an independent entity, for the duration of the project only.

5. Does not normally have executive authority but merely recommends.

6. Is normally led by a champion or project leader whose task-related knowledge and leadership abilities qualifies him or her for this role.

7. Goals are usually clearly defined in terms of cost incurred, quality of end result, and time to completion. The team is measured accordingly as a group.

8. The effectiveness of the team depends among other things on human chemistry.

9. Collective ownership cannot be disputed.

10. Group peer pressure will have a strong influence on individual behavior.

The Coexistence of Both Approaches

Molecular (Organic) Hybrid Structure. The classic structure resembles a crystal lattice in physics with legitimate, stable states defined, but also containing unsatisfied states, as in the valency shell of an electron. Task forces, on the other hand, resemble free electrons wandering through the lattice till it finds some kind of vacuum or unsatisfied need, rather like the impurities introduced into the intrinsic silicon.

Since both organizational approaches seem to complement or compensate for the other in terms of strengths and weaknesses, perhaps even possess a natural affinity for each other, is it possible that a state in which they can permanently coexist can be developed. This, in fact, is what we have attempted to do with the formation of our module teams (see Figures 6-22 and 6-23). In the hybrid system formed by integrating these module teams into our existing organization, the classic structure remains in its original form. It is still there to provide stability, continuity, and order, but its negative attributes of inertia, unresponsiveness to change, limited communication traffic capability, and long cycle-time decision making are compensated for by the module teams. Like task forces, these teams are task focused, multi-disciplined, self-sufficient, and self-managing but differ in that they are neither transitory nor reactionary. Neither are they simply committees, whose grist is discussion and whose output is policy, but agents of change, prime movers, whose mandate is analysis and action. Forming covalent bonds as it were within the organizational structure, the module teams are, in a manner of speaking, the cement binding the functional bricks into a cohesive whole.

MANUFACTURING EXCELLENCE FOR TOTAL CUSTOMER SATISFACTION

Manufacturing System Subcomponents

1. **Manufacturing Engineering:**

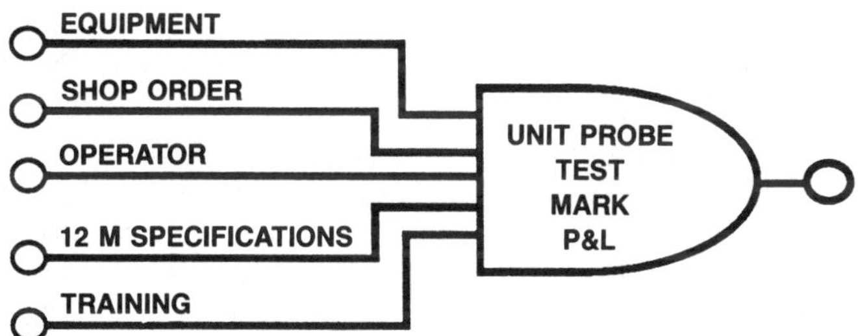

A. **Customer:** The Unit Managers

B. **Charter:** Making the Best Use of What We Have

C. **Expected Output:** (The ingredients of total customer satisfaction)—A production worthy, value adding process complement under statistical process control

D. **Scope:** A central service to all modules including the unit probe, test, mark, and P&L operations

E. **Functional Method:** A "bundling" operation to take:

(1) a piece of equipment
(2) a process of 12 M specification
(3) a product shop order
(4) an operator
(5) appropriate training—and **integrate** these ingredients to produce the expected output.

F. **Required Inputs:**

External:

(1) Equipment from MTD group
(2) Shop order form product engineering
(3) Operator from Unit Manager

Intrinsic:

(1) 12 M equipment process specification
(2) Operator training
(3) Statistical process control methodology

ORGANIZATION AS A TASK FOCUSED SYSTEM

In January 1988, we most convincingly demonstrated to ourselves (and others), the module concepts' ability to provide three (quality, cost, and on-time delivery) of the five ingredients of total customer satisfaction. This was done in a mutually inclusive way, across a wide product portfolio, to a large customer base. We are now continuing to develop and enhance the evolution of this concept, building on what we now know works, to solve the problem of dealing with the fourth ingredient of total customer satisfaction—that of absorbing new technology into the manufacturing system. While the module concept works extremely well on reasonably mature products, even this highly focused approach has difficulty dealing with the challenge of absorbing new products, processes, equipment, and packages into production without faltering. Our approach in dealing with this is based on the view that the major problem in bringing technological innovation to the marketplace is more a function of organizational inadequacy rather than of the difficulties inherent in any new technology per se. As we discussed earlier, most organizational structures are built (usually in disregard of the task required of them), either from the bottom up or from the top down, in a hierarchical, pyramid of power, whose main purpose is to perpetuate the existing order rather than to manage change, such as that which new technology epitomizes. The tasks as defined by these boxes are then staffed—matching tasks required to be done to skills available—and then somehow "bolting" this, usually less than elegantly, on to the manufacturing system. In effect, this organization structure becomes to all intents and purposes, the system, with all of its white space and functional parochiality and not surprisingly, usually has difficulty fulfilling the task required. fulfilling the task required.

We departed from this classical approach in that we defined the desired end-result first and then designed the manufacturing system we thought best able to produce this. (See Figure 6-24.) We extended this approach into the subcomponents of the system, defining the expected output of each of these in terms of the ingredients of total customer satisfaction (see Figure 6-25) and then used these system subcomponents as system building blocks. (An example of subsystem component design is shown in Figure 6-26.)

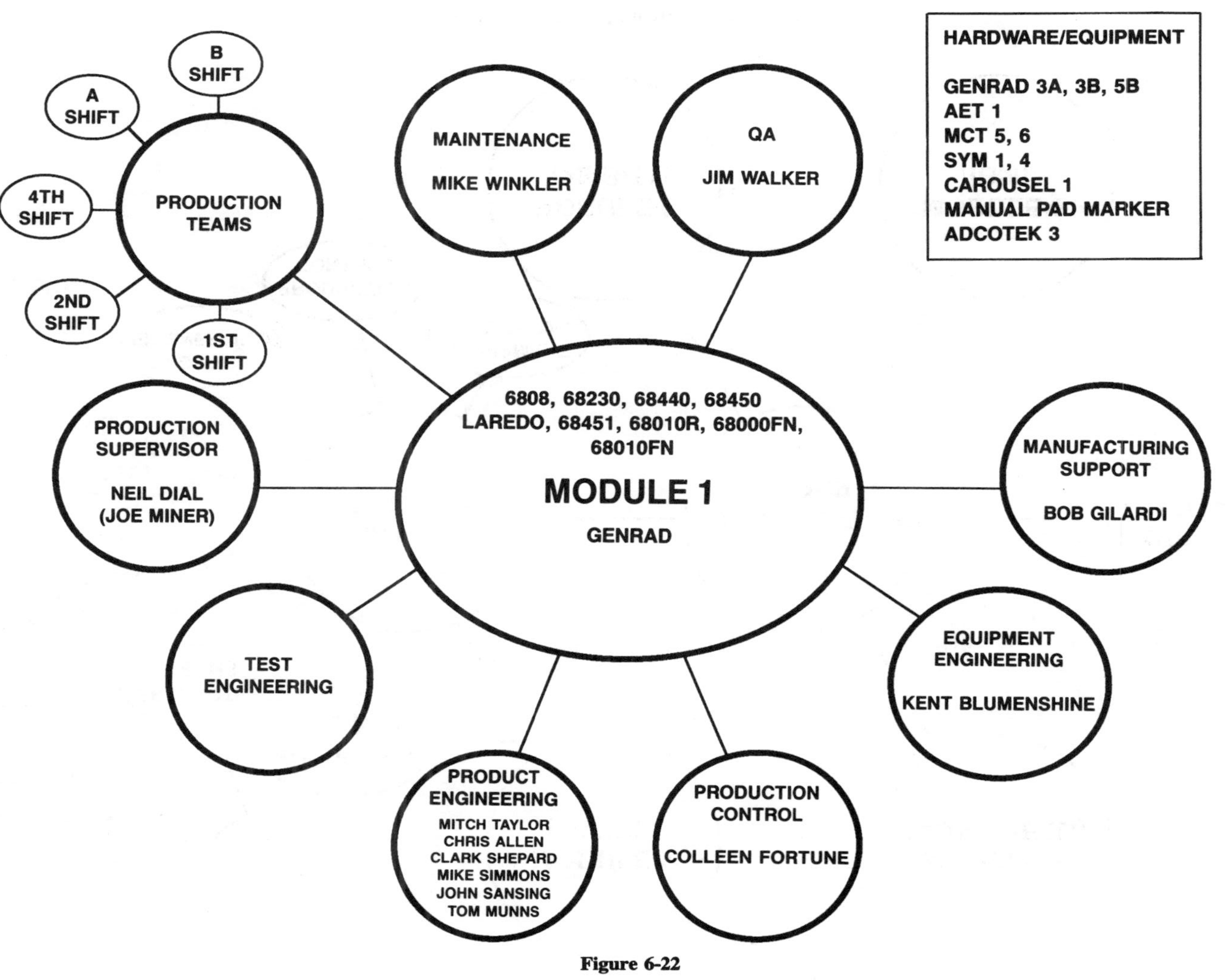
HARDWARE/EQUIPMENT
GENRAD 3A, 3B, 5B
AET 1
MCT 5, 6
SYM 1, 4
CAROUSEL 1
MANUAL PAD MARKER
ADCOTEK 3
B SHIFT
A SHIFT
4TH SHIFT
2ND SHIFT
1ST SHIFT
PRODUCTION TEAMS
MAINTENANCE
MIKE WINKLER
QA
JIM WALKER
6808, 68230, 68440, 68450
LAREDO, 68451, 68010R, 68000FN,
68010FN
MODULE 1
GENRAD
PRODUCTION SUPERVISOR
NEIL DIAL
(JOE MINER)
MANUFACTURING SUPPORT
BOB GILARDI
TEST ENGINEERING
EQUIPMENT ENGINEERING
KENT BLUMENSHINE
PRODUCT ENGINEERING
MITCH TAYLOR
CHRIS ALLEN
CLARK SHEPARD
MIKE SIMMONS
JOHN SANSING
TOM MUNNS
PRODUCTION CONTROL
COLLEEN FORTUNE

Figure 6-22

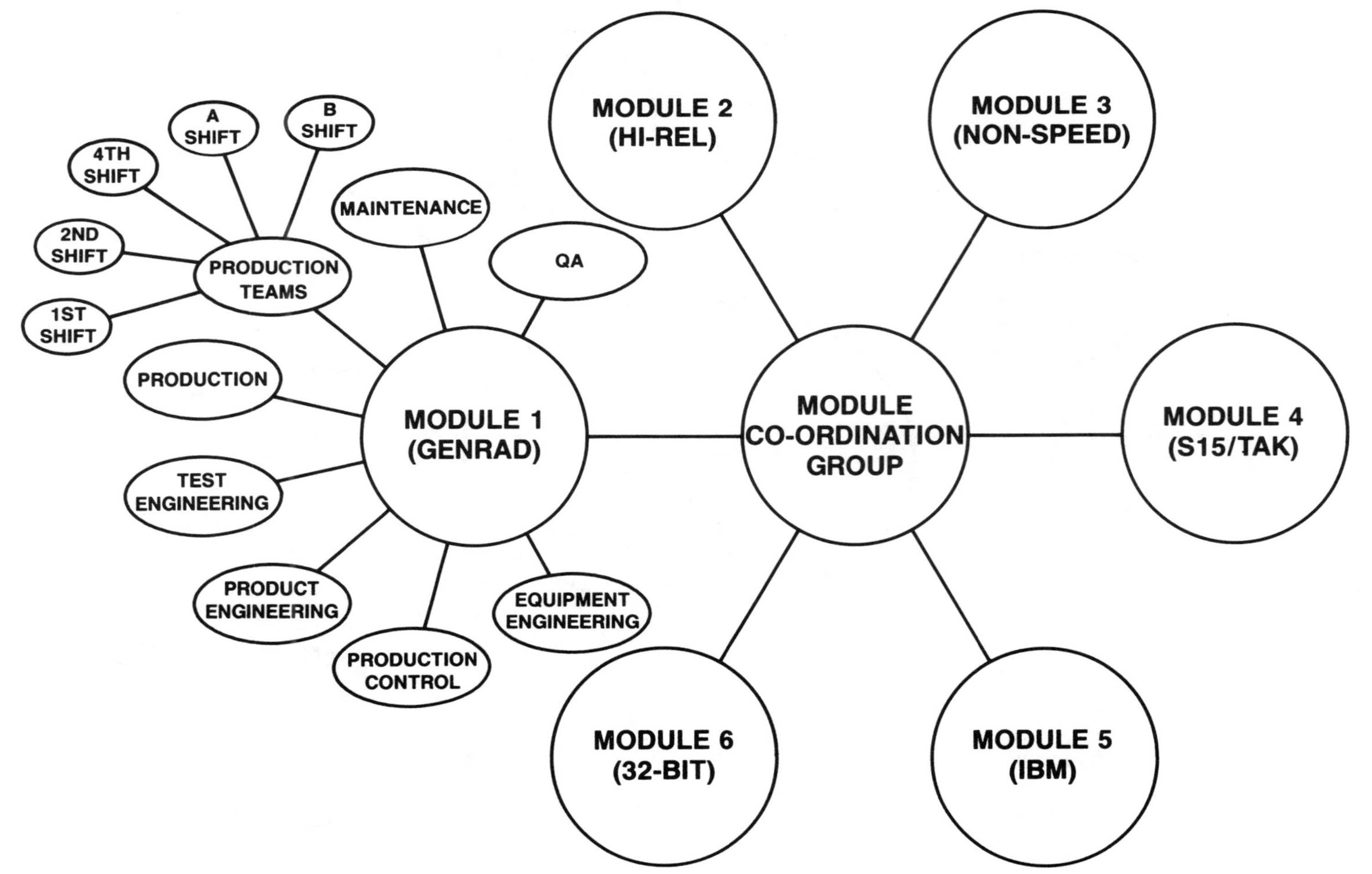

Figure 6-23 PMP—As It Was Meant To Be?

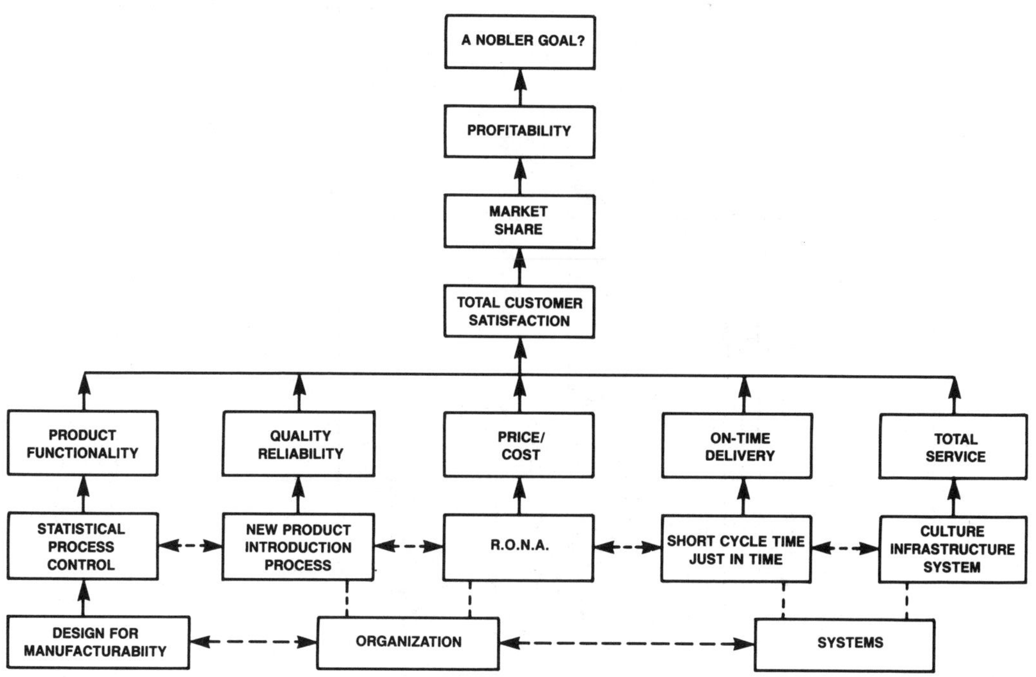

Figure 6-24 Strategic Hierarchy

Figure 6-25 Manufacturing Excellence for Total Customer Satisfaction

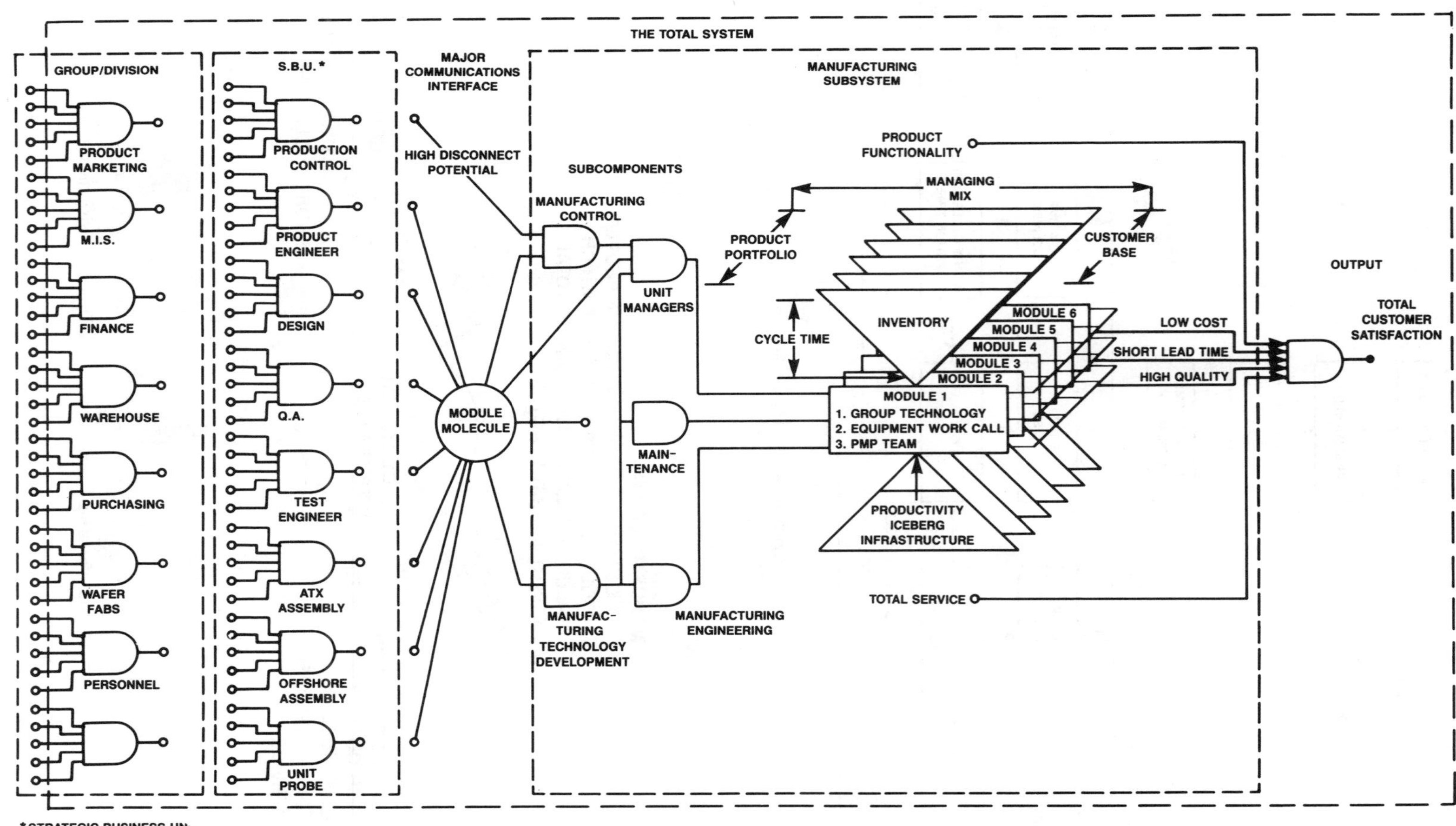

Figure 6-26 Manufacturing Excellence for Total Customer Satisfaction

Only then did we address the design of the people organizational structure most compatible with this. In effect, we worked back from the point where the system can be defined in the least ambiguous way, the desired output, then migrated backwards through each subcomponent, deep into the system infrastructure. This approach helps to ensure that controversial decisions are made against the criteria of "what makes best sense" for the system and each subcomponent, in terms of the desired end result, rather than that of self-interest and personal preference. The methodology of this approach can be summarized as follows:

STEP 1. Define the desired end result in terms of the ingredients of total customer satisfaction for:

A. The total system or subsystem.

B. The major subcomponents within the system or subsystem.

STEP 2. Design the system to best achieve this desired end result, working back from the output. (Define the desired end result for each subcomponent. Identify who is the intermediate, internal customer of each subcomponent. What are the ingredients of total satisfaction for this customer?)

STEP 3. Define each subcomponent in detail, including:

Its charter
Expected output
Scope
Functional method
Inputs required
Required skills mix

STEP 4. Agree on ownership: assign individuals to subcomponents.

STEP 5. Link subcomponent inputs and outputs: identify any real or potential communication disconnects (white space).

STEP 6. Match tasks to skills available. Identify subcomponents without names/names without subcomponents and skills shortfall.

STEP 7. Design people organizational structure most compatible with the system. (To all intents and purposes, this should be the subcomponent hierarchy.)

STEP 8. Develop infrastructure implementation plan.

STEP 9. Develop potentially surplus resources redeployment plan.

STEP 10. Develop human resources training and development plan.

Perhaps worthy of particular mention are our manufacturing engineering and manufacturing technology development subcomponents. These two functions, in conjunction with maintenance, formerly constituted our fairly classical, equipment engineering department. The expected output or desired end result we are trying to optimize in restructuring and aligning these subcomponents as we have are:

1. To allow the manufacturing subcomponent to be as self-sufficient as possible in running day-to-day operations.

2. To allow the manufacturing engineering subcomponent to focus its primary thrust on "making best use of what we already have." Integrating the ingredients necessary, the equipment, the process specification, the product specification, the operator, the training component, into a self-sufficient, self-contained productive entity under statistical process control. With this defined in terms of Cpk, which can be "plugged" into the manufacturing process as a fait accomplis rather than engineering it in situ in production as has historically been the case. To facilitate this, we considered it necessary to free it of the maintenance burden, now a stand-alone subcomponent, and to protect it from the time-consuming distractions of the "red herrings" or immaturity of new technology. The manufacturing technology development subcomponent serves this latter purpose by screening new technology prior to releasing it to its primary, internal customer.

3. To facilitate a smooth transition of new technology into the manufacturing system—new products, packages, processes, equipment, and so on—either instigated by our SBU development groups, design, equipment OEMs, or product engineering, or initiated by the manufacturing technology development group itself. While we expect only small but very frequent improvements in our existing manufacturing process from the manufacturing engineering group, over a continuum of time, the charter of the manufacturing technology development group is to produce radical, albeit much less frequent, step function improvements by identifying or developing technology whose capability spectrum, defined in terms of Cp, begins where our existing manufacturing technology ends. Since the manufacturing engineering subcomponent is this groups internal custom, it must be convinced of the potential production worthiness of this new technology by this group.

Consistent with the principle of measuring all subcomponents in the same parameters as measured by the "customer," all subcomponents within the system are measured in terms of quality, cost, and on-time (cycle-time) delivery. Although, while it is relatively easy to define and measure the expected output of product producing functions in these terms, others less directly involved in this process are measured in terms of operating or project budget costs and projected completion date time milestones.

WHERE DO WE GO FROM HERE?

The Manufacturing Continuum

Of the eight possible approaches to manufacturing (shown in Figure 6-27) each have their individual merits—but none unfortunately, has all of the attributes required to satisfy the needs of world class manufacturing—high quality, low cost, short lead time—over a mix of products, of different lot sizes, with different flows, methods, equipment, and so on. At one extreme, we have the project and job shop approach, with extremely high flexibility, but lacking in almost all other attributes. At the other extreme, we have continuous flow, clearly well endowed with the potential at least, to score highly in all attributes—except flexiblity. This approach, we know already, is usually single model/single process and cannot readily accommodate mix or volume perturbations, or different lot sizes, methods, and so on. It is manufacturing management's challenge to develop hybrid solutions, combining the best characteristics of all of these approaches in striving towards **flexible, continuous flow, zero defect processing**. Like perfection, this goal will never be completely realized, but it can be asymptotically approached. Focused factories are one such hybrid compromise towards this objective. Focused factories are not predicated on some recently discovered or developed, radically new manufacturing

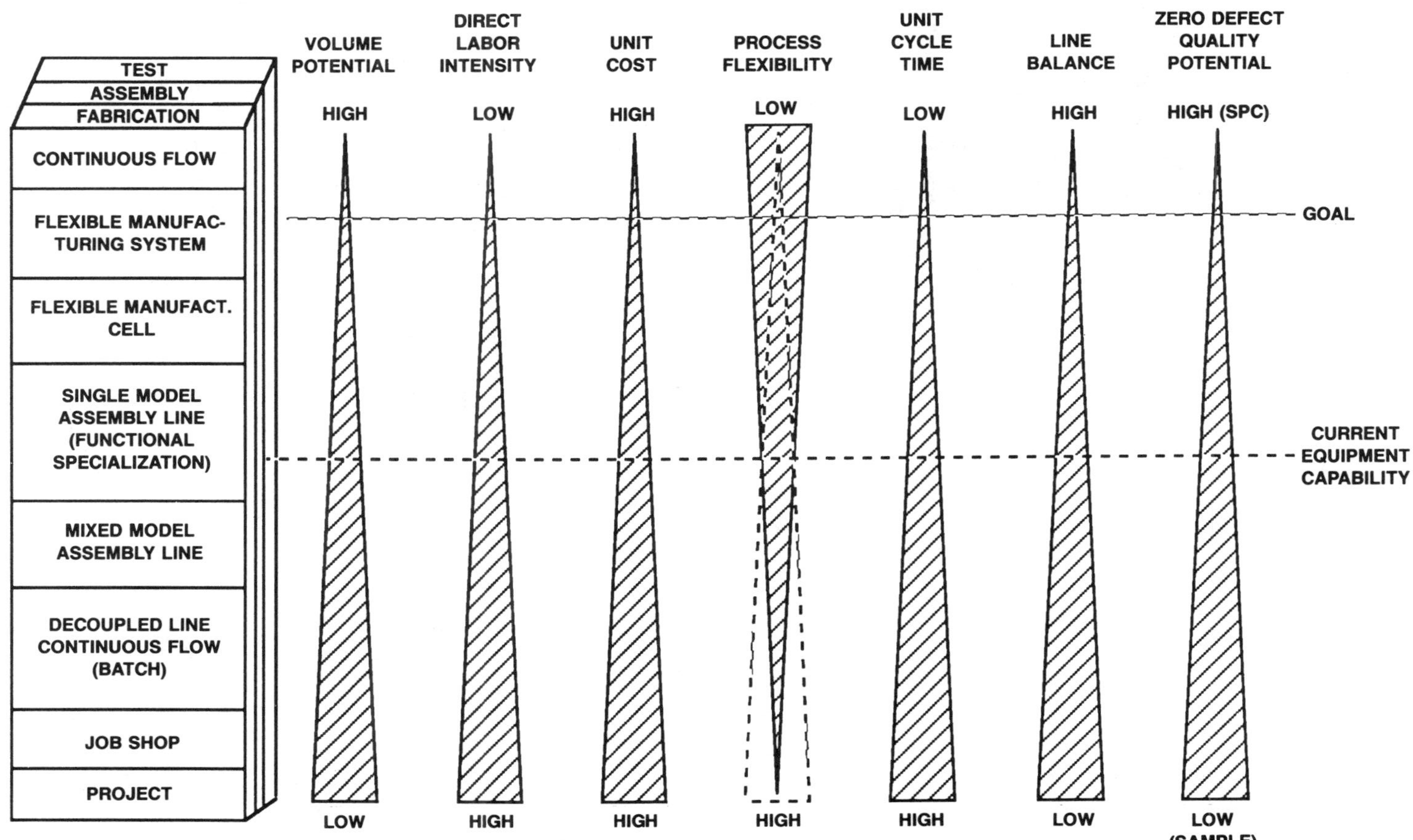

Figure 6-27 The Manufacturing Continuum Process Attributes

principle. They are predicated on nothing more than common sense. If the matrix of variables is too large to handle, with different product flows, methods, or equipment changes, it must surely make sense to treat this portfolio as groups of products with from a manufacturing point of view, in order to make the mix more manageable.

While focused factories or modules, as we have chosen to describe these small factories within a factory, are a distinct improvement over the functional approach to manufacturing, they are an intermediate rather than an ultimate solution in the journey towards world-class manufacturing.

The holy grail of manufacturing is **flexible, continuous flow, zero defect processing**. The search for this is the mission of manufacturing management, taking the form of evolutionary, rather than revolutionary incremental developments up the manufacturing continuum towards this goal. The quest has parallels to that of developing competence in SPC, the difference being that in SPC, steps are taken to insulate the process from undesirable variability. In flexible, continuous flow manufacturing, the challenge is to accommodate desired variability in mix, volume, lot size changes, and so on without missing a beat.

The integrated manufacturing cell, the next evolutionary step beyond modules, represents the harnessing of the best attributes of all of these approaches in which, for a range within the manufacturing continuum, the desired end result—high quality, 100 percent on-time delivery, and low cost, across a mix of products with different lot sizes and product flows, and so on—is not compromised. The process of moving up this continuum continues beyond the integrated manufacturing cell with flexible manufacturing cells, ultimately arriving at integrated arrangements of these cells in the form of a flexible manufacturing system.

Why An Integrated Manufacturing Cell?

To understand why it is necessary to develop and build these integrated manufacturing cells for the back end processes in semiconductor manufacturing, we must first accept that all manufacturing takes place on a continuum ranging from project through/job shop/ decoupled line flow/mixed model assembly line/to flexible continuous flow, as depicted graphically in Figure 6-27. Next we must understand, based on this spectrum of manufacturing processes, where on the continuum we must operate. Our contention is that our highly proliferate product portfolio requires that we must operate between job shop and mixed model mode assembly line. The following is a brief discussion which brings us to this realization.

Mixed Model Assembly Line

Each MC68000 product, for example, will have a different speed sort and marking, yet all move down an assembly line according to a predetermined sequence. An analogy might be GM producing midsized Oldsmobiles, each having a different color, engine, and options, yet all moving down a single conveyorized assembly line according to a predetermined sequence.

Decoupled Line Flow

When we change over from product A to product B—MC68000 to MC68010 for example—we are operating in a **decoupled line flow process**, defined as essentially standardized batch mode. This process is generally adopted when a business has developed a relatively stable line of products, each of which is produced periodically in batches, of different lot sizes, to customer order. Most of these products follow the same flow pattern within the factory. The volume of each model of products is not sufficient to justify specialized, dedicated equipment for any single class of product, yet it enables the business to use a process that is more specialized than job shop mode.

Job Shop

When we change over from a PGA package to a dual-in-line or quad pack, we operate as a job shop. Any single product or job may use only a small part of the production system's resources in skills or equipment. Some processing steps may require such a large capital investment (e.g., an LSI tester) that one can justify incorporating them into the facility only if they can be used in the production of many products.

Accepting the area of the continuum in which we operate, we realized we must now develop a manufacturing strategy which allowed us to operate as efficiently as possible within this range. In the past we have mainly focussed our attention on optimizing the job shop. We must now address optimization of decoupled line flow and mixed model assembly line if we are to continue to reduce manufacturing costs and achieve manufacturing competitiveness. The integrated manufacturing cell is the vehicle we intend to use to address optimization of decoupled line flow and mixed model assembly line.

Our existing job shop, while enhanced with manual implementation of decoupled line flow, seldom produced actual productivity greater than 30 percent of theoretical equipment ability. The 70 percent loss in productivity is due to many factors, such as long set-up times, frequent jamming of handling equipment, high rework requirements, and the inability to develop an efficient scheduling system which can run such a complex proliferation of product and flows—all in a modified job shop mode. To address the problem, we first defined the kind of a system needed to optimize decoupled line flow and mixed module flow without jeopardizing the flexibility of our job shop mode operation. The system definition evolved as follows:

1. Integrate the most common product flow in our product portfolio but have the flexibility to change in the future. The product flow which would encompass the largest unit volume in our factory is shown in Figure 6-28.

The addition of a lead inspect as a first step is essential to obtain low jam rates. We will sort rejects to a lead straighten rework bin immediately after lead inspect. An additional benefit to this flow will be to monitor incoming material and ultimately improve incoming quality by providing quantitative feedback to the assembly sites.

2. The changeover/set-up time when operating in either mixed model mode or decoupled line flow will be under ten minutes. Mixed model flow only involves mark changeover and possibly test program reload. We chose to incorporate a multiple pad marking scheme which allows the ink mix and cliche change to be an external set-up and reduces internal set-up time to less than **two** minutes. This process has also shown to yield high quality mark definition and good permanency results when using a two part epoxy ink. The possible test program reload can occur simultaneously with the mark changeover.

Decoupled line flow will be the same scenario as mixed model changeover with the addition of load board changes on both test sites. Using quick connect interfacing between the test head and test site, changeover will be less than **three** minutes per test site.

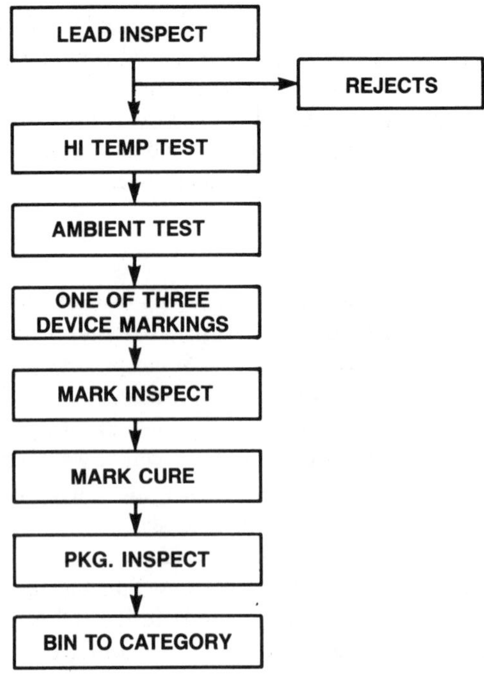

Figure 6-28

3. Changeover/set-up time when operating as a job shop will be kept to a minimum—understanding that there will be cost of equipment design to manufacturing cost trade offs. Depending on complexity, the time will vary from 30 minutes to a maximum of one eight hour shift. The key here is to understand what elements of the changeover require the most time and how to make as many of the modules within the cell multi-function. This necessarily leads to a discussion of the possible configurations of the integrated manufacturing cell. The transport of devices from module to module will, to a large degree, determine how flexible the cell is and how long a changeover will take. The transport system, where ever possible, needs to be mechanically universal, requiring only minor to no changes in hardware and a cell program reload to accommodate a package change. Hardware changeovers would be minimized if pick and place equipment was used to position the parts. Device nests and end of arm effectors can be multidevice tooled thus eliminating hardware changeover in some cases. It is likely that 10 × 10 PGA, 13 × 13 PGA, LCC, and possibly PLCC packages can be accommodated with one set of tooling using this approach. All DIL could be accommodated with an alternate set of tooling. The major portion of a changeover could then be accomplished with software.

There are however other approaches to transport functions such as rail feeds, walking beams, rotary tables, and so on. These would no doubt be more mechanically involved changeovers, but software development becomes a much simpler task. The potential tradeoff will be cost versus flexibiity and changeover time. As far as making the modules within the cell able to accommodate a number of different packages is concerned, the input, lead inspect, mark, mark inspect, and package inspect should be an order of magnitude simpler than the controlled environment test sites.

4. The jam rate for the entire integration will be less than 1 in 10,000 units. There are three main areas that classically cause jams which this system addresses. Addition of a lead inspect and sort as a first operation will eliminate jams due to devices with bent leads in the system. The elimination of gravity feed and designing the system around all positive positioning mechanisms will eliminate jams caused by random positioning and movement—a major problem with the type of equipment used today.

This system will be designed to achieve a 1200 UPH (3 sec cycle rate)—a very conservative number for most operations at today's standards. At 1200 UPH many of the jamming problems associated with handling devices at higher speeds are minimized.

Note: While these rates may seem slow when comparing them to some equipment used today, one must remember that during decoupled line flow and mixed model assembly line modes, 1200 UPH represents the aggregate of all of the operations in the process of converting raw stock to finished goods, an overall, aggregate rate never before achieved in our back end operation—despite the very high speeds which each isolated island of automation is individually capable.

5. The system will introduce no more than 5 PPM lead or package defects. This is possible primarily because interoperation handling involves no human intervention and equipment jamming will be minimal. (Once again we see that productivity, low cost, and quality are not mutually exclusive.)

6. The system needs to occupy less floor space than today's conventional equipment. (Typically; two handlers, a marker, and lead/pack/mark inspect will occupy 70 square feet and typically 60 percent of the machine will be used for input/output staging.) The integrated manufacturing system has only one input/output and by implementing technology to allow devices to stabilize at temperature in the test environment in a time no greater than two minutes, the design allows for a minimum staging of product in a process between actual operations. The maximum amount of staging required to achieve 1200 UPH will be 20 units. With the previously mentioned information, it does not seem unreasonable to strive for 35 square feet as the design objective for the cell. See Figure 6-29.

7. The operation of the system will be integrated through a main CPU which can be preprogrammed for varying products and will accommodate future CIM/SPC philosophy. Given the future direction of manufacturing, this will ultimately be a mandatory requirement for any equipment intended for production use.

DEVELOPING THE STRATEGIC ALLIANCES

As a company, to facilitate this project we needed to develop a strategic or joint venture relationship with one or more equipment manufacturers. While we have much of the expertise and experience available internally, we also needed to acknowledge that much additional specialized knowledge and expertise exists out of our company. In addition, to reduce a program of this size to practice in less than one year, required more resources than any one company was willing or able to bring to bear in these austere times.

Once we collected our thoughts on why an integrated manufacturing cell was required and what was needed to accomplish it, we focused on how to reduce our concepts to practice in the most timely, cost efficient manner. The options that were most obvious were:

1. Work with a number of manufacturers designing interchangeable operation modules. Use vendors with expertise in each respective operation and select a system integrator and software house. This approach would be very difficult to coordinate and

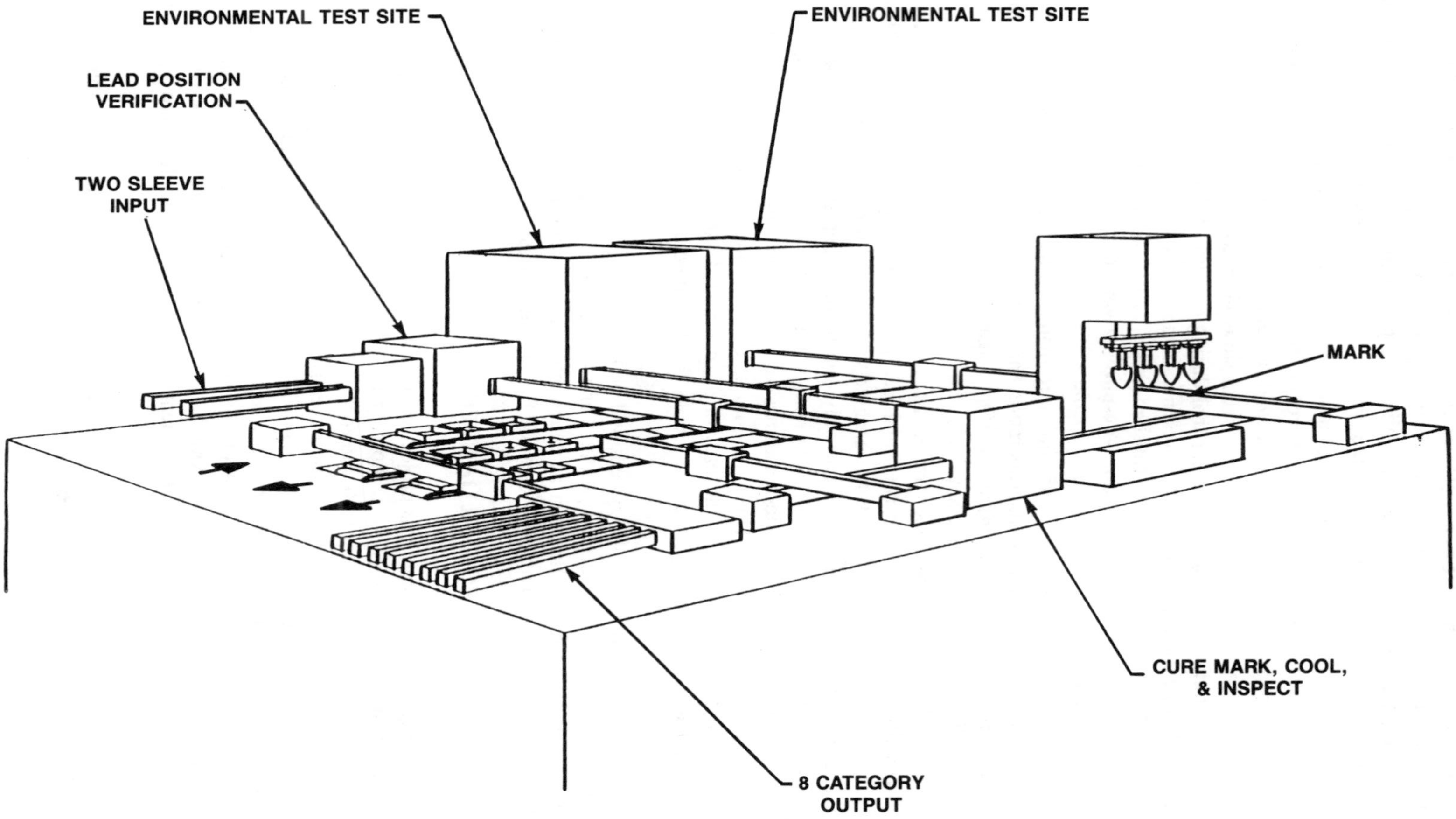

Figure 6-29 Artist Conception of Integrated Manufacturing Cell

held little promise of attracting any vendor on more than a contractual basis. (Nothing in it except a P.O. for the vendors. No potential win/win scenario.)

2. Find one vendor willing to take on the whole project. This approach forces the vendor and us to protect ourselves with rigid specifications and legally enforceable non-disclosure agreements and drives cost up to cover unforeseen pitfalls as there is no end product for the vendor to include in his product portfolio.

3. Identify vendors who have mutual interests in all or portions of this system and therefore an interest in sharing development cost. This approach will tend to develop mutual dedication to its successful completion as the vendor will be developing something that will eventually be part of his standard product portfolio offering in the future. In addition, a program of this type offers the environment for all participating companies to share technology, experience, and expertise. Upon successful completion of a relatively small venture such as this, the foundation is laid for a more encompassing relationship in the future, built on the working relationship and mutual trust developed during the initial cooperative relationship. The advantage to our company is obvious in developing a path which allows us to have manufacturing equipment which won't be available to our competitors for a considerable length of time after we have it in production.

We decided the best way to test our perceptions would be to talk to a number of potential vendors. We needed to present our program to existing equipment manufacturers, both large and small, and we needed to also talk to some competent mechanical engineering and automation houses who have not classically been involved in semiconductor backends. We also made a conscious decision to present only the manufacturing concept and basic design objectives so as not to stifle any creative thinking on the part of the potential vendors. What we presented gave these vendors much more latitude to be creative than in the past. We also presented the program in such a way that it was apparent to them that they were free to be involved with as much or little of the program as they wished. In addition, we asked that they consider what their companies internal plans were and that their proposals attempt to create as much synergy as possible between their programs and ours.

Our initial exploratory contacts included four established test handler manufacturers, varying in size from large to small, two contract mechanical engineering/automation houses, and one automation consultant. All but one vendor received and understood our manufacturing philosophy and were anxious to pursue the program further. As the initial proposals came in, it became obvious that there is even more creativity and talent out there in the marketplace than we had initially envisioned. The initial proposals also showed us that it would not be in our best interest if we continued with vendors totally unfamiliar with semiconductor backend manufacturing. Their lack of experience showed in oversimplified or incompatible approaches to handle "ICs." They had the intrinsic ability, but we felt that the learning curve for them would jeopardize our time schedule. As we continued down the road with the established manufacturers, it became obvious that the very small company was not adequately resourced for a program of this magnitude and consequently would not be likely to evolve as the major long term strategic partner. Ultimately we focused on the two major handler manufacturers. Both companies were allowed to evolve the design conception with us but all information from all vendors was held in strict confidence by us. As it turned out, both companies were interested in developing the test sites, transports, integration, and software and felt more comfortable having us develop multiple pad mark, mark, cure, and vision inspections. We would work with them integrating these operations into the system with them providing the transport mechanism, transport software, and interface. Both proposals evolved in directions having considerable synergy with the vendor's internal programs and this was one of the key elements which allowed us to begin making our decision between the two. Company "A" had an internal program which if we wanted to maintain synergy with would have forced us to compromise some of our initial design objectives. Also their proposal was a test vehicle well on the way to the final system, 18 months down the road.

We favored company "B's" proposal in that it had almost total alignment with our initial objectives and significant synergy with their future plans. Also "B" is smaller than "A" and appeared to be able to make decisions faster and at lower levels. "B" is extremely strong in the software area which we have come to perceive as one of the most important aspects of the manufacturing cells.

Note: Capital dollars involved with "A" or "B" were essentially the same.

The Planned Evolution of the System

In addition to satisfying the initial objectives, the integrated manufacturing cell will have software "hooks and handles" with adequate hardware flexibility to allow an evolution to true, real time, statistical process control (SPC), and ultimately computer integrated manufacturing (CIM). With this system architecture, one can easily envision running control devices or standards intermixed with production product. The ability to do real time, total manufacturing process monitoring will allow us to successfully apply SPC and eliminate the need for any form of QA Gates. With such a process in place, the next stage in the evolution to CIM is a realistically feasible possibility.

ORGANIZATIONAL CONSIDERATIONS IN THE NEXT PHASE IN THE EVOLUTION OF MODULES

For a variety of reasons, we are continuing to steer the evolution of our module concept towards the end result defined in Figure 6-30. Only by carrying the principles of unambiguous ownership and self-sufficiency further can we hope to bring to bear the degree of control in execution necessary to deal with continued strong growth, increasing complexity of products and processes, the increasing proliferation associated with our widening product portfolio as more new products emerge from the engineering phase into production and last, but by no means least, the ever-escalating customer expectations for higher quality, lower cost, and 100 percent on-time delivery across a wide product spectrum and customer base.

All of these goals demand much tighter cross functional communication, more ownership focus, a greater sense of urgency, and even closer control of execution than we have historically been accustomed to. The structure we are proposing is the one which in our opinion best facilitates these needs. One of the main differences between what we are proposing and the way we are currently organized within the test area operation itself, is that the unit supervisors will have vertical responsibility for a unit consisting of two modules through all shifts, rather than horizontal responsibility across all modules—but on one shift only—as at present. This approach, the primary intention of which is to improve shift to shift continuity and consolidate the ownership principle, will not be implemented without difficulty and will require adjustments in both our expectations of our supervisors and possibly even their classification within the job grade structure but, again in our opinion, the advantages will far outway the disadvantages. It is also worth

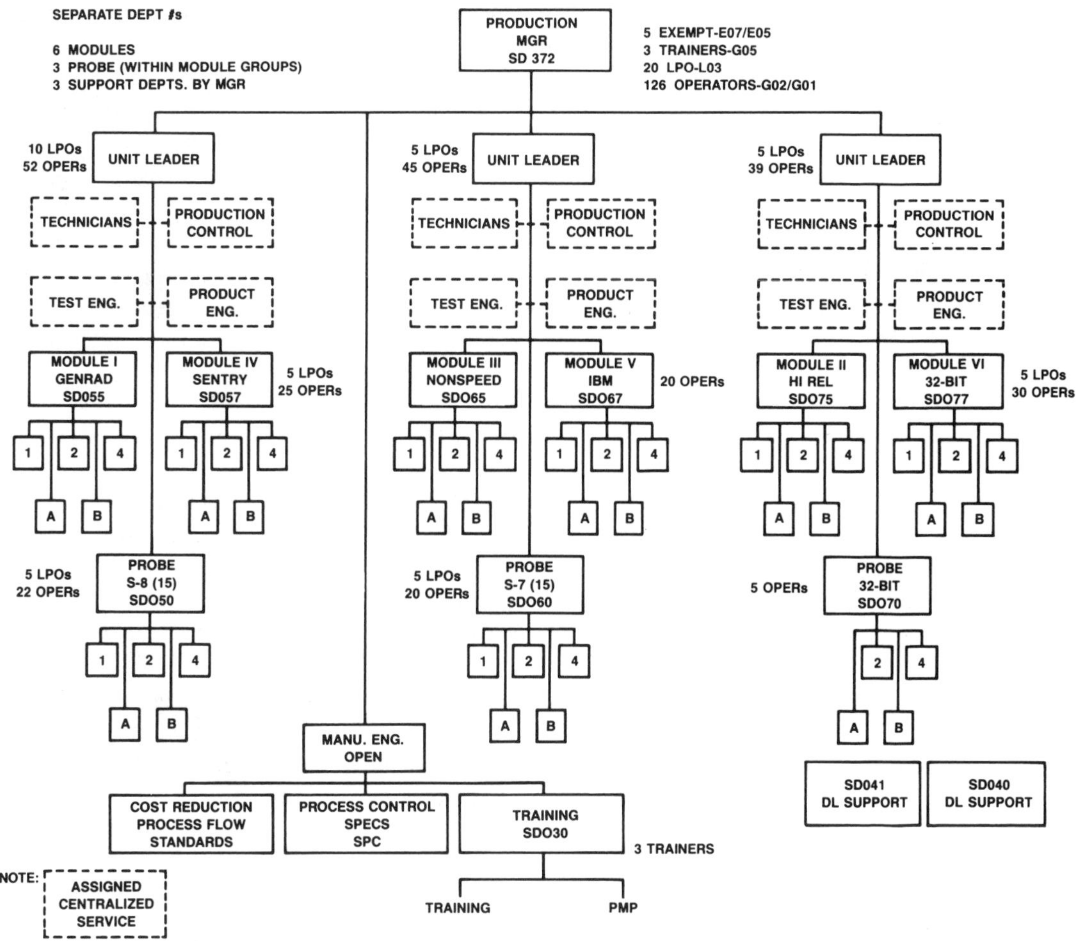

Figure 6-30 Phase II

mentioning that we shall be increasingly more reliant on our "LPOs" (lead production operators—now called group leaders) in this system and this in all fairness, will have to be acknowledged. Apart from the virtually immediate operational benefits, this approach will also provide the career development and increased job satisfaction opportunities that many of our people so richly deserve.

We also need to continue the process of restructuring and modifying the skills mix of our organization in anticipation of successful development, and subsequent implementation of the IMC concept, the first prototype of which will be available to us in 1987–1988. Migrating towards the structure required to support this will obviously not be an overnight transition, but will involve fairly significant redeployment and training, particularly with regard to our maintenance technicians. The first step in this second phase is that of opening up the discussion to a wider group of people with a vested interest in its implementation and ultimate success.

For information purposes only, some general issues/comments are as follows:

1. Unit supervisors will still be required to work shifts, though the operationally preferred schedule will of necessity have to be very flexible and as such not likely to fit into an existing shift pattern.

2. Probe responsibility for the products specific to each module is included in the unit supervisor's responsibility.

3. With regard to improving on-time delivery, we already have a task force consisting of marketing, production control, and manufacturing people addressing this issue. This group is of the opinion that to accept a 100 percent on-time delivery goal to all customers across all products would probably result in a no better than 80 percent actual performance. We obviously cannot be all things to all people and the consensus opinion is that we should focus on a top-ten list of OEMs for each "unit" of two modules for whom 100 percent on-time delivery would be both our goal and hopefully also our actual performance. We would accept, at least initially, an 80 percent goal or better for all of the others. (We need to include product and test engineering in this task force in the near future.)

4. The three "units" are not universal in their degree of difficulty, complexity, and strategic importance and this will be reflected in the skills and grade level classification of each of the respective unit supervisors.

5. We need to resolve those support roles which can and must be assigned on a dedicated basis and those which as a matter of practical of necessity must remain as a central service. For example, we foresee maintenance technicians, while remaining part of the equipment engineering group, would be dedicated and assigned by module (or unit) while process and equipment engineering would remain as a centralized service to all three units.

6. It is probably far too much to expect that our product and test engineers would ever be available on a shift coverage basis to provide fastest possible resolution of product problems encountered spontaneously and sporadically on the off-shifts. In the absence of this, they must be closely focused by module on day shift at least.

The Measurement System Profit and Loss Accounting and Semiconductor Economics

7

Components and Structure of P&L Operating Statement

In a standard cost accounting system, we are required to forecast what we think our performance will be in a given period. We are not asked to forecast what we **would like** to happen or **needs** to happen or **might** happen—but what we think **will** happen, or be **made** to happen!

This forecast then becomes a criteria against which we are measured (**setting our own objectives**).

At the end of the period, **actual** performance is compared to **forecasted** performance, and **variations** are then quantified in relation to several criteria:

1. Actual to forecast
2. Actual to budget
3. Actual to worldwide standard
4. Actual to local standard

Note: The highest volume producer's local standard is also worldwide standard. Lower volume producers are required to set local standards acknowledging their lower volume.

There are two major elements in an operating statement: profit and loss (P&L).

1. Billings (revenue, income)
2. Costs (expenditure, cash outlay, costs incurred)

We will analyze each of these in terms of their constituent parts, examine how they are treated in a standard cost accounting system, and identify which variations are quantified.

We may not be held accountable in the short term for a bad P&L result; e.g., due to inadequate sales (economic downturn, low backlog).

We are held accountable for the **accuracy** of the forecast.

In this respect, we want as few **adverse variations** as possible in order not to rely on **compensating errors**.

Table 7-1 Billings Analysis

	Forecast			Actual			Variance			Type
	Units	ASP	Total	Units	ASP	Total	Units	ASP	Total	
Device 1	1000	3.5	3500	500	3.5	1750	-500	0	-1750	Volume
Device 2	500	6.0	3000	500	5.8	2900	0	-0.2	-100	ASP
Device 3	2000	1.2	2400	3000	1.0	3000	+1000	-0.2	+600	VOL/ASP
Device 4	100	2.5	250	50	2.4	120	-50	-0.1	-130	VOL/ASP

Table 7-2 Variations

1. Volume	— Higher or lower actual than forecast (quantum effect)
2. ASP	— Higher or lower actual than forecast (quantum effect)
3. Device Mix	— Different mix of product sold than forecast
4. Package Mix	— Different quantity of package type by device
5. Exchange Rates	— Set prices in dollars, income in basket of mixed currencies
6. DPP	— Distributor price protection
7. DSR	— Distributor sale or return protection
8. RMR	— Credit issued to customer for reject product
9. Inflation	— Varying purchasing power of currencies

Accounting systems do not necessarily provide this analysis (automatically).

COST GROUPING AND VARIATIONS IN MARGIN 1

In a standard cost accounting system **inventoriable costs** are grouped into labor, material, and overhead costs. Standard costs are costs which should be realized: i.e., achievable goals.

Worldwide standard costs are set by facility producing highest volume: i.e., most cost effective for comparison between different locations. Local **standard** costs are set by local facilities: i.e., their own particular most cost effective forecast.

Differences between worldwide standard costs and local standard costs result in **"procedural variations."**

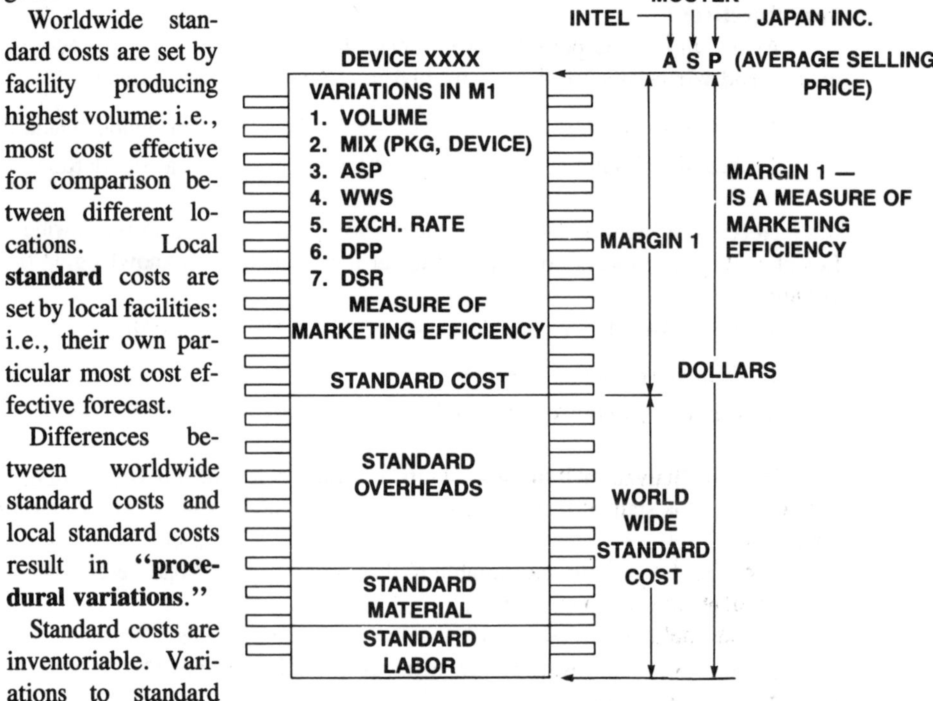

Standard costs are inventoriable. Variations to standard costs are not valued in inventory but are a debit from the operating statement at the time of occurrence.

Standards are set for six month periods, perhaps October–March, April–September, for example. Should be achieved, **on average**, during the period.

ACTUAL OR M2 (MARGIN 2) COSTS

M2 costs are costs **actually** incurred in producing the product. M2 costs are a measure of **manufacturing** efficiency.

The desired end result is for **manufacturing efficiency** to be such that M2 inventoriable costs = standard costs: i.e., for M2 to equal M1. Differences result in favorable or adverse variations (usually adverse). However, some M2 costs are expected and normal and are not inventoriable: e.g., freight/duty. M2 therefore can never exactly equal M1.

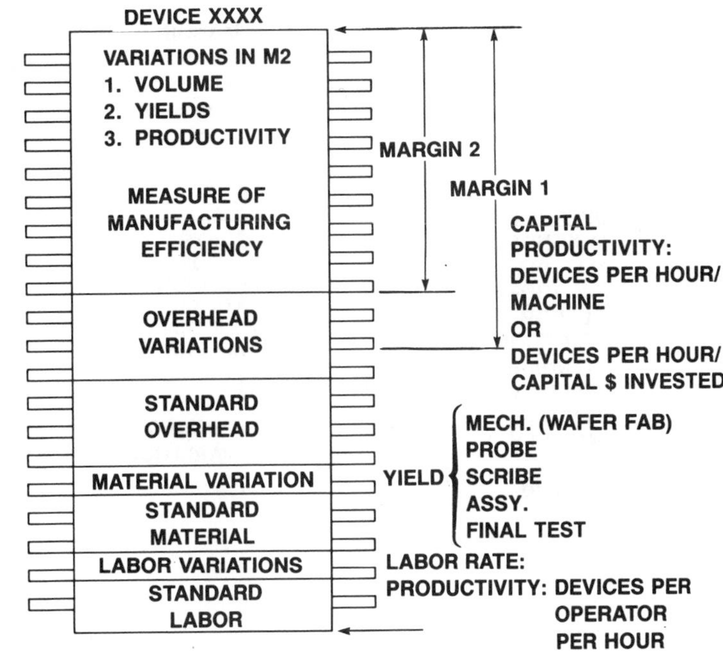

M2 costs are **factory costs**—Do not include product engineering, product marketing, design, etc.

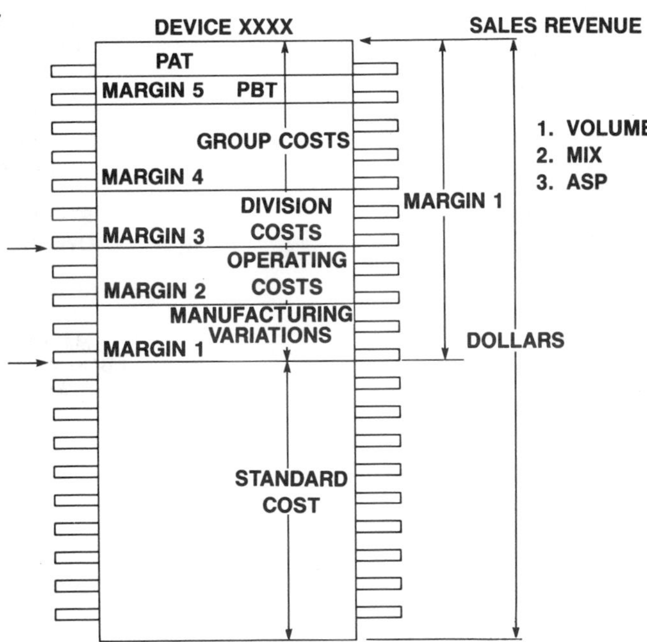

Margin 1—(sales revenue—standard cost of sales)

Standard cost of sales—cost at which product should be manufactured set by major supplier.

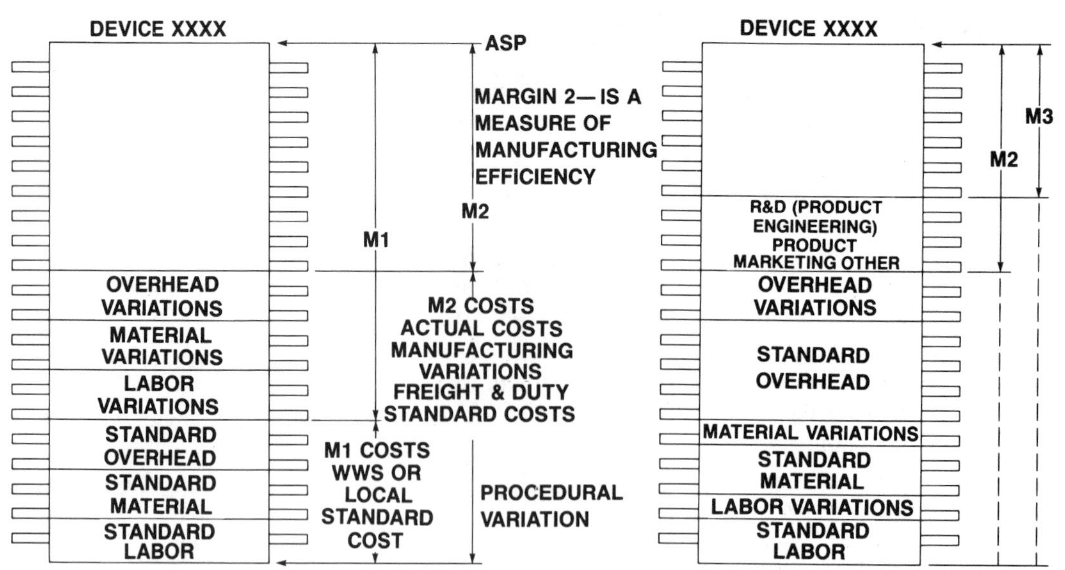
DEVICE XXXX
ASP
MARGIN 2—IS A
MEASURE OF
MANUFACTURING
EFFICIENCY
M1
M2
OVERHEAD VARIATIONS
MATERIAL VARIATIONS
LABOR VARIATIONS
STANDARD OVERHEAD
STANDARD MATERIAL
STANDARD LABOR
M2 COSTS
ACTUAL COSTS
MANUFACTURING
VARIATIONS
FREIGHT & DUTY
STANDARD COSTS
M1 COSTS
WWS OR
LOCAL
STANDARD
COST
PROCEDURAL
VARIATION
DEVICE XXXX
M3
M2
R&D (PRODUCT ENGINEERING) PRODUCT MARKETING OTHER
OVERHEAD VARIATIONS
STANDARD OVERHEAD
MATERIAL VARIATIONS
STANDARD MATERIAL
LABOR VARIATIONS
STANDARD LABOR

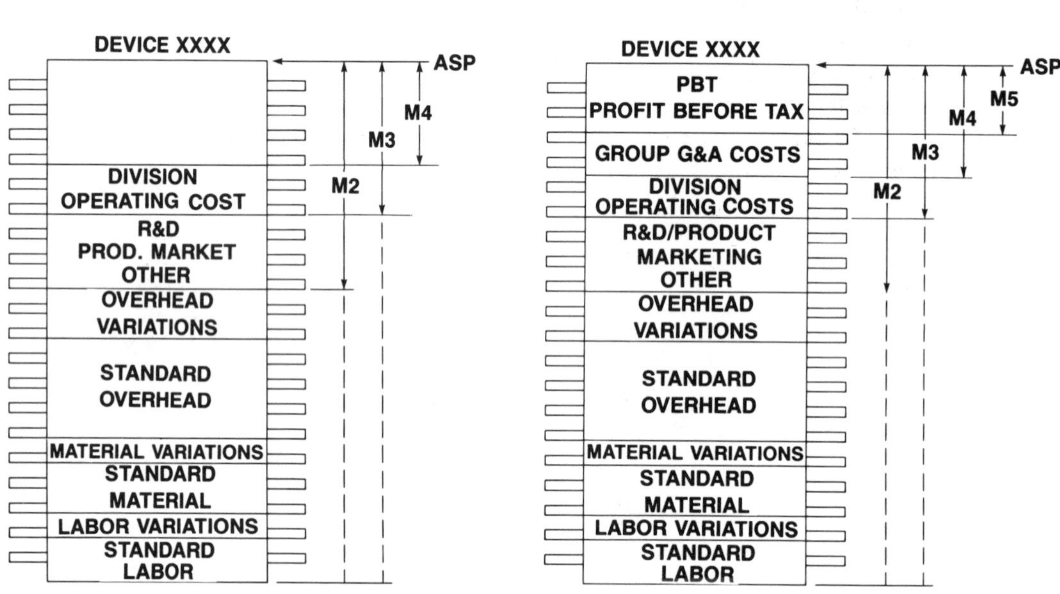
DEVICE XXXX
ASP
M4
M3
M2
DIVISION OPERATING COST
R&D PROD. MARKET OTHER
OVERHEAD VARIATIONS
STANDARD OVERHEAD
MATERIAL VARIATIONS
STANDARD MATERIAL
LABOR VARIATIONS
STANDARD LABOR
DEVICE XXXX
ASP
M5
M4
M3
M2
PBT
PROFIT BEFORE TAX
GROUP G&A COSTS
DIVISION OPERATING COSTS
R&D/PRODUCT MARKETING OTHER
OVERHEAD VARIATIONS
STANDARD OVERHEAD
MATERIAL VARIATIONS
STANDARD MATERIAL
LABOR VARIATIONS
STANDARD LABOR

Worldwide Standard (WWS)	Set by factory producing highest volume **on the assumption** that it will be the most efficient. Set for major manufacturing criteria, such as probe yield, final test yield etc., giving rise to worldwide standard cost: e.g., finished goods, raw stock, die. For major facility—worldwide standard is their **local standard**.
Local Standard	Set by subsidiary on same basis as major producer—reflects local expected performance. **Self-imposed "goals"** against which measurement can be made.

In both cases, standards are set for six month periods, usually **April to September** and **October to March**. Confidence in meeting them should be virtually 100 percent. A minimum acceptable realistically achievable yardstick met with high confidence, **on average**, over the six-month period.

Ideally, there should be an upward trend from one standards period to another to reflect planned improvement. (Again ideally, actual performance will be less than standard for first three months and greater than standard for next three months.) A standard should not be based on historical performance plus 10 percent improvement. It should be based on what is theoretically possible minus some small allowance for life's imperfections.

Forecasts	A "standard" is in effect a **long-term forecast**. But forecasting is an inexact "science" and the further out, the less exact. Forecasts are therefore introduced to: 1. Allow for "fine-tuning" within the standards period to accommodate short-term and, hopefully temporary, perturbations. 2. Allow future performance criteria to be set for those activities which, for obvious reasons, standards are not set: e.g., bookings, billings, RMRs, accruals against which actual performance can be measured.
Goals	A goal is neither a standard nor a forecast, both of which are **best assessments** of **what we think will happen**. A goal is an aspiration of what we **would like** or may **need to happen**. **Goals do not feature, and should not feature, in a P&L forecast.**

For example, on a particular device, the WWS cost for finished goods may be $2, the local standard $3. But we may, if the market ASP is $2, have a product cost goal of $1, realizing this goal may be the only alternative to not selling this product. A goal, therefore, should have an associated action plan to achieve it—**out with the P&L forecast**. See Figure 7-1.

Actual Performance

At the end of the relevant accounting period, actual performance (now history) is quantified and compared to local standard, WWS, budget and forecasts.

Variations (favorable or adverse) are also quantified/explained and their effects factored into the P&L **and** inventory accounts.

SUMMARY

- Margin 1—Net sales less total standard cost of sales
- Margin 2—Margin 1 less total manufacturing variation, freight, duty
- Margin 3—Margin 2 less total inventoriable, operating expense
- Margin 4—Margin 3 less division operating expense
- Margin 5—Margin 4 less group operating expense

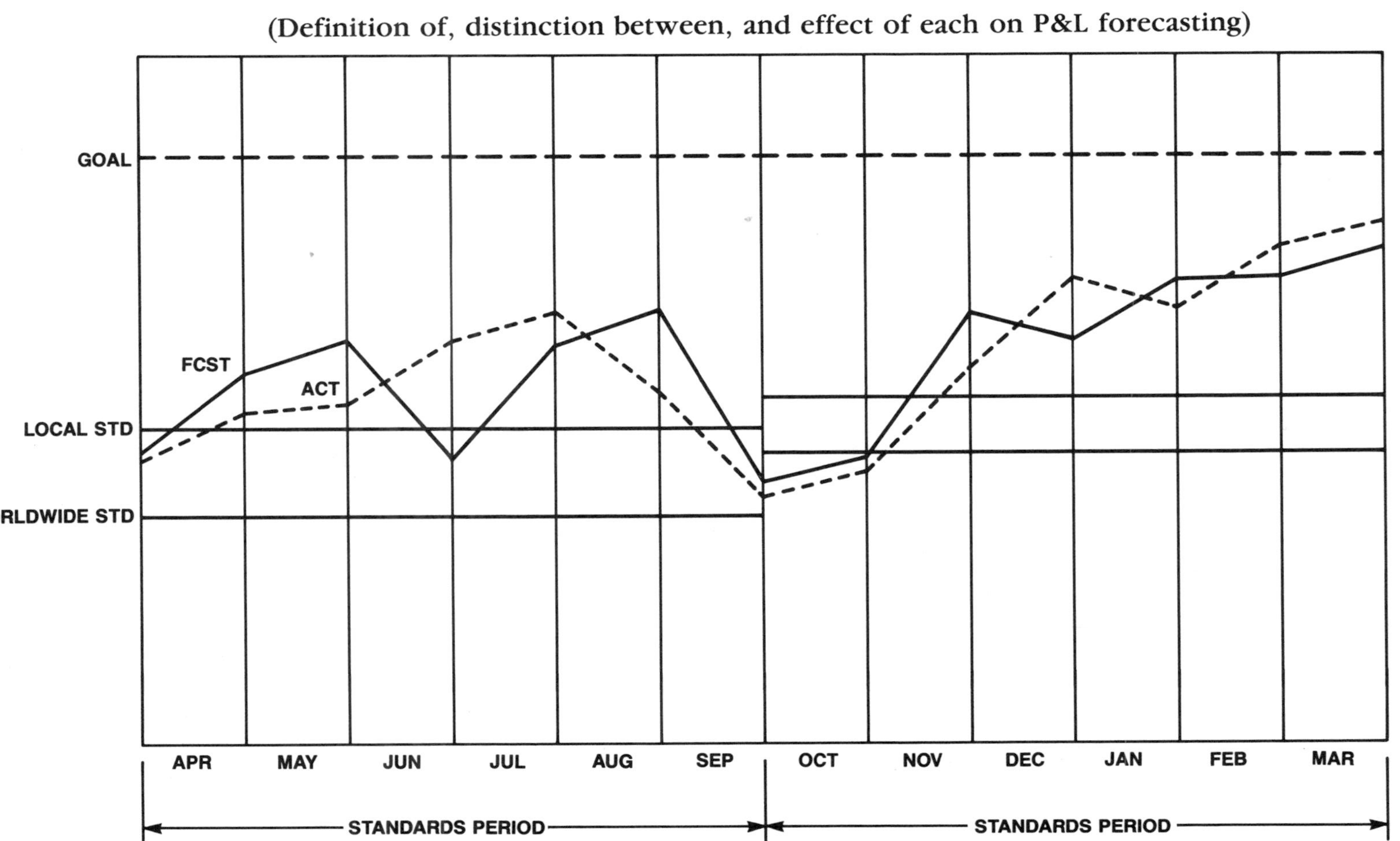

Figure 7-1 Standards, Forecasts, Goals, and Actual Performance

8

Product Cost Structure, Pricing, and Overhead Recovery

RELATIONSHIP BETWEEN PRICE AND COST

There are two boundaries within which the ASP of a product lies:

1. Market Price (price customer is prepared to pay)

2. Minimum Acceptable Price (price below which we as a vendor cannot sell the product profitably)

$ ↑	Market Price Minimum Acceptable Price	} PROFIT	$ ↑	Minimum Acceptable Price Market Price	} LOSS

Minimum Acceptable Price (for locally manufactured product).

Margin 1 (M1) = ASP – Worldwide Standard (WWS) Cost

$$\text{Margin } 1\% = \frac{\text{ASP} - \text{WWS Cost}}{\text{ASP}}$$

ASP (for 70% M1)

$$70\% = \frac{\text{ASP} - \text{WWS Cost}}{\text{ASP}}$$

$$70\% = 1 - \frac{\text{WWS Cost}}{\text{ASP}}$$

$$70\% + \frac{\text{WWS Cost}}{\text{ASP}} = 1$$

$$\frac{\text{WWS Cost}}{\text{ASP}} = 1 - 70\%$$

$$\because \text{ASP} = \frac{\text{WWS Cost}}{1 - 70\%}$$

$$= \frac{\text{WWS Cost}}{0.3}$$

$$= 3.33 \times \text{WWS}$$

ASP (for 50% M2)

$$50\% = \frac{\text{ASP} - \text{M2 Cost}}{\text{ASP}}$$

$$50\% = 1 - \frac{\text{M2 Cost}}{\text{ASP}}$$

$$50\% + \frac{\text{M2 Cost}}{\text{ASP}} = 1$$

$$\frac{\text{M2 Cost}}{\text{ASP}} = 1 - 50\%$$

$$\because \text{ASP} = \frac{\text{M2 Cost}}{1 - 50\%}$$

$$= \frac{\text{M2 Cost}}{0.5}$$

$$= 2 \times \text{M2 Cost}$$

Usually, but not always 70 percent M1, 50 percent M2 are percentage margins required to meet or exceed minimum profit before tax (PBT) after M3, M4, M5 costs have been absorbed. (In a highly competitive market, a company may have to structure itself to be profitable at 55 percent and 35 percent, respectively.)

This represents a cost plus margin approach to pricing—not likely to be tenable in a highly competitive market.

The other extreme is to forecast what market ASP is likely to be and then determine what product cost needs to be in order to remain competitive and profitable in that scenario.

M2 costs are **actually** incurred in producing the product.

The desired end result is for manufacturing efficiency to be such that M2 inventoriable costs = standard costs; i.e., for M2 to equal M1. Differences result in favorable or adverse variations (usually adverse).

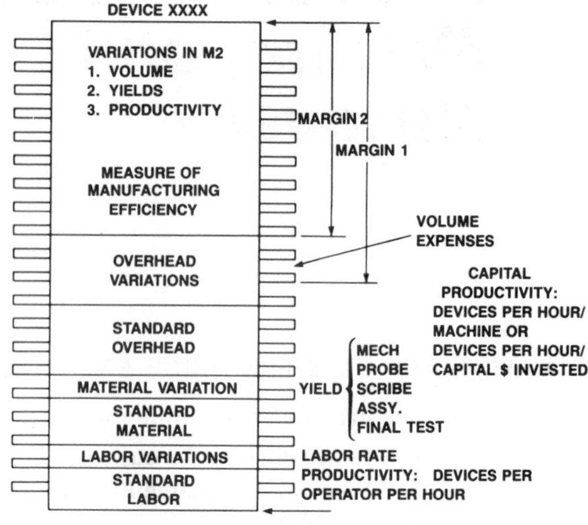

Figure 8-1 Actual or M2 (Margin 2) Costs

The difference between dollar revenue realized from the sale of a product and the cost incurred in supplying it is profit (margin).

$$\text{Profit} = \text{ASP} - \text{Cost}$$

$$\%\ \text{Profit} = \frac{\text{ASP} - \text{Cost}}{\text{ASP}}$$

Optimized margins require ASPs to be as high as the market will bear and costs to be as low as can be achieved.

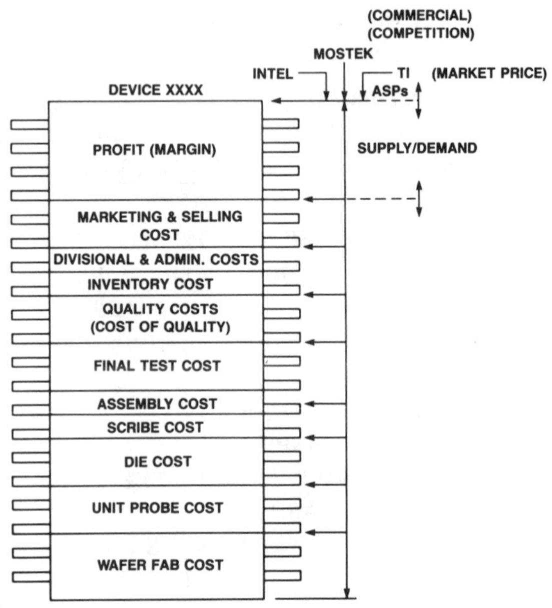

Figure 8-2 Elements of Cost

MARGIN 2 (M2) COSTS

1. Wafer Cost $= PC + \frac{BOH}{V}$

   PC = Prime (Variable) Costs
   V = Volume
   BOH = Burden & Overhead

2. Die Cost $= \frac{\text{Wafer Cost}}{\text{GDPW} \times \text{Prb. Yld.}}$

   GDPW= Gross Die Per Wafer

3. Die Probe Cost $= PC + \frac{BOH}{V}$

4. Die Scribe Cost $= PC + \frac{BOH}{V}$

   Labor
   Material
   Overhead

5. Assembly Cost $= PC + \frac{BOH}{V} + \text{Profit}$

6. Import Duty on Raw Stock = 18% × (TFP + Duty Adder) TFP = Raw Stock Transfer Price

7. Final Test Cost $= PC + \frac{BOH}{V}$

8. Indirect Manufacturing Overhead Cost

WAFER COST

Any function that is capital intensive carries a high cost in the form of depreciation (facilities, equipment). This cost is incurred **independently of volume**. There is a high cost of doing nothing.

In the case of wafer cost we saw that:

$$\text{Wafer Cost} = PC + \frac{BOH}{V}$$

PC = Prime or variable costs in the form of labor and material (silicon, gases). In effect, labor cost may not be considered to be variable. (Cost accounting, like economics, is more of a social than a pure science.)

Total prime costs vary in direct proportion to volume. Unit prime costs remain fixed. In the short term the most effective way to reduce wafer cost is to increase volume (without increasing BOH). It may be the case that volume is a function of the manufacturing base (the range of products which can be manufactured in wafer fab).

The narrower the range of devices over which capacity needs to be absorbed, the more difficult it may be to do so **profitably** or even at all.

Example:

In our example, the monthly BOH **load** to be absorbed is in the region of $500K's.

Therefore, if we produce 5,000 wafers in a month, the BOH element in the cost of each wafer is:

500,000/5,000 = $100's

The sum of labor and material costs is in the region of $40's.

Therefore, wafer cost = 40 + 100 = **$140**

If we produce 10,000 wafers, the BOH element is:

500,000/10,000 = $50's

And the wafer cost is reduced to:

40 + 50 = **$90's**

Therefore, given that BOH is fixed, wafer cost is a function of volume. In turn, volume may be a function of width of **manufacturing base**, and manufacturing base may be a function of **new product introduction**.

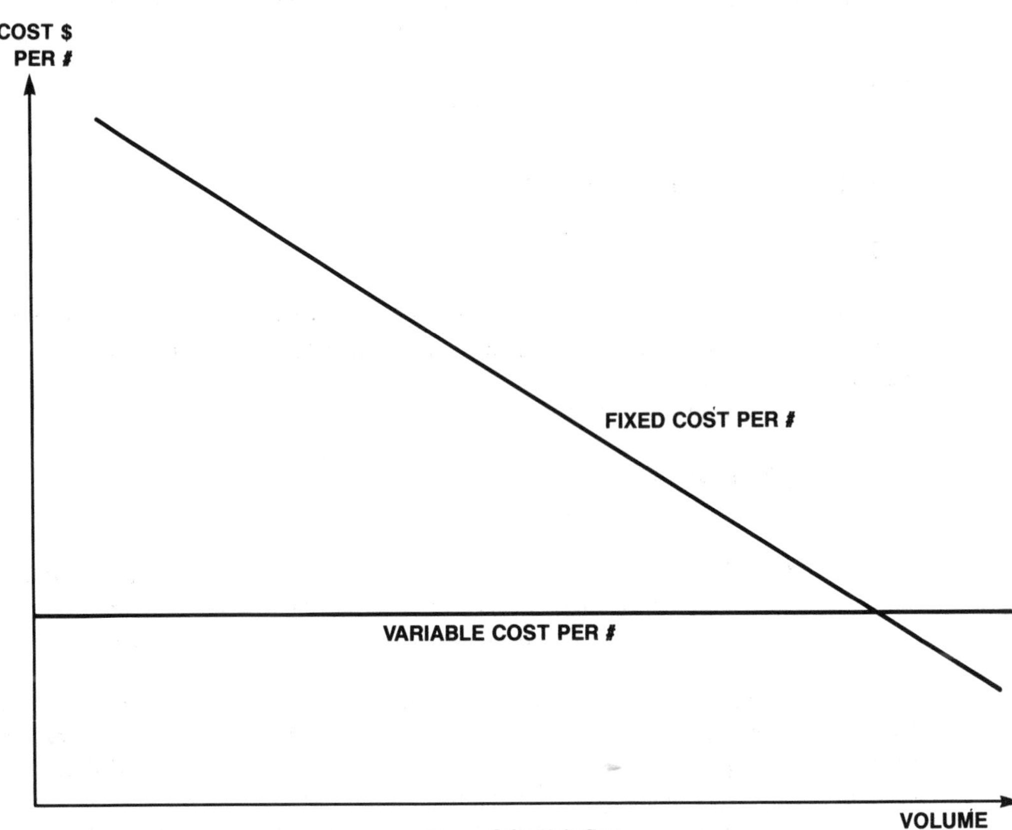

Figure 8-3 Unit Cost

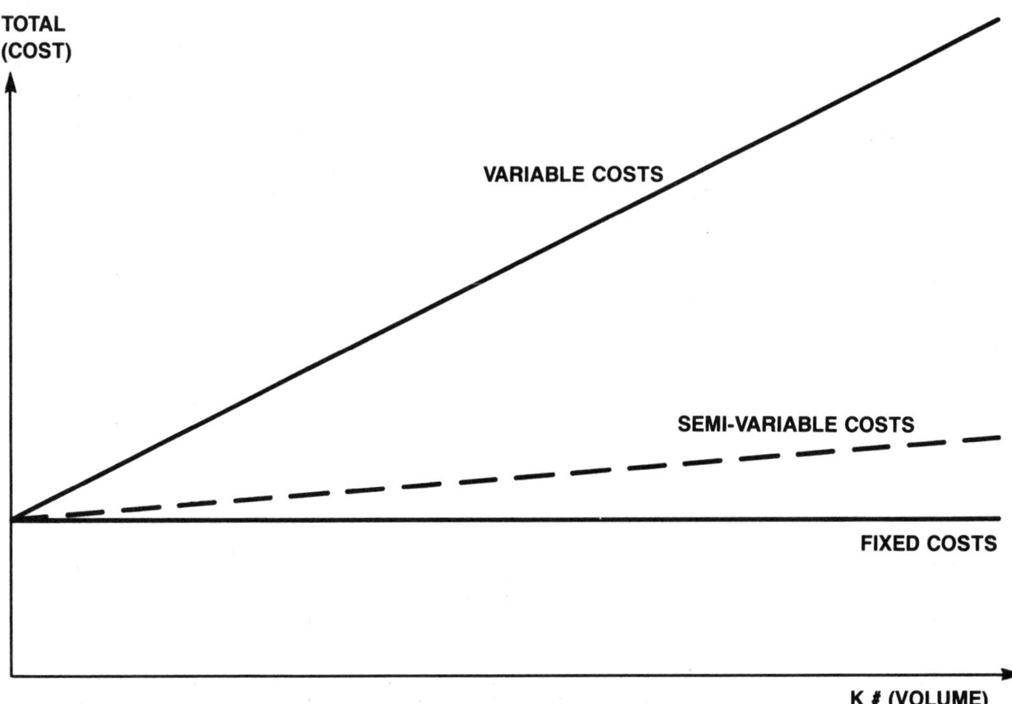

1. Fixed Costs—Depreciation, Rent, Rates
2. Semi-Variable Costs—Masks, Clothing
3. Variable Costs—Wafers, Gold, Gases, Chemicals

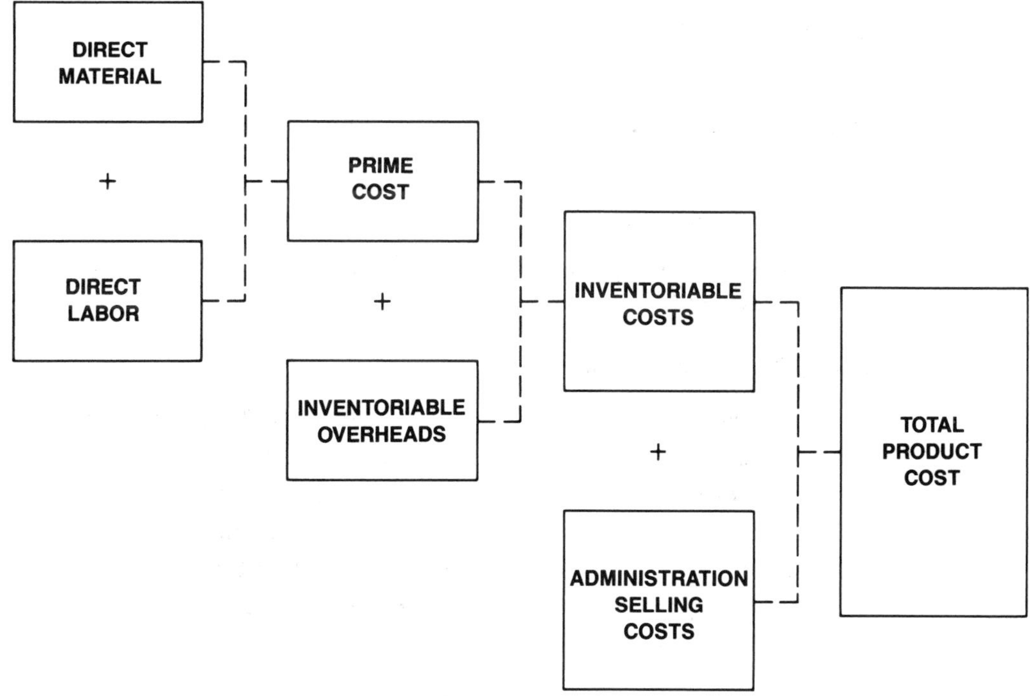

Figure 8-4 Total Costs

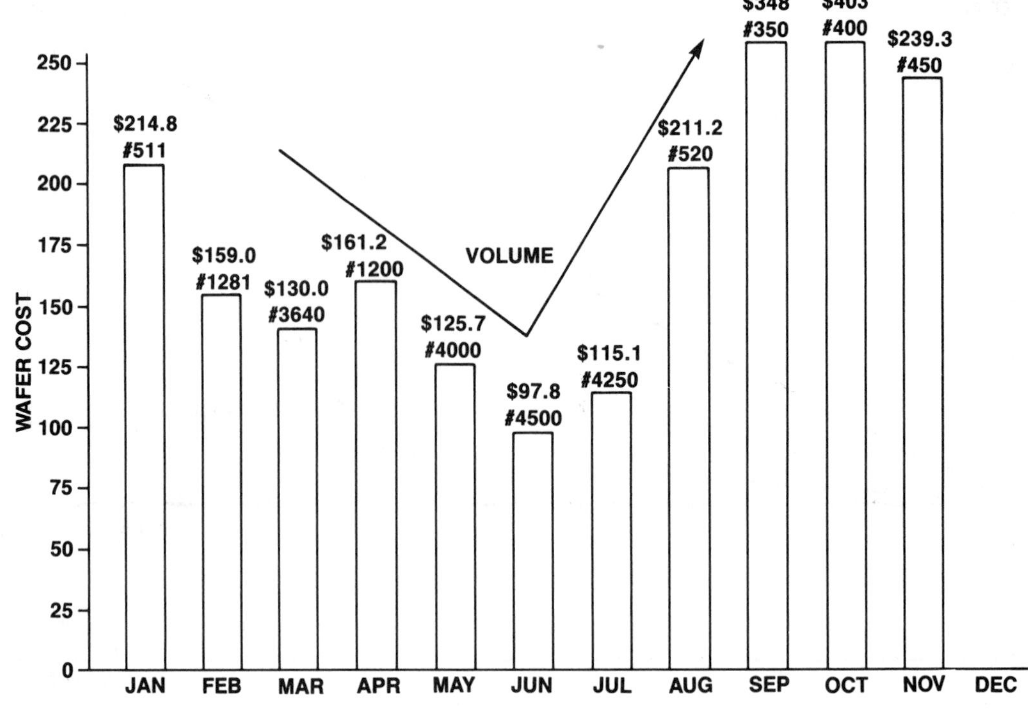

Figure 8-5 Wafer Cost

DIE COST

Die cost is a function of:

1. Wafer Cost
2. Good Die Per Wafer
3. Unit Probe Cost

Good die per wafer is a function of:

1. Gross Die Per Wafer (function of wafer/die size)
2. Unit Probe Yield

Unit probe yield is a function of:

1. Logic Design
2. Computer Simulation
3. Circuit Design
4. Circuit Layout
5. Mask Quality
6. Diffusion (implant) Process Integrity
7. Photolith Process Integrity
8. General Workmanship
9. Test Program
10. Test Equipment
11. Finger Problems
12. Procedures

TEST COSTS

Unit probe and final test costs are a function of:

1. Initial cost of the equipment
2. Ability to provide device with access to the CPU (number of test stations, handlers, probers, and index time of these)
3. Device test times
4. Yield
5. Test system or peripheral down time
6. Batch size
7. Retest factor
8. Engineering time
9. QC requirements
10. Operator efficiency
11. Interaction of elements (1) through (10)

Effect of Technology on Wafer/Die/Test Cost Relationship

Table 8-1 illustrates the extent to which costs by stage of completion are sensitive to die size. The changes in die cost as a proportion of total cost for SSI, MSI, and LSI are shown.

TECHNOLOGY/COST SENSITIVITY

Table 8-1 Wafer Cost

Device	$60			$120		
	SSI	MSI	LSI	SSI	MSI	LSI
Gross Die/Wafer	5510	395	267	5510	395	267
Good Die/Wafer	4794	140	92	4794	140	92
Probe Cost/Wafer	15.70	13.36	8.52	15.70	13.36	8.52
Probed Die Cost	0.016	0.524	0.745	0.028	0.953	1.397
Assy. Cost	0.063	0.237	0.731	0.063	0.237	0.731
Assy. Yield percent	96.0	92.0	89.0	96.0	92.0	89.0
Final Test Yield percent	94.0	90.0	83.0	94.0	90.0	83.0
Test Cost	0.02	0.362	0.308	0.02	0.362	0.308
M2 FG Cost	0.106	1.298	2.241	0.119	1.817	3.143
Die Cost as percent of Total Cost	15.1	40.4	33.2	23.5	52.4	44.4
*Revenue/Wafer Start $	865.2	311.8	456.0	865.2	311.8	456.0
Contribution/Wafer Start $	406.6	161.3	303.7	350.4	101.2	242.4
ASP	0.20	2.69	6.71	0.20	2.69	6.71
*Test Cost as percent of Total Cost	18.8	27.8	13.7	16.8	19.9	9.0

Margin 1 Misconceptions

The consequences of using a standard cost system for measurement and decision making can be seriously misunderstood by many people other than a few outside of the finance environment.

Margin 1 is hypothetical, margin 2 is real. Not only is margin 2 also misunderstood, it is not usually readily visible at device level. In product portfolios in which there is a significant spread between lowest and highest ASPs and product costs, compensating errors cannot be relied upon to permit the use of averages. Averages in this context are meaningless.

For example, when wafer fab capacity is less than required, loading decisions may be made on revenue per wafer start or margin 1 contribution. **The correct criteria is margin 2 contribution**.

Overhead Recovery

Since the P&L account is one of the benchmarks by which a company is measured, it is important to understand the content of such a document and the relationships between costs.

The following example shows how the costs of production flow into the **P&L and inventory.**

Helpful hints—Think in terms of:

1. **P&L Account** — Variations | **Inventory Account** — Local or WWS value of product
2. **Actual** costs incurred will be compared to **standard** costs.
3. Costs which **should be** recovered will be compared to costs which **are** recovered.

Example

This example takes 150 wafer starts and follows them through to the finished goods stage, at which point they are sold.

Assumptions

150 wafer starts. Cycle time through wafer fab/probe four weeks (period 1). Assembly/final test four weeks (period 2). Wafer fab inventory held at local standard. (Same as WWS in the case of U.S. factories.) Shipped die at WWS value. No opening inventory.

Period 1

Wafer Fab

The following information relates to the local standard cost of an unprobed wafer (i.e., costs which **should be** incurred).

Material	$ 10.00	
Labor	$ 15.00	Yielded cost @ 80 percent process yield (mechanical yield) in wafer fab
Overheads	$ 75.00	
	$100.00	(Standard cost of wafer)

1. Production (Actual Yield 80%)

150 wafers are started; however, only 100 starts are completely processed. This equates to 80 wafer outs (80% yield in fab). The remaining 50 are only half processed

(i.e., 50 @ 80% = 40 ÷ 2 = 20 equivalent outs). This **equates to 20 equivalent outs.** Therefore, the recoveries based on local standard are on 100 equivalent outs (i.e., **80 actual + 20 equivalent**).

(Recoveries: Absorption of fixed overhead cost over volume)

Earned Recoveries
(Recovered Costs)
(Costs which should have been incurred in producing 100 wafers)

Material	$10 × 100 = $ 1000
Labor	$15 × 100 = $ 1500
Overheads	$75 × 100 = $ 7500
	$10000

However **actual** costs are as follows (actually measured during the period)

Material	$ 1100
Labor	$ 1550
Overheads	$ 7650
	$10300

From the preceding information, we see that the wafer fab cost was $300 more than we had accounted for in the local standard, so we have a negative variation to local (worldwide) standard.

We will now follow the progress of the 80 wafer outs from wafer fab into probe and through to the die stage.

Probe

The following information relates to the local standard cost of probe (per wafer).

Labor	$10.00
Overheads	$30.00
	$40.00

We now have a total probed wafer cost of $140 (i.e.,—$100 fab + $40 probe).
The standard die out is 70 good die (expected output) per wafer.
This gives us a local standard cost of die $2.00 (i.e., $140/70 = $2.00).
The WWS die cost at $1.50.
In this example our standard yield is 70 die; however, we find our actual yield is 35 die.

2. Production (wafer starts 80)

Standard die out	5600	(80 wafers × 70 die per wafer)
Actual die out	2800	(80 wafers × 35 die per wafer)
Yield Variation	2800	@ standard cost = $5600 (local standard to actual)

Earned recoveries will be based on the 80 wafer starts.

∵ **Earned Recoveries**

Labor	$10 × 80 = $ 800
Overheads	$30 × 80 = 2400
	$3200

However, actual costs are as follows (measured):

Labor	$ 800
Overheads	2200
	$3000

From the preceding information, we see that the probe cost was $200 less than we had accounted for in the local standards, so we have a positive variation to local standard.

Based on actual yields, we see that our output is 2800 die valued at local standard $2.00 = $5600. However, when we ship the die out of the factory for assembly (buy/sell), we value the inventory, not at local standard, but WWS value, the difference being a negative **procedural variation** (local standard to WWS).

i.e., Local	$5600	(2800 × 2.00)
WWS	$4200	(2800 × 1.50)
Procedural Variation	$1400	

At this point let us summarize our position.

Production	80 wafers out of wafer fab	
	20 equivalent builds still in wafer fab	
	2800 good die produced (actual)	
	Our total costs are as follows:	
Costs	Wafer fab	$10300
	Probe	$ 3000
	Total Costs	$13300

Now let us look at the impact on the P&L.

Wafer Fab/Probe		**$**	**P&L Impact $ (FAV)**
A. Material—	Earned	1000	
	Actual	1100	
	Variation		100
B. Labor —	Earned	2300	
	Actual	2350	
	Variation		50
C. Overheads—	Earned	9900	
	Actual	9850	
	Variation		(50)
Yield Variation			5600
Procedural Variation			1400
Total Variations			7100

A. Material—No material involved at probe
B. Labor—Wafer Fab—1500 + Probe – 800 = 2300
C. Overhead—Wafer Fab—7500 + Probe – 2400 = 9900

We see that the P&L shows cost of $7,100, but we know out total costs incurred are $13,300. Where is the Δ$6,200? The answer is in the inventory value (note that the P&L account is only charged with the actual to standard cost **delta**).

Inventory Valuation

Wafer fab—20 equivalent builds (left in inventory)	
i.e., 20 @ \$100 =	\$ 2000
Die (valued at WWS) i.e., 2800 @ \$1.50	\$ 4200
Total inventory valuation	\$ 6200
If we add to the inventory value the costs released to the P&L	\$ 7100
This equates our total costs	\$13300

(**Actual** good material is sold out of P&L account into inventory account at WWS value.)

Period 2

The product (die) has now been shipped out for assembly and final test. (The assumption at this point is that no more wafer fab production takes place in this period.)

Let us first of all look at assembly.

Assembly (2800 good die in)

The following information relates to the **standard cost** of assembly.

Material	\$1.00	This being the yielded assembly cost @ 90 percent yield.
Labor	\$0.10	
Overhead	\$0.40	
	\$1.50	The actual yield achieved is 90 percent.

However, for assembly we find that the actual cost of assembly is \$1.60 (yielded). Not only this, but the WWS assembly fee is \$0.01 lower than the "pooled" fee being charged (pooled fee being average in-house assembly the assumption being that there are several assembly sites).

3. Production

2800 assembly starts equates to raw stock = 2520 outs (yield 90%)

Based on those outs 2520, we see that we have a variation of \$0.10 being standard \$1.50—actual \$1.60. We therefore have a dollar variation in assembly of \$252 ($2800 \times 0.9 \times 0.1$).

We also incur an assembly margin; i.e., (the delta between the assembly fees) × (assembly starts)(volume loading variance), i.e., $2800 \times 0.01 =$ \$28 (ASMOP).

For inventory valuation purposes we must calculate a raw stock WWS value, this being (die WWS yielded at assembly) + (yielded assembly cost):

i.e., 1.666 + 1.50* = \$3.166 per # raw stock

*Local standard yielded assembly cost

($1.5 \div 0.9 = 1.66$)—WWS die cost

Therefore, our inventory value of raw stock will be 2520 @ 3.166 = \$7980.

At this point let us summarize what has happened in assembly.

Inventory value has increased from \$4200 (die at WWS) to \$7980 (RS at WWS) = \$3780 of an increase.

We have incurred an assembly variation of \$252 (local standard to actual).

We have also incurred an ASMOP charge of \$28 (local standard to WWS).

Our total costs are:

2520 × 1.60 =	\$4032	(Raw stock out × actual cost)
2800 × 0.01 =	\$ 28	(Die started × (actual − standard))
Actual assembly cost	\$4060	

This ties back to the P&L/inventory account as follows:

Inventory increase	\$3780	Inventory account
Assembly variations	\$ 252	P&L account
ASMOP	\$ 28	
	\$4060	

Let us now turn our attention to final test.

Final Test

The following information relates to the local standard cost of final test.

Labor	\$0.10	Final test yield standard 85% Raw stock WWS \$3.166 Finished goods WWS \$4.100
Overheads	\$0.20	
	\$0.30	

We now have to compute a local standard finished goods cost which, for final test, we value our inventory at, although this is adjusted back to finished goods WWS when we transfer the product into finished goods store.

Local standard finished goods cost = (3.166 + 0.30)/85% = \$4.078
(Raw stock WWS + local standard test cost)/(final test yield)

4. Production (Actual Yield 90%)

We start 2520 raw stock and yield 2268 finished goods out:

Standard finished goods out	2142 (Standard yield 85%)
Actual finished goods out	2268 (Actual yield 90%)
Yield variation (favorable)	(126) @ Standard cost (4.078) = (\$513)

Earned recoveries will be based on 2520 starts:

Earned Recoveries

Labor $0.10 × 2520 = $252
Overheads $0.20 × 2520 = $504
$756

However, actual costs are as follows:

Labor	$300
Overheads	$550
	$850

From the preceding calculations, we see that the final test cost was $94 more than we had accounted for in the standards, so we have a variation to local standard.

Based on actual yields, we see that our output is 2,268 finished goods valued at local standard $4.078 = $9249.

However, when we transfer the finished goods from production to the finished goods warehouse, we value the inventory not at local standard but WWS value, the difference being a procedural variation:

i.e., Local standard	$9249
WWS value	$9299
Procedural variation	$ 50

Let us again summarize our position.

Production	Final test starts	2520
	Finished goods out	2268
Costs	$850	

The P&L impact for final test shows

			P&L Impact
Labor—earned	actual	$252	
	variations	300	48
Overheads—earned	actual	504	
	variations	550	46
Yield variations			(513)
Procedural variations			(50)
			(469)

Once again, the P&L impact does not reflect the true cost. Again it is in inventory. Inventory value increase

$7980 to $9299 = $1319
Total cost $ 850

We have now reached the end of period 2 and enter period 3. No more manufacture takes place. At the end of period 2 we sell 1134 units @ $12.0/# and the remainder in period 3; i.e., 1134# @ $12.0/#. In order to complete this example we need to look at the P&L and inventory in each period.

What are our total manufacturing costs?

Wafer fab	$10300
Probe	$ 3000
Assembly	$ 4060
Final test	$ 850
	$18210
Total Sales 2268 × 12.0	$27216
Net Margin	$ 9006

	Period 1	Period 2	Period 3	Total
Sales	—	13608	13608	27216
COS (WWS)	—	4649	4650	9299
Margin 1	—	8959	8958	17917
Margin 1%				65.8%
Assy. Var.	—	252	—	252
ASMOP	—	28	—	28
Mat. Var.	100	—	—	100
Lab. Var.	50	48	—	98
O'Head Var.	(50)	46	—	(4)
Yield Var.	5600	(513)	—	5087
Proc. Var.	1400	(50)	—	1350
TOTAL VAR.	7100	(189)	—	6911
Margin (P&L)	(7100)	9148	8958	11006
Margin 2%				40.4%
Inventory	6200	6650	2000	2000
Net				9006

If local standard **cost** is higher than WWS **cost**, then the greater the throughput, the better is overhead recovery, but the worse is the **procedural variation**. Product produced goes into inventory account at WWS and P&L is charged with adverse variation. Though the local standard and actual probe yield, for example, may be better (higher) than WWS, if the cost is higher (high wafer cost), then adverse procedural variations will occur.

P&L HINTS

1. Local standards, WWS, forecasts, goals, and actuals.
2. Think in terms of variations into P&L account.
3. Think in terms of inventoriable costs into inventory accounts.

Why not simplify things by disposing of local standards and measure everything against WWS?

Local standards (forecasts) allow measurement against self-imposed objectives and, in accordance with inventory policy, reflect variation effect in inventory when it occurs as opposed to when it crosses a boundary.

INABILITY TO COMPENSATE FOR SAVAGE ASP EROSION

The products which experience most dramatic ASP erosion are primarily those which factories are most capable of producing; i.e., mature products at or near the end of their life cycle.

The major forces behind ASP erosion are: (1) economic recession, (2) opportunity curve, but perhaps more importantly, (3) the **Japanese propensity to compete.**

ASPs can recover after a recessionary cycle due to:

1. General economic recovery giving rise to a capacity limited situation
2. A capacity limited situation brought about by vendors' departures from the market
3. Introduction of new, high-technology, high ASP products sufficiently early in their life cycle to carry an ASP premium over manufacturing cost
4. Enhancing ASPs and hence contribution by offering prime product; i.e., niche market segments

Benefits brought about by new product introduction are the least uncertain of these major forces.

EXPERIENCE CURVE POSITION

Experience curve theory relates the unit cost of product to cumulative volume produced. It is based on laws that have been developed from observation of experimental data from actual manufacturing situations that show that unit cost is related to **cumulative volume produced**.

Progress down an experience curve is also a **function of the number of cycles of learning**. The manufacturing cycle time determines the number of cycles of learning. There are, therefore, two major factors that determine progress down an experience curve—cumulative volume produced **and** cycle time.

The position that a company occupies on the experience curve determines unit cost if cycles-times are the same. **The product engineer uses the experience curve theory and present unit cost to project the future unit cost versus volume** required to **maintain a market position** or, if required, **to gain increased market share.**

Present and future experience curve positions are essential ingredients in annual planning.

NEW PRODUCT SUPPORT

In the competitive marketplace there are three strategies to achieve gain in market share:

1. Reduce unit cost on mature product at a rate which exceeds competition.
2. Introduce new products to established markets with improved customer appeal.
3. Create new markets with new products.

The first strategy involves the support of mature products as discussed in the previous section. The other two strategies involve the support of new products—also a key responsibility of the product engineering group.

EXPERIENCE CURVE ANALYSIS—THE PROGRESS FUNCTION

The variation of product cost with time was first studied in the aircraft industry during World War II. The results obtained have since been verified to **hold for all volume manufactured products**. The data accumulated show that in **manual** volume production situations the cumulative labor hours required to produce a unit decrease exponentially with the cumulative number of units produced.

$$T = AX_{n+1} \qquad \text{Equation 1}$$

Where:

T = Cumulative Incurred Labor Hours
A = Labor Hours to Produce the First Unit
X = Cumulative Number of Units Produced
n = Cost Reduction Rate Where:

$$-1 < n < 0 \qquad \text{Equation 2}$$

Cost reduction for competitive pricing with profit in the manufacture of silicon integrated circuits is realized only in the manufacture of large volumes of identical circuits. Thus, **one of the most significant economic factors that must be considered** in the decision to manufacture an integrated circuit is the **market volume potential**. Building integrated circuits in large volumes offers a manufacturer the **opportunity** and **incentive** to gain a tremendous amount of knowledge about a product in a relatively short time. The integrated circuit manufacturer, with the knowledge gained, can proceed to **reduce costs by product or manufacturing improvements**. As he **progresses** down the cost-reduction path, prices can be lowered. (The means to do so must be provided.)

The product becomes more price competitive. With a properly directed price strategy, the integrated circuit manufacturer can simultaneously increase his share of the available market.

> The unit cost of manufacturing integrated circuits of a given type tends to decline exponentially with the total number of units produced.

EXAMPLES OF TOOLS TO IMPROVE YIELD (REDUCE PRODUCT COST)

1. Identification of mask defects
2. Assessment of yield loss due to mask defaults
3. Assessment of "true" wafer process/defect yield
4. Early recognition of position related yield losses; e.g., doughnut problem
5. Quantification of loss due to edge die failure

a. EXAMPLE OF TWO-DIMENSIONAL WAFER MAP

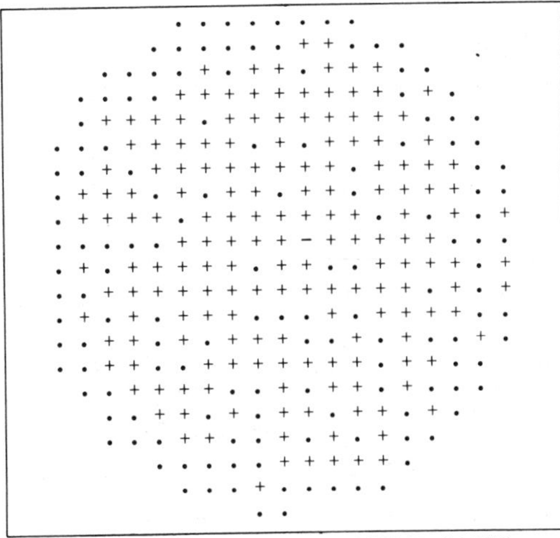

PASS: 175 FAIL: 147 YIELD: 54.35%

b. EXAMPLE OF CUMULATIVE WAFER MAP

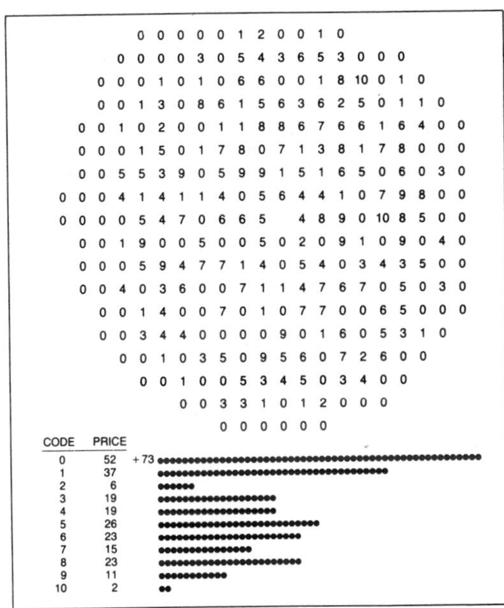

Figure 8-6 Wafer Maps

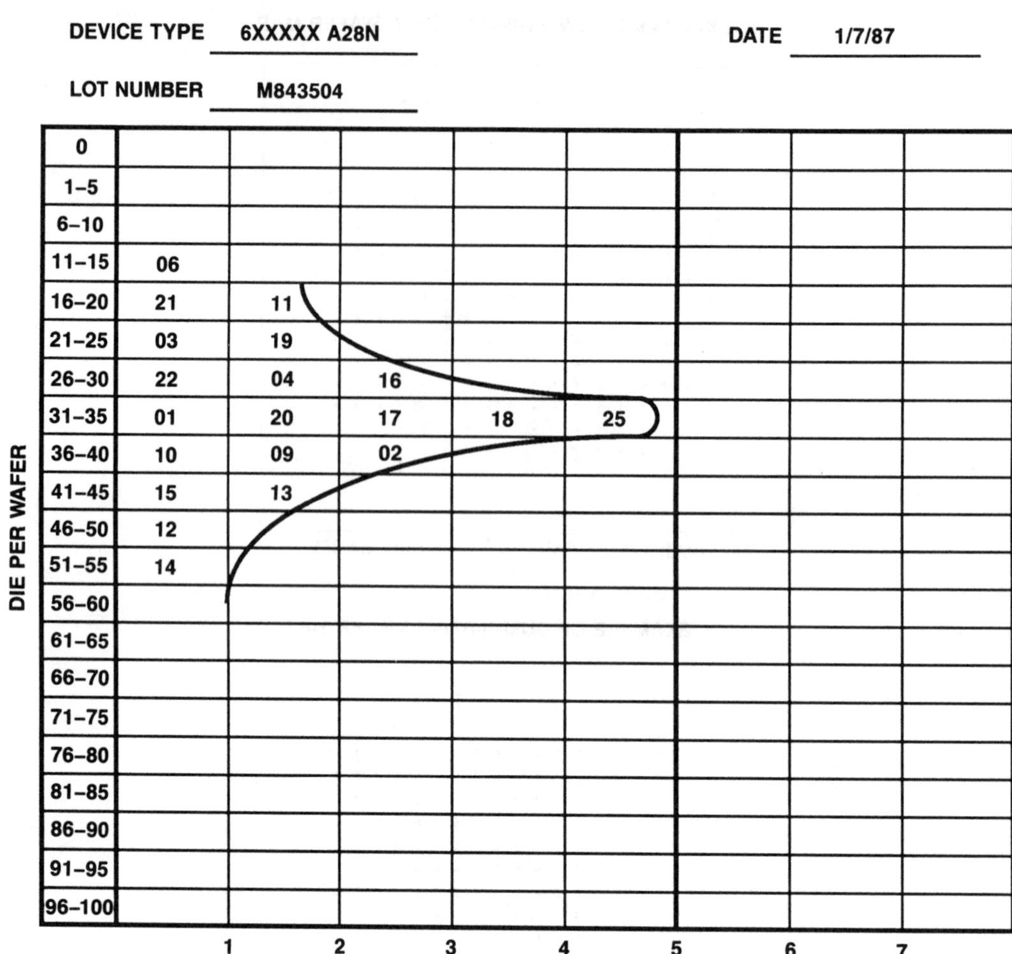

Figure 8-7 Yield Histogram

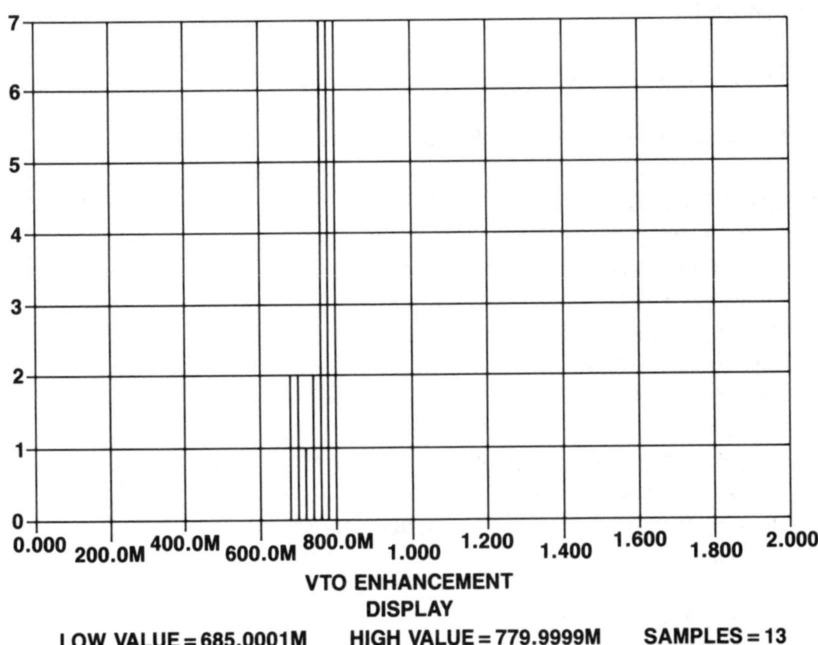

Figure 8-8 Example of Process Control Parameter Distribution

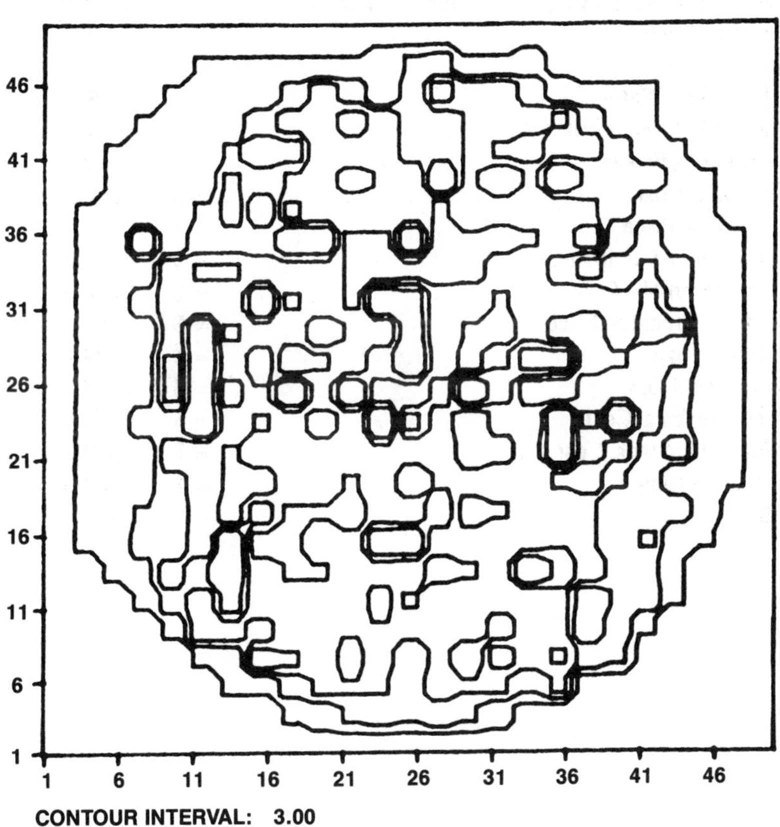

Figure 8-9 Example of Contour Wafer Map

Cost Model

To calculate actual and **forecasted** product costs.

PACKAGE TYPE IS 40 PIN PLASTIC:

The Stored Values are as follows:

1. Scribe Yield	=	1.00
2. Wafer Fab Yield	=	0.82
3. Final Test Yield	=	0.87
4. General Administration Profit Adder	=	0.18
5. Duty Adder % * .01	=	0.05
6. Duty Rate % * .01	=	0.17
7. Duty Drawback Rate % * .01	=	0.09
8. Freight Charge (export + import freight) % *	=	0.03
9. Yielded (unprobed) Wafer Cost	=	$125.00
10. Mode — Calc. A.S.P. = 1, Calc Actual Margin = 0	=	0
11. No Changes		

Device Type XXXX		
Die Size (mils)	=	160 × 111
Shrink	=	15%
Wafer Cost Yielded at 82.0% Wafer Mechanical Yield	=	$125.0
Gross Die/Wafer	=	855
Probe Yield %	=	61
Good Die Per Wafer	=	521
Yielded Die Probe Cost	= $	0.1800
Die Cost Into Probe	= $	0.2399
Yielded Die Cost	= $	0.4199
Die Transfer Price	= $	0.4955
Freight + Duty Component	= $	0.1499
Yielded Assembly Cost	= $	0.3929
Raw Stock Transfer Price	= $	0.9435
Raw Stock Cost	= $	1.1602
Yielded Test Cost	= $	0.1000
Yielded Marking Cost	= $	0.1500
Yielded F.G. Stock Cost	= $	1.4102
A.S.P. at Present	= $	3.00
Margin 2	= %	52.99

Table 8-2 Example of Yield Trend Analysis

Device	Probe Yield				F.T. Yield			
	Current Actual	Last Q Avge	F/Cast Next Q	Goal Next Q	Current Actual	Last Q Avge	F/Cast Next Q	Goal Next Q
Device 1	32	32	35	40	86	84	84	86
Device 2	—	—	60	60	70	73	76	76
Device 3	—	—	55	56	80	83	76	77
Device 4	—	40	40	40	79	76	70	75
Device 5	—	—	40	40	—	—	70	75
Device 17	—	—	55	62	—	92	90	90

Table 8-3 Example of Contribution Analysis

Device	Tech	SCE	Status	Revenue Per Wafer Start			Contribution Per Wafer Start		
				L	S	P	L	S	P
Device 1	NMOS	E	PROD	649.42	—	257.21	92.44	—	−36.62
Device 2	NMOS	E	PROD	—	—	486.42	—	—	5.70
Device 3	NMOS	E	PROD	—	—	539.38	—	—	155.51
Device 4	NMOS	E	PROD	—	—	193.88	—	—	110.91
Device 5	NMOS	E	ENG	—	—	217.00	—	—	−60.72
Device 17	NMOS	E	PROD	—	—	215.80	—	—	−146.59

TEST SYSTEMS LAYOUT UTILIZATION AND EFFICIENCY

It is the intention in this section to outline the major aspects that ought to be considered in any proposed test system configuration. There are essentially two goals to which system configuration should be directed:

1. Devices per operator hour (labor efficiency)
2. Central processor (computer) efficiency (machine utilization)

As will be shown, these two goals need not be compatible since one can be optimized at the expense of the other.

First, consider central processor unit (CPU) efficiency. In any test system, it is the CPU time available in conjunction with the time taken to test a device (not including handling) which determines the **maximum** throughput in devices/hour which could be delivered.

Therefore, in one hour (3600 secs) with a test time of 250 msec (typical for SSI gates) the maximum attainable throughput per hour would be $3600/250 \times 10^{-3} =$ 14.4 k devices/hour.

This ideal case would represent 100 percent CPU utilization since all available CPU time is being utilized in testing devices.

The difference between actual throughput and maximum throughput per hour is due to the following:

1. Ability to provide device access to the CPU [number of test stations: (A) handlers, (B) probers]
2. Device test times
3. Yield
4. Test system or peripheral down time
5. Batch sizes
6. Retest factor
7. Engineering time required on M/Cs
8. QC requirements
9. Operator efficiency
10. Interaction of elements (1) through (9)

(Average units per hour would comprehend system downtime.)

1. Ability to Provide Device Access to CPU

The method used to overcome this constraint is to provide more than one test station per system to allow queuing of devices so that in theory whenever the CPU has completed testing a device, there is a high probability that another station contains a device waiting to be tested. Therefore, test stations simply provide access to the CPU, and since the CPU is a unique commodity to the system shared between stations, it can only service one station at a time. Automatic handlers (and in a limited sense, probers) are simply extensions of the test stations, which increase the probability of a device waiting to be tested as the CPU becomes available, by minimizing handling times. Number of peripherals required is a function of test time and yield and index time, and, until now, we have not been able to accurately quantify this. (This assumes CPU multiplexed test system.)

a. Electromechanical device for loading and unloading devices in packaged form to and from the test socket on the test system.

b. Electromechanical device for loading and unloading devices in 5/6″ diameter wafer form to and from the test socket.

2. Device Test Times

The constraints in this respect manifest themselves more at final test than at probe. At final test, the test times are determined by the number and variety of tests required to be done as stipulated in the device data sheet or spec and by the time taken to perform each test as determined by the machine. Throughput at this point can only be improved by faster measurement capability.

At least, initially, these same considerations should apply at probe, but as experience and knowledge of the product improves, tests can be eliminated from probe programs provided that this does not adversely affect final test yields.

3. Yield

This is a function of program integrity, system capability, peripheral equipment, wafer processing quality, device design, process design, mask quality, and so on.

Until now, these variables have constituted the major obstacles to accurately determine:

a. Optimum system configuration

b. CPU utilization

c. Throughput/hour (per operator or per system)

Items 1 to 3 are variable and interactive.

4. Test System or Peripheral Downtime

In general it can be argued that as system complexity increases, either in its own right or as a function of additional peripheral equipment in the form of probers or handlers, the probability of downtime occurring increases. The approach recommended, therefore, is to design the optimum configuration for the volume required and to have sufficient peripherals and functional modules to operate a modular replacement system on production equipment, with faulty items being repaired on an engineering system isolated from production.

5. Batch Sizes

In this respect, change is nonproductive. Both batch size and system configuration should be designed to minimize the effects of change and incorporate product rationalization (test times) with respect to machines available. Products with similar test times should be tested on systems optimally configured to these test times. (We shall discuss short cycle-time manufacturing (SCM) later.)

6. Retest Factor

Retesting obviously utilizes system time retesting devices instead of raw stock. Interaction with QC should be such as to minimize the need to allocate system resources for this purpose. (A technique to eliminate or minimize this, RFT, will be discussed later.)

7. Engineering Time

This is a prerequisite to production in preparing test programs but is in itself, nonproductive and uses system time, which would be better employed testing product. A large proportion of the engineering activity does not require a full system, most of which would be expensively redundant. It is far better to maintain an off-line facility.

8. QC Requirements

In the situation, desirable or otherwise, where QC uses production resources, the need to datalog uses a disproportionate amount of system time due to slow-speed peripherals. This effect can be minimized by datalogging on a fast peripheral (disc, where possible, but alternatively magnetic tape) and converting to hard copy off line. This is another justification for an off-line system.

9. Operator Efficiency

Devices per operator hour is an important figure of merit but can not be considered in isolation. It is possible to maximize this figure by providing unlimited equipment resources and at the expense of CPU utilization. This is obviously unsatisfactory and should be considered in system configuration. On the other hand, it would be equally futile to establish in theory that it was possible for one operator to attend four probers if the probers were so far apart that this was physically impossible.

The merits of not utilizing the equipment during coffee breaks, lunch breaks, and shift changes should also be considered.

10. Interaction of Items 1 through 9

It should be apparent that none of the preceding items can be manipulated with disregard for the others. It has been the effects of this dynamic interaction and our inability to quantify the effects of these variables, which has, to some extent, restricted our ability to make optimum use of the resources at our disposal. We are all familiar with our current level of performance. What has remained less than satisfactory until now has been the ability to predict, other than by "gut feel," what our level of performance should be under varying conditions and the ability to manage these variables to our maximum advantage.

Being aware of both these levels of performance, as well as the reasons why they differ, may well indicate the approach necessary to reduce this margin.

Production departments require stability to perform efficiently. It should be the goal of every service department to eliminate or minimize the effects of change on production departments by management of the variables with which they are concerned.

Hopefully, what has been written here will help in that respect.

MATHEMATICAL TEST CAPACITY MODEL

Capacity is vested in the computer and not in a handler or prober, and the following calculations refer to **system capacity** with the number of handlers as a variable.

The general equation (derived in the Calculations section) is:

$$\text{Capacity (units into test/hour)} = \frac{3600.E}{R.\,TA} \quad \frac{1-X}{TA} + \frac{N}{X}$$

Where E = Machine efficiency (i.e., uptime)
R = Retest factor (e.g., for 20% retest R = 1.2)
TA = Average test time (seconds)
X = Index time of handler or prober (seconds)
N = Number of handlers or probers

The expression in square brackets is the machine utilization and must be considered when deciding the optimum number of handlers (or probers) to use on each test system.

For N = 1 Capacity C_1

$$= \frac{3600.E}{TA.R}\left(1-\left(\frac{X}{(TA+X)}\right)\right)$$

$$= \frac{3600.E}{(TA+X)R}$$

For N = 2 Capacity C_2

$$= \frac{3600.E}{TA.R}\left(1-\left(\frac{X}{(TA+X)}\right)^2\right)$$

$$= \underline{C_1(1+Z)} \text{ (see Appendix D)}$$

$$\text{Where } Z = \frac{X}{TA+X}$$

$$\text{Similarly } C_3 = C_1(1+Z+Z^2)$$

$$\text{And } C_4 = C_1(1+Z+Z^2+Z^3)$$

This format shows directly the increase in throughput gained adding each additional handler. If Z is large (i.e., 1/2), then there is a case for increasing the number of handlers or probers. Reduction of test time will have little effect unless an adequate number of peripherals are in use.

If Z is small (i.e., 1/2), then there is not such a good case for increasing the number but a better case for concentrating on a reduction of test time.

For most SSI devices, Z is greater than 1/2 at final test but less than 1/2 at probe. This is a result of the different values of X: 500 ms at final test and 150 ms at probe.

FINAL TEST

At final test the handler (control) index time is 500 ms. Calculated throughputs, in thousands of raw stock per hour for different test times and number of handlers, are shown in the table below. E and R are not included in these figures (i.e., E = R = 1) and are considered later with handler efficiency and unused time to derive an overall efficiency.

Table 8-4

Test Time (ms)	Number of Handlers				Z
	1	2	3	4	
150	5.5	9.8	13.1	15.6	0.77
200	5.1	8.8	11.5	13.3	0.71
250	4.8	8.0	10.1	11.6	0.67
300	4.5	7.3	9.1	10.2	0.63
400	4.0	6.2	7.5	8.1	0.56
500	3.6	5.4	6.3	6.8	0.50
700	3.0	4.3	4.8	5.0	0.42
1000	2.4	3.2	3.5	3.6	0.33

It can be seen in the 150–250 ms region with two or three handlers a 20 percent decrease in test time only increases the throughput by 10 percent due to a drop in utilization, whereas, an additional handler may increase throughput by 30 percent.

With an average test time of 500 ms and three handlers, the indicated rate is 6.3 K raw stock per hour. Why is this more than twice our achieved long-term averages? The answer is efficiency.

Types of Efficiency:

1. Machine efficiency (E) is actual time machine is in use and not sitting idle due to breakdowns, batch/type change, device tube transfer, engineering time, and so on. This corresponds closely to the 73 percent efficiency observed by industrial engineering in test area environments.

2. Handler efficiency—with three handlers on a system we have usually only two running at a given moment due to inefficient tube change, jams, and so on. This corresponds to a utilization drop of 17 percent, i.e., **83 percent**.

3. Unused time due to nonstaggered coffee/lunch breaks, and so on—**88 percent**.

4. Retest (R) about 15 percent of all devices are tested twice due to reject rescreen and QC screen/reject **87 percent**.

This corresponds to an overall efficiency of 46 percent.

This could be raised to over 80 percent (a 75 percent increase) by increasing (1) to 90 percent (eliminate idle and tube transfer); (2) to 100 percent (by adding a fourth handler, i.e., three effective handlers); (3) to 100 percent (by staggering coffee/lunch breaks); and (4) to 91 percent (by solving the reappearing QC return problem and reducing R from 1.15 to 1.1).

Current throughput = 6.3 × 46 percent

= 2.9 K raw stock per hour

Note: While the preceding table is of raw stock against average test time, it can reasonably be used for finished goods against pass test time as there is very little difference when yields are over 90 percent.

PROBE TEST

At probe, similar arguments apply. The chief difference is the lower index time (150 ms). This reduces the incentive to increase the number of probers.

The weighted average number of die/wafer at probe is 1150 and the entries in the table below have been divided by this number giving rates in wafers per hour rather than K units per hour.

Table 8-5

Average Test Time (ms)	Number of Probers				Z
	1	2	3	4	
150	10.4	15.6	18.3	19.6	0.50
200	9.0	12.8	14.4	15.1	0.43
250	7.8	10.8	11.9	12.3	0.38
300	7.0	9.3	10.1	10.3	0.33
400	6.7	7.2	7.7	7.8	0.27
500	4.8	5.9	6.2	6.2	0.23
700	3.7	4.3	4.5	4.5	0.18
1000	2.7	3.1	3.1	3.1	0.13

With three probers per CPU and an average test time of 250 ms the indicated rate is 11.9 wafers per hour. This corresponds to seven wafers per hour at an efficiency of 60 percent. This efficiency is higher than at final test due to less frequent interruptions and the better optimized number of peripherals.

CALCULATIONS

$$\text{Capacity } C = \frac{3600.E}{R} \times \frac{1}{TA} \times U$$

Where U is CPU utilization.

If X is the handler index time the total cycle time with one handler will be TA + X.

$$\text{Thus, utilization } U_1 = \frac{TA}{TA + X}$$

$$\text{CPU idle time} = 1 - U_1 \text{ or } \frac{X}{TA + X}$$

If we assume that a second handler will utilize this idle time to the same degree that the first utilized the total time, the idle time for a two handler system is:

$$\frac{(X)2}{(TA + X)}$$

$$\text{And CPU utilization } U_2 = \frac{1 - (X)2}{(TA + X)}$$

Similarly for N handlers:

$$U_N = 1 - Z^N$$

$$\text{where } Z = \frac{X}{TA + X}$$

$$\text{Thus capacity } C_N = \frac{3600.E(1 - Z^N)}{R.TA \qquad (\ )}$$

For N = 1 capacity C_1

$$= \frac{3600.E(1 - X)}{TA.R\ (\ TA + X)}$$

$$= \frac{3600.E}{(TA + X).R}$$

Note: Z^N represents the probability that CPU time will be available for use by a subsequent handler and gives rise to the binomial $1 - Z^N$ for machine utilization.

For N = 2 Capacity C_2

$$= \frac{3600.E\ (1 - (\ )^2)}{TA.R\ (\ (TA + X)\ )}$$

$$= \frac{3600.E((TA + 2X)TA)}{TA.R \qquad (\ (TA + X)^2)}$$

$$= \frac{3600.E\ X\ 1\ X(1 + X)}{R\ TA + X(\ TA + X)}$$

$$= C_1\ (1 + Z)$$

$$\text{Similarly, } C_3 = C_1\ (1 + Z + Z^2)$$

$$\text{And } C_4 = C_1\ (1 + Z + Z^2 + Z^3)$$

If one wishes to consider the test time on each station rather than an overall average test time, the equation for two stations is:

$$\text{Capacity } C_2 = \frac{(3600.E)}{(R)} \quad \frac{(Ta + Tb)}{(Ta^2 + Tb^2)} \quad \frac{((X)(X))}{(1 - (Ta + X)(Tb + X))}$$

If a long test time LSI circuit is being tested on the same system as a gate, Ta and Tb will be very different. There is a popular myth that this setup is a poor way to utilize a system. In fact, it is a very good setup as the LSI station is in test most of the time, but when it is indexing the gate station can be testing, and utilizations very close to 100 percent can be achieved.

The drawback is that labor and handler efficiency can be low because the gate station only gets a small percentage of CPU time and has a throughput similar to the LSI station, i.e., low.

Productivity

Perhaps because of the traditional origins of the subject, there is a tendency for those most concerned with productivity to approach it from the direct operator point of view and, in a capital-intensive, highly mechanized situation, treat the symptoms rather than the cause in determining what is and is not feasible in terms of direct operator target setting and measurement. Though in some instances this remains important, it is becoming less frequent. Has the productivity of the mining industry increased. For example, because the exhortations to get miners to work harder has been successful in getting them to use bigger picks and shovels, or is it because more productive, capital-intensive coal cutting and loading machinery and the attendant organization and methods to sustain them at optimum working capacity have been introduced?

Productivity in an environment where, in accordance with specialization and the division of labor, many, if not all, of the direct manufacturing jobs have been deskilled to the level of simply loading and unloading machines, is more a function of asset utilization than direct human effort.

This is not to say that the human element is not important but rather takes a different form in the sense that productivity is sought in "pre-engineering" equipment to operate at its optimum. As a result of this, many direct operator activities are relegated to the loading and unloading categories. Skill, in the traditional sense, is still required during the production activity to keep the machine running at optimum performance. This calls for a quasi-technical ability of the setter caliber and is not generally possessed by direct production operators. In pursuing productivity goals, it is the overall scheme of things, machine downtime, machine dependability, scheduling, layout, product flow, and manning which needs to be considered.

Motivation

Power in the economic sense has passed from its historical association with land and capital to the recent infrastructure of knowledge and skills which comprise the organization. Not surprisingly, there have been changes in the motivation to which people respond. Compulsion was historically associated with the ownership of land. Pecuniary motivation came to be associated with capital. In today's economic climate, however, with the plethora of legislation on industrial matters attempting to regulate relationships between employees and employers, there is little opportunity to administer either. The "carrot and the stick," because of fundamental changes in the nature of modern industrial activity, tend to be replaced by identification and adaptation.

Specialized knowledge and its coordination has now become the decisive factor in economic activity. This requires that people work in groups and, as a result, power passes to these groups. Participants are normally adequately compensated, though few regard their compensation dispassionately. In associating with a group, however, an **individual can find himself being attracted or repelled by its goals**, depending on the degree to which they are compatible with his own. This recognition and the subsequent efforts at conciliation are the process of **identification** and **adaptation**.

Given any individual, there is obviously a **complex system of motivations**. In the entrepreneurial organizations, in which the primary concern is for income or profit, pecuniary motivation may be strong throughout the organization. In the mature corporation, **identification** and **adaptation** may be much more important, especially so if it has a **strong scientific** and **technical orientation**. It will also be different at different levels of participation.

Circumstances inducing identification and adaptation:

1. If a goal is seen not to be hostile to the interests of the group

2. If the group can or believes it can modify the goals of the organization to its own

3. If the prestige of the group or organization attracting identification is high and widely perceived

4. If there is frequent interaction between individuals who comprise the organization

5. If a substantial number of the needs of the individual are satisfied within the organization

6. If competition between members of the organization is minimized

The real key to motivation is in creating the circumstances in which the initiative for the individuals to motivate themselves can flourish.

PRODUCT TRANSFER PRICING

Transfer price is the price at which a commercial transaction involving change of ownership on the sale of goods between strategic business units within the same legal entity takes place. A point of equilibrium at a price the buyer is willing to pay equals the price the seller is willing to accept (average selling price—ASP).

There are two kinds of transfer price:

Legal—Applies to transactions between independent legal entities within a corporation where prices are established in accordance with **transfer price policy rules** (see later) using invoices which are **visible out with the legal entity to customs and inland revenue authorities**. These are used as a **basis for computation of import duty and corporation tax** obligations.

Operational—Applies to transactions between operations groups, albeit within the same legal entity, but as independent product P&L centers. Reflects price at which transaction is **seen** to take place by **product P&L**.

Operational transfer pricing allows for **concessions by agreement** between product P&L managers in which legal transfer price is **operationally adjusted** within the business and business management **measurement system**. It is desirable but not essential for operational transfer prices to be the same (equal) as legal transfer prices.

1. Legally—The transfer price policy is as follows:

The United States Internal Revenue code sets forth **four basic transfer pricing methods**. These methods are to be **applied sequentially**, and each must be examined in order **until an appropriate method is determined**. The following four paragraphs set forth each of the methods and when they are to be utilized.

a. **The comparable uncontrolled price method**. This method is to be applied when each of the individual terms and conditions of sale are comparable between an independent third party and a sale to a related entity. Some of the factors to consider in determining comparability would be volume, market into which sale is made, level of distribution, and the local competitive situation. Historically, sales to subsidiaries are not considered comparable to outside sales. **This method, therefore, is not used as a basis for transfer prices**.

b. **The resale price method**. This method involves determining the **ultimate resale price in the country of sale** and discounting that by the costs of disposition plus a reasonable profit to the seller.

c. **The cost-plus method**. The basic premise of this method is that all costs of manufacture (full absorption costs) are to be computed and an adder applied thereto for a reasonable profit to the manufacturing entity.

   The cost-plus method is essentially the complement of the resale price method. The determining factor as to which of the two methods are to be utilized is as follows:

   (1) If the costs incurred between the intercompany sale and the ultimate customer sale are easier to measure than the costs incurred up to the point of the intercompany sale, the resale price method is to be utilized.

   This is true and applies in the case of finished goods.

   (2) If the costs up to the point of the intercompany sale are easier to measure than those incurred by the selling entity, the cost-plus method is to be used.

   This is true and applies in the case of die/raw stock/wafers.

d. **Any other method**. This is the standard Internal Revenue Service caveat that allows any other method which can be justified and yields a reasonable answer at the bottom line to be utilized if none of the preceding methods are appropriate.

   For example, products shipped from the U.S.A. to Europe, legal transfer pricing would be as follows:

* Finished goods	—**Base price** discounted by 18%
Raw stock	—WWS + ADDER
Unprobed wafers	—WWS + ADDER
Die	—WWS + ADDER

The **base price** is defined as the lowest of the following:

(1) The lowest actual ultimate customer unit selling price within the previous six months.

(2) The low-ball price as published in the price matrix and down to which the salespersons in the field are authorized to accept orders without individual approval from the relevant factory.

(3) The resale price established in a transnational or other contract.

*Low-ball ASP—average of lowest three original equipment manufacturer (OEM) ASPs (excluding internal) over the last six-months backlog.

2. Operationally—The transfer price policy is:

Whatever is mutually acceptable and agreed between buyer and seller within the stated framework. This is why transfer pricing is always such a **controversial issue**, why it takes up a disproportionate amount of management time, why it is used to **optimize product P&Ls** and **does nothing to increase incremental wealth from a worldwide P&L point of view**. Not only can it be nonproductive, it can be counterproductive. What is agreed between buyer and seller, and there is **no obligation on either to buy or sell**, depends, like all other commercial transactions, on prevailing **supply/demand conditions**. The current **legal** transfer price policy is adequate for products whose prices are stable; i.e., mature products in a normal supply/demand situation.

It does not lend itself to:

a. An ecomonic upturn
b. An economic downturn
c. New products whose ASP is high initially but reduces rapidly as it actually comes or is wished down the learning curve.

In these circumstances, the **buyer and seller attempt to arrive at transfer prices which optimize each P&L**.

The seller seeks:

Highest possible transfer price: real in the case where the buyer is willing to accept; contrived where WWS can be manipulated downwards to reflect a low cost of sale to the sellers P&L or by manipulating low-ball ASP, which maximizes the contribution from the associated MOP at the time of sale, since adverse variations to WWS have already been incurred by the P&L in some prior period. This can result in an uncompetitive ASP to the buyer due to necessary markups to cover freight/duty and selling costs in the simplest case, and overhead recovery problems in those situations where the buyer has locally incurred manufacturing overheads to absorb, the full burden which has to be carried by the balance of locally manufactured product in any given sales number. It can also result in **backlog pressure from the customer** and **loss of credibility** since, by the time he receives the product, the prevailing **market ASP may be very much lower than that for which he is billed**.

It also results in paying unnecessary import duty. The **buyer's interest** is obviously to secure the **lowest possible transfer price** for exactly the same product P&L optimization reasons.

Considering the three previous cases:

An **upturn obviously favors the seller**, in some cases to the extent that TPs are almost academic since price/demand elasticity is low and products may be on allocation. The seller can charge high prices, confident that the intermediate buyer and end customer will accept. This is the worst case as far as paying unnecessary duties is concerned.

A downturn obviously favors the buyer, who can now adopt the following approach to obtaining competitive TPs:

a. If the prevailing ASP/TP/markup relationship does not drive the local product P&L negative below margin two, he can accept the TP and place back-to-back orders on the shipping source.
b. If the prevailing ASP/TP/markup relationship does drive the product P&L negative below margin two, he can **apply pressure to the shipping source** to reduce the TP by arguing it is not in the best interest of his product P&L to proceed

with the transaction. However, he would be willing to **act as an agent on behalf** of the shipping source, since it may still be in the interest of that P&L to proceed at a TP which does not adversely effect the agent's P&L (**factory loading**).

Approximately 35 percent M2 is typically required to break even at M5, but any contribution at M2 between 0 and 35 percent absorbs buyer's fixed costs.

In all of the negotiation and adjustment of financial parameters such as WWS or TPs, it is usually difficult if not impossible to see where **real margin two costs** are comprehended. In the case of new products, at least initially, ASPs are very high; so too are transfer prices and probably real margin two costs. WWS are usually set very low in anticipation of meeting these costs some time in the future. However, customers with an interest in such products, while willing to pay a high price for small volume in the early stages, will not commit without being given budgetary prices for the future. Obviously, **budgetary prices based on a backlog/billed ASP bear no relationship to what the price will be in one or two years time**. Situations can arise where competitive pressure drives the ASP down further and faster than was anticipated from the learning curve projections. In any transfer price related activity it is worth remembering that "**rules are for the obedience of fools and the guidance of wise men**."

1. Page 1—Basic Transfer Pricing Methods

None of these four methods makes provisions for:

a. Different competitive situations in buyer/seller locations.
b. Price projections based on learning curve expectations on new, high ASP products whose price will decrease rapidly.
c. Options (B)—**The resale price method can be wrongly interpreted** to mean the U.S. resale price and not, as is literally stated, the ultimate **resale** price in the **country of sale**.

2. There is normally no automatic system of providing these. They are usually computed manually, which is cumbersome and time consuming.

The Mechanics of a Transfer Price Transaction:

Recall the notion of two accounts:

1. The inventory account and
2. The P&L account

In a transfer price transaction there will be two sets of these, one for both buyer and seller.

The Buyer's Position	The Seller's Position
WWS value of purchased product goes into inventory account (until time of sale).	P&L credited with sale at transfer price. Cost of sale hits operational P&L as transfer of product value at WWS from inventory to P&L account.
Difference between transfer price and WWS value of product hits P&L account as MOP (margin on purchases) adverse cost.	
Other costs incurred in procuring product hits P&L account at appropriate line item; i.e., freight, duty, inventory cost.	These costs are incurred by the buyer.

Transfer Price—Administration and Management

Product Marketing	Define and **substantiate** what ASPs need to be in order to be competitive—by product/by package/by region/by time frame.
Materials Control (Business Analysis)	Compute transfer price required in relation to these ASPs. Identify those products where ASP/TP relationship is not economically viable. Convey to finance.
Finance (P&L Analyst)	Prepare above for submission to transfer price group.
Operations Management	Review and control the above.

All of the above should be completed on a quarterly basis.

Exceptions to normal policy

Market penetration pricing applies to high technology products which are subject to intense competition and rapid price erosion. Under these conditions, transfer price will be 82 percent of competitors' quotes or such other base price deemed necessary by the manufacturing location as required to penetrate the local market. Reduced TPs will be used for both legal and operational purposes.

TRANSFER PRICING

The following is a method of establishing, **for a given transfer price**, what the break-even ASP value would need to be at margin two and margin five (seller's market).

		% of TSP	$ TSP
Transfer price	plus freight	1%	
	duty	17%	
	other costs (sales allowances)	4%	
			________
Cost at margin 2	plus product mkt.		
	purch./dist.	1.1%	
	div. G&A	0.2%	
	group	0.6%	
		19.6%	________
Cost at margin 5			
			________

Cost at Margin 2

For example, TSP, freight, delay, and others are variable costs which are incurred solely by purchasing the product. Thus, if we do not purchase product, we will not incur **any** of those costs down to margin 2. We therefore need to look very carefully at the contribution at this margin: i.e. (ASP—margin 2 cost). If it is negative, then the cost of the product is greater than the revenue, and we should not purchase this product. However, any such decision needs to be channeled through the operations managers; in many cases, it may not be purely a purchase/nonpurchase decision based on the previous information which should be made. It does highlight a problem.

Note: In a buyer's market, it is more appropriate to take ASP as given and compute what the transfer price needs to be.

Cost at Margin 5

Excluding margin 2 product marketing, purchasing/distribution, division G&A, and group are all costs that are more or less fixed; i.e., they will be incurred although we do not purchase product.

If the contribution of this product is positive, then we have made a profit on this sale. However, if it is negative, then on the profit-before-tax line we have made a loss on this sale. Although **if the contribution at margin 2 was positive, then this sale has contributed to our overhead recovery**; i.e., more revenue to cover the fixed costs, reducing the impact on the profit by these costs.

In summary, the purchase/nonpurchase decision is not self-evident. There are many considerations to be taken into account in such a decision.

This does highlight a problem if one exists in purchasing product. In terms of profitability, it raises such questions as:

1. Is the transfer price the problem?

2. Is it an ASP problem?

3. Do we need to probe this product?

4. If we do not purchase this product to meet our billings forecast, may this be beneficial to the profit in the P&L?

5. Is the product margin 2 cost the problem?

The real problem is in the rules by which transfer pricing is arrived.

The formula is **82 percent of the current U.S. low-ball billings ASP**.

This is adequate and fair for established products which are released to production and are not subject to frequent price reductions or to new products whose initial value is not high. However, on products like the 64K or the MC68000, the combination of high initial cost and status on the learning curve leads to frequent price reductions. Indeed, so frequent and so significant that, in some cases, we find ourselves **shipping product to a customer at an ASP that, because of the time difference between booking and billing the product, is higher than the customer would be required to pay if he bought the product on the open market**.

The only way to avoid the serious consequences of such a practice is for the formula for **transfer prices for such products to be linked to the forecast booking ASPs**.

Recommended Changes to Operational Transfer Price Policy

1. **Stable Products**

   For products at or near the end of the learning curve, no changes are required.

2. **New Products**

   a. Low-ball highlight ASP to be used as **base price**.

   b. Budgetary transfer price projections to be given for the same reasons that budgetary end customer ASPs (should include unprobed wafers and die) are required.

   c. All product line TPs to be provided.

3. **Economic Upturn**

   a. Ensure internal support sales budget commitments are honored or changed only with the mutual agreement of buyer/seller.

   b. Low-ball booking ASP to be used as **base price**.

4. **Economic Downturn**

   a. Low-ball booking ASP to be used as base price.

   b. Buyer reverts to role of agent when local product P&L would be driven negative at margin 5 by prevailing ASP/TP/selling-cost relationship.

In all cases, legal and operational invoicing to be reconciled by finance.

General

1. If WWS and local standards are set unrealistically low (April to September, October to March), then favorable margins at time of sale are only realized at expense of adverse manufacturing variations absorbed by product P&L in some prior period.

2. Manufacturing source P&L should provide analysis of contribution at margin 2/margin 5 for both locally manufactured product (LMP) and imported finished goods (IFG).

9

Cost Accounting for Short Cycle-Time Manufacturing

THE OLD WAY—A TRADITIONAL COST ACCOUNTING SYSTEM

Most cost accounting systems in use today evolved around the functional approach to manufacturing: the so-called just-in-case (JIC) approach in which **uncertainty is addressed by means of inventory**. This and the more contemporary method of manufacturing, as well as an in-depth treatment of a traditional cost accounting system, are discussed at length elsewhere in the book but are summarized here for convenience. The major characteristics of the functional method, in strict accordance with the principle of specialization and the division of labor, are narrowly defined, production operative tasks, functionally specialized processes, with a high degree of fixed function mechanization or automation, often separated by large distances and coupled together by pipeline inventory and queuing work-in-process, with work shuttled to and from inventory banks and these value-adding operations on the factory floor. This results in much **work-in-process zig-zag**, with **many clerical and accounting transactions** when a product lot is moved from one cost block or inventory bank to another. As a consequence of this, **cycle-times, the time between start and completion of a product, are usually very long**.

Inventory is defined by accounting convention to be an asset in this approach and is rigorously accounted for in usually very **large and elaborate inventory bank networks supported by computerized tracking**. Frequent inventory audits are required. The focus is on direct labor and product cost although these are generally difficult to quantify accurately for a variety of reasons. Normally these accounting systems are not real-time and with the long cycle-times involved, **manufacturing costs incurred in any period do not correspond to the sales revenue in that same period**. Product cost standards, by key stages of completion, are established by quantifying expected values for the major manufacturing variables such as yield and throughput for the standards period. These standards are normally set twice per year, covering two six-month periods. Following the notion that **direct labor adds value to the product**, many of these systems are entirely direct labor based. (Since value is considered to be added only by direct labor, you can have as much of this wealth creating resource as you want, but you cannot employ a technician to make the machine work better since this is an indirect, "nonwealth-creating" resource.)

Overhead is allocated across the product portfolio based on direct labor hours.

Because it is a standard cost accounting system, total actual costs are captured from which variations to standard are quantified. The operating statement is credited with the standard cost value of any inventory produced, with the product transferred to the inventory account where it is held at standard value. In effect, the **product is sold to the inventory account from the operating profit and loss account**. This can encourage the building of inventory for which there is no customer demand. The value of this inventory is then written up or down accordingly as the standards change, further confusing our factory manager. All of the preceding costs are further classified into **inventoriable** and **non-inventoriable**. Inventoriable costs are those labor, material, and direct factory overhead costs provided for in the standards. Noninventoriable are the indirect factory overhead costs, some of which are provided for in the standard, and some of which are not, which may then appear as negative variations to standard. These costs are further complicated by the concept of **procedural variation**, the difference between local and worldwide standard performance. The "cost of sales" in any period is the standard cost of the product. From this, margin 1—sales revenue minus cost of sales—is calculated. Margin 2 is based, not on the actual cost of the material being sold, but on the cost of the material being manufactured at that time. When, as is most often the case, actual performance is worse than standard, whether the standard or actual manufacturing performance was the culprit, will be debated at great length, usually to no avail. Yet another major shortcoming of such systems is that any individual product costs cannot be isolated but appear as averages.

Pay-for-performance schemes in this system are usually based on forecasted improvements in standards net of current cost and on overhead recovery, not on revenue, profit, quality, product cost, or on-time shipments to the customer. Again, because of long cycle-times, distortions due to mix changes, for example, can confuse the picture. **There is a compelling propensity in this system for the manufacturing organization to produce if material, machine capacity, and people are available—not just if that particular product is needed.** The emphasis is on machine and operator utilization (not necessarily efficiently) rather than the **effectiveness of the overall system**.

THE NEW WAY

The contemporary approach to manufacturing employs **short cycle-time instead of inventory to deal with uncertainty** as shown in Figure 9-1. (There are other equally important differences, such as using statistical process control to **control process variation** and build quality into the product rather than inspect out defects. These, as we shall see, are relevant in our cost accounting context.) **Any inventory which is either not immediately sellable or having value added to it is considered to be a liability rather than an asset in this approach** and techniques such as group technology, dedicated equipment, with dedicated multiskill teams, are collectively employed in organizing the manufacturing resources into focused factories, called cells or modules on a smaller scale. See Figure 9-2.

These cells normally operate in a just-in-time, "zero" inventory materials management mode in which **material is processed serially and continuously in order to reduce cycle-time**. In this way, the very costly consequences of WIP zig-zag are avoided. The emphasis is on producing only that material which is sellable, when it is required. This approach acknowledges that machines, not just direct labor, add value to the product;

SHORT CYCLE TIME MANUFACTURING

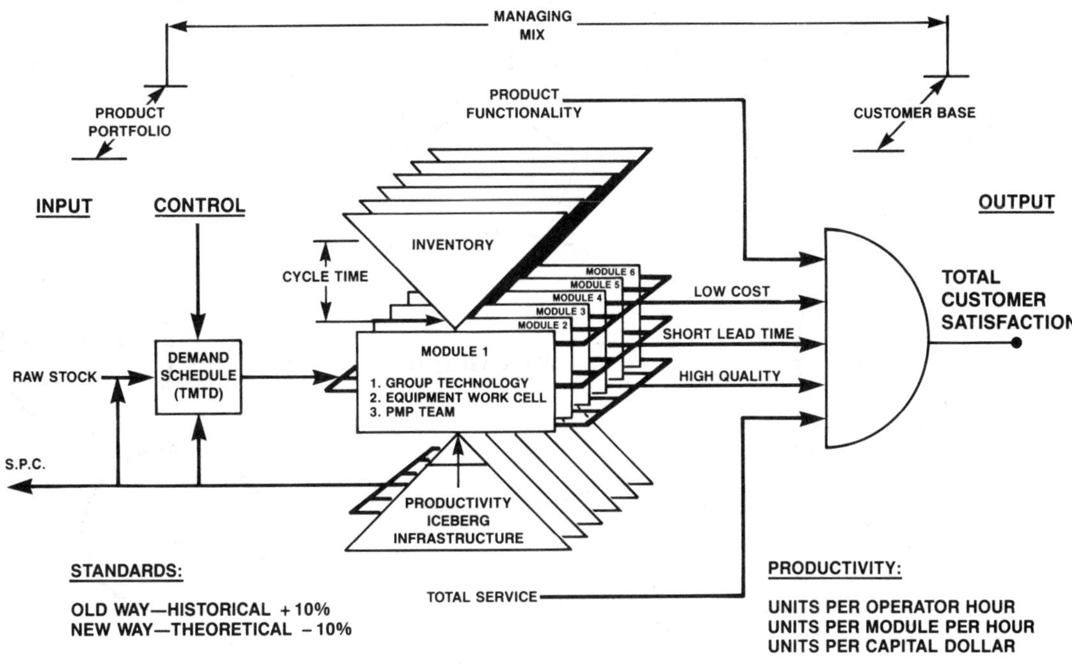

Figure 9-1 Group of Six Cell Models Over Which Product Portfolio is Spread

that manufacturing is becoming much more capital intensive; that fixed cost and material are becoming a higher proportion of product cost relative to direct labor cost. The emphasis in this approach is on the process—that **the quality of the product, and the associated cost, is a function of the quality of the process by which it is designed and manufactured**. Anything which impedes the free flowing of material is attacked. Cycle-time, linearity of inputs and outputs to all operations, line balancing and managing mix, generally ignored in the functional approach, are key operating parameters in this approach. **The system is in fact designed to maximize revenue and profit by maximizing total customer satisfaction, not just to minimize costs.**

WHAT SHOULD BE MEASURED?

As cost accounting's internal customer, **what would the manufacturing community define as total customer satisfaction in this new kind of manufacturing environment?** Why can't it simply be: What is the selling price of the product? How much did it cost? The difference is profit (or loss). Must the information we need be hidden in a fog of obscurity of accounting convention, professional jargon and rules which have not withstood the test of time? Other than providing employment for accountants, what good is an accounting system to the factory manager and his people, or anyone else for that matter, which requires a PhD in finance and ten years of effort to understand—and even then does not tell him what he needs to know?

Our interest in this question is **in the context of manufacturing excellence**. To answer our question then, we must begin by first **defining excellence, then devise a**

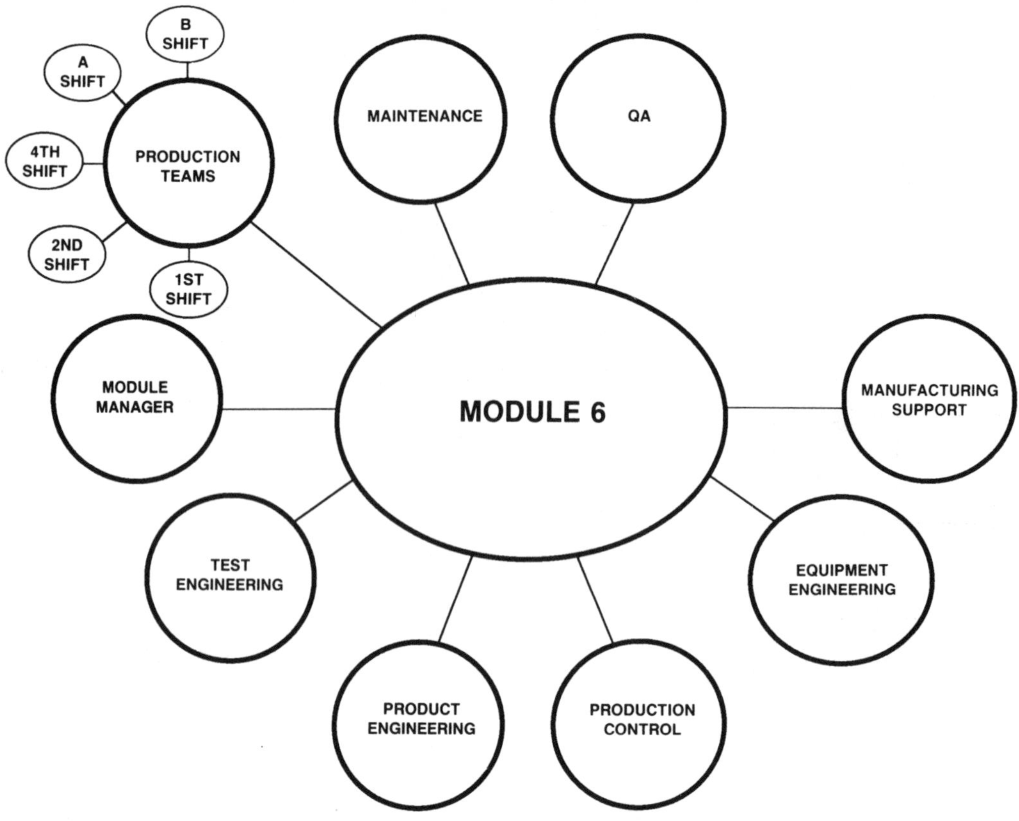

Figure 9-2 People Organization in the Cell
Task Focused, Cross Functional

system which measures variation to this. In the book *The Goal*, Goldratt and Cox identified **throughput, inventory, and operating expense** as the critical parameters in manufacturing. Can it really be this simple? There is indeed truth here, but not the whole truth. The reader at this point, is referred back to our strategic hierarchy discussion. In this exercise, we **identified manufacturing's primary contribution to total customer satisfaction as quality, cost, and on-time delivery**.

A standard cost accounting system can help on only one of these, namely costs, albeit in a limited way, as we have already discussed. That after all is what it is designed to do. But such systems do not help much, if at all, on quality and on-time delivery—the erstwhile "intangibles" ignored by the traditional cost accounting system, not because these other parameters are less important than cost but because they cannot be quantified in dollars. **Traditional cost accounting systems cannot put a dollar value on good or even superior quality of outgoing product or on-time delivery, even though customers obviously place a high value on these.** This is also true of traditional accounting investment justification techniques such as return on investment (ROI). Bad quality they at least attempt to deal with in the form of the dollar value of returned materials, or yield of the manufacturing processes. Here we begin to understand the problem perhaps. **Traditional accounting systems place too much emphasis on operations which relate only to cost and not enough on those which relate to adding value, in the complete sense and not just to inventory,** for the internal as well as the external customer. Since

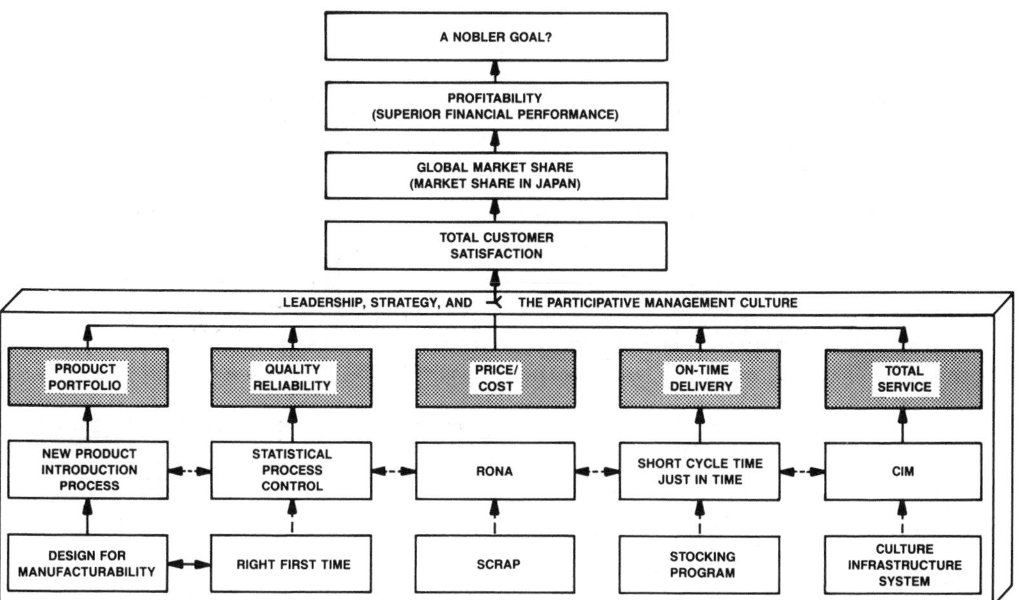

Figure 9-3 Strategic Hierarchy of Business Imperatives

inventory is considered to be an asset in the traditional system, any activity which creates inventory is ''adding value'' and is by definition therefore, good. In fact, this is the only way which added value (or reduced cost) can be measured in such systems. (Since the modern approach is to minimize inventory in the system, any action to do so must, again by definition, be considered bad in the traditional approach.) Either way, the manufacturing community's customers, both external and internal, are denied total customer satisfaction. How can we fix this in the new model? Might it be possible that we can demonstrate to the accounting community **that cost is a function of quality and on-time delivery; that it is in fact possible to place a value on these things, measurable indirectly if not directly in dollars?** If this is so, and we measure these parameters and the things they are affected by, can we come closer to total customer satisfaction?

Quality

Scrap is the reciprocal of yield. By using right first time discipline and statistical process control to build in quality rather than inspect out defects which incurs additional cost in the form of rework and/or scrap, waste of material, capacity, and time is minimized or eliminated. (See Figure 9-3.) **By improving quality in this way, that is, by reducing scrap, we are also reducing cost in a quantifiable way.** Reducing scrap is the reciprocal of adding value. This also contributes to our on-time delivery objective since material which is on engineering hold, or being reworked, or scrapped is not being processed in the shortest possible cycle-time.

On-Time Delivery

In the case of on-time delivery, this is nothing more than **shipping the required volume, to the prescribed mix, at the right time**. On-time delivery is, among other things, a function of cycle-time, which also contributes to our low cost objective, since **the lower**

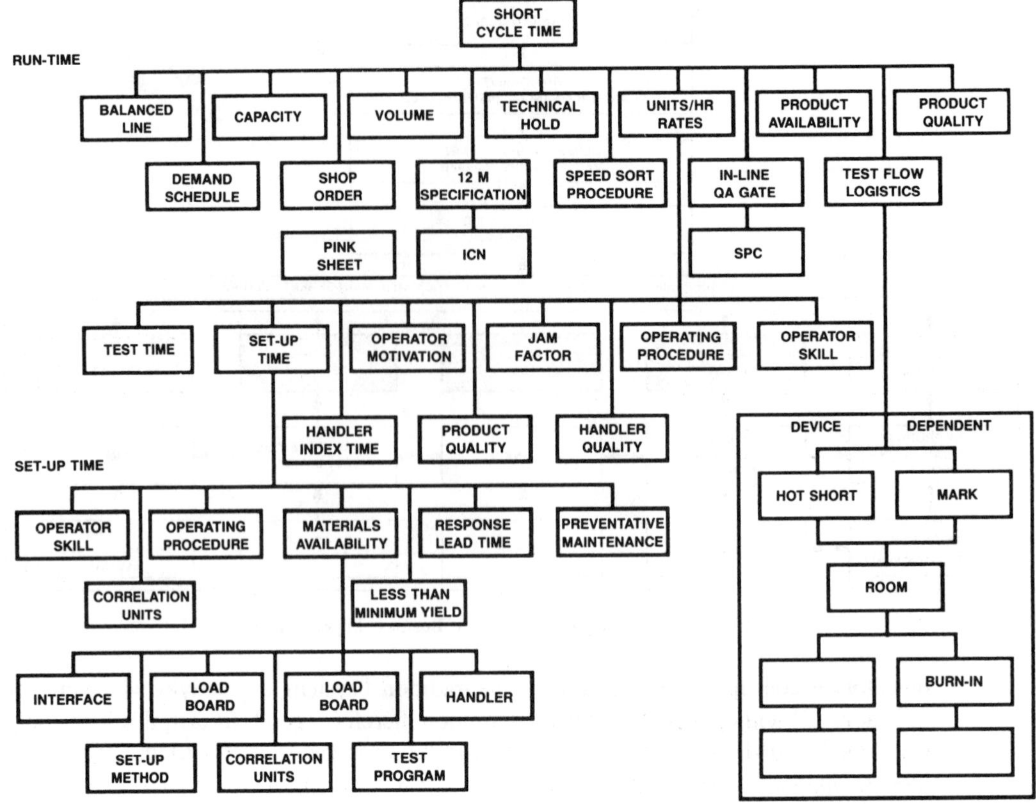

Figure 9-4 Produtivity Infrastructure

the cycle-time, the more units which can be processed with a given amount of capacity, in a given amount of time. So by reducing cycle-time we are also reducing cost. Again it is possible to establish the correlation quantitatively as we shall see later. (Also, by including linearity, building only that product which is immediately sellable rather than that which there is capacity and material for, **revenue and profit are maximized**.)

Low Cost

Low cost is **a function of high productivity—of machine capacity, material, and time—not just of direct labor**. Material in unsaleable finished goods, or staged work in process, or queued up in the line, is not productive use of inventory, or the cash needed to fund it. Again, short cycle-time and high quality require less inventory in the system, so inventory productivity and therefore low cost are optimized. Since high productivity is a function of high quality and low cycle-time, **all of the variables which effect cycle-time**, as shown in Figure 9-4, **must be attacked**.

So there is indeed a quantifiable relationship between quality, on-time delivery, and cost. That relationship manifests itself in the form of cycle-time. So if we can **quantify the hourly cost of operating a cell**, and we know the **theoretical cycle-time for a product** (or product lot, or mix of products) then we can not only **determine the theoretical capacity for that product or mix of products through the cell**, but we can also **set a standard cost for the product** (including overhead recovery) **based on**

cycle-time and the cost of running the process, rather than on direct labor. The actual cycle-time for the product, or lot, would capture any and all **inefficiencies or variances**, for whatever reason. Both standard and the actual product costs calculated in this way would be much more accurate than is possible in a conventional system. **Cycle-time is in fact, the super, superordinate, all encompassing measurement of manufacturing excellence.**

Assume for example, that a product has a theoretical cycle-time of three seconds. The maximum theoretical units per hour which could be processed would be 3600/3 = 1200 units. If the measured cycle-time were six seconds (UPH is 600 units per hour), then the cell is running at only 50 percent utilization. **The other 50 percent represents waste in some form.** While actual cycle-times are certainly not fixed and irreducible, neither are theoretical. Over the course of time, these too can be attacked and reduced.

MEASURING MANUFACTURING PERFORMANCE

In pursuing manufacturing excellence, we must **set standards for the parameters of quality, cost, and on-time delivery, and for all of the major variables which affect them, based on what is theoretically possible** minus some small allowance for life's imperfections—**not history plus 10 percent. We can then compare actual performance to theoretical in order to quantify variances**. (Historical performance plus 10 percent perpetuates mediocrity, not excellence.) So what do we need to measure in order to capture these parameters? In any given accounting period, using the parlance of Goldratt and Cox, manufacturing operations management needs to know:

Throughput

- **Good units processed**—the volume of units across which the total cost of the cell is to be absorbed.
- **Output linearity**—the degree to which material flow is continuous. **This must be measured hourly, daily, and cumulatively.**
- **On-time delivery**—the degree to which factory schedule and customer on-time delivery commitments are met.
- **Cycle-time of good units**—the shorter the cycle-time, the higher the volume, the lower the fixed cost per unit.
- **Total cycle-time**—including clerical transactions, staging inventory, work in process, and so on, capturing not only manufacturing inefficiencies, but **the inefficiencies of the total system, from order entry to shipping**.
- **Quality of the outgoing product**—to measure the degree to which excellence in this parameter is being achieved.
- **Units scrapped**—waste in the form of material and capacity: **a measure of the quality of the incoming material and defects introduced by the receiving process itself**.
- **Units reworked**—the amount of waste in the form of people and machine capacity due to misprocessing. (An example of how these parameters are measured and reported in an outgoing final test operation is shown in Figures 9-5 and 9-6.)

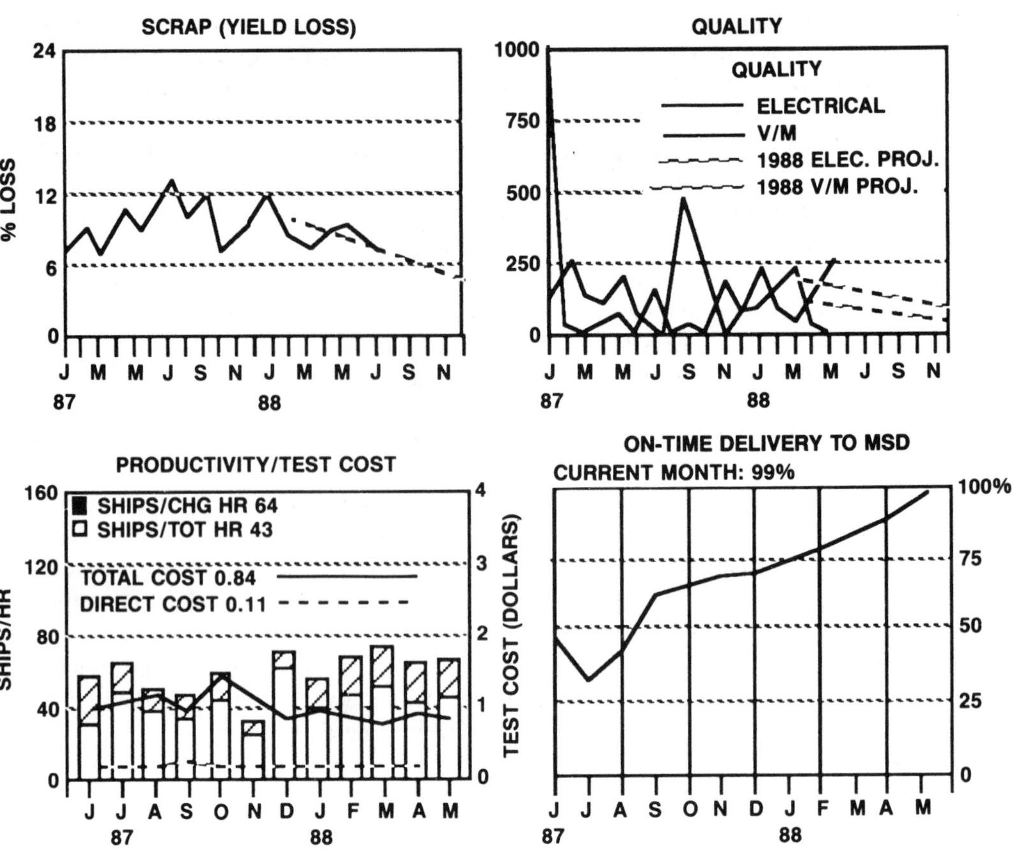

Figure 9-5 Module 4: Sentry 15

Inventory

In this case, we need to quantify inventory by volume, by stage of completion, and its cycle-time through all operations, including nonvalue adding operations. Inventory productivity is measured in turns—the average value of the next three months sales forecast divided by the value of the inventory at standard cost. As can be seen from Figure 9-7, the absolute value of inventory has increased as shipments increased, but the turns ratio has remained more or less the same. (Six turns is not good!)

Costs

In order to determine the cost per hour of the cell, we need to capture the following major components of cost as follows:

- **Equipment depreciation**—the major "fixed cost" component.
- **Cell facility cost**—based on floor space occupied.
- **Power costs.**
- **Cell hours worked**—the cell is available, but may not be working, for 168 hours per week. The degree to which it is not is again waste.
- **Total hours worked (team labor)**—to determine the cost of direct labor input.
- **Direct operating expenses.**
- **Set-up time**—nonproductive use of capacity and people.

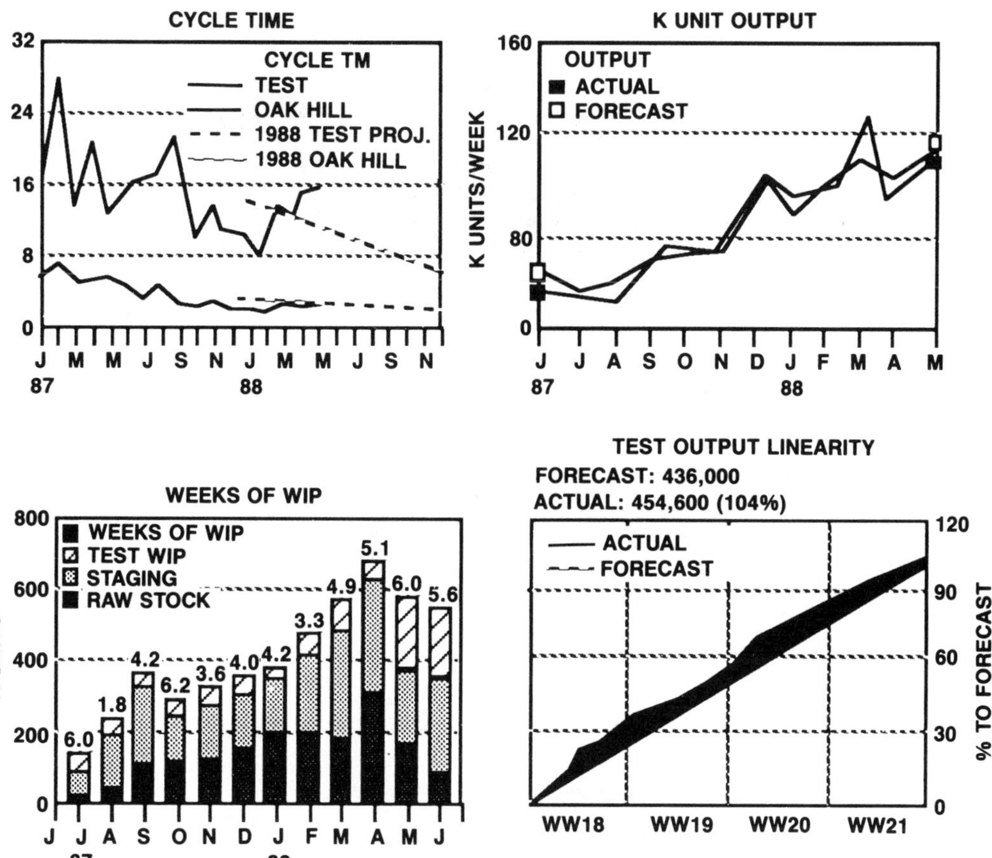

Figure 9-6 Module 4: Sentry 15

- **Cell downtime**—nonproductive use of capacity.
- **Queuing time**—nonproductive use of material, cost of inventory. (Set-up time, cell downtime,and queuing time constitute **nonproductive cycle-time**.)
- **Engineering hours by cell**—nonmanufacturing cost.
- **Material**—input value.
- **Quality assurance cost**—with statistical process control, this becomes an integral part (and cost) of the manufacturing process rather than the cost of an independent quality control department. (Up to this point, these are all easily captured, direct costs.)
- **Administration/engineering/production control cost**—allocated to cells based on estimated effort. (An example of how these can be measured and reported is shown in Figure 9-8 and Tables 9-1 through 9-4.)

This does not represent the new model used in cycle-time, but is a modification of the standard cost accounting system. Moreover, since resources are assigned by module, the unit costs are more accurate then can be obtained in the purely functional system.

This is not quite as simple as: What can we sell it for? How much does it cost to produce? The difference is profit. But it is much closer. Obviously, the lower the cost associated with each of these, the lower the cost per hour of the cell. The overall business results in using such an approach are shown in Figure 9-4.

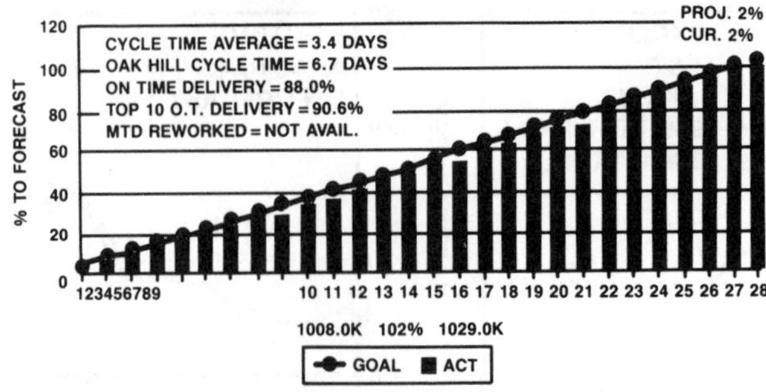
CUMULATIVE SHIPMENTS: SHIPMENTS FOR MAY 1986
PROJ. 2%
CUR. 2%
CYCLE TIME AVERAGE = 3.4 DAYS
OAK HILL CYCLE TIME = 6.7 DAYS
ON TIME DELIVERY = 88.0%
TOP 10 O.T. DELIVERY = 90.6%
MTD REWORKED = NOT AVAIL.
% TO FORECAST
120
100
80
60
40
20
0
123456789
10 11 12 13 14 15 16 17 18 19 20 21 22 23 24 25 26 27 28
1008.0K 102% 1029.0K
GOAL
ACT

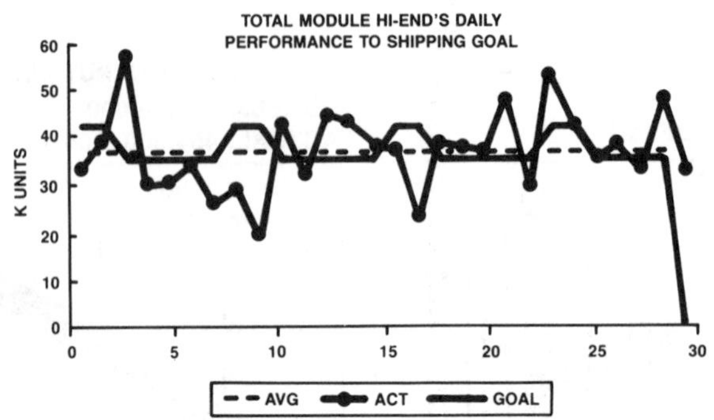
TOTAL MODULE HI-END'S DAILY
PERFORMANCE TO SHIPPING GOAL
K UNITS
60
50
40
30
20
10
0
0 5 10 15 20 25 30
AVG
ACT
GOAL

MODULE 4: SENTRY 15 SHIPMENTS FOR MAY 1986
PROJ. 4%
CUR. 4%
CYCLE TIME AVERAGE = 2.3 DAYS
OAK HILL CYCLE TIME = 19.0 DAYS
ON TIME DELIVERY = 98.7%
TOP 10 O.T. DELIVERY = 98.3%
MTD REWORKED = NOT AVAIL.
% TO FORECAST
120
100
80
60
40
20
0
123456789
10 11 12 13 14 15 16 17 18 19 20 21 22 23 24 25 26 27 28
436.0K 104% 454.6K
GOAL
ACT

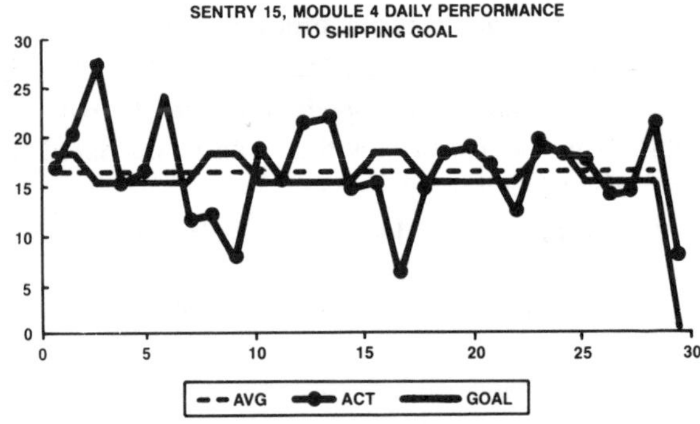
SENTRY 15, MODULE 4 DAILY PERFORMANCE
TO SHIPPING GOAL
30
25
20
15
10
5
0
0 5 10 15 20 25 30
AVG
ACT
GOAL

Figure 9-7

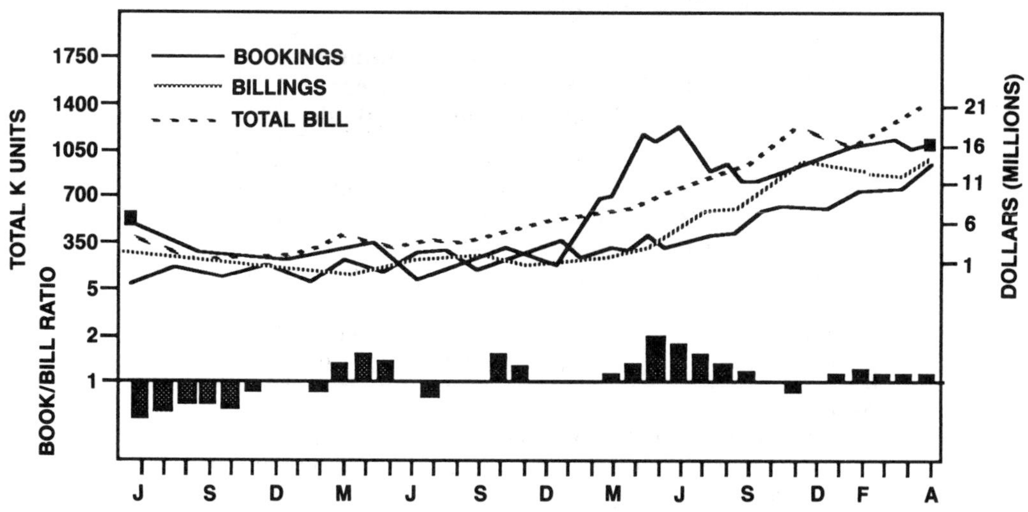
DOMESTIC BOOKINGS/BILLINGS
THREE MONTH MOVING AVERAGE
BOOKINGS
BILLINGS
TOTAL BILL
TOTAL K UNITS
1750
1400
1050
700
350
5
2
1
BOOK/BILL RATIO
DOLLARS (MILLIONS)
21
16
11
6
1
J S D M J S D M J S D F A

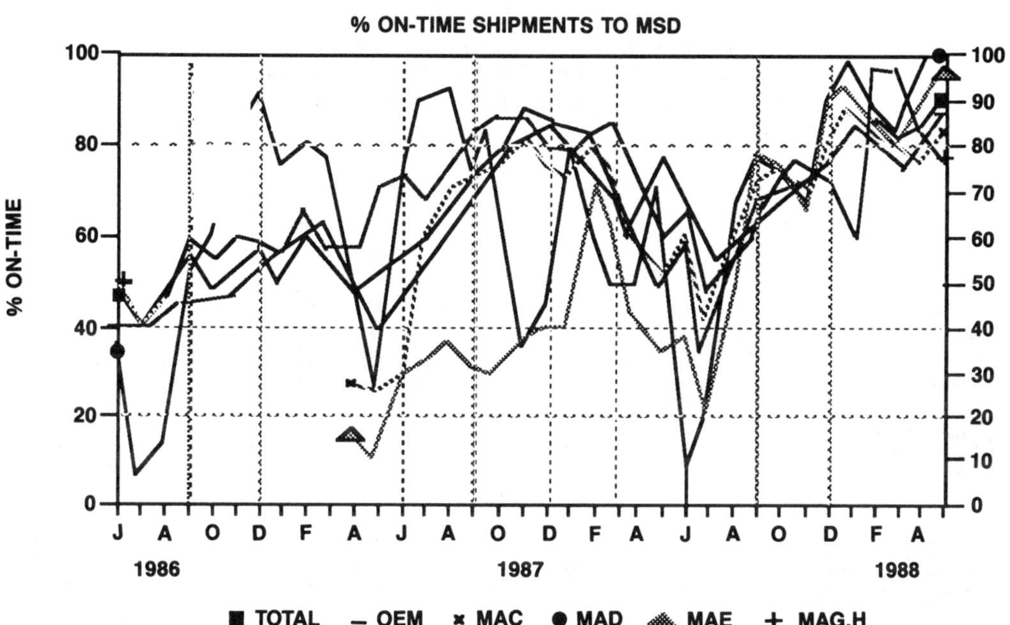
% ON-TIME SHIPMENTS TO MSD
% ON-TIME
100
80
60
40
20
0
90
70
50
30
10
J A O D F A J A O D F A J A O D F A
1986
1987
1988
TOTAL
OEM
MAC
MAD
MAE
MAG,H

Figure 9-8

Table 9-1 Test Module Cost Report
Square Footage and Depreciation Per Module
(Used as Allocation Bases Per Module)

Module	Sq. Ft. Test	% of Total	Annual Depr./ Module	Monthly Depr./ Module	% of Total
1	802	7.6	481.1	40.1	23.1
2	251	2.4	187.2	15.6	9.0
3	383	3.6	81.5	6.8	3.9
4	2640	25.0	532	44.3	25.5
5	755	7.1	232.9	19.4	11.2
6	2374	22.5	568.0	47.3	27.3
Other		31.8	0	0.0	0.0
Total		100.0	2082.7	173.6	100.0

NOTES:

1. The sq. ft. %/module is used to allocate mfg. engr. EXPS and DFO building costs (SD372), e.g., brick and mortar, electricity, etc.
2. The square footage per module was obtained from manufacturing planning based on actual measurement.
3. The depr./module % is used to allocate the monthly test depreciation out of SD372 (DFO) to each module.
4. The annual depr./module is based on breaking out each asset and its depreciation from SD372 (DFO) to its respective module.

Table 9-2 Test Module Cost Report
Base Input Data

ITEM	COST DESCRIPTION	ALLOC METHOD	1987 MAY	JUN	JUL	AUG	SEP	OCT	NOV	DEC	1988 JAN	FEB	MAR	APR	MAY
SD372	MONTHLY DEPRECIATION	IDENT	116.4	172.5	133.5	136.9	229.2	187.0	187.0	237.0	157.3	157.0	239.1	231.3	235.1
SD372	500 S/C'S EXCL DEPR	SQ FT	40.7	50.4	53.0	51.1	59.4	40.1	44.9	43.2	53.8	49.1	64.5	49.9	51.7
SD372	TOT EXPS LESS 500'S	D.L	156.1	221.7	178.7	190.7	206.7	200.5	223.0	298.0	254.8	270.2	272.1	271.4	247.8
SD191	COB EXPENSES	D.L	63.6	74.9	64.7	64.7	80.1	71.0	75.0	86.0	82.8	78.0	79.7	77.5	78.2
SD055	DIRECT LABOR K$	IDENT	60.7	88.4	85.3	92.9	146.8	118.6	122.5	144.8	134.2	142.3	179.7	155.9	159.7
SD055	INVENTORY BURDEN	D.L	142.9	183.5	185.1	152.3	202.4	159.6	163.5	204.0	174.7	175.2	240.3	203.6	223.0
SD055	NON-INVENTORY BURDEN	D.L	30.1	44.7	19.2	33.4	51.3	35.9	33.4	34.2	35.4	31.1	40.5	38.3	42.1
QA	TOTAL P & L EXPS	D.L	97.0	128.0	119.0	90.0	125.0	114.0	124.0	133.0	103.0	109.0	122.0	110.0	112.0
MFG ENG	TOTAL P & L EXPS	SQ FT	42.0	53.0	57.0	72.0	88.0	84.0	89.0	84.0	61.0	84.0	145.0	115.0	149.0
	TOTAL TEST EXPS - - ➤		749.5	1017.1	895.5	884.0	1188.9	1010.7	1062.3	1264.2	1057.0	1095.9	1382.9	1252.9	1298.6
M1 KU	TOTAL MONTHLY KUNITS PER MOD		70.0	87.5	75.4	77.1	104.4	83.5	93.8	91.3	83.5	86.8	101.2	94.7	78.0
M2 KU	TOTAL MONTHLY KUNITS PER MOD		0.9	1.5	0.8	1.7	2.4	0.7	2.6	2.4	4.7	1.4	1.9	0.7	1.6
M3 KU	TOTAL MONTHLY KUNITS PER MOD		213.3	281.0	181.4	209.6	37	213.7	157.9	197.1	320.9	206.5	279.2	212.3	189.3
M4 KU	TOTAL MONTHLY KUNITS PER MOD		156.9	279.0	201.0	176.8	364.1	290.1	305.5	493.6	375.1	416.8	555.1	421.7	454.6
M5 KU	TOTAL MONTHLY KUNITS PER MOD		43.3	48.8	56.5	50.8	81.5	52.0	52.1	63.2	77.9	92.2	125.6	114.4	177.8
M6 KU	TOTAL MONTHLY KUNITS PER MOD		62.7	92.0	73.7	83.1	149.2	99.0	140.2	130.0	104.2	97.1	126.3	128.7	127.7
	TOTAL KUNITS . . ➤		547.2	789.8	588.9	599.0	1038.6	738.9	752.1	977.6	966.3	900.8	1189.3	972.5	1029.0
M1 DL	TOTAL MTHLY D.L. HRS PER MOD		1492.6	1638.1	2180.2	2652.4	2697.6	1942.9	2393.1	2884.5	2296.4	2310.4	2963.0	26464.7	2265.8
M2 DL	TOTAL MTHLY D.L. HRS PER MOD		83.3	152.9	63.5	71.4	390.3	279.2	724.6	738.2	525.5	496.5	708.9	751.5	672.5
M3 DL	TOTAL MTHLY D.L. HRS PER MOD		1469.9	1903.1	1805.2	1887.5	2962.8	1580.9	2157.6	2298.8	2021.1	1673.8	2317.5	1929.8	1758.1
M4 DL	TOTAL MTHLY D.L. HRS PER MOD		2840.4	4588.1	3940.4	3669.1	6153.2	8407.8	5912.6	7065.0	6322.1	6301.6	7936.4	6800.1	7154.2
M5 DL	TOTAL MTHLY D.L. HRS PER MOD		1207.6	1816.9	2150.5	2179.8	3089.6	1866.3	1562.4	1813.2	1881.5	2698.3	4159.7	3380.2	3846.6
M6 DL	TOTAL MTHLY D.L. HRS PER MOD		1781.0	2909.8	2424.6	2892.0	5087.0	3461.4	4778.2	5582.9	5054.3	5260.0	7026.9	6438.9	7069.1
	TOTAL DL HRS - - ➤		8874.8	13008.9	12564.4	13352.2	20380.5	17538.5	17528:5	20382.6	18100.9	18740.6	25112.4	21765.2	22766.3
	DL RATE/HR - - ➤		$6.80	$6.80	$6.80	$6.80	$6.80	$6.80	$7.00	$7.00	$7.00	$7.00	$7.00	$7.00	$7.00
	TOT DL K$ PER PRODUCTION - - ➤		60.3	88.5	85.4	90.8	138.6	119.3	122.7	142.7	126.7	131.2	175.8	152.4	159.4
	TOT DL K$ PER BURDEN RPT - - ➤		60.7	88.4	85.3	92.9	146.8	118.6	122.5	144.8	134.2	142.3	179.7	155.9	159.7
	DELTA(-)= EXCESS PROD K$ - - ➤		0.4	-0.1	-0.1	2.1	8.2	-0.7	-0.2	2.1	7.5	11.1	3.9	3.5	0.3

Table 9-2 (continued)

* * ALL COST PER UNIT * *

MODULE	COST ELEMENT	←-1987-							→	←-1988-				→
		MAYJUNJUL			AUG	SEPOCTNOV			DECJANFEB			MAR	APR	MAY
	LABOR COST/UNIT	0.123	0.112	0.133	0.141	0.115	0.197	0.132	0.097	0.115	0.103	0.097	0.113	0.110
TOTAL	INV BURDEN/UNIT	0.291	0.232	0.289	0.237	0.168	0.264	0.181	0.143	0.163	0.141	0.137	0.151	0.154
MODULE	NON-INVEN/UNIT	0.061	0.057	0.030	0.052	0.043	0.059	0.037	0.024	0.033	0.025	0.023	0.028	0.029
4	DEPRECIATION/UNIT	0.069	0.057	0.061	0.072	0.161	0.165	0.156	0.123	0.107	0.096	0.110	0.140	0.132
(6800)	DFO/UNIT EXCEL DEPR	0.372	0.317	0.372	0.399	0.229	0.380	0.298	0.240	0.288	0.260	0.196	0.231	0.200
	IFO/UNIT	0.130	0.095	0.101	0.101	0.066	0.117	0.083	0.060	0.077	0.063	0.045	0.057	0.054
	QA/UNIT	0.198	0.162	0.186	0.140	0.104	0.188	0.137	0.093	0.096	0.088	0.069	0.081	0.077
	MFG ENGR/UNIT	0.055	0.039	0.100	0.144	0.085	0.102	0.103	0.060	0.057	0.071	0.092	0.068	0.082
	TOTLA MOD4 COST/UNIT --->	$1.30	$1.07	$1.27	$1.28	$0.97	$1.47	$1.13	$0.84	$0.94	$0.85	$0.77	$0.87	$0.84

** ALL COST PER UNIT **

MODULE	COST ELEMENT	MAY	JUN	JUL	AUG	SEP	OCT	NOV	DEC	JAN	FEB	MAR	APR	MAY
		<-----1987						--->	<------1988					--->
	LABOR COST/UNIT	0.110	0.112	0.145	0.152	0.133	0.161	0.163	0.146	0.131	0.146	0.148	0.157	0.155
	INV BURDEN/UNIT	0.261	0.232	0.314	0.254	0.195	0.216	0.217	0.209	0.181	0.194	0.202	0.209	0.217
	NON-INVEN/UNIT	0.055	0.057	0.033	0.056	0.049	0.049	0.044	0.035	0.037	0.035	0.034	0.039	0.041
	DEPRECIATION/UNIT	0.213	0.218	0.227	0.229	0.221	0.253	0.249	0.242	0.163	0.174	0.201	0.238	0.228
ALL	DFO/UNIT EXCL DEPR	0.360	0.344	0.393	0.404	0.256	0.326	0.356	0.349	0.319	0.354	0.283	0.330	0.291
MODULES	IFO/UNIT	0.116	0.095	0.110	0.108	0.077	0.096	0.100	0.088	0.086	0.087	0.067	0.080	0.076
(1-6)	QA/UNIT	0.177	0.162	0.202	0.150	0.120	0.154	0.165	0.136	0.107	0.121	0.103	0.113	0.109
	MFG ENGR/UNIT	0.077	0.067	0.097	0.120	0.085	0.114	0.118	0.086	0.063	0.093	0.122	0.118	0.145
	TOTAL MOD COST/UNIT --->	$1.37	$1.29	$1.52	$1.47	$1.14	$1.37	$1.41	$1.29	$1.09	$1.20	$1.16	$1.28	$1.26

** ALL COSTS % OF TOTAL **

MODULE	COST ELEMENT	MAY	JUN	JUL	AUG	SEP	OCT	NOV	DEC	JAN	FEB	MAR	APR	MAY
		<-----1987						--->	<------1988					--->
	LABOR COST/UNIT	8.1%	8.7%	9.5%	10.3%	11.7%	11.8%	11.5%	11.3%	12.1%	12.1%	12.7%	12.2%	12.3%
	INV BURDEN/UNIT	19.1%	18.0%	20.7%	17.3%	7.1%	15.8%	15.4%	16.2%	16.6%	16.2%	17.4%	16.3%	17.2%
	NON-INVEN/UNIT	4.0%	4.4%	2.1%	3.8%	4.3%	3.5%	3.1%	2.7%	3.4%	2.9%	2.9%	3.1%	3.2%
	DEPRECIATION/UNIT	15.5%	17.0%	14.9%	15.5%	19.4%	18.5%	17.6%	18.8%	15.0%	14.5%	17.3%	18.5%	18.1%
ALL	DFO/UNIT EXCL DEPR	26.3%	26.8%	25.9%	27.4%	22.5%	23.8%	25.2%	27.0%	29.4%	29.4%	24.4%	25.7%	23.1%
MODULES	IFO/UNIT	8.5%	7.4%	7.2%	7.3%	6.8%	7.0%	7.1%	6.8%	7.9%	7.2%	5.8%	6.2%	6.0%
(1-6)	QA/UNIT	12.9%	12.6%	13.3%	10.2%	10.6%	11.3%	11.7%	10.5%	9.8%	10.0%	8.8%	8.8%	8.6%
	MFG ENGR/UNIT	5.6%	5.2%	6.4%	8.2%	7.5%	8.3%	8.4%	6.7%	5.8%	7.7%	10.5%	9.2%	11.5%
	TOTAL MOD COST/UNIT --->	100.0%	100.0%	100.0%	100.0%	100.0%	100.0%	100.0%	100.0%	100.0%	100.0%	100.0%	100.0%	100.0%

MODULE	COST ELEMENT	MAY	JUN	JUL	AUG	SEP	OCT	NOV	DEC	JAN	FEB	MAR	APR	MAY
		<-----1987							--->	<------1988				--->
	DIR LABOR PER UNIT	0.145	0.127	0.197	0.234	0.176	0.158	0.173	0.215	0.187	0.181	0.199	0.177	0.203
1	TOTAL O/H PER UNIT	2.014	1.910	2.206	2.253	1.505	1.472	1.534	1.933	1.583	1.554	1.700	1.489	1.735
	ACTUAL O/H RATE	1389%	1501%	1123%	963%	856%	930%	884%	900%	847%	859%	854%	841%	853%
	DIR LABOR PER UNIT	0.600	0.674	0.518	0.294	1.106	2.667	1.895	2.092	0.760	2.412	2.537	7.515	2.942
2	TOTAL O/H PER UNIT	22.406	19.912	27.312	14.463	17.716	47.803	19.322	23.408	8.492	28.597	29.517	67.974	28.390
	ACTUAL O/H RATE	3734%	2953%	5269%	4915%	1602%	1793%	1020%	1119%	1117%	1186%	1163%	905%	965%
	DIR LABOR PER UNIT	0.047	0.046	0.068	0.061	0.060	0.050	0.093	0.079	0.043	0.055	0.056	0.064	0.065
3	TOTAL O/H PER UNIT	0.435	0.395	0.524	0.420	0.329	0.314	0.576	0.515	0.264	0.359	0.334	0.347	0.357
	ACTUAL O/H RATE	928%	858%	774%	686%	551%	625%	620%	650%	617%	651%	592%	546%	549%
	DIR LABOR PER UNIT	0.123	0.112	0.133	0.141	0.115	0.197	0.132	0.097	0.115	0.103	0.097	0.113	0.110
4	TOTAL O/H PER UNIT	1.114	0.902	1.109	1.091	0.813	1.217	0.958	0.720	0.788	0.719	0.650	0.729	0.699
	ACTUAL O/H RATE	905%	807%	832%	773%	708%	617%	728%	740%	688%	700%	669%	646%	635%
	DIR LABOR PER UNIT	0.190	0.253	0.259	0.292	0.258	0.244	0.204	0.195	0.164	0.199	0.225	0.207	0.151
5	TOTAL O/H PER UNIT	2.265	2.757	2.303	2.355	1.628	1.744	1.647	1.625	1.186	1.315	1.313	1.228	0.857
	ACTUAL O/H RATE	1195%	1090%	809%	806%	632%	714%	807%	833%	722%	661%	583%	594%	566%
	DIR LABOR PER UNIT	0.193	0.215	0.224	0.237	0.232	0.238	0.232	0.292	0.330	0.368	0.378	0.350	0.387
6	TOTAL O/H PER UNIT	2.087	2.050	2.088	1.922	1.685	1.905	1.733	2.253	2.327	2.600	2.499	2.301	2.462
	ACTUAL O/H RATE	1081%	954%	933%	812%	727%	801%	748%	771%	705%	706%	660%	657%	635%
	DIR LABOR PER UNIT	0.110	0.122	0.145	0.152	0.133	0.161	0.163	0.146	0.131	0.146	0.148	0.157	0.155
ALL MODS	TOTAL O/H PER UNIT	1.204	1.119	1.343	1.265	0.954	1.159	1.205	1.110	0.918	1.024	0.978	1.089	1.066
	ACTUAL O/H RATE	1091%	999%	926%	835%	715%	718%	739%	761%	700%	703%	661%	695%	688%

Table 9-3 Forecast Report

FACTORY DEVICE	\$, S	ASP	#, S	CRD DELINQ	MSD DELINQ	O.CRD BASE	O.MSD BASE	SHIP AHEAD	BAL CM+1	CM+2	FINISH GOOD	FINAL TEST	RAW STOCK	STOCK IN T
DEVICE 1	0.00	—	0.00	0.00	0.00	—	0.00	0.00	0.00	—	0.08	0.00	0.00	0
DEVICE 2	0.00	—	0.00	—	—	—	—	0.00	0.00	—	0.00	0.00	1.41	0
DEVICE 3	0.00	—	0.00	—	—	—	—	0.00	0.00	—	—	—	—	—
DEVICE 4	2070.80	77.50	26.72	2.72	2.72	19.00	19.00	5.00	15.00	15.00	0.00	1.29	0.00	0
DEVICE 5	0.00	—	0.00	0.00	0.00	0.00	0.00	0.00	0.00	—	0.00	0.00	0.00	0
DEVICE 6	135.00	75.00	1.80	0.00	0.00	1.60	1.60	0.20	0.60	1.00	0.07	0.67	0.53	0
DEVICE 7	1153.66	90.13	12.80	5.66	1.81	9.06	10.30	0.68	5.16	7.48	0.00	1.42	1.20	0
DEVICE 8	3581.92	116.07	30.86	5.36	0.00	29.01	24.69	6.17	12.29	19.55	0.41	4.65	7.69	5
DEVICE 9	0.00	—	0.00	0.00	0.00	—	—	0.00	0.50	—	0.00	0.00	0.00	0
DEVICE 10	1074.78	144.46	7.44	3.11	0.05	5.59	5.24	2.15	3.67	7.14	0.00	0.02	0.07	0
DEVICE 11	55.80	186.00	0.30	0.30	0.30	—	—	0.00	0.00	—	0.04	0.48	0.00	0
DEVICE 12	374.24	66.71	5.61	0.95	0.02	6.55	4.64	0.95	3.95	3.71	0.19	0.29	0.00	0
DEVICE 13	1442.63	91.19	15.82	2.50	0.00	15.40	11.97	3.85	9.81	17.85	0.01	1.06	4.79	3
DEVICE 14	82.50	150.00	0.55	0.00	0.00	0.25	0.25	0.30	0.45	0.35	1.11	1.65	0.00	0
DEVICE 15	65.87	65.87	1.00	—	—	1.00	1.00	0.00	0.00	—	0.00	0.00	0.00	0
DEVICE 16	948.79	148.48	6.39	2.09	0.13	4.78	4.15	2.12	5.23	5.37	0.10	0.65	0.00	0
DEVICE 17	895.87	37.50	23.89	0.00	0.00	18.89	18.89	5.00	15.00	15.00	0.00	3.11	0.00	0
DEVICE 18	516.25	175.00	2.95	0.00	0.00	2.95	1.60	1.35	1.50	1.69	0.11	2.12	0.00	0
DEVICE 19	221.75	201.59	1.10	0.06	0.00	0.91	0.88	0.22	0.89	0.97	0.44	0.58	0.00	0
DEVICE 20	213.56	109.52	1.95	0.04	0.00	1.91	1.95	0.00	1.38	2.85	0.58	1.07	2.38	0
DEVICE 21	1172.39	172.41	6.80	0.30	0.01	6.50	6.47	0.32	2.61	3.46	0.00	0.44	2.44	0
DEVICE 22	0.00	—	0.00	—	—	—	—	0.00	0.00	—	0.37	0.01	0.00	0
DEVICE 23	1576.15	329.05	4.79	1.88	0.07	3.00	4.20	0.52	2.51	2.44	0.05	0.99	1.82	1
DEVICE 24	19.87	110.40	0.18	0.00	0.00	0.24	0.18	0.00	0.05	0.06	0.12	0.02	0.00	0
SUBTOTAL 6666	16136.42	105.44	153.04	26.28	5.32	128.23	118.13	29.61	82.35	106.11	4.58	22.60	23.20	11
TOTAL MA	23210.04	22.11	1049.59	361.30	72.73	809.60	810.67	166.29	660.62	708.88	128.04	165.16	391.71	103

ALL VALUES ARE IN THOUSANDS EXCEPT ASP IN U.S. DOLLARS.
CRD DELINQ. BACKLOG ARE 010183:080187.
MSD DELINQ. BACKLOG ARE 010183:080187.

CRD BACKLOG ORDERS ARE 08/30/87:10/03/87.
MSD BACKLOG ORDERS ARE 08/30/87:10/03/87.
CM + 1 BACKLOG ORDERS ARE 10/10/87:10/31/87.
CM + 2 BACKLOG ORDERS ARE 11/01/87:11/28/87.

GOAL FOCUSED ACTION—VISIBILITY/EXECUTION/CONTROL

Now that we have our resources organized as we would like, and our measurement system set up, how do we orchestrate the realization of the objectives on the factory floor? Any manufacturing strategy must contain the elements: **visibility, execution,** and **control**. With increasing complexity of products and processes, escalating customer expectations of quality, cost, and on-time delivery across a wide product portfolio to a wide customer base, execution of the manufacturing tasks is in itself difficult enough. To allow the manufacturing organization to focus on this exclusively, the visibility and control elements are addressed by means of the following manufacturing control system:

CONCLUSION

We set out to demonstrate that the traditional standard cost accounting system no longer serves the needs of modern manufacturing; that like the inventory it so rigorously accommodates, it has become a liability rather than an asset. But it is not enough just to criticize. We are obliged to offer a solution. Since world-class manufacturing requires world-class accounting, we defined what excellence in manufacturing means, including what should be measured and how, in order that the new accounting model may be developed around this. We also have tried to develop the nucleus of a new, more appropriate model built around JIC, SPC, and SCM all of which are designed to reduce the need for inventory in the system by reducing cycle-time and eliminating waste which is representative of what happens on the floor of a modern factory. In doing so, we focused on cycle-time and process cost rather than direct labor, attempting to show that cost is a quantitatively measurable function of quality and on-time delivery and that these value-adding characteristics can be quantitatively measured. We require our cost accounting system for short cycle-time manufacturing to measure process cost—the cell cost per hour—as well as product cost and value in inventory. This means we need to

Table 9-4 Factory Control Report

TMTD STATUS REPORT

PRODUCED DAILY TO CONTROL TEST AREA. REQUIRED TEST UNITS COLUMN IS DIMINISHING BALANCE. EACH DEVICE DROPS OFF REPORT WHEN DECREMENTED TO ZERO.

		TOTAL MSD KEY CUST. MSD																
FACTORY DEVICE	REQD TEST UNITS	DELQ THRU 09/10	09/11	09/ 12	09/13	WEEK 09/14 09/15	WEEK 09/16 09/30	WHSE	QA	P&L	ROOM COLD	BURN IN	MARK	HOT TEST	COMBO STAGE	R.S. STAGE	RAW STOCK	STOCK IN TR
DEVICE 1	17.59	4.80 3.70	0.86 0.86	— —	— —	0.09 —	6.45 4.67	5.41	1.45	0.00	0.00	0.00	—	—	0.45	6.49	0.00	0.00
DEVICE 2	18.21	2.32 2.32	6.79 6.79	— —	— —	— —	8.21 8.21	9.12	0.00	0.00	0.00	0.00	—	—	—	7.26	0.00	0.00
DEVICE 3	4.88	1.09 0.13	0.85 —	— —	— —	0.51 0.06	2.51 0.15	0.02	0.00	0.00	0.00	0.00	—	—	0.00	0.00	0.00	0.00
DEVICE 4	6.85	1.04 0.23	0.52 0.50	— —	— —	0.47 0.22	4.04 0.92	0.00	0.00	0.00	0.00	0.00	—	8.75	—	0.06	2.89	8.64
DEVICE 5	2.98	0.90 0.83	0.02 0.02	— —	— —	0.29 0.17	0.35 0.25	0.00	0.00	0.00	0.00	0.00	—	—	0.29	4.98	0.52	0.40
DEVICE 6	1.24	0.83 0.83	— —	— —	— —	0.05 0.05	0.85 0.85	1.01	0.00	0.00	0.00	0.00	—	—	—	0.00	0.00	0.00
DEVICE 7	1.54	0.80 —	— —	— —	— —	0.06 —	0.27 0.15	0.23	0.00	0.00	0.00	0.00	—	—	0.03	0.00	0.00	0.00
DEVICE 8	3.21	0.72 0.52	— —	— —	— —	0.04 0.02	1.29 1.01	0.00	0.00	0.00	0.00	0.00	—	—	0.18	0.13	0.00	0.00
DEVICE 9	6.83	0.36 0.36	— —	— —	— —	0.50 0.50	2.76 2.24	0.14	0.04	0.00	0.00	0.00	—	—	0.17	2.04	0.77	0.00
DEVICE 10	3.75	0.15 —	— —	— —	— —	0.66 —	0.81 0.49	0.01	0.00	0.00	0.00	0.00	—	0.38	0.09	0.97	3.91	1.28
DEVICE 11	1.50	0.14 —	— —	— —	— —	— —	1.08 1.08	0.04	0.00	0.00	0.36	0.00	—	—	—	2.21	0.00	0.00
DEVICE 12	0.96	0.10 0.10	0.20 0.20	— —	— —	0.31 0.12	0.20 0.20	0.00	0.09	0.00	0.00	0.00	—	—	—	2.05	0.00	0.00
DEVICE 13	1.51	0.05 —	0.03 0.03	— —	— —	0.01 —	0.95 —	0.00	0.00	0.00	0.00	0.00	—	—	—	0.05	0.00	0.00
DEVICE 14	0.40	0.01 —	— —	— —	— —	0.00 —	0.32 0.31	0.00	0.00	0.00	0.00	0.00	—	—	0.11	1.13	0.00	0.00
DEVICE 15	52.40	— —	10.00 10.00	— —	— —	— —	42.66 42.66	12.86	0.00	0.00	6.48	0.00	—	—	—	4.11	0.00	0.00
DEVICE 16	1.09	— —	2.00 2.00	— —	— —	0.02 —	— —	0.92	0.00	0.00	0.00	0.00	—	—	—	0.54	0.00	0.00
DEVICE 17	25.24	— —	1.97 1.97	— —	— —	2.80 2.00	11.22 5.92	0.35	0.53	0.00	0.00	0.00	—	—	0.49	21.24	0.00	0.00
DEVICE 18	0.67	— —	0.67 —	— —	— —	— —	— —	0.00	0.00	0.00	0.00	0.00	—	0.79	—	0.00	0.00	0.00
DEVICE 19	0.49	— —	0.25 —	— —	— —	— —	0.25 —	0.01	0.57	0.00	0.00	0.00	—	—	—	0.00	0.00	0.00
DEVICE 20	0.14	— —	0.10 0.00	— —	— —	— —	0.04 —	0.00	0.00	0.00	0.00	0.00	—	—	—	0.01	0.00	0.00
DEVICE 21	0.49	— —	— —	— —	— —	— —	0.52 0.03	0.03	0.00	0.00	0.00	0.00	—	—	0.16	1.96	0.98	0.00
DEVICE 22	1.75	— —	— —	— —	— —	— —	1.75 1.75	0.07	0.00	0.00	0.00	0.00	—	—	0.80	2.00	0.00	0.00
DEVICE 23	0.01	— —	— —	— —	— —	— —	0.31 0.31	0.35	0.00	0.00	0.00	0.00	—	—	0.06	2.35	5.49	3.37
DEVICE 24	0.05	— —	— —	— —	— —	— —	0.11 —	0.05	0.00	0.00	0.00	0.00	—	—	0.83	0.00	0.00	0.00
DEVICE 25	5.56	— —	— —	— —	— —	— —	3.64 3.59	0.69	0.00	0.00	0.00	0.00	—	—	0.02	6.41	77.41	11.54
DEVICE 26	0.79	— —	— —	— —	— —	— —	0.54 0.25	0.60	0.00	0.00	0.00	0.00	—	—	0.26	2.00	0.00	0.00
DEVICE 27	0.44	— —	— —	— —	— —	— —	— —	0.06	0.00	0.00	0.00	0.00	—	—	0.49	11.18	0.46	0.43
DEVICE 28	0.12	— —	— —	— —	— —	— —	0.24 —	0.48	0.00	0.00	0.00	0.00	—	—	0.25	1.56	0.00	0.00
DEVICE 29	1.81	— —	— —	— —	— —	— —	— —	0.00	0.00	0.00	0.00	0.00	—	—	0.02	1.80	0.00	0.00
DEVICE 30	0.56	— —	— —	— —	— —	0.05 —	0.26 0.16	0.00	0.00	0.00	0.00	0.00	—	—	—	0.40	0.00	0.00
DEVICE 31	0.26	— —	— —	— —	— —	0.02 —	0.20 0.10	0.01	0.00	0.00	0.00	0.00	—	—	3.69	0.50	0.00	0.00
DEVICE 32	0.32	— —	— —	— —	— —	— —	0.78 0.78	0.46	0.00	0.00	0.00	0.00	—	—	—	0.00	0.00	0.00
SUBTOTAL	163.64	13.48 9.02	24.27 22.37	0.00 0.00	0.00 0.00	5.90 3.14	92.69 76.08	35.30	2.98	0.00	7.08	0.00	0.00	9.91	12.00	86.54	95.94	25.92

measure the productivity of material, overhead, and indirect costs as well as direct labor. That the productivity of all of these are embraced within cycle-time.

Also, by focusing on the three ingredients of total customer satisfaction for which manufacturing is primarily responsible—those of quality, cost, and on-time delivery, we argued that pay-for-performance schemes should and can be based on measurable improvements to the customer, not on forecasted improvements on hypothetical standards or not necessarily productive, overhead recovery. People behave as they are measured. Not only the accounting system, but the resources of the organization must be cohesively focused on these same objectives, providing **a direct line-of-sight link between what the factory does and the customer needs.**

Contemporary manufacturing systems are encumbered by accounting systems which have outlived their usefulness, institutionalized by rules, and dogma to resist the necessary changes in manufacturing. We defend this as being financial prudence. In the Great

Britain of the late 1970s and early 1980s, these would be called restrictive practices. The accounting profession has much to account for. The most highly refined form of the above is IMC.

While this is an accurate reflection of process cost, how do we compute:

1. **Theoretical process cost**
2. **Standard product cost**
3. **Actual product cost**

CYCLE-TIME TUTORIAL

Introduction

Traditional cost accounting systems are predicated on the accounting convention that it is direct labor which adds value to the product. As manufacturing becomes more highly automated, and therefore capital intensive, it is the process equipment which assumes the role of adding value to the the product rather than direct labor. In the extreme, the direct labor contribution diminishes to one of simply loading and unloading the machines. As a result, product costs become more a function of material and overhead (capital cost) with the direct labor component diminishing. The productivity of material and capital equipment therefore, becomes much more critical. Indeed, it can be shown that as the productivity of capital equipment increases, direct labor cost per unit will diminish. This tutorial examines the major factors which determine the productivity of capital equipment in relation to cycle-time, supporting the case for cycle-time rather than direct labor being used as the cost accounting base. (A further convention is that inventory is an asset and must therefore be valued. This is discussed later.)

Definitions

Operation. A single step (station) in the process.

Process. A series of operations or steps.

Cycle-Time. Cycle-time is the time which elapses from:

1. the start of an operation to the completion point of that operation or;

2. the start of the first operation in a series of operations to the completion of the last operation.

Theoretical Cycle-Time. Theortical cycle-time of an operation, or series of operations, is the time which should elapse, or be consumed, in definitions (1) and (2) above—**exclusive of non-value adding activities**—that is, **waste**. A "value adding" activity usually changes the physical form of the product. Transporting, storing, or clerical transactions in the manufacturing environment are cost not value adding activities. Reducing cycle-times of these activities is no less important than that of reducing the sum of the cycle-times of the individual value adding processes. (Elimination is even better.) Even theoretical cycle-times should be considered irreducible. Intrinsic cycle-times can be reduced through innovative improvements to the process. Nonvalue adding activities such as machine index time, may or may not be considered to be part of the theoretical cycle-time depending on whether or not, the index time can be used productively.

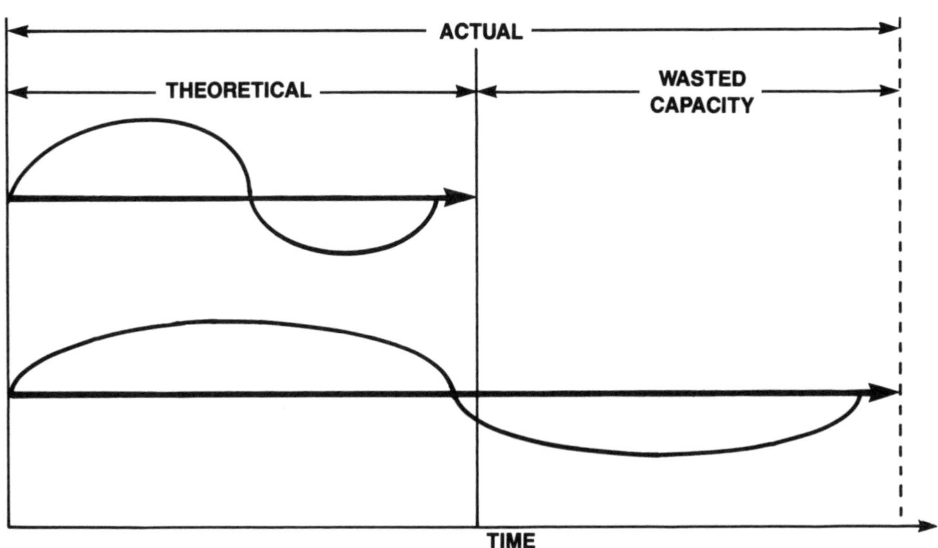

Figure 9-9. Theoretical and actual cycle-time.

Actual Cycle-Time. Actual cycle-time is always greater than the theoretical, due to inefficiencies encountered in the real world. This is shown graphically in Figure 9-9. We shall identify these inefficiencies and their effect on capacity, and therefore cost.

Index Time. Index time is a very specific form of transport time. It is the time required, usually by an automated piece of equipment, sometimes a human operator, **to present a unit to the actual value adding process**. (The time to remove a unit should or should not be included in the index-time depending on whether it affects value adding cycle-time or not.)

Lot Sizes of One (Unit) = The "Unit of Work"

As we shall see later, **lot size has a significant effect on cycle-time**. Recalling our definition of cycle-time, we must be clear in what we consider to be the start and stop events—unit or lot. This means **we must define the cycle-time according to the "unit of work."** What is one unit of work? A single device? A container or rail containing several units? A number of containers or rails? The answer—depends on what we are interested in measuring. Lot size has more meaning to the human than to the machine, but lot size will affect the average cycle-time of each unit through the machine. The "correct" lot size or unit of work is whatever the system is most optimally designed to handle. What we consider to be the start clock/stop clock events in the process must also be identified.

Note: The smaller the lot size, the more frequent the equipment changeover the longer will be the total changeover time, resulting in a longer average actual cycle-time per unit. While **smaller lot sizes will result in a shorter average cycle-time per lot, the average cycle-time per unit will be longer**. If, for customer service related reasons smaller lot sizes are desirable, then the system must be designed or redesigned accordingly in order not to pay a penalty in increased cost or reduced throughput.

Transport Time. The time required to transport a "unit of work" between value adding operations.

Set-Up (Change-Over) Time. The time required to prepare the equipment to do productive value adding work. (At the start of a shift for example, or during a model change-over.)

Downtime. The time during which a machine is either not available to perform its value adding function due to planned maintenance or to some malfunction.

Throughput. **Saleable** output in UPH (**good** units per hour). Note the emphasis on saleable and good.

Note: A machine which is processing material, no matter how efficiently, simply because there is capacity and/or inventory available, not necessarily saleable, will be recovering overhead costs—**but is not generating revenue**. This is the difference between efficiency and effectiveness. (Nothing is so futile as to do well that which should not be done at all.) Because of process yield, or more meaningfully scrap, a machine's input rate will be higher than its good unit output rate per hour. Like cycle-time we must always be clear to which we are referring when we talk rates and capacities.

Theoretical Throughput (in Good UPH). Assumes 100 percent product and process yield (zero scrap) no downtime or material shortages. In fact, a "perfect universe" where there is no waste of material, capacity, or time.

Theoretical Capacity. Theoretical capacity = theoretical (UPH × 168 hours per week).

Relationship Between Cycle-Time and Capacity

Consider a final test operation in a factory.

Assume: Test Time = 5 s
Index time = 1 s

Therefore, theoretical cycle-time (CTt) = 5 + 1
= 6 s

and maximum theoretical throughput = 3600/6
= 600 UPH

Note: 1 hour = 3600 seconds

Note: While we have included index time in our theoretical cycle-time in this example, it is not necessarily productive value adding time, as we shall see later.

With this information, we can now calculate the theoretical capacity of our machine.

Theoretical capacity = (168 hours per week) × 600 UPH = 100.8 K units

This information can be used in two ways.

1. To determine the theoretical capacity of a piece of equipment (or module, or factory) which already exists.

2. To determine the theoretical capacity required to support the sales volume in units. For example, in an annual sales budget or five year plan.

We can represent this graphically as shown in Figure 9-10 where area represents capacity. For example, consider **declared capacity available**. The more hours per week which a piece of equipment is used, the longer the horizontal line, therefore the greater the capacity as represented by area. The greater the UPH, the longer the vertical line, therefore the greater the capacity available in Figure 9-10(a) or the less the capacity required in Figure 9-10(b).

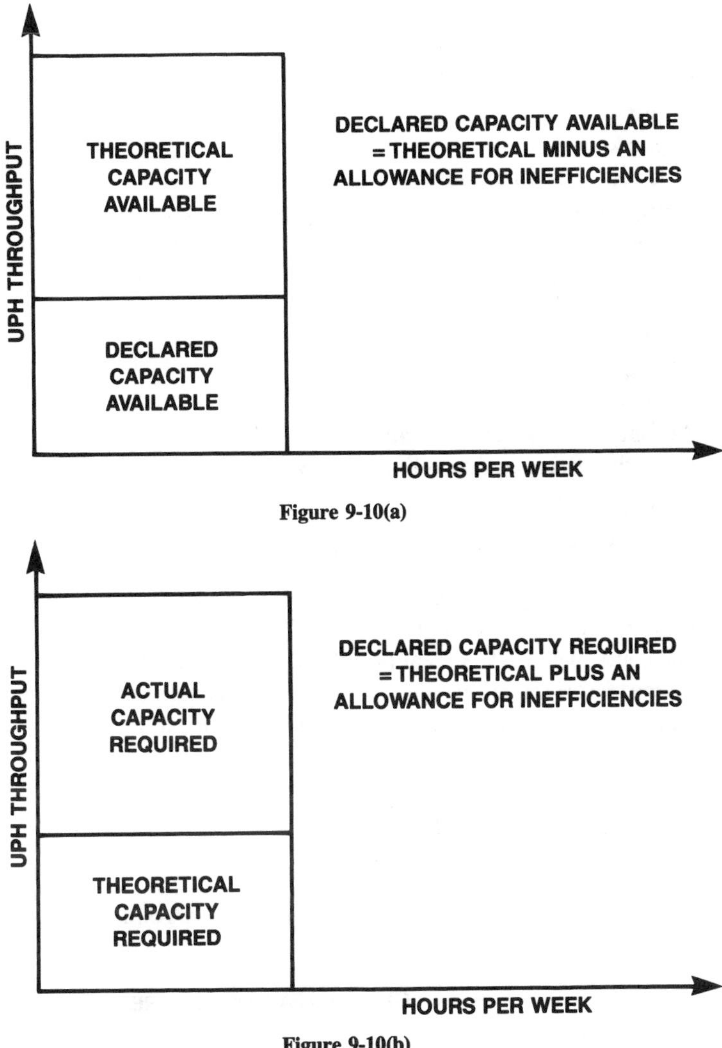

Figure 9-10(a)

Figure 9-10(b)

Actual Throughput in UPH. The measured number of good, saleable units produced, on average, every hour.

Note: This is always less than theoretical for a variety of reasons. Process yields are not 100 percent, scrap is not zero, and no machine runs continuously.

For the piece of equipment in our theoretical example, assume that empirical measurements show that the average actual throughput over a long period of time is 200 UPH. This is low, but typical of a highly automated piece of equipment in the U.S. semiconductor industry. The actual cycle-time is 3600/200 = 18 seconds. Therefore, **asset**

utilization = 200/600 or 6/18 = 33 percent and **actual capacity** = 200 UPH × number of machine hours available for productive use. (Not necessarily used productively.) Assuming the same 168 hour week used to calculate theoretical capacity, this equates to 200 × 168 = 33.6 K units per week compared to the 100.8 K theoretical. Few organizations run their capital equipment 168 hours per week. As manufacturing becomes more capital intensive, however, the compulsion to do so increases. Some of the major capacity stealers are listed as follows:

Engineering time
Set-up (change-over) **time**
Scrap (the reciprocal of yield)
Retest
Rework
Planned or unplanned down-time
Equipment jams (average actual index time increases)
Material shortages
Material staging
Product on hold
Process on hold
Transport time
Clerical transaction time
Accounting transaction time
Quality control gating (eliminated with SPC)
Absenteeism

Measuring Asset Utilization in Terms of Cycle-Time

Let's now return to Figure 9-10 and modify it to reflect the effect of these inefficiencies or components of waste (see Figure 9-11). First we must set up the machine. Say that takes four hours. Then 2.5 percent (4/168) of the time available is used for this purpose. Then assume, for example, that our process yield was not 100 percent but a more realistic 90 percent. Then 10 percent of our capacity is being used to produce rejects. Also assume,

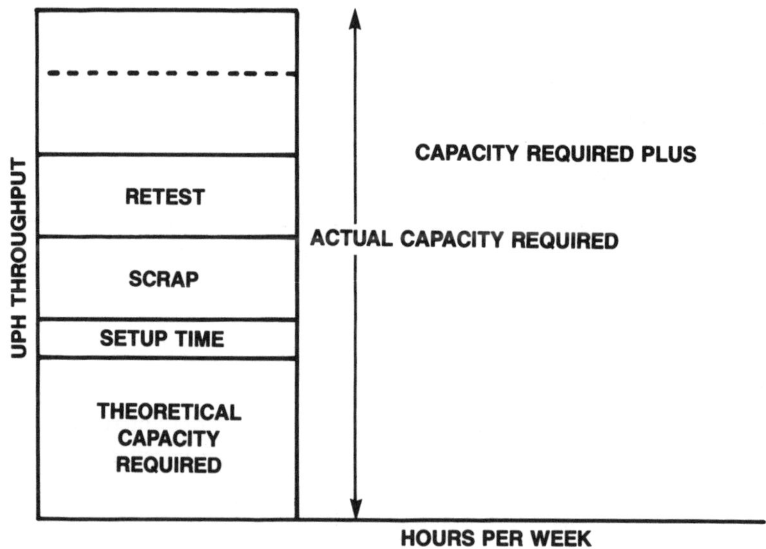

Figure 9-11.

not having right first time discipline, that we retest 10 percent of the product. We "waste" a further 10 percent of our capacity on this inefficiency. We could go through the whole list, downtime, material shortages, and so on, eventually quantifying the amount of capacity wasted due to each component.

In fact, **waste of capacity** = theoretical UPH – actual UPH or CTa-CTt

Relationship Between Cycle-Time and Inventory

Cycle-time and inventory are highly interdependent. If inventories are high, cycle-times will be long. If process cycle-times are long, inventories will be high. In embarking on a cycle-time reduction program to break this vicious circle, most efforts focus initially on draining work in process out of the system. As queuing and pipline WIP are reduced, cycle-time will reduce. Reducing cycle-time by reducing inventory is only part of the solution. All too often efforts cease at this point, and further potential gains by pursuing reductions in non-value adding activity cycle-time and in intrinsic cycle-times of the value adding processes remain unrealized. Since capacity is a function of cycle-time, which in turn is a function of inventory, it is often the case that we have installed capacity because we have inventory, not necessarily because its needed. See Figure 9-12.

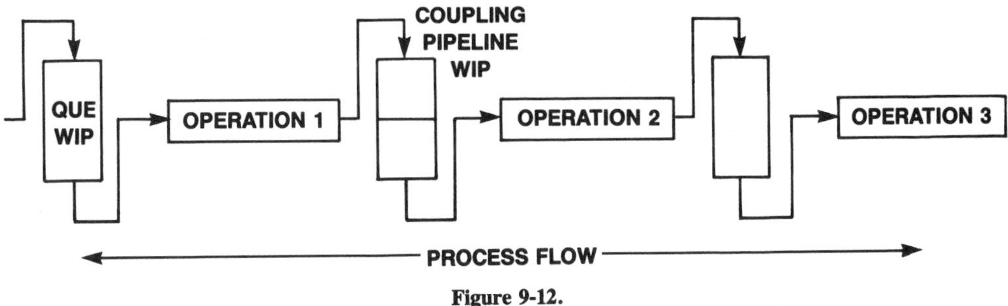

Figure 9-12.

Note: Queue WIP is due to demand/capacity mismatches. Pipeline WIP is due to geographically separated operations.

Relationship Between Cycle-Time and Throughput

Misguided efforts to reduce cycle-time often result in a trade-off in the form of higher cost, or lower throughput. Cycle-times can be reduced by adding more capacity, but this will increase costs. Reducing lot sizes will also reduce average lot cycle-times. But without commensurate reductions in change-over times, this will also reduce throughput. Smaller lot sizes will also require more frequent quality control gating. Without statistical process control, this will also add to non-value adding cycle-time.

For One Operation

For a single stand-alone independent operation throughput is simply: 3600/CT(t or a).

For a Series of Operations

In a functionally organized factory each operation is independent of every other. If the throughput rates of operations differ, and they invariably do, inventory buffers conceal this by insulating each operation from the other. Line balancing is either "not considered to be required," or impossible to manage. In a module or cell such a cavalier attitude cannot be tolerated.

Consider the first unit in a lot being processed through a JIT cell (see Figure 9-13). Its cycle-time through the series of operations will be the sum of the cycle-times of each individual operation in the series—CT1 + CT2 + CT3 + CT4. This is also true for every unit in the lot. Is the throughput of the system then 3600/(CT1 + CT2 + CT3 + CT4) = 3600/34.2 = 105 units per hour?

Since four units are being processed simultaneously within the cell, one at each operation, the throughput of the cell is 3600 divided by the cycle-time of the slowest operation. In this case—3600/12 = 300 UPH.

Operation 3 has the lowest throughput per hour. It is the bottleneck which determines the throughput of the cell. Since the other operations are capable of higher throughput rates per hour, this represents wasted capacity. Improving the throughput rate of operation 3 improves the utilization of all of the resources in the cell.

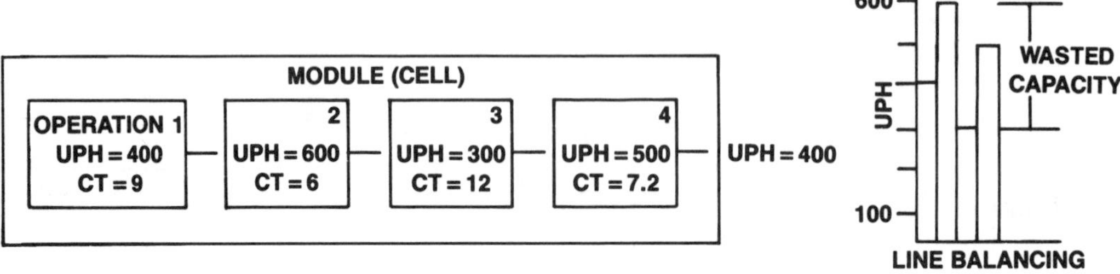

Figure 9-13.

Relationship Between Cycle-Time and Productivity

Cycle-time is a direct measure of productivity since a machine can produce twice the throughput if the cycle-time is halved, assuming no additional resources are necessary. We are concerned with productivity in its most complete sense. The productivity of capital equipment and material, not just direct labor. Cycle-time captures all of these. None of these factors of production can vary, for better or worse, and not be captured in the actual cycle-time measurement. If inventory increases or decreases, if the machine goes down, if there is too much absenteeism, if there are product or process quality problems, any and all of these perturbations will be captured in the cycle-time measurement. Cycle-time is the super, superordinate measurement of manufacturing excellence.

Relationship Between Test (Operation) Time and Index Time

In an automatic test equipment (ATE) manufacturing environment, the host computer in a test cell (the central processor) may be a common resource shared between test stations each of which may have an automatic handler connected. The handler function is to precondition the devices and present them to the tester. (See Figures 9-14 and 9-15.) Assume that handler 1 indexes and inserts a device into the test socket on the station. A signal is sent to the central processing unit (CPU) requesting it to start controlling the test station in the testing of the product. The CPU is then dedicated to the control of station 1. Assume that a few milliseconds later, handler 2 indexes a device into the test socket on station 2. Station 2 will likewise send a signal to the CPU requesting its undivided attention. Since the CPU is already preoccupied with station 1, station 2 must wait until station 1 has completed testing. If station 1 finds the unit to be defective it will relinquish control, perhaps within a few milliseconds of the start test signal having been sent. The time will vary according to the nature of the defect in the product. The flow of the test program determines when it is encountered in the test cycle. On the other hand, if station 1 contains a good unit, it will retain the use of the CPU for the full five seconds, the test time of a good unit in our example. Station 2 meanwhile, is still waiting unproductively. If we consider only one station, the minimum cycle-time to test a unit would be $3600/5 + 1 = 3600/6 = 600$ units per hour. The second station can only make productive use of the CPU while the first is indexing the next unit and vice versa. In practice, the test stations are not synchronized and each infringes on the other. The shorter the test time in relation to the index time the greater the throughput gained by the addition of a second station. The aggregate throughput of two stations therefore is not double that of one, but double times some factor less than one according to the relationship of the test to index ratio. (The mathematics of this is dealt with in Chapter 6.)

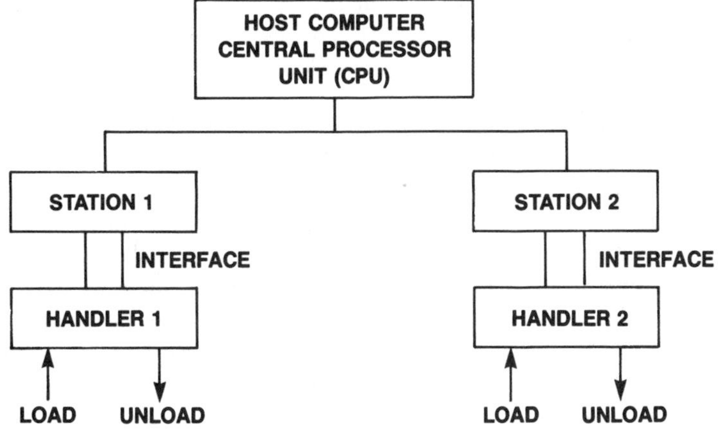

Figure 9-14. Automatic test equipment.

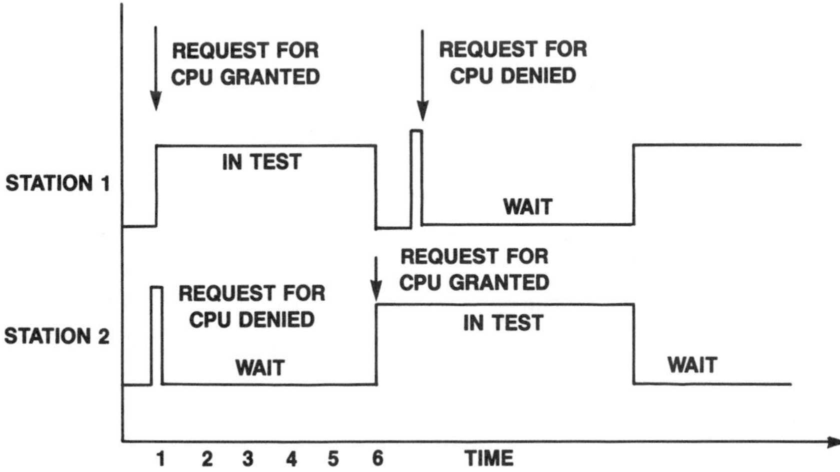

Figure 9-15. Relationship between test time and index time.

The Effect of Mix on Capacity—Aggregate UPHs

We have seen that the capacity of a single operation is 3600/CT. Capacity will obviously change as CT changes. For example, a product which requires a longer processing time.

For a series of operations, capacity is the operation with the lowest throughput per hour. Again, this will change as CT changes.

In a situation where mix has to be comprehended, capacity of the equipment will vary according to the mix being run. In this situation constant capacity is the capacity of the central processing unit. All other numbers are relative to a given mix.

We can deal with this in one of two ways: (1) normalize cycle-times or (2) compare actual aggregate cycle-time CTa to theoretical, aggregate cycle-time CTt for that mix, weighted by relative volumes.

Setting Standards for Theoretical Cycle-Times

Standards need not be set for every product or every operation but may be categorized according to the attribute which is most important. Test times, for example, may be the same for all products within a family. This approach reduces the level of detail involved in setting standards and measuring actual performance to no more than is required.

Using Cycle-Time Instead of Direct Labor to Value Inventory, Cost Product, and Measure RONA

If the cost per hour of a cell is known, and there is no reason why even a traditional cost accounting system should not be able to provide this, then product costs can be based on cycle-time rather than direct labor. Theoretical cycle-times times cost per hour for the cell, weighted by volume, would provide product cost standards. That is costs which should be realized. Actual cycle-times will ensure that all costs are fully recovered in the product cost, each product's share proportional to its use of the cells total resources. This rationale could be equally applied to valuing inventory. In this way the performance measurement system would be fully supportive in the pursuit of manufacturing excellence—the reduction of cycle-time.

Summary

- Quantify theoretical cycle-times.
- Measure actual cycle-times.
- Identify reasons for differences and attack.
- Inventory and cycle-time are highly interdependent.
- Capacity is a function of aggregate cycle-time relative to mix.
- Slow, but continuous processing is better than fast spurts and long pauses.
- Fuel growth with cycle-time reduction (productivity) not capital and direct labor profligacy. Fund resources required to reduce cycle-time with reduction in inventory carrying costs.
- Overhead recoveries, inventory valuation, product costs, should be based on cycle-time—not direct labor.
- There is much more to addressing product cost competitiveness than direct labor.

- In the modern, capital intensive factory, there is much less need for "unskilled direct labor" and a much greater need for equipment and process engineers and technicians to make the process more productive.
- Comment on "entitlement"—in effect, setting a "standard" less than excellence.
- Make the measurement system consistent with the pursuit of manufacturing excellence.

10

Definition of Terms

This chapter addresses those line items found in a typical profit and loss operating statement. The materials includes:

1. A list of these typical line items in the order in which they occur in the operating statement. An example of this statement is shown in Table 10-1.

2. A description, in accounting terms, of each line item.

3. How these line items are grouped together within the margins 1 through 5 within the structure of the statement.

4. Some typical reports produced from such an accounting data base structure.

OPERATING STATEMENT DEFINITIONS

1. Gross Bookings $
2. Net Bookings $
3. Net/Gross Ratio
4. Demand Turns
5. Shipped Turns
6. Turns %
7. Backlog Current — CR
8. Backlog 1-13 Wk — CR
9. Backlog Total — CR
10. Back Delinquent — CR
11. % To Total
12. Net Booking ASP
13. Backlog ASP
14. Sales: G/ASP
15. Sales: N/ASP
16. Net Units
17. Book/Bill Ratio
18. Gross Sales Value $
19. Gross Sales Nonvalue
20. Total Gross Sales
21. Returns
22. Allowances
23. Net Sales $
24. Std Cost $
25. Std Margin $ (1)
26. Freight
27. Duty
28. Mfg Variances
29. Actual Material
30. Less Earned Material
31. Purch Price Variation
32. Gold Adder Adjustment
33. Usage/Mix Variation
34. Scrap/Obsolete
35. Scrap Reclaim
36. Total Mtl Variation
37. % To Earned Material
38. Actual Labor
39. Less Earned Labor
40. Rate Variation
41. Productivity Var
42. Total Labor Var
43. $ To Earned Labor
44. DFO
45. QA
46. IFO
47. Total Inventoriable O/H
48. Less Earned Overhead
49. Less Capacity Variation
50. Total Mfg OH Var
51. % To Earned Labor
52. Total Earned (M.L.O.)
53. Yield Variation
54. % To Total Earned
55. Wafer Variations
56. Total Factory Var
57. Procedural Var
58. Translation Rate Var
59. Total Mfg Var
60. Mfg Margin (2)
61. Inventory Adj
62. Adj to Phy RM
63. Adj to Phy Interco
64. Adj to Phy WIP/FG
65. STD Change
66. Valuation Change
67. Scrap RMR
68. Total Inventory Exp
69. R&D Engr
70. Prod Market
71. Tech Service P&L
72. Other Period Ex
73. Wafer Period Expenses
74. Capacity Variation
75. Subtotal Op Cost
76. OP Margin (3)
77. Purchase & Distribution
78. Capital Expense

79. Division G&A
80. Subtotal Div Op Ex
81. Total Period Expense
82. Division Margin (4)
83. Group Marketing
84. Group Admin
85. Group R&D
86. Non Dept
87. PS & Scrp
88. Corp G&A & HR
89. Other
90. Interest
91. Overhead Eliminations
92. Sub Total G&A
93. Group Margin
94. Taxes
95. Profit After Taxes

LINE ITEM DEFINITIONS

1. Gross Bookings $
End customer bookings during current month:
a. New acknowledged orders booked, including:
(1) New will advise orders (for variety of reasons, no FSD given).
(2) Excluding new customer to advise orders (contingent on customer order entered with no CRD).
b. Increase in price and/or quantity against existing orders.
c. Changes from customer to advise orders to acknowledged orders.

2. Net Bookings $
Gross bookings minus:
a. Cancellations of booked orders.
b. Decreases in price and/or quantity against existing orders.
c. Device title changes (decrement one family and increment another family).
d. Changes from acknowledged orders to customer to advise orders (contingent on customer).

3. Net/Gross Ratio %
Net bookings divided by gross bookings (item 2 divided by item 1).

4. Demand Turns $
New orders booked in current month—customer required during current month plus two weeks.

5. Shipped Turns $
The actual amount of demand turns shipped during current month.

6. Turns %
Shipped turns divided by demand turns (item 5 divided by item 4).

7. Backlog Current $
End customer orders required to be shipped during the next month plus one week.

8. Backlog 1-13 Weeks $
End customer orders required to be shipped during the next 13 weeks.

9. Backlog Total $
Total end customer orders required to be shipped.

10. Backlog Delinquent $
End customer orders required in prior periods or current month but not shipped.

11. **Percentage Delinquent**
Backlog delinquent divided by backlog total (item 10 divided by item 9).

12. **Net Bookings ASP $ (End Customer)**
Net dollars booked divided by net units booked (item 2 divided by related units).

13. **Backlog ASP $ (End Customer)**
Backlog dollars divided by backlog units (item 9 divided by related units).

14. **Gross Sales ASP $ (End Customer)**
Gross sales dollars divided by gross units sold (item 20 divided by related units).

15. **Net Sales ASP $ (End Customer)**
Net sales dollars divided by net units sold (item 23 divided by related units).

16. **Net Units Sold (End Customer)**
Gross units sold less adjustments for returns.

17. **Book/Bill Ratio $ (End Customer)**
Net bookings dollars divided by net sales dollars (item 2 divided by item 23).

18. **Gross Sales—Valued $**
End customer sales of valued product.

19. **Gross Sales—Nonvalued $**
End customer sales of nonvalued product.

20. **Total Gross Sales $**
Gross sales valued plus gross sales nonvalued (line 18 plus line 19).

21. **Returns $**
End customer returns of product.

22. **Allowances $ (End Customer)**
Any reduction in gross sales—excluding the returns of product, such as distributor price protection, cash discounts, and so on.

23. **Net Sales $**
Total gross sales less returns and allowances (line 20 less lines 21 and 22).

24. **Standard Cost $**
WWS cost of valued product sold to an end customer (standard cost included material, labor, burden, and overhead).

25. **Standard Margin 1$**
Net sales less total standard cost of sales (line 23 less line 24).

26. **Freight $**
Freight charges associated with shipping product to and from subsidiaries as well as end customers.

27. **Duty $**
Import tax on product received from international locations.

28. **Manufacturing Variance (Section Title Line)**

29. **Actual Material**
Actual cost of material (raw wafers, piece parts and in-process plating).

30. **Earned Material $**
Standard cost of material input to work-in-process.

31. **Purchase Price Variation $**
Delta between actual cost and standard cost of issues to line bank (or receipt into stockroom).

32. **Gold Adder $**
Delta between the actual cost of gold and standard cost of plating an item.

33. **Usage/Mix Variation $**
    a. Usage variation—delta between earned material and actual usage of material in work-in-process.
    b. Mix variation—delta between earned material and alternate material used in work in process.

34. **Scrap & Obsolescence $**
Reserve for write-off of scrap and/or obsolete material in line banks and stockroom.

35. **Scrap Reclaim $**
Credit for reclaimed gold.

36. **Total Material Variation $**
Total lines 31 through 35.

37. **Percentage to Earned Material %**
Material variation over earned material (line 36 divided by line 30).

38. **Actual Labor $**
Payroll for direct labor (excludes burden).

39. **Less Earned Labor $**
Standard labor input to work in process.

40. **Rate Variation $**
Difference between standard rate and actual rate times actual hours paid.

41. **Productivity Variation $**
Actual hours worked times standard rate minus standard hours worked times standard rates.

42. Total Labor Variation $
Rate variation plus productivity variation (line 40 plus line 41).

43. Percentage to Earned Labor %
Total labor variation divided by earned labor.

44. Direct Factory Overhead (DFO) $
a. DFO departments.
b. Plus share of charge back (charge back equals a department's share, if any, of committed costs, building services, tool and die amortization, and formal work order maintenance).
c. Inventoriable burden.

45. Quality Assurance (QA) $
Quality assurance departments (standard QA and hi-rel QA) plus share of charge.

46. Indirect Factory Overhead (IFO)
a. Indirect factory departments.
b. Process engineering projects.
c. Plus share of chargeback.

47. Total Inventoriable Overhead $
Total inventoriable cost from direct factory overhead, quality assurance and indirect factory overhead (line 44 plus 46).

48. Less Earned Overhead $
Standard overhead input to work in process.

49. Less Capacity Variance $
Percent of earned labor over full capacity labor times total fixed portions of inventoriable overhead (not to be used initially).

50. Total Manufacturing Overhead Variation $
Inventoriable overhead input variance after capacity variance and earned overhead relief.

51. Percentage to Earned Overhead %
Total manufacturing overhead variation over earned overhead (line 50 divided by line 48).

52. Total Earned Material, Labor, and Overhead (MLO)
Standard material, labor, and overhead earned (line 30 plus lines 39 and 48).

53. Yield Variation $
The cost of (or income) generated by producing units at a level below (or above) standard unit output.

54. Percentage to Total Earned %
Yield variation over total earned MLO (line 53 divided by line 52).

55. **Wafer Variations**
If wafer families are used, the amount of wafer variation charged to benefiting final families with offset wafer family.

56. **Total Factory Variance $**
Total material variation plus total labor variation plus total overhead variation plus yield variation (line 36 plus lines 42–50 and 53).

57. **Procedural Variance $**
Difference between a local factory standard and WWS.
A procedural variance is taken by writing the product up or down to WWS (if not already at WWS) when product is moved to finished goods or transferred to another factory.

58. **Translation Rate Variance**
Gains and losses from foreign currency revaluation.

59. **Total Manufacturing Variation $**
Total factory variation plus procedural variation plus translation rate variation (line 56 plus lines 57 and 58).

60. **Manufacturing Margin (2) $**
Margin 1 less total manufacturing variation less freight and duty (line 25 less lines 26, 27, and 59).

61. **Inventory Adjustments (Section Title Line)**

62. **Adjustment to Physical Raw Material $**
Cycle audit and/or physical inventory count adjustments at factory standard for material in stockroom and line bank.

63. **Adjustment to Physical Intercompany $**
Adjustment at WWS made by the shipping factory for difference between invoice and physical count on shipments of valued product.

64. **Adjustment to Physical WIP & Finished Goods**
Cycle audit and/or physical inventory count adjustment at appropriate standard for material in work in process and finished goods.

65. **Standard Change $**
Reserve for standard change.

66. **Valuation Change $**
Reserve for value/nonvalue adjustment plus lower of cost or market adjustment (cost being defined as standard).

67. **Scrap RMR $**
Valued units returned by external and internal customers times WWS less WWS value of units placed back in inventory for resale.

68. Total Inventory Expense $
Total lines 62 through 67.

69. R&D Engineering $
Division controlled R&D—formerly noninventoriable product engineering portion of engineering sustaining plus share of charge back.

70. Product Marketing $
Operation management controlled marketing departments plus charge back.

71. Tech Service Profit or Loss
Profit or loss from support operation (materials, EPI, plating, and parts).

72. Other Period Expense $
Warranties, licensing fees, noninventoriable burden expenses.

73. Wafer Family Period Expense
If wafer families are used, the amount of wafer period expense charged to benefiting final families with offset on wafer family. See Table 10-2.

74. Capacity Variance $
The charge to the P&L for percent of earned labor over full capacity labor times fixed portion of inventoriable direct and indirect factory overhead (not to be used initially).

75. Subtotal Operating Expense $
Total lines 69 through 75.

76. Operating Margin (3) $
Margin 2 less total inventory expense less total operating expense (line 60 less lines 68 and 75).

77. Purchasing & Distribution $
Departments for specification, warehousing, purchasing and customer service including their share of chargeback.

78. Capital Expense $
Expense portion of capital work orders for equipment and facilities.

79. Division G&A
Administrative departments' charges controlled by division management plus appropriate charge back.

80. Subtotal Operating Expenses $
Purchasing and distribution plus capital expenses plus division G&A (line 77 plus lines 78 and 79).

81. Total Period Expense $
Operating expense plus subtotal division operating expense (lines 75 and 80).

82. **Division Margin (4) $**
Margin 3 less division operating expense (line 76 less line 80).

83. **Group Marketing $**
Departments for marketing and selling—includes marketing and selling, strategic marketing and advertising, plus share of chargeback.

84. **Group Administration $**
Administration functions controlled by group management plus their chargeback.

85. **Group R&D $**
R&D functions controlled by group management plus share of chargeback.

86. **Nondepartment Expense $**
Workmen's compensation, patent awards, suggestion awards, and state income tax.

87. **Profit Sharing and Supplementary Contributory Retirement Plan Costs $**
Assigned by corporate.

88. **Corporate G&A and Human Relations $**
Assigned by corporate.

89. **Other $**
Other income and expense.

90. **Interest $**
Interest income and expense.

91. **Overhead Eliminations**
Elimination PII caused by inventorying technical services' wafer and piecepart at a WWS based upon transfer price.

92. **Subtotal G&A $**
Total lines 83 through 91.

93. **Group Margin $**
Margin 4 less G&A (line 82 less line 92).

94. **Taxes**
Appropriate tax rate applied to regional profits.

95. **Profit After Taxes**
Group margin less taxes (line 93 less line 94).

Table 10-1 Family Operating Statement

Measurement: Amounts in Thousands

Gross Booking Line Item	USA ($)	USA (%)	Total Europe ($)	Total Europe (%)	Asia Pacific ($)	Asia Pacific (%)	Rest of Amer ($)	Rest of Amer (%)	Total World ($)	Total World (%)
Bookings Net $	2721		1359				50		4130	
Net Gross Ratio	.907		.964				.947		.925	
Shipped Turns			146						146	
Turns %			31.6						8.5	
Backlog Current	1805		2323				127		4255	
Backlog 1-13 Wks	3924		3230				211		7366	
Backlog Total $	14244		8512				620		23377	
Backlog Delqnt	1528		1719				53		3300	
% To Total	10.7		20.1				8.6		14.1	
ASP Bookings	.959		.475				.623		.714	
ASP Backlog	.939		.606				.602		.773	
ASP Gross Sal	.593		.597		.412		.423		.567	
ASP Net Sales	.561		.597		.408		.420		.551	
Net Sales #	2880		2624		841		226		6571	
Book/Bill Ratio	1.683		.867				.522		1.140	
Gross Sales V$	1805	111.6	1681	107.2	349	101.6	96	100.7	3931	108.5
Gross Sales NV$	4	.2							4	.1
Returns $$	−129	−7.9	−102	−6.5	−6	−1.7		−.1	−237	−6.5
Allowances	−63	−3.9	−11	−.6			−1	−.6	−75	−2.0
Net Sales $$	1616	100.0	1568	100.0	343	100.0	95	100.0	3623	100.0
Std Cost Net	627	38.8	540	34.4	141	41.2	41	43.0	1349	37.2
Std Margin (1)	989	61.1	1028	65.5	202	58.7	54	56.9	2273	62.7
Freight	58	3.5	28	1.7	3	.8			89	2.4
Duty	38	2.3	269	17.1	19	5.5	8	7.9	333	9.1

Table 10-1 Family Operating Statement (Continued)

Actual Material	12	.7	56	3.5	731	212.9	1	.5	799	22.0
Earned Material			54	3.4	738	214.7			792	21.8
Purch Price Var	11	.6	2	.1					13	.3
Usage/Mix Var					-6	-1.8			-6	-.1
Scrap/Obsolete	9	.5					1	.5	10	.2
Scrap Reclaim	-9	-.5							-9	-.2
Tot Mtrl Var	11	.6	2	.1	-6	-1.8	1	.5	8	.2
% To Ernd Mat	4416.7		4.3		-.8				.9	
Actual Labor	20	1.2	53	3.3	61	17.6			134	3.6
Earned Labor	15	.9	68	4.3	99	28.9			182	5.0
Rate Var	1				-4	-1.2			-4	-.1
Productivity Var	5	.2	-15	-.9	-34	-9.9			-45	-1.2
Tot Labor Var	5	.3	-15	-.9	-39	-11.2			-49	-1.3
% To Ernd Lab	36.0		-22.7		-38.8				-26.7	
DFO	95	5.8	221	14.1	315	91.7			632	17.4
QA	54	3.3	16	1.0	20	5.7			90	2.4
IFO	22	1.3	30	1.9	9	2.6			61	1.6
Tot Inv OH	171	10.5	268	17.0	344	100.2			783	21.6
-Earned OH	81	5.0	382	24.3	425	123.7			888	24.5
-Capacity Var										
Tot Mfg OH Var	89	5.5	-114	-7.2	-81	-23.4			-106	-2.9
% To Ernd OH	109.6		-29.9		-18.9				-11.9	
Tot Earned MLO	96	5.9	504	32.1	1262	367.4			1862	51.4
Total Yield Var	27	1.6	1		34	9.9			62	1.7
% To Tot Ernd	27.9				2.7				3.2	
Wafer Variations	33	2.0							33	.9
Tot Factory Var	166	10.2	-127	-8.0	-91	-26.5	1	.5	-52	-1.4
Procedural Var	6	.3	253	16.1	-88	-25.5			172	4.7
Translation Var										
Tot Mfg Var	172	10.6	127	8.0	-179	-52.1	1	.5	120	3.3

Table 10-1 Family Operating Statement (Continued)

Measurement: Amounts in Thousands

Line Item	**USA** ($)	(%)	**Total Europe** ($)	(%)	**Asia Pacific** ($)	(%)	**Rest of Amer** ($)	(%)	**Total World** ($)	(%)
Adj to Phy RM	38	2.3	3	.1					41	1.1
Adj to Phy Intco	83	5.1			- 108	- 31.5			- 26	- .7
Adj to Phy WIPFG	- 120	- 7.4	5	.2					- 116	- 3.2
Std Change	25	1.5							25	.6
Valuation Change	10	.6	7	.4	3	.7			20	.5
Scrap RMR	33	2.0	30	1.9					64	1.7
Tot Inv Ex	69	4.2	45	2.8	- 106	- 30.7			8	.2
Mfg Margin (2)	652	40.3	559	35.6	464	135.2	46	48.4	1722	47.5
R&D Engr	161	9.9	12	.7					173	4.7
Product Market	29	1.8			2	.5			31	.8
Tech Service P/L	- 19	- 1.1							- 19	- .5
Other Period Ex	25	1.5	5	.3	14	4.1			45	1.2
Wafer Period Ex	20	1.2							20	.5
Capacity Var										
Tot Operating Ex	218	13.4	17	1.0	16	4.6			251	6.9
Op Margin (3)	435	26.8	542	34.5	448	130.5	46	48.4	1471	40.6
Purchase/Dist	79	4.8	16	1.0	10	2.8			105	2.8
Capital Ex	6	.3	3	.1					9	.2
Division G&A	35	2.1	95	6.0					129	3.5
Tot Division Ex	119	7.3	113	7.2	10	2.8			242	6.6
Div Margin (4)	315	19.5	429	27.3	438	127.7	46	48.4	1229	33.9
GRP Marketing	121	7.4	194	12.3	29	8.5	6	6.2	350	9.6
GRP Admin	68	4.1	82	5.2	69	20.0	2	1.9	221	6.0
Group Finance	21	1.2							21	.5
GRP R&D	25	1.5							25	.6
Non Dept	22	1.3			5	1.3			27	.7
P/S-Scrp-I/B	44	2.7	14	.8				.3	58	1.6
Corp G&A & H.R.	37	2.2	2	.1				.2	39	1.0
Interest			13	.8	- 6	- 1.8		- .3	7	.1
OTH (Inc) Ex	7	.4	58	3.6	- 6	- 1.7	- 1	- .7	58	1.6
OH Eliminations										
Tot Group Ex	345	21.3	363	23.1	91	26.3	7	7.8	806	22.2
GRP Margin (5)	- 29	- 1.8	66	4.1	348	101.3	39	40.6	423	11.6
Taxes									190	5.2
Prof Aft Tax									233	6.4

Table 10-2 Example of Wafer Family

	Wafer Family for A&B	P&L Family A	P&L Family B	Total A&B
Bookings				
Net Sales		500	1000	1500
Std. Cost		250	500	750
Earned Material	100	100	200	400
Purchase Price Var	10	1	2	13
Earned Labor	50	100	200	350
Rate Var	(5)	4	(4)	(5)
Productivity Var	2	1	2	5
Total INV OH	160	200	400	760
Earned OH	150	190	405	645
OH Variation	10	10	(5)	15
Yield**	(5)	10	10	15
Wafer Variations*	(12)	4	8	0
Total Mfg Var	0	30	13	43
Adj to Phys	1	0	1	2
Other Period Exp***	3	5	5	13
Wafer Period Exp*	4	2	2	0
Sub-Total OP Costs		7	8	15
OP Margin	0	213	479	692

*New line items

**Total wafer variations must be input as an offset amount

***Total wafer period cost must be input as an offset amount

11

Business Forecasting

WHAT IS A P&L FORECAST?

A P&L forecast is our **best collective assessment** of what the **financial outcome** of all the related business/manufacturing activities will be in a given period in the future.

WHY DO WE FORECAST?

We forecast because we are **in business to make a profit** and we would prefer to see, at the earliest possible moment, what the course of actions will give rise to rather than wait until it happens (i.e., what will be **probable financial outcome of projected scenario**). The former approach permits corrective action (change of direction) to take place if probable profit is less than desired because it is financially prudent to reconcile **anticipated income** with **planned expenditure** in order that they be **balanced** on the **profit fulcrum**. We forecast in order to assess risk, to determine the feasibility of a proposed scenario, and to be able to detect and correct or compensate for major deviations to plan.

We forecast in order to reach out and shape the future rather than passively await its arrival.

Examples of forecasting forms and charts are shown in Tables 11-1 and 11-2 and in Figure 11-1.

Table 11-1 Schedule Of Forecast Time Periods

	Jul	Aug	Sep	Oct	Nov	Dec	Jan	Feb	Mar	Apr	May	June	Jul	Aug	Sep	Oct	Nov	Dec
Aug FCST	EST	FCST	FCST	Forecast Quarter			Forecast Quarter			Forecast Quarter			Forecast Quarter			Forecast Quarter		
Sep FCST		EST	FCST	FCST	FCST	FCST												
Oct FCST			EST	FCST	FCST	FCST												
Nov FCST				EST	FCST	FCST	Forecast Quarter			Forecast Quarter			Forecast Quarter			Forecast Quarter		
Dec FCST					EST	FCST	FCST	FCST	FCST									
Jan FCST						EST	FCST	FCST	FCST									
Feb FCST							EST	FCST	FCST	Forecast Quarter			Forecast Quarter			Forecast Quarter		
Mar FCST								EST	FCST	FCST	FCST	FCST						
Apr FCST									EST	FCST	FCST	FCST						
May FCST										EST	FCST	FCST	Forecast Quarter			Forecast Quarter		
Jun FCST											EST	FCST	FCST	FCST	FCST			
Jul FCST												EST	FCST	FCST	FCST			

WHAT, WHEN, AND HOW DO WE FORECAST AND FOR WHAT FUTURE PERIODS?

Item	Detail	Due Date	Responsibility	Source
1. Aged bookings	Each major device by A. Units B. ASP C. Package	WD 1	Product Mktg.	A. Historical trends B. Field Fcsts.
2. Billings **External**	Each major device by A. Total dollars B. Units C. ASP D. Package	WD 3	Production Cont.	A. Turns bookings Fcst B. Delinquencies C. Open orders for per D. Ship aheads
Internal	Each major device by A. Total dollars B. Units C. ASP D. Package	WD 3	Production Cont.	A. Open orders
Credits	RMR, DPP, DSR		Production Cont. Finance	A. Historical trends B. Forecasts
	Reconciliation of Bookings/Billings—Manufacturing Plans/Purchases			
3. Manufacturing plan (by device)	Wafer Fab A. Starts B. Outs C. Moves D. Mech. Yield E. Probe Yield *(End inv. cycle time)	WD 1	Wafer Fab Mgr.	A. Wafer outs/reqd. schedule B. Run rates
	Unit Probe A. Wafers probed B. Yield *(End inventory)			
	Assembly A. Starts B. Yield		Materials Mgr.	
	Final test A. Starts B. Outs C. Yield		Manufacturing Mgr.	
4. Purchases	A. Raw stock, finished goods purchases to be recd. by factory	WD 4	Materials Mgr.	Order Backlog
	B. Quantify MOP by device by stage of completion	WD 5	Materials Mgr.	
5. Operating expenses	Details of any significant anticipated over/under expenditure compared to budget/current run rates	WD 3	All Dept. Mgrs.	

WHAT, WHEN, AND HOW DO WE FORECAST AND FOR WHAT FUTURE PERIODS (Continued)

Item	Detail	Due Date	Responsibility	Source
6. Complete 1st pass P&L Fcst.	3 months by month, remainder of year by qtr. (input to MOPLACS but not released)	WD 5	P&L Analysis	
7. Review of 1st pass P&L	Sales by device, units ASP, yields, run rates	WD 6	OPS + Dept. Mgrs.	
8. Amendments to 1st pass P&L	Depending on outcome of review	WD 6	P&L Analyst	
9. Proposed P&L	For final review	WD 7	P&L Analyst + OPS Mgrs.	
10. Final amendments		WD 7	P&L Analyst	
11. Final P&L		WD 7	P&L Analyst	

These timescales are probably as good as can be achieved with a manual system, leaving little or no time for review. A system in which "number crunching" is automated has significant advantages.

NOTE 1

A. Production control should schedule wafer fab on an **outs required** basis. This will not be a forecast or manufacturing plan until it has been reconciled with wafer fab's **can do** response.

B. Production control should provide wafer fab with visibility into outs requirements by means of a **six-month wafer outs required rolling forecast** by device, reviewed and reissued monthly.

C. Production control should provide a one-month outs requirement to wafer fab on a monthly basis in addition to the weekly outs required schedule.

D. Product/device engineering should make available a probe yield forecast, **mutually agreed**, for the next month and for the year, by quarter, reviewed and reissued quarterly.

Table 11-2 Forecasting Factory Drive Chart

	Jul	Aug	Prior Sept	Est Sept	3Q86	Prior Oct	Curr Oct	Nov	Dec	4Q86
Cm Bklg Aged	5425	4935	7084	7084		7852	6950	6304	7171	20425
- Pr Mo Ship Ahd	—	—	—	—		- 2000	—	- 600	- 600	
+ Net Book Aged	348	920	650	1767	1767	1245	950	850	1650	3450
+ Begin Dlq	3090	2373	1710	1710		1900	1920	2000	2000	
+ Ship Aheads	1427	1827	2000	1471		600	600	600	1275	
Total Available	10290	10055	11444	12032		9597	10420	9154	11496	
- End Dlq Bklg	- 2373	- 1710	- 1900	- 1920		- 1700	- 2000	- 2000	- 2000	
- Ret & Allow	- 847	- 877	- 600	- 502		- 500	- 500	- 500	- 625	
- Xcels & Push	—	—	—	—		—	—	—	—	
- Otp Adjustment	- 238	- 221	- 217	- 217		- 138	- 73	- 121	- 65	
Current F'cst	7294	7472	8727	9627	24393	7259	7847	6533	8806	23186
Budget	6791	6791	8488	8488	22070	6900	6900	6900	8700	22500
Delta to Budget	503	681	239	1139	2323	359	947	- 367	106	686

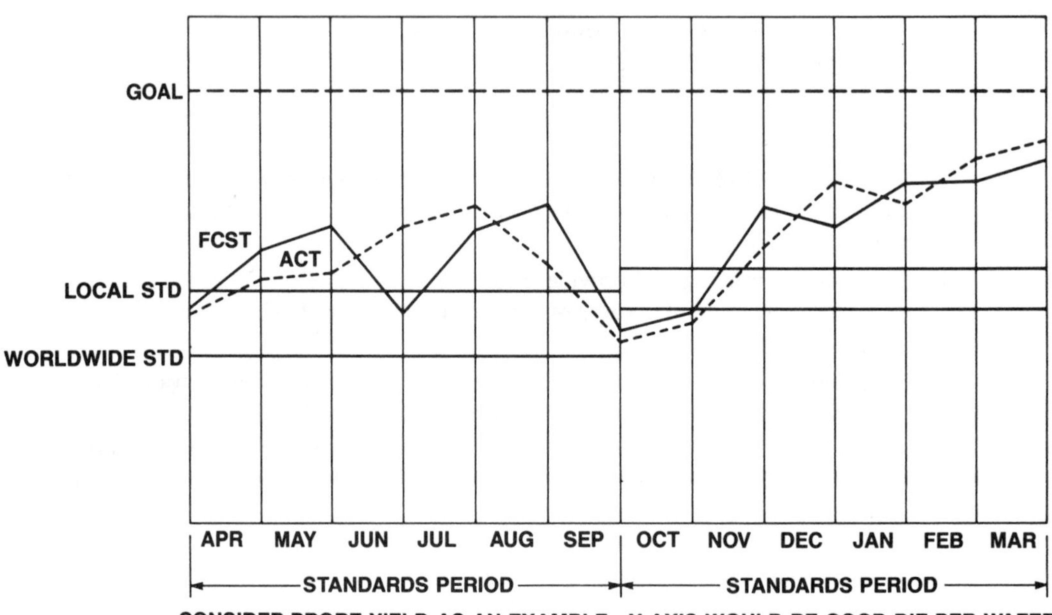

Figure 11-1 Standards, Forecasts, Goals, and Actual Performance
(Definition of, distinction between and the effect of each on P&L forecasting)

If the criteria for a good forecast is + 5 percent, - 0 percent; that is, the actual sales, pbt, and so on, should certainly not be less than forecast and should not exceed forecast by more than 5 percent, then it is difficult to see how this degree of control can be achieved by such crude means. Lacking in the detail necessary to assess the quality of what these numbers represent, this approach, while useful as a broad guideline or test of a forecast number, it has little value in helping to manage at the product line level, in producing an accurate forecast. Mix, with all of its implications, is not comprehended in this approach.

12

Integrated Business Information System (IBIS)

VISIBILITY, EXECUTION, AND CONTROL

Except for clairvoyants and astrologers, no one claims to be able to see into the future with any degree of certainty. But in business, if we are to be proactive rather than reactive, the need for us to attempt to do so is real. We differ from the seers by placing our faith in what we know and our expectation, our judgment, about what we think will be factual in the future, rather than in a "sixth" sense. This "science" however, is still very inexact and the boundaries of uncertainty can not be precisely defined, so we take out an insurance policy against unforeseen events in the form of inventory. One significant factor determining the amount of this inventory which we think we should hold is the cycle-time, from start to finish, of our manufacturing process. If, for example, it takes 120 days to build product and we assume it would be prudent to have this product immediately available when the customer demands it, then we need to forecast what we think the aggregate demand of our customer order base will be in four months time and start the appropriate mix of products in our manufacturing process now. (Forecasting customers' behavior, over whom we have perhaps some influence but certainly not control, can be particularly inexact.) This forecast will contain two major elements, backlog and bookings.

1. **Backlog**—Orders already placed by customers on our books for delivery in some future period. The precise date the customer requires the product to be delivered is customer required date (CRD). Our commitment to deliver is factory schedule date (FSD). Ideally, these dates should be the same.

2. **Bookings**—Orders yet to be placed by customers in some future period for delivery in some future period. (An important subcategory of bookings is turns bookings—orders placed sometime during the current month for delivery in the same month.)

As Figure 12-1 shows, the further we go out in time, the greater will be the bookings portion of our sales (billings) forecast and the smaller will be the actual current backlog portion. (The relationship between CRD backlog, FSD backlog bookings forecast, delinquencies—orders already past due for delivery—and capacity are shown graphically.) Ideally, the bookings forecast portion would be constructed using inputs from the field (the marketplace) incorporating what we know or think we know of our customer's

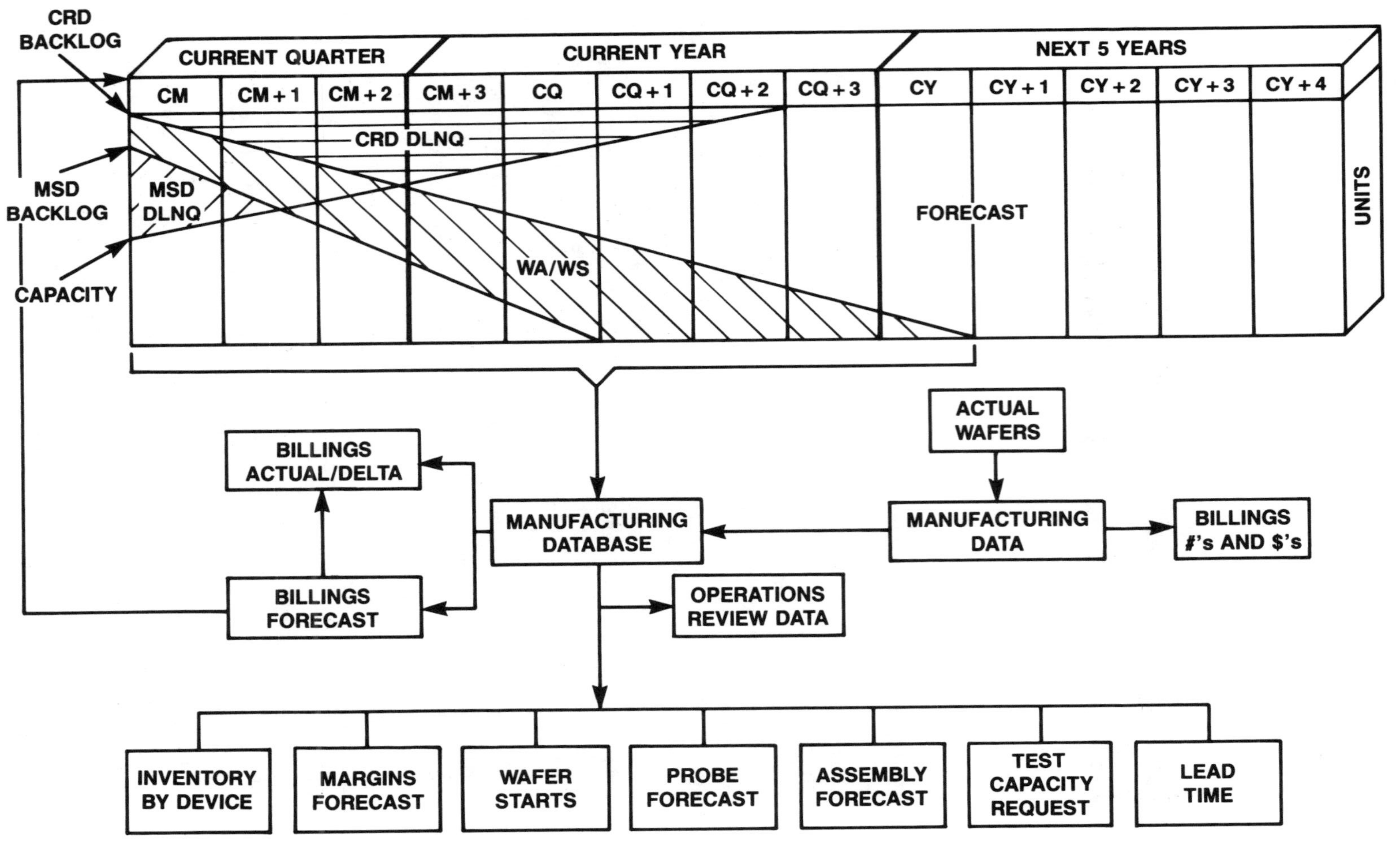

Figure 12-1 IBIS Forecasting Time Profile

intentions to place orders. (Sometimes the use of the term **market** conceals more than it reveals and we forget that aggregate demand is composed of the behavior of individual human beings.) This distillation process begins with inputs from each individual customer throughout the world and is refined through the field sales offices in the regions and finally through product marketing, usually located back in the factories. To be meaningful, this information needs to be by individual device type, not aggregate dollars. Factories do not know how to build dollars for sale in some future period, only units in a prescribed mix. This is the ideal, proactive approach. For a variety of reasons, however, the task of deciding this most often falls by default on the production control organization who, in the absence of anything better, fulfill this requirement by extrapolating history. However, regardless of how the sales forecast is produced, there is still risk because of uncertainty.

In the light of these difficulties, we might choose to simply not forecast at all and only build to order, provided of course that our manufacturing cycle-time is acceptable to our customers. This approach would mean foregoing the opportunity to service sporadically and spontaneously occurring needs for immediate or short lead-time delivery product in some future period. (On semi-custom or full-custom products, build to order is the only alternative. Cycle-time from order entry to delivery of order is very often the deciding factor in who gets the order.) Even if we do forecast, since forecasting is an inexact science, we cannot possibly call the aggregate demand mix precisely. The risk in this approach of course, is that we shall build the wrong mix and will have available in our inventory too little of what is subsequently demanded and too much of what isn't—not only in our finished goods warehouse but dispersed throughout the system. This may manifest itself in both sales and inventory jeopardy—sales opportunities we cannot service (turns billings) and inventory which we cannot sell and may have to write off. At best, we get to fund the holding of it.

We can deal with this uncertainty of supply and demand in one of two ways—by working to refine the accuracy of our forecasting process, or by improving our responsiveness through shorter manufacturing cycle-times (or both). For example, if overall cycle-time can be reduced from 120 days to 60 days, the amount of insurance inventory in jeopardy due to this window of uncertainty can be halved. Even by selectively reducing cycle-time, due to the value added effect on inventory by stage of completion, if we were able to reduce only the last operation cycle-time, final test say, from four weeks to two days, then we would only need to hold two days of finished goods inventory since that is how long it would take to replenish this inventory if it were totally consumed in servicing some unforeseen windfall opportunity. Obviously, the further back into the process we apply this approach, the greater we benefit. Reducing manufacturing cycle-times to improve responsiveness has been discussed elsewhere but what about other, nonmanufacturing but nevertheless equally important cycle-times? A factory usually has to process information before it can even begin to process product. One such process is the very forecasting cycle we have just been discussing. (A practical equivalent example is the actual order entry, scheduling and factory loading cycle. This is also an integral part of product lead-time from order entry to delivery is it not?) This process, represented schematically in Figure 12-2, is essentially universal for every business. The data to be processed will be different from business to business, from product to product, from day to day (or month to month, year to year)—but the actual cycle of events in the process is, or should be, the same.

Despite the cyclical nature of this process, it is still widespread practice for this (forecasting, planning, factory loading, actual performance to plan comparison and the

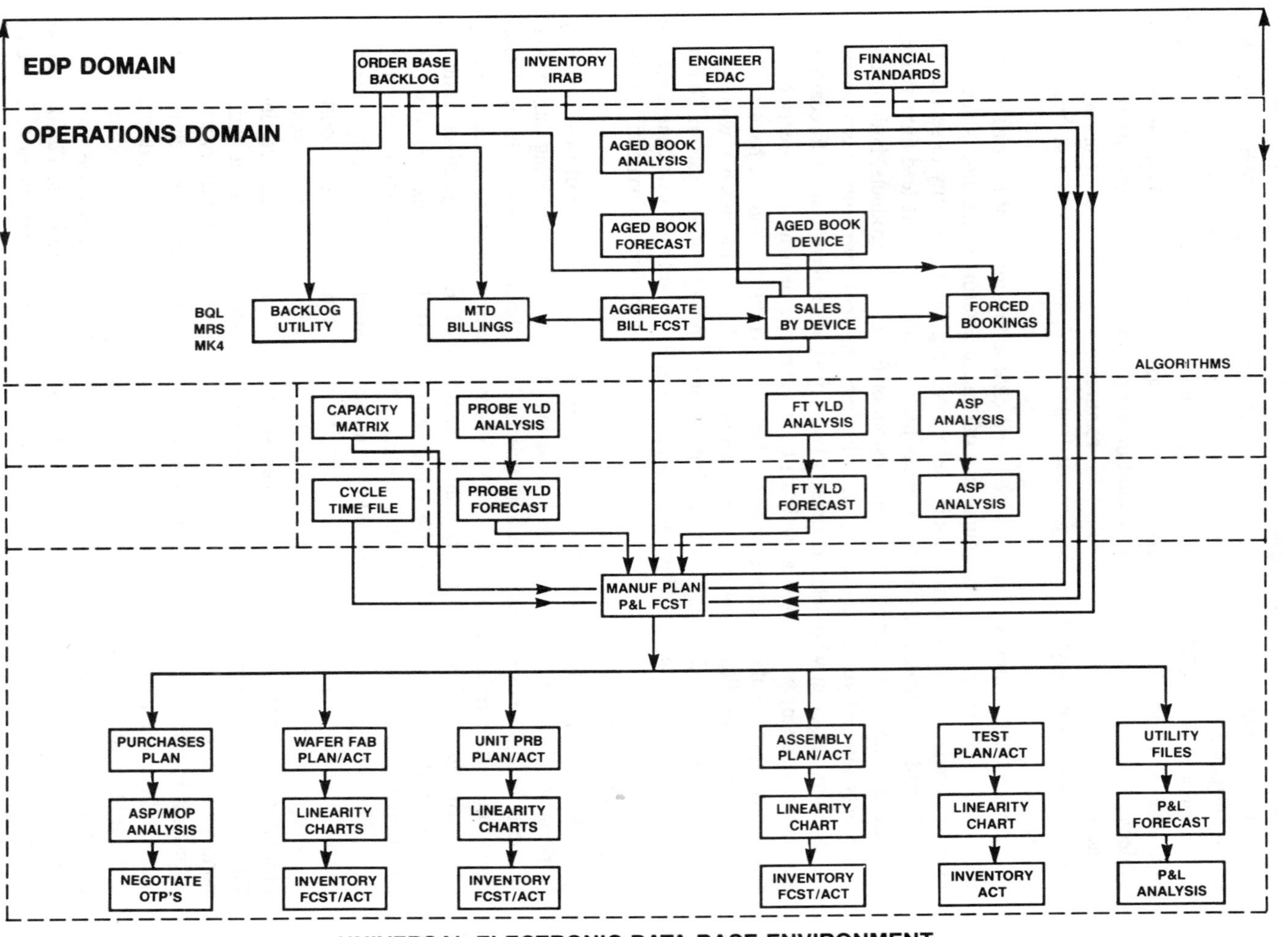

Figure 12-2 IBIS Integrated Business Information System

financial quantification of this activity—the operating profit and loss forecast statement)—to be produced by manual methods rather than with computer software. In all too many enterprises, this ritualistic frenzy can be seen at the beginning of every month. Armed with an eight inch thick EDP (electronic data processing) report, calculators, and pencils, the production control group in its entirety, scribble frantically for days on end to produce on the back of a cigarette packet, a forecast already condemned due to these methods and the need to meet a deadline, to a level of detail too crude to be useful. Accuracy and or speed are invariably compromised. Because of time pressure, drive charts such as the example shown in the previous chapter are typically used, after which a bottom up plan by device is produced. This is the cart before the horse.

We are all familiar with the expression "islands of automation." Information processing, creating and communicating the visibility which precedes execution and control on the factory floor, is all too often limited by similar "islands of information." Each functional department, in their understandable if not excusable typically parochial fashion, maintains their own particular databases in some nonuniversally accessible environment, incapable of sharing this information with other equally isolated islands except through additional cycles of redundant keyboard entry. Execution on the factory floor can only be optimized if the many dynamically changing variables can be captured, processed and communicated speedily. It is entirely typical for the ingredients of the forecasting process to reside in different domains. The raw data, the information on backlog and inventory profile, for example, normally reside in some "universal" corporate data base, only made available to the user in some prescribed fashion. EDP factories are usually as remiss as the rest of us in "marketing what their factories can produce" rather than learning to build what their customers want. The yield data, the manufacturing variables, process flows, and so on, all of which must be brought together, not only to build a forecast but to build the product itself, are all equally likely to reside in different and isolated data bases. All of these have to be fed into the main number crunching engine at some point.

The traditional inability (or unwillingness) of a typical EDP organization to provide the data to the user (customer) in the form desired, at an affordable cost, when it is required (quality, on-time delivery and cost are universal parameters) in conjunction with the user's inability (or unwillingness) to precisely define the end product required, ensures a less than optimal outcome. There is a language barrier. This can only be resolved by either giving the user the authority to access and the means to process the data base for himself, or for the custodians of the corporate part of the data base to take the responsibility to process the data in the form required by the user. Since each EDP customer normally prefers to have a customized solution, the EDP leadtime can understandably deteriorate due to a high project backlog, often beyond limits acceptable to the internal customer. This almost invariably encourages the proliferation of self-help solutions. With the recent availability of fourth level language data base interrogation tools such as Nomad and Focus, the former approach is now feasible.

IBIS seeks to facilitate this by integrating these "islands of automation" in a common electronic data base, universally accessible to, and supported by all parties involved and by automating the processing of the data.

Tables 12-1 through 12-10 are examples of the automating of this process.

Table 12-1 Forecast Report

(This is the last page of a 20 page 250 line item bottom up forecast, produced automatically in less than 1 hour)
Produced day 1 each month—perhaps 2/3 iterations to hit final number

	Forecast			Backlog							Work In Process			
	$,S	ASP	#,S	CRD Delinq	MSD Delinq	O.CRD Base	O.MSD Base	Ship Ahead	Bal CM + 1	CM + 2	Finish Good	Final Test	Raw Stock	Stock In TR
Device 1	29.09	2.53	11.50	—	—	11.50	11.50	—	0.00	—	4.12	1.51	—	—
Device 2	32.20	5.65	5.70	5.68	5.68	7.20	7.20	—	—	—	0.75	4.08	6.00	—
Device 3	0.48	4.77	0.10	—	—	0.10	0.10	—	—	—	0.23	0.25	6.04	—
* * Subtot	173.68	2.57	67.71	5.75	5.68	49.61	49.68	20.73	14.70	25.67	44.44	96.91	21.35	4.9
Device 4	130.07	4.89	26.60	1.40	1.00	15.70	16.10	10.00	11.65	5.30	21.25	58.68	—	0.8
Device 5	—	4.50	—	—	—	—	—	—	—	10.00	0.87	—	—	—
Device 6	39.88	7.25	5.50	—	—	5.50	5.50	—	1.00	1.00	—	5.72	—	—
Device 7	0.28	13.96	0.02	—	—	0.02	0.02	—	—	—	0.35	—	—	—
Device 8	93.34	5.43	17.19	0.09	0.09	11.86	11.86	5.23	8.19	10.95	19.79	0.06	3.94	—
Device 9	1.72	11.44	0.15	—	—	0.15	0.15	—	—	0.05	—	0.24	—	—
Device 10	4.94	12.05	0.41	0.04	0.03	0.37	0.38	—	0.10	—	2.76	—	—	—
Device 11	—	19.75	—	—	—	0.00	0.00	—	—	0.00	0.49	—	—	—
Device 12	—	—	—	0.00	0.00	0.00	0.00	0.00	0.00	0.00	—	—	—	—
Device 13	3.48	29.00	0.12	—	—	0.12	0.12	—	0.10	—	0.06	—	—	—
Device 14	—	—	—	0.00	0.00	0.00	0.00	0.00	0.00	0.00	—	—	1.08	—
Device 15	0.40	4.48	0.09	—	—	0.09	0.09	—	0.95	0.60	4.12	—	—	—
* * Subtot	274.11	5.47	50.08	1.53	1.12	33.81	34.22	15.23	21.99	27.90	49.69	64.70	5.02	0.8
Device 16	6.88	10.27	0.67	0.07	0.00	0.21	0.21	0.03	0.04	0.04	0.06	—	2.54	2.3
Device 17	30.00	5.00	6.00	—	—	—	—	6.00	18.00	10.08	24.26	—	—	—
Device 18	—	—	—	0.00	0.00	0.00	0.00	0.00	0.00	0.00	—	—	—	—
Device 19	0.15	14.51	0.01	1.16	0.00	—	1.15	—	—	—	0.98	2.01	5.20	—
Device 20	—	26.00	—	—	—	—	—	—	—	0.08	0.27	0.16	—	—
* * Subtot	37.03	5.54	6.68	1.23	0.00	0.21	1.36	6.03	18.04	10.20	25.57	2.17	7.74	2.3
* * Total	587.04	4.54	129.31	10.47	7.61	88.12	90.26	42.29	60.26	67.57	143.28	168.54	43.06	8.0
Total	6026.33	21.03	286.56	29.51	17.31	215.57	214.74	83.01	128.23	165.15	353.88	402.18	273.81	22.8

All values are in thousands except ASP in U.S. dollars
CRD delinq. backlog orders are 010183: 08/24/85
MSD delinq. backlog orders are 010183: 08/24/85
CRD backlog orders are 08/25/85:09/28/85
MSD backlog orders are 08/25/85:09/28/85
CM + 1 backlog orders are 10/05/85:10/26/85
CM + 2 backlog orders are 10/27/85:11/23/85

Table 12-2 MTD Status
Produced daily to **Control Execution** to the forecast—**status in dollars**

	Fcst $	Sup. $ Bklg.	ASP	MTD Bill $	MTD Bill $ — Fcst $	OFI Hold $	OFI $	Total F.G. Whse. $	In Tran $	Lot P $	QA $	P&L $ TM80	Last Test $	Mid WIP $
Device 1	183.39	50.83	4.42	144.95	-38.43	0.00	0.00	108.78	0.00	0.00	0.00	6.39	0.00	0.00
Device 2	—	0.00	5.25	—	0.00	0.00	0.00	4.57	0.00	0.00	0.00	0.00	0.00	0.00
Device 3	39.88	0.00	7.25	28.05	-11.82	0.00	0.00	9.00	0.00	0.00	0.00	0.00	5.78	6.79
Device 4	0.28	0.00	13.96	0.35	0.07	0.00	0.00	4.48	0.00	0.00	0.00	0.00	0.00	0.00
Device 5	110.14	4.19	5.24	97.90	-12.25	0.96	0.00	61.88	0.00	0.00	0.00	0.00	0.00	0.00
Device 6	1.72	0.00	11.50	1.68	-0.05	0.00	0.00	3.31	0.00	0.00	0.00	0.00	0.00	0.00
Device 7	9.37	2.04	13.02	7.36	-2.02	0.00	0.00	26.51	0.00	0.00	0.00	0.00	0.00	0.00
Device 8	—	0.00	19.75	—	0.00	0.00	0.00	9.62	0.00	0.00	0.00	0.00	0.00	0.00
Device 9	—	—	—	—	0.00	—	—	—	—	—	—	—	—	—
Device 10	0.00	0.00	29.00	—	0.00	0.00	0.00	0.00	1.88	0.00	0.00	0.00	0.00	0.00
Device 11	0.99	0.00	2.84	0.97	-0.02	0.00	0.03	10.64	0.00	0.00	0.00	0.00	0.00	0.00
Device 12	10.00	8.26	43.46	—	-10.00	0.00	0.00	0.00	0.00	—	0.00	0.00	0.00	0.00
Device 13	—	0.00	15.00	—	0.00	0.00	0.00	0.00	0.00	0.00	0.00	0.00	15.40	0.00
Device 14	0.10	0.00	10.33	0.02	-0.08	0.00	0.00	10.27	0.00	0.00	0.00	0.00	0.00	0.00
Device 15	—	—	—	—	0.00	—	—	—	—	—	—	—	—	—
Device 16	72.86	37.51	33.73	7.12	-65.74	0.00	0.00	27.25	0.00	0.00	2.39	0.00	0.00	0.00
Device 17	—	—	—	—	0.00	—	—	—	—	—	—	—	—	—
Device 18	—	—	—	—	0.00	—	—	—	—	—	—	—	—	—
Device 19	—	—	—	—	0.00	—	—	—	—	—	—	—	—	—
Device 20	—	—	—	—	0.00	—	—	—	—	—	—	—	—	—
Device 21	25.99	0.00	49.04	1.57	-24.42	0.00	0.00	35.36	0.00	0.00	0.00	0.00	10.59	0.00
Device 22	0.06	0.46	5.78	-7.11	-7.17	0.00	0.35	35.32	0.00	0.00	0.00	0.00	0.00	0.00
Device 23	2.83	0.00	4.35	2.83	0.00	0.00	0.00	53.98	0.00	0.00	0.00	0.00	0.00	0.00
Device 24	2.79	0.00	6.50	2.44	-0.36	0.00	0.00	4.65	0.00	0.00	0.00	0.00	0.00	0.00
Device 25	0.99	0.00	6.60	0.03	-0.96	0.00	0.00	8.83	0.00	0.00	0.00	0.00	0.00	0.00
Device 26	—	0.00	8.20	—	0.00	0.00	0.00	1.84	0.00	0.00	0.00	0.00	0.00	0.00
Device 27	0.00	0.07	3.27	-1.35	-1.35	0.00	0.00	7.69	0.00	0.00	2.45	0.00	0.00	0.00
Device 28	—	—	—	—	0.00	—	—	—	—	—	—	—	—	—
Device 29	8.95	10.15	2.03	-1.71	-10.66	0.00	0.51	22.71	0.00	0.00	0.00	18.10	0.00	0.00
Device 30	—	—	—	—	0.00	—	—	—	—	—	—	—	—	—
Device 31	55.49	7.41	2.16	48.15	-7.34	0.00	0.00	1.50	0.00	0.00	0.00	0.00	0.00	0.00
Device 32	—	—	—	—	0.00	—	—	—	—	—	—	—	—	—
Device 33	9.38	0.00	3.35	8.01	-1.37	0.00	0.00	4.53	0.00	0.00	0.00	0.00	0.00	0.00
Device 34	—	—	—	—	0.00	—	—	—	—	—	—	—	—	—
Device 35	56.42	2.32	2.52	38.23	-18.19	0.00	4.03	92.39	0.00	0.00	0.00	0.00	0.00	0.00
Device 36	20.23	14.01	2.38	13.36	-6.87	0.00	0.00	0.00	0.00	0.00	0.00	0.00	4.43	14.07
Device 37	25.42	0.00	5.65	23.28	-2.14	0.00	1.90	0.00	0.00	0.00	0.00	0.00	0.00	0.00
Device 38	0.48	0.00	4.77	0.48	0.00	0.00	0.00	0.62	0.00	0.00	0.00	0.00	0.00	0.00
Device 39	3.35	0.00	7.12	2.41	-0.94	0.00	0.32	2.21	0.00	0.00	0.00	0.00	0.00	0.00
Device 40	205.00	0.00	5.00	118.25	-86.75	0.00	32.76	0.00	0.00	0.00	24.18	0.00	0.00	0.00
Device 41	—	—	—	—	0.00	—	—	—	—	—	—	—	—	—
Device 42	0.87	0.00	14.51	0.74	-0.13	0.00	0.29	65.43	0.00	0.00	0.00	0.00	0.00	0.00
Device 43	—	0.00	26.00	—	0.00	0.00	0.00	11.21	0.00	0.00	0.00	0.00	0.00	0.00
* * Total	846.98	137.25	4.62	538.01	-308.99	0.96	40.19	624.58	1.88	0.00	29.02	24.49	36.20	20.86
Total	6809.83	1022.01	18.18	3359.86	-3449.95	13.71	124.44	3537.30	799.62	83.95	388.12	100.70	808.62	802.61

Table 12-3 MTD Status
Produced daily to **Control Execution** of the forecast—**Status in Units**

	CRD,ORD Base	SUP,ORD Base	MSD,ORD Base	Qty Held	Fcst $,S	MTD Bill $	Delta #	OFI Hold	OFI	F.G. Whse	In Tran	Lot P.	Q.A.	P&L	Last Test	Mid WIP
Device 1	12.50	11.50	12.50	1.00	41.49	32.79	-8.69	—	—	24.61	—	—	—	1.4	—	—
Device 2	—	—	—	0.00	—	—	0.00	—	—	0.87	—	—	—	—	—	—
Device 3	1.63	—	1.63	0.00	5.50	3.87	-1.63	—	—	1.24	—	—	—	—	0.8	0.94
Device 4	—	—	—	0.00	0.02	0.02	0.00	—	—	0.32	—	—	—	—	—	—
Device 5	2.74	0.80	2.39	0.00	21.02	18.68	-2.34	0.2	—	11.81	—	—	—	—	—	—
Device 6	—	—	—	0.00	0.15	0.15	0.00	—	—	0.29	—	—	—	—	—	—
Device 7	0.16	0.16	0.16	0.00	0.72	0.56	-0.15	—	—	2.04	—	—	—	—	—	—
Device 8	—	—	—	0.00	—	—	0.00	—	—	0.49	—	—	—	—	—	—
Device 9	—	—	—	0.00	—	—	0.00	—	—	—	—	0.00	—	—	—	—
Device 10	0.12	—	0.12	0.12	0.00	—	0.00	—	—	—	0.06	—	—	—	—	—
Device 11	0.01	—	0.01	0.00	0.35	0.34	-0.01	—	0.01	3.75	—	—	—	—	—	—
Device 12	0.23	0.19	0.12	0.00	0.23	—	-0.23	—	—	—	—	0.00	—	—	—	—
Device 13	0.04	—	0.02	0.00	—	—	0.00	—	—	—	—	—	—	—	1.0	—
Device 14	0.01	—	—	0.00	0.01	0.00	-0.01	—	—	0.99	—	—	—	—	—	—
Device 15	0.01	—	—	0.00	—	—	0.00	—	—	—	—	0.00	—	—	—	—
Device 16	1.98	1.11	1.54	0.00	2.16	0.21	-1.95	—	—	0.81	—	—	0.07	—	—	—
Device 17	—	—	—	0.00	—	—	0.00	—	—	—	—	0.00	—	—	—	—
Device 18	—	—	—	0.00	—	—	0.00	—	—	—	—	—	—	—	—	—
Device 19	—	—	—	0.00	—	—	0.00	—	—	—	—	—	—	—	—	—
Device 20	0.00	—	0.00	0.00	—	—	0.00	—	—	—	—	0.00	—	—	—	—
Device 21	1.00	—	1.00	0.00	0.53	0.03	-0.50	—	—	0.72	—	—	—	—	0.2	—
Device 22	0.08	0.08	0.06	0.00	0.01	-1.23	-1.24	—	0.06	6.11	—	—	—	—	—	—
Device 23	—	—	—	0.00	0.65	0.65	0.00	—	—	12.41	—	—	—	—	—	—
Device 24	0.05	—	0.05	0.00	0.43	0.38	-0.05	—	—	0.71	—	—	—	—	—	—
Device 25	—	—	—	0.00	0.15	0.00	-0.14	—	—	1.34	—	—	—	—	—	—
Device 26	—	—	—	0.00	—	—	0.00	—	—	0.22	—	—	—	—	—	—
Device 27	0.02	0.02	—	0.00	0.00	-0.41	-0.41	—	—	2.35	—	—	0.75	—	—	—
Device 28	—	—	—	0.00	—	—	0.00	—	—	2.36	—	—	—	—	—	—
Device 29	5.28	5.00	5.25	0.00	4.41	-0.84	-5.25	—	0.25	11.18	—	—	—	8.9	—	—
Device 30	—	—	—	0.00	—	-0.22	-0.22	—	—	—	—	—	—	—	—	—
Device 31	3.43	3.43	3.40	0.00	25.69	22.29	-3.40	—	—	0.69	—	—	—	—	—	—
Device 32	—	—	—	0.00	—	—	0.00	—	—	—	—	0.00	—	—	—	—
Device 33	0.41	—	0.41	0.00	2.80	2.39	-0.41	—	—	1.35	—	—	—	—	—	—
Device 34	0.21	—	0.01	0.00	0.01	—	-0.01	—	—	0.94	—	—	—	—	—	—
Device 35	7.30	0.92	7.22	4.27	22.39	15.17	-7.22	—	1.60	36.66	—	—	—	—	—	—
Device 36	5.89	5.89	5.89	0.00	8.50	5.61	-2.89	—	—	—	—	—	—	—	1.9	5.91
Device 37	1.56	—	1.56	1.56	4.50	4.12	-0.38	—	0.34	—	—	—	—	—	—	—
Device 38	—	—	—	0.00	0.10	0.10	0.00	—	—	0.13	—	—	—	—	—	—
Device 39	0.13	—	0.08	0.00	0.47	0.34	-0.13	—	0.04	0.31	—	—	—	—	—	—
Device 40	17.38	—	17.38	0.00	41.00	23.65	-17.35	—	6.55	—	—	—	4.84	—	—	—
Device 41	—	—	—	0.00	—	—	0.00	—	—	—	—	0.00	—	—	—	—
Device 42	1.13	—	1.13	1.13	0.06	0.05	-0.01	—	0.02	4.51	—	—	—	—	—	—
Device 43	—	—	—	0.00	—	—	0.00	—	—	0.43	—	—	—	—	—	—
**Total	63.30	29.10	61.93	8.08	183.35	128.70	-54.62	0.2	8.87	129.64	0.06	0.00	5.66	10.3	3.9	6.85
Total	134.60	45.85	123.50	14.22	374.58	265.81	-108.68	0.6	15.58	327.41	5.64	1.16	10.61	11.4	17.4	13.26

Table 12-4 Billable Status
This report quantifies **billable** product by stage of completion.
Used to determine extent to which "actual" billings are on track to forecast.

	Fcst $	ASP	MTD Bill $	MTD Bill $ — Fcst $	OFI Hold $	OFI $	Shippable F.G. Whse $	In Tran $	Lot P $	QA $	P&L $/ TM80	Last Test $
Device 1	1.72	11.50	1.68	-0.05	0.00	0.00	0.00	0.00	0.00	0.00	0.00	0.00
Device 2	9.37	13.02	7.36	-2.02	0.00	0.00	2.04	0.00	0.00	0.00	0.00	0.00
Device 3	0.99	2.84	0.97	-0.02	0.00	0.03	0.00	0.00	0.00	0.00	0.00	0.00
Device 4	10.00	43.46	0.00	-10.00	0.00	0.00	0.00	0.00	0.00	0.00	0.00	0.00
Device 5	0.10	10.33	0.02	-0.08	0.00	0.00	0.10	0.00	0.00	0.00	0.00	0.00
Device 6	72.86	33.73	7.12	-65.74	0.00	0.00	27.25	0.00	0.00	0.00	2.39	0.00
Device 7	25.99	49.04	1.57	-24.42	0.00	0.00	35.36	0.00	0.00	0.00	0.00	10.59
Device 8	0.06	5.78	-7.11	-7.17	0.00	0.35	0.12	0.00	0.00	0.00	0.00	0.00
Device 9	2.83	4.35	2.83	0.00	0.00	0.00	0.00	0.00	0.00	0.00	0.00	0.00
Device 10	2.79	6.50	2.44	-0.36	0.00	0.00	0.36	0.00	0.00	0.00	0.00	0.00
Device 11	0.99	6.60	0.03	-0.96	0.00	0.00	0.00	0.00	0.00	0.00	0.00	0.00
Device 12	8.95	2.03	-1.71	-10.66	0.00	0.51	10.22	0.00	0.00	0.00	0.00	0.00
Device 13	55.49	2.16	48.15	-7.34	0.00	0.00	1.50	0.00	0.00	0.00	0.00	0.00
Device 14	9.38	3.35	8.01	-1.37	0.00	0.00	1.39	0.00	0.00	0.00	0.00	0.00
Device 15	0.00	0.00	0.00	0.00	0.00	0.00	0.00	0.00	0.00	0.00	0.00	0.00
Device 16	56.42	2.52	38.23	-18.19	0.00	4.03	14.37	0.00	0.00	0.00	0.00	0.00
Device 17	20.23	2.38	13.36	-6.87	0.00	0.00	0.00	0.00	0.00	0.00	0.00	4.43
Device 18	25.42	5.65	23.28	-2.14	0.00	1.90	0.00	0.00	0.00	0.00	0.00	0.00
Device 19	0.48	4.77	0.48	0.00	0.00	0.00	0.00	0.00	0.00	0.00	0.00	0.00
Device 20	3.35	7.12	2.41	-0.94	0.00	0.32	0.64	0.00	0.00	0.00	0.00	0.00
Device 21	205.00	5.00	118.25	-86.75	0.00	32.76	0.00	0.00	0.00	24.18	0.00	0.00
Device 22	0.87	14.51	0.74	-0.13	0.00	0.29	16.14	0.00	0.00	0.00	0.00	0.00
* * Total	846.98	4.62	538.01	-308.99	0.96	40.19	187.21	1.88	0.00	24.18	2.39	18.42
Total	6809.83	18.18	3359.86	-3449.95	13.71	124.44	725.45	782.98	31.03	160.59	224.80	668.92

Table 12-5 TMTD Status Report
Produced daily to control test area. Required test units column is **diminishing balance**.
Each device drops off report when decremented to zero.

	Total Plan	Reqd Test Units	MTD Bill #	Delq Thru 09/24	Week 09/25 10/05	Week 10/06 10/16	Week 10/17 10/27	Week 10/28 11/07	Whse	L.P.	QA	P&L	Last Test	MID WIP	S.P. Stage	First Test	Raw Stock	Stock In TR
Device 1	5.50	0.39	3.87	1.63	—	1.00	—	—	1.24	—	—	—	0.80	0.94	—	2.99	—	—
Device 2	27.00	4.01	22.29	0.03	3.40	3.60	0.15	13.50	0.69	—	—	—	—	—	0.04	—	13.01	—
Device 3	8.70	3.09	5.61	1.34	4.55	—	—	—	—	—	—	—	1.86	5.91	—	—	—	—
Device 4	4.70	0.24	4.12	1.56	—	—	—	—	0.34	—	—	—	—	—	—	—	—	—
Device 5	1.67	0.98	0.34	0.02	0.11	0.16	—	0.06	0.35	—	—	—	—	—	—	—	1.88	0.75
Device 6	41.00	10.80	23.65	17.38	—	12.50	—	—	6.55	—	4.84	—	—	—	—	2.98	—	—
**Subtot	255.61	19.51	163.80	34.68	31.35	56.25	27.47	77.77	204.54	11.11	5.21	0.00	4.77	6.85	144.10	17.29	148.88	64.83
Device 7	0.15	0.15	0.00	0.23	0.07	—	—	0.10	—	—	0.20	0.04	0.04	1.00	—	0.27	—	—
**Subtot	0.35	0.15	0.20	0.40	0.07	0.20	0.00	0.10	1.31	0.32	0.20	0.04	0.52	1.00	0.89	0.27	0.38	0.00
Device 8	2.44	0.43	1.80	0.01	0.14	0.39	0.48	0.16	0.21	—	—	—	1.73	—	0.02	—	11.89	3.92
Device 9	6.00	0.24	3.54	0.11	1.04	0.44	0.41	1.66	2.23	—	0.36	—	—	—	0.38	1.75	137.25	13.86
Device 10	0.10	0.10	0.00	0.04	—	—	—	—	—	—	—	—	—	—	—	—	—	—
Device 11	0.38	0.15	0.00	—	0.38	—	—	—	0.23	—	—	—	—	0.25	—	—	—	—
Device 12	0.85	0.13	0.72	0.03	0.10	—	0.20	—	—	—	—	—	—	—	0.77	—	—	—
Device 13	2.36	1.51	0.85	1.06	0.60	0.41	1.12	—	—	—	—	—	—	—	1.83	—	—	—
Device 14	2.30	1.28	0.21	1.67	0.30	0.15	—	0.35	0.81	0.07	—	—	—	—	—	1.06	—	0.98
Device 15	0.23	0.23	0.00	0.23	—	—	—	—	—	—	—	—	—	—	—	—	—	—
Device 16	0.40	0.40	0.00	0.40	—	—	—	—	—	0.45	—	—	—	—	—	—	—	—
**Subtot	120.91	4.47	82.86	8.38	16.53	31.29	11.38	24.60	115.54	0.52	0.54	0.00	2.76	3.12	104.22	3.47	201.39	20.73
Device 17	0.10	0.10	0.00	0.13	—	—	—	—	—	—	—	—	0.15	—	—	—	—	—
Device 18	0.63	0.59	0.03	1.06	0.46	0.19	0.08	0.01	—	0.46	—	—	0.22	0.51	0.00	—	0.61	—
**Subtot	0.73	0.69	0.03	2.34	0.55	0.19	0.08	0.01	0.00	0.93	0.03	0.00	0.37	0.51	0.00	0.00	0.61	0.00
Device 19	0.80	0.16	0.61	0.07	—	—	—	—	0.02	—	—	—	1.41	—	0.09	—	—	—
Device 20	13.60	6.39	7.21	0.65	6.60	0.15	—	6.60	—	—	—	—	4.94	0.87	0.02	—	—	—
Device 21	1.90	1.77	0.07	1.60	0.20	—	0.01	0.30	0.05	—	0.33	—	—	—	0.32	—	—	—
Device 22	0.22	0.10	0.12	0.05	0.01	0.00	—	2.31	0.00	—	—	—	—	—	0.84	0.38	1.47	0.83
Device 23	5.70	3.63	1.53	3.01	1.27	1.01	0.84	0.40	0.54	—	0.10	1.10	0.95	—	—	—	—	—
Device 24	0.80	0.59	0.00	1.63	—	0.50	—	—	0.21	—	—	—	—	0.74	—	—	—	—
Device 25	0.30	0.30	0.00	1.07	—	2.00	—	—	—	—	—	—	0.04	—	—	0.13	—	—
Device 26	0.08	0.08	0.00	0.07	0.01	—	—	—	—	0.11	—	—	0.08	—	—	—	—	—
Device 27	1.67	0.28	0.72	0.95	—	—	—	—	0.67	—	—	—	0.30	0.01	0.02	—	—	—
Device 28	0.23	0.11	0.11	—	0.13	—	—	—	0.01	—	—	—	0.24	—	0.01	—	2.12	—
Device 29	0.05	0.01	0.00	0.05	—	—	0.32	—	0.03	—	—	—	0.05	—	—	—	—	—
Device 30	0.38	0.09	0.05	—	0.14	0.05	—	—	0.23	—	—	—	—	—	—	—	0.01	—
Device 31	0.42	0.20	0.21	0.16	0.17	0.46	0.01	0.16	0.01	0.00	—	—	—	—	0.03	1.36	0.62	—
Device 32	2.30	1.03	0.59	0.82	0.86	0.43	1.22	0.45	0.69	—	—	—	0.03	0.01	0.01	—	—	—
Device 33	2.80	1.34	0.61	1.57	0.82	0.56	0.37	1.41	0.84	—	—	—	0.78	0.15	0.11	—	—	—
Device 34	1.80	0.60	0.53	3.30	1.22	0.97	0.98	0.89	0.67	—	—	—	0.16	—	—	—	0.26	—
Device 35	0.35	0.35	0.00	2.29	0.31	0.39	0.15	0.25	—	—	—	—	—	—	—	—	—	—
**Subtot	49.47	17.03	21.57	19.35	21.47	7.71	4.78	23.29	27.97	0.70	2.58	1.10	9.20	1.78	56.87	2.59	11.66	0.83
Total	427.62	41.85	269.00	65.92	70.44	95.64	43.71	125.77	349.36	13.58	8.56	1.14	17.62	13.26	306.08	23.62	362.92	86.39

Table 12-6 Unique Product Tracking Chart
Produced daily—used to control **custom**—one customer/one device products.

	Delq Thru 09/24	Week 09/25 10/01	Week 10/02 10/08	Week 10/09 10/15	Week 10/16 10/22	Week 10/23 10/29	Week 10/30 11/05	Week 11/06 11/12	Week 11/13 11/19	Week 11/20 05/20	Whse	QA Lot P.	Test WIP	In Tr FM Assy	Back End Assy	Front End Assy	Die	Probe	Fab
Device 1	0	0	0	0	0	0	0	18000	0	0	1882	0	21138	0	0	0	28137	0	0
Device 2	0	0	0	0	0	0	0	0	0	0	846	0	1151	0	0	0	5389	0	0
Device 3	0	0	0	0	0	0	0	0	0	0	68	0	0	0	0	0	16238	0	0
Device 4	0	0	0	0	0	0	0	0	0	0	324	0	0	0	0	0	4451	0	0
Device 5	0	0	0	0	0	10000	0	8000	0	8000	2749	0	16046	0	0	6153	154	0	120
Device 6	0	0	0	0	0	0	0	0	0	0	1808	0	4421	0	0	0	19302	0	0
Device 7	0	0	0	12000	0	0	0	0	0	0	2041	0	12906	0	0	0	0	0	0
Device 8	0	0	0	0	0	0	0	0	0	2000	3005	0	3431	0	0	0	26641	1	0
Device 9	0	0	0	0	0	0	0	2000	0	2000	698	0	0	0	7820	0	0	1	0
Device 10	0	0	0	0	0	0	0	0	0	0	562	0	0	0	0	0	10070	0	0
Device 11	0	0	0	0	0	0	2000	0	0	2000	2515	0	2357	0	0	0	13004	0	0
Device 12	0	0	0	0	0	0	0	0	0	0	2018	0	0	194	0	0	0	0	0
Device 13	0	0	0	0	0	0	0	0	0	0	345	0	11211	0	0	0	6124	0	0
Device 14	0	0	0	0	0	0	0	2000	0	2000	151	0	0	0	2711	0	1025	0	24
Device 15	0	0	0	0	0	0	2000	0	0	0	2892	0	0	0	0	0	367	0	0
Device 16	0	0	0	0	0	0	0	0	0	0	2209	0	0	0	0	0	0	0	0
Device 17	0	0	0	0	0	0	0	0	0	0	0	0	0	0	0	0	0	0	0
Device 18	0	0	0	0	0	0	0	0	0	0	327	0	0	0	0	0	1691	0	0
Device 19	0	0	0	0	0	0	0	0	0	0	1375	0	16668	0	0	0	43207	0	0
Device 20	0	0	0	0	0	0	0	2000	0	2000	705	0	735	0	0	2792	13881	0	0
Device 21	0	0	0	0	0	0	0	424	0	3576	424	0	0	0	0	0	0	19	69
Device 22	0	0	0	0	0	0	0	0	0	0	239	0	0	0	0	0	0	0	0
Device 23	0	0	0	0	0	0	0	2000	0	2000	440	0	0	0	2688	0	4667	0	0
Device 24	0	0	0	0	0	0	0	0	0	0	0	0	0	0	0	0	0	0	0
Device 25	0	0	0	0	0	0	0	2000	0	2000	358	0	0	0	4920	0	1576	0	0
Device 26	0	0	0	0	0	0	0	2000	0	0	197	0	642	0	3075	0	0	0	0
Device 27	0	0	0	0	0	0	0	0	0	0	781	0	5146	0	0	0	15787	0	0
Device 28	0	0	0	0	0	0	2000	0	0	0	2833	0	0	0	0	0	420	0	0
Device 29	0	0	4500	0	0	0	0	4000	0	4000	5425	0	0	0	0	4992	1586	0	44
Device 30	0	0	0	0	0	0	0	0	0	0	828	0	0	1263	0	0	0	0	0
Device 31	0	0	0	0	0	0	0	2000	0	0	692	0	0	3013	0	0	0	0	0
Device 32	0	0	0	0	13000	0	0	12000	0	12000	8333	0	4884	0	11297	10102	16036	0	0
Device 33	0	0	0	0	0	0	0	0	0	0	240	0	0	0	0	0	8010	0	0
Device 34	0	0	0	0	0	0	0	0	0	0	932	0	0	0	0	0	4712	0	0
Device 35	0	0	0	0	0	0	0	2000	0	2000	1376	0	0	0	0	0	6759	0	0
Device 36	0	0	0	0	0	0	0	2000	0	2000	254	0	568	0	0	0	8459	0	0
Device 37	0	0	0	0	0	0	0	2000	0	2000	109	0	0	0	0	0	3441	0	24
Device 38	0	0	0	0	0	0	0	0	0	0	968	0	3515	0	0	0	4859	0	0
Device 39	0	0	0	0	0	0	0	0	0	0	798	0	3059	0	0	0	97	0	0
Device 40	0	0	0	0	0	0	0	2000	0	0	545	0	0	0	0	0	2785	0	0
Device 41	0	0	0	0	0	0	0	0	0	0	0	0	0	0	0	0	0	0	0
Device 42	0	0	0	0	0	0	0	0	0	0	0	0	0	0	0	0	0	0	0
Device 43	0	0	0	0	0	0	0	0	0	0	0	0	0	0	0	0	0	0	0
Device 44	0	0	0	0	0	0	0	0	0	0	0	0	0	0	0	0	0	0	0
Device 45	0	0	0	0	0	0	0	0	0	0	0	0	0	0	0	0	0	0	0
Device 46	0	0	0	0	0	0	0	0	0	0	0	0	0	0	0	0	0	0	0
	0	0	4500	12000	13000	10000	6000	64424	0	47576	52292	0	107878	4470	32511	24039	268875	21	281

Table 12-7 Forced Bookings

	Forecast K Dollars	Forecast ASP	Forecast K Units	Backlog K Dollars	Backlog ASP	Backlog K Units	Delta K Dollars	Delta ASP	Delta K Units
Device 1	$140.00	$4.00	35.00	$218.60	$4.11	53.20	– $78.60	$4.32	– 18.20
Device 2	$127.20	$4.31	29.51	$219.50	$4.72	46.50	– $92.30	$5.43	– 16.99
Device 3	$80.50	$8.73	9.22	$355.70	$12.18	29.20	– $275.20	$13.77	– 19.98
Device 4	$62.00	$1.24	50.00	$41.30	$1.27	32.40	$20.70	$1.18	17.60
Device 5	$44.30	$5.24	8.45	$61.60	$5.45	11.30	– $17.30	$6.08	– 2.85
Device 6	$38.10	$3.47	10.98	$46.00	$3.24	14.20	– $7.90	$2.45	– 3.22
Device 7	$33.10	$13.04	2.54	$24.00	$12.00	2.00	$9.10	$16.90	.54
Device 8	$24.10	$6.03	4.00	$29.60	$6.17	4.80	– $5.50	$6.85	– .80
Device 9	$21.70	$1.24	17.50	$25.00	$1.26	19.80	– $3.30	$1.43	– 2.30
Device 10	$18.70	$3.46	5.40	$80.90	$3.68	22.00	– $62.20	$3.75	– 16.60
Device 11	$16.80	$5.45	3.08	$17.00	$5.48	3.10	– $.20	$11.47	– .02
Device 12	$13.50	$35.00	.10	$.67	$67.00	.01	$12.83	$142.56	.09
Device 13	$11.70	$11.70	1.00	$12.50	$12.50	1.00	– $.80	– $1.00	
Device 14	$10.90	$1.17	9.32	$16.80	$1.23	13.70	– $5.90	$1.35	– 4.38
Device 15	$8.80	$88.20	.10	$2.60	$104.00	.03	$6.20	$82.92	.07
Device 16	$8.70	$8.73	1.00	$10.60	$8.15	1.70	– $1.90	$6.26	– .30
Device 17	$5.30	$2.44	2.17	$9.00	$2.50	3.60	– $3.70	$2.59	– 1.43
Device 18	$4.50	$3.19	1.41	$6.00	$3.16	1.90	– $1.50	$3.07	– .49
Device 19	$2.20	$72.33	.03	$14.50	$20.71	.70	– $12.30	$18.37	– .67
Device 20			– 1.00	$71.80	$17.95	4.00	– $71.80	$14.36	– 5.00
Total:	$672.10		189.82	$1266.67		261.74	– $591.57		– 74.92

Table 12-8 Manufacturing Matrix

Final Test System	Device	NUM LDS	Ft Test Time	Ft Units Per Hour Hot	Ft Units Per Hour Room	Ft Units Per Hour Cold	Ft Yld	Mark Units Per Hour	P&L Units Per Hour	Load Brd	Skt	HNLR	Mkr	Test Flow
System 1	Device 1	16	4.00	565	600	40	80	2174	1099	191	81	HAND	—	9
	Device 2	40	3.00	346	417	40	80	909	500	209	99	MCT	—	10
	Device 3	40	8.00	—	—	—	88	—	—	—	—	—	—	33
	Device 4	40	3.00	395	448	40	80	1667	1000	209	99	MCT	—	10
	Device 5	40	3.00	395	448	40	80	1667	1000	209	99	MCT	—	—
	Device 6	40	3.00	395	448	40	80	1667	1000	209	99	MCT	—	—
	Device 7	28	3.00	395	448	40	80	1667	1000	209	111	MCT	—	10
	Device 8	40	3.00	990	1163	40	5	2174	1099	188	83	MCT	—	9
	Device 9	40	3.00	990	1163	40	80	2174	1099	188	83	MCT	—	11
	Device 10	16	4.00	787	855	40	80	2174	1099	191	81	HAND	—	9
	Device 11	28	3.50	877	935	40	93	2174	1053	187	77	MCT	—	10
	Device 12	28	3.50	877	935	40	93	2174	1053	187	77	MCT	—	10
	Device 13	28	3.50	877	935	—	93	2174	1053	187	77	MCT	—	10
	Device 14	40	3.00	395	448	40	80	1667	1000	209	99	MCT	—	10
	Device 15	40	12.00	503	613	200	90	1667	1000	226	17	—	—	45
	Device 16	28	6.00	398	613	40	92	1667	1000	—	—	—	—	—
	Device 17	40	3.00	395	448	40	80	1667	1000	209	99	MCT	—	—
System 2	Device 18	100	30.00	78	86	40	60	327	187	806	128	—	—	6
	Device 19	100	30.00	78	86	40	70	327	187	809	136	—	—	6
	Device 20	100	30.00	78	86	40	70	327	187	811	138	—	—	—
	Device 21	100	4.50	228	294	40	88	327	187	804	124	—	—	—
	Device 22	100	4.00	—	—	—	90	—	—	804	124	—	—	—
System 3	Device 23	28	3.50	877	935	40	93	2174	1053	187	77	MCT	—	30
	Device 24	28	3.50	877	935	40	93	2174	1053	187	77	MCT	—	56
	Device 25	48	3.00	465	526	40	—	719	180	168	372	MCT	—	21
	Device 26	48	3.00	469	526	40	—	719	180	168	372	MCT	—	21
	Device 27	48	3.00	469	526	40	—	719	180	168	372	MCT	—	57
	Device 28	28	3.50	617	741	40	93	2174	1053	187	77	MCT	—	10
	Device 29	28	3.50	617	741	40	93	2174	1053	187	77	MCT	—	10
	Device 30	28	3.50	617	741	40	93	2174	1053	187	77	MCT	—	10
	Device 31	48	3.00	588	645	40	65	1538	180	168	372	MCT	—	21
	Device 32	48	3.00	588	645	40	25	1538	180	168	372	MCT	—	21
	Device 33	48	3.00	588	645	40	—	1538	180	168	372	MCT	—	57
	Device 34	28	3.50	877	925	40	93	2174	1053	187	77	MCT	—	30
System 4	Device 35	64	2.50	422	495	40	12	1099	130	700	—	SYM	—	50
	Device 36	48	1.50	645	746	40	80	187	130	519	519	MCT	—	47
	Device 37	64	2.50	422	495	40	12	1408	4000	513	—	SYM	—	24
	Device 38	64	2.50	422	495	40	74	1408	4000	513	—	SYM	—	24
	Device 39	64	2.50	422	495	60	7	1099	130	513	—	SYM	—	18
	Device 40	64	2.50	422	495	60	7	1099	130	700	—	SYM	—	24
	Device 41	64	2.50	422	495	60	2	1099	130	513	—	SYM	—	18
	Device 42	64	2.50	422	495	60	2	1099	130	513	—	SYM	—	24
	Device 43	64	2.50	422	495	60	83	1099	130	513	—	SYM	—	18
	Device 44	64	2.50	422	495	—	83	1099	130	513	—	SYM	—	24
	Device 45	64	2.50	422	495	—	83	1099	130	513	—	SYM	—	36
	Device 46	64	2.50	422	495	60	12	187	130	700	—	SYM	—	18
	Device 47	64	2.50	422	495	60	69	187	130	700	—	SYM	—	18
	Device 48	64	2.50	422	495	60	12	187	130	700	—	SYM	—	18
	Device 49	64	2.50	422	495	60	69	187	130	513	—	SYM	—	18
	Device 50	64	2.50	422	495	60	69	187	130	700	—	SYM	—	—

This file contains Manufacturing Variables used in

(a) Capacity Planning
(b) Machine Loading
(c) Manufacturing Cell Balancing

Table 12-9 Q4 Test Capacity Requirements As of 12/16/85 06:40:53

Device	K-Unit Fcst Qtly	Ft Device Per Hour	Final Test System	Time Req. For Testers
* *Subtot Negates	525		N/A	71295.00
Device 1	30	40.80	Sentry 2	1224.00
Device 2	2	32.10	Sentry 2	64.20
* *Subtot Sentry	32		N/A	1288.20
Device 3	60	122.80	Sentry 7	7368.00
Device 4	4	173.60	Sentry 7	694.40
Device 5	4	173.60	Sentry 7	694.40
Device 6	15	175.40	Sentry 7	2631.00
Device 7	45	175.40	Sentry 7	7893.00
Device 8	4	175.40	Sentry 7	701.60
Device 9	2	* * * * *	Sentry 7	3921.40
Device 10	80	180.10	Sentry 7	14408.00
Device 11	90	180.10	Sentry 7	16209.00
Device 12	20	174.20	Sentry 7	3484.00
Device 13	262	180.10	Sentry 7	47186.20
Device 14	300	116.10	Sentry 7	34830.00
Device 15	70	116.10	Sentry 7	8127.00
Device 16	20	238.60	Sentry 7	4772.00
Device 17	40	116.10	Sentry 7	4644.00
* *Subtot Sentry	1016		N/A	157564.00

Device	K-Unit Fcst Qtly	Ft Device Per Hour	Final Test System	Time Req. For Testers
Device 18	21	144.30	Series 10	3030.30
Device 19	9	144.30	Series 10	1298.70
Device 20	16	144.30	Series 10	2308.80
Device 21	25	144.30	Series 10	3607.50
Device 22	3	134.20	Series 10	402.60
Device 23	50	174.20	Series 10	8710.00
Device 24	55	174.20	Series 10	9581.00
Device 25	25	180.10	Series 10	4502.50
* *Subtot Series 1	204		N/A	33441.40
Device 26	8	130.80	Takeda	1046.40
Device 27	10	130.80	Takeda	1308.00
Device 28	22	130.80	Takeda	2877.60
Device 29	10	130.80	Takeda	1308.00
Device 30	25	130.80	Takeda	3270.00
Device 31	2	130.80	Takeda	261.60
Device 32	4	142.00	Takeda	568.00
Device 33	4	130.80	Takeda	523.20
Device 34	4	130.80	Takeda	523.20
Device 35	35	136.60	Takeda	4781.00
Device 36	140	136.60	Takeda	19124.00
Device 37	110	136.60	Takeda	15026.00
Device 38	10	305.80	Takeda	3058.00
Device 39	275	305.80	Takeda	84095.00
* *Subtot Takeda	659		N/A	137770.00
Total MA	2858		N/A	444740.00

Table 12-10 Inventory Status As Of 04/15/85 12:54:02

Factory Device	#,S	Assemb End	Assemb Start	Die	Probe WIP	Probe Stage	Fab End	Fab Start
* * Subtot MAHC	0.25	0.00	0.00	45.36	0.00	0.00	0.00	0.02
Device 1	0.13	0.00	0.00	0.00	0.00	0.00	0.00	0.00
Device 2	0.96	0.00	0.00	0.00	0.00	0.00	0.00	0.00
Device 3	0.00	0.00	0.00	0.00	0.00	0.00	0.00	0.00
Device 4	0.95	0.00	0.00	0.00	0.00	0.00	0.00	0.00
Device 5	0.00	0.00	1.92	272.65	0.00	0.00	0.00	0.00
* * Subtot MAHF	2.04	0.00	1.92	272.65	0.00	0.00	0.00	0.00
Device 6	0.00	0.00	0.00	101.81	0.00	0.00	0.00	0.00
Device 7	0.00	0.00	0.00	0.00	0.00	0.00	0.00	0.00
* * Subtot MAHG	0.00	0.00	0.00	101.81	0.00	0.00	0.00	0.00
Device 8	6.57	0.00	0.00	423.81	0.43	0.00	0.00	0.00
Device 9	0.00	0.00	0.00	0.00	0.00	0.00	0.00	0.00
Device 10	22.01	4.68	0.00	178.43	0.44	0.00	0.00	0.00
Device 11	0.10	0.00	0.00	0.00	0.00	0.00	0.00	0.00
Device 12	0.00	0.00	0.00	0.00	0.00	0.00	0.00	0.00
Device 13	0.00	0.00	0.00	0.00	0.00	0.00	0.00	0.00
Device 14	10.00	0.00	0.00	417.40	0.70	0.00	0.00	0.00
Device 15	2.00	0.00	0.00	0.00	0.00	0.00	0.00	0.00
Device 16	0.00	0.00	0.00	0.00	0.00	0.00	0.00	0.00
Device 17	0.00	0.00	0.00	0.00	0.00	0.00	0.00	0.00
* * Subtot MAHM	40.68	4.68	0.00	1019.64	1.57	0.00	0.00	0.00
Device 18	12.04	3.01	5.97	54.27	0.11	0.00	0.00	0.00
Device 19	0.00	0.00	0.00	0.00	0.00	0.00	0.00	0.00
Device 20	0.00	0.00	0.00	0.00	0.00	0.00	0.00	0.00
Device 21	12.16	9.25	0.00	87.98	0.02	0.00	0.00	0.00
Device 22	0.00	0.00	0.00	0.00	0.00	0.00	0.00	0.00
Device 23	0.00	0.00	0.00	0.00	0.00	0.00	0.00	0.00
Device 24	0.00	0.00	0.00	0.00	0.00	0.00	0.00	0.00
Device 25	0.00	0.00	0.00	0.00	0.00	0.00	0.00	0.00
Device 26	2.20	0.00	0.00	0.00	0.00	0.00	0.00	0.00
Device 27	0.52	0.00	0.00	0.00	0.00	0.00	0.00	0.00
Device 28	0.00	0.00	0.00	0.00	0.00	0.00	0.00	0.00
* * Subtot MAHN	26.92	12.26	5.97	142.25	0.13	0.00	0.00	0.00
Device 29	1.00	4.96	26.93	24.84	0.13	1.35	0.42	0.38
Device 30	8.20	0.00	0.00	0.00	0.00	0.00	0.00	0.00
Device 31	0.00	0.00	0.00	0.00	0.00	0.00	0.00	0.00
Device 32	0.10	0.00	0.00	0.00	0.00	0.00	0.00	0.00
Device 33	0.00	0.00	0.00	0.00	0.00	0.00	0.00	0.00
Device 34	0.00	0.00	0.00	0.00	0.00	0.00	0.00	0.00
* * Subtot MAHP	9.30	4.96	26.93	24.84	0.13	1.35	0.42	0.38
* * Total MAH	79.19	21.90	34.82	1606.55	1.83	1.35	0.42	0.40
Total MA	360.43	141.27	141.28	2692.74	5.06	3.46	11.85	10.82

THE SEQUENCE OF EVENTS IN THE CYCLE

- **Input aged bookings forecast** (from aged bookings analysis)
- **Verify manufacturing variable parameters file** (unit probe, assembly, final test yields, throughput rates, manufacturing flows, and so on.)
- **First pass forecast data base** (production control commit to a unit forecast by device based on aged bookings forecast, backlog and WIP profile. This could be produced by an algorithm.)
- **Unit forecast by line item entered into data base**
- **First pass of sales forecast run** (subtotals and totals)
- **First iteration of sales forecast** (if required)
- **First pass capacity required to support forecast**
- **Run mix capacity analysis—by package type/by module**
- **First pass margins forecast generated**
- **Factory loading plans generated**
- **Daily tracking charts generated** (actual performance to plan—sales, unit shipments, and so on)
- **Other utility reports generated** (defined at run time)

What used to require many man hours to produce an end product of extremely limited usefulness can now be generated speedily and accurately within a few minutes. Prior to this, all too often the human contribution in the process was almost totally consumed in the data gathering and number crunching part of the task rather than in the analysis, judgement, presentation and identification of action items. With the IBIS approach, these proportions can be reversed but perhaps even more importantly, the business can be managed as a system, integrating not only the data, but the efforts of the specialists functional departments as well, in a common thrust. The demand side of the equation, the CRD and FSD backlog profile is captured as it changes, as new orders are placed and old orders drop off as product is shipped against them. CRD and FSD mismatches are identified. The supply side, also dynamically changing as material is processed from one stage of completion to the next, is also captured. These changes are processed automatically on a daily, or more frequently, if required, basis and then communicated to all who need to be aware of these changes as they effect factory loading schedules, etc.

THE CHANGING NATURE OF DEMAND

As with inventory, people have become accustomed to feeling insecure if total backlog doesn't vastly exceed the capacity to service it far into the future. There may be early indications however that we shall have to live without this comfort factor in the future. Backlog of orders greater than say 13 weeks out in time is a disappearing phenomenon. On the other hand, short-term backlog shows evidence of growing, even during recessions. For whatever reason, customers are no longer inclined to place orders with the kind of long leadtimes of six to nine months and greater that we have become accustomed to in the past. It may be that they themselves do not have the visibility or confidence in what they can see of their own immediate future. It may be that they have come to expect faster responsiveness from suppliers due to the introduction of techniques to reduce manufacturing cycle-times. It may simply be that they assume, as they have in the past, that we are in the phase of the business cycle where supply exceeds demand. Whether this persists when the wheel goes full circle and demand yet again "appears" to exceed supply remains to be seen. What does seem to be clear is that short-term demand endures, even during recessionary periods, and the supplier who can respond fastest to this, either with inventory or short cycle-time manufacturing, or both, will weather any future "uncertainty" better than most. Whichever service strategy is employed, being able to first assimilate and then communicate the variables, speedily and accurately, will be a distinct advantage.

FORECASTING

Crawl Charts

In Figure 12-3:

The Y axis represents the dollar value of orders on the order backlog.

The X axis represents weeks prior and weeks into a quarter time period.

The curves to the left of the zero weeks reference point on the X axis represent the cumulative profile of orders entered, starting thirteen weeks prior to the beginning of the quarter up to the beginning of the quarter, for delivery during that quarter. The opening value represents orders placed earlier than thirteen weeks before the start of that quarter, for delivery in that quarter. Changes in buying behavior may become apparent from observing changes or differences in (a) the respective opening values for each quarter, (b) the slope of each individual curve, and (c) the relative slopes of the curves. For example, if the opening values, the slopes and the ending values are essentially similar, then stable business conditions with little or no growth may be assumed. On the other hand, if each successive quarter's opening value is higher than the preceding one, then a growth phase may be imminent, leading to an expectation that the sales forecast should be increased over the previous forecast. For successively declining values, the converse may be the case. The slope of the curves also provide some insight into whether customer confidence, in either their own future visibility or in their suppliers ability to respond to short lead time orders (or both) is improving or deteriorating.

The three quarters prior to the current quarter (now history), are shown for comparison to support forecasting by historical extrapolation. For a growing business for example, we would expect to see the graphs for each successive quarter offset higher on the Y axis than that for the preceding quarter. The curves to the right of the zero weeks reference point on the X axis, the start of the 13-week quarter, consists of two components: (a) actual sales billed out of the backlog and (b) sales yet to be billed. The negative going cusp, from zero weeks to approximately two weeks into the quarter, represents ship aheads out of the current quarter, that is orders due for shipment within this time frame shipped at the end of the prior quarter. This is complemented by the sharply escalating tail at the end of each 13-week period. Current quarter backlog plus delinquencies (CQ + DEL) is also tracked in order to determine whether turns bookings, business booked during the quarter for delivery in the same quarter, is being serviced or falling into delinquencies. In the latter case, the displacement between the curves would be increasing. In effect, this is a measure of the responsiveness of the factory (or inventory availability). In addition to hopefully providing insight into the growth performance of a business, both actual and potential, as well as changes in buying behavior, this chart can also be applied as a common sense test to a sales forecast as discussed earlier.

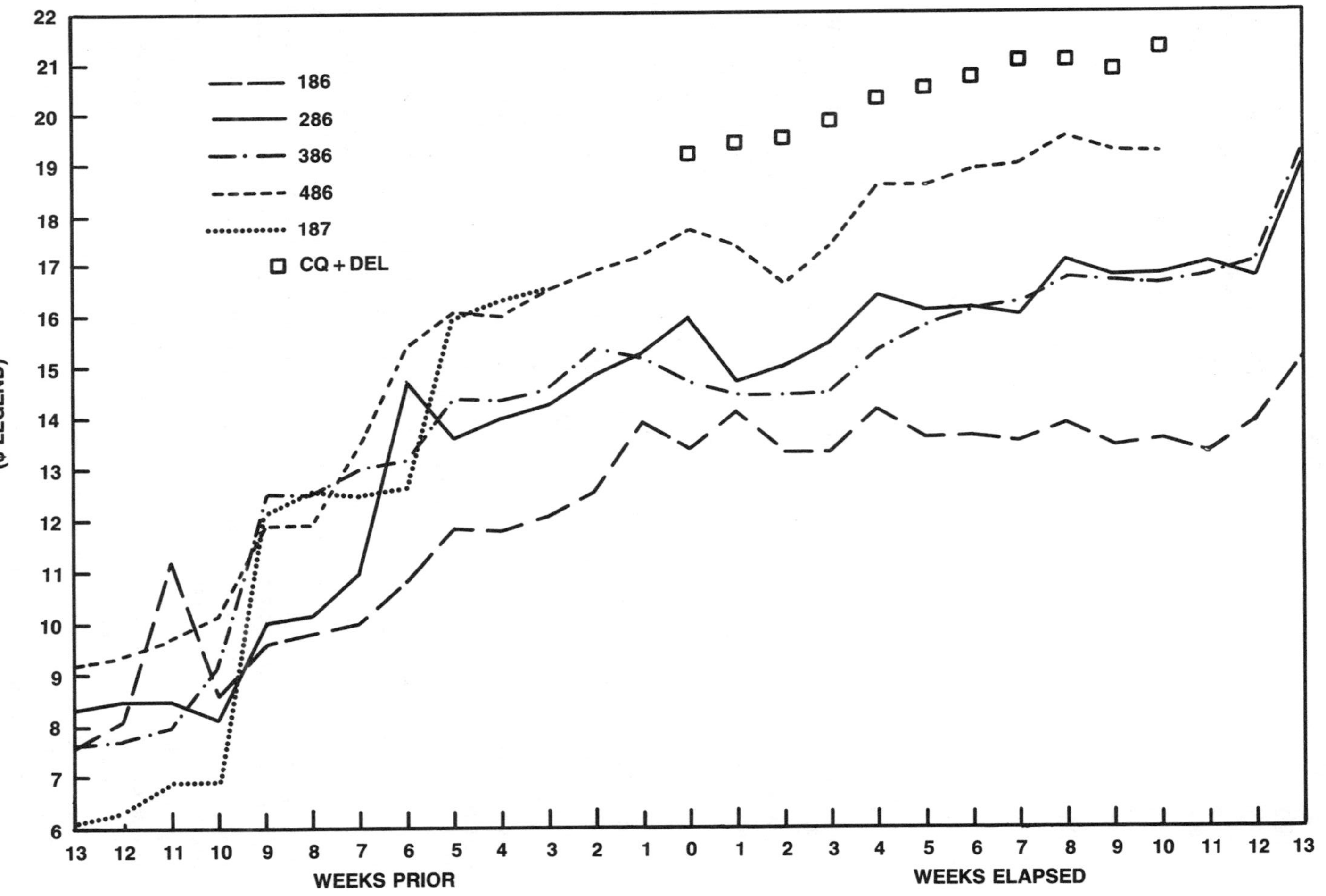

Figure 12-3 Open Order (CRD)—Crawl Chart

MAKING AND MEETING AGGRESSIVE COMMITMENTS

In a highly competitive marketplace, aggressive lead-time delivery quotes will often be necessary to win business, but if these given in the heat of battle are based on nothing more than wishful thinking, overzealousness, or desperation and are subsequently shown to have been nothing more than empty promises by late actual shipment, then at the very least, repeat patronage will be jeoparized. A late shipment is indicative of one of two things. A commitment being made which could not possibly be honored in the first place—at best optimism, at worst, dishonesty or lack of control in execution, perhaps because of engineering or manufacturing problems, or having taken an order which should not have been accepted. Both, though not necessarily equally, are harmful to one's image as a reliable supplier. Since delivery is almost always a function of a great many internal commitments in an organization, this parameter should be measured, reported, and made visible throughout the organization. Good on-time delivery performance is a function of a well-integrated organization, not of independent fiefdoms.

ON-TIME DELIVERY

In this section we will discuss:

- Definition of on time.
- Why is on-time delivery so important?
- Setting a realistic (attainable) goal.
- Nature and scope of the problem.
- Treatment—(there is no quick fix panacea).

Why is On-Time Delivery so Important?

Like quality, an on-time delivery commitment given by the supplier at order entry time, is one which the customer has no choice but to accept up front in good faith—a commitment verifiable only after product has shipped—or gone delinquent. Whether that commitment is honored in the future remains to be seen. To subsequently default may in all probability cause major difficulty to the customer—since his business and operational plans will have been predicated on this. The supplier too is affected in that to default is a reflection on the competence and integrity of his organization, methods, control, and in some cases his personnel. Since it is one of the essential ingredients of total customer satisfaction, the need for exemplary performance here is no less than that for the other ingredients of high quality and low cost. Like these others, it is no less difficult to achieve—arguably perhaps, even more so—and this section inquires into the major factors which must be managed in order that it be maximized.

What Does On-Time Mean?

The ultimate objective is to meet the customer's customer required date (CRD) profile to deliver to the customer's receiving dock—exactly the right amount of units, at exactly the right times, as prescribed by the customer.

It does not mean:

Shipping **late**

Shipping **early**

Shipping only **partial** quantities

Shipping **less than all of the line items** in a multiline item order

If, at order entry time, there is cause to believe, for a variety of reasons, that the customer's CRD cannot be met with high confidence, the factory will schedule a date (FSD) which will extend beyond the customer's CRD by some period. This becomes the commitment to the customer against which the organization will subsequently be measured. Some of the reasons for this practice are as follows.

The customer's requirement may be unrealistic—placing a large order today for delivery tomorrow, for example. More likely, there may be internal operational reasons preventing product being available in the quantities and schedules required. Some of those internal constraints will be discussed later. In the extreme, this internal uncertainty may be so great that the factory will not be willing or able to commit to an FSD at all at that time. In the past, the tendency was to accept such orders, considering them to be bookings—thus allowing them to show on the order backlog—and to reflect their uncertain delivery status with some form of factory to advise (FTA) code. The equivalent from the customer's point of view is customer to advise (CTA)—where the customer has sufficient confidence to place an order but cannot be specific on the required delivery profile. This practice is fairly typical in a business upturn and sometimes represents the customer's attempt to "reserve" a block of capacity—"just in case." Another set of circumstances giving rise to the same behavior is that of new product start up, where the customer has too many variables and uncertainties to deal with in his manufacturing build plan to be definitive about his specific needs. In both cases, these practices distort the "truly billable" backlog of an organization, creating perhaps a false euphoria, possibly resulting in imprudent investment in more capacity. This can lead to financial difficulty if the anticipated volumes do not materialize.

In the event that the FSD offered extends beyond the CRD, there is always the possibility that this will be unacceptable to the customer and he will exercise his prerogative to place the order elsewhere. Even if acceptable, this approach results at best in a double parameter—CRD and FSD—measurement system, with performance to FSD, by custom and practice, becoming the primary internal measurement and thus disguising or de-emphasizing actual performance in relation to the customer's real need. The degree to which a customer's CRD is "reasonable" is again a function of many factors and differs according to whether the product in question is a standard commodity product, a semi-custom product (customized standard product) or a full-custom product. It also depends on the degree of production worthiness of the product and manufacturing process and the prevailing relationship between supply and demand.

As was stated at the beginning, **measuring the organization's actual on-time delivery performance to CRD only is the ultimate objective**. But to do so may require control in regulating supply and demand to pass from the factory to the field and product marketing deciding the "degree of reasonableness" of the CRD profile being asked for before accepting it as a commitment. To do so, these functions would also require an intimate knowledge of the supply situation. For any organization, this will most certainly involve a very significant educational task to modify both customer and field sales force behavior in an attempt to linearize both aggregate demand and supply and for this reason, scheduling is likely to remain within Production Control's jurisdiction for the foreseeable future.

Setting a (Realistically) Attainable Goal

How long is a piece of string? What is a reasonable goal for one organization—a strategic business unit in a corporation consisting of many such business units, for example—may not be reasonable for another. At one extreme, for a business which consists of a single-product portfolio, shipping a mature, standard commodity product to perhaps only one major customer—a 100 percent on-time all the time delivery goal could be considered reasonable. At the other extreme, for a business supplying a broad portfolio of new state-of-the-art, customer specific products across a diverse customer base in a rapid growth phase might not be considered so reasonable. A universal goal to deliver **100 percent on-time, all the time, on all products in the portfolio** (in whatever state of production worthiness) **across the total customer base at no "lost opportunity" cost** would not be a realistically, attainable goal, and as such, meaningful commitment to achieving it is not likely to extend beyond lip service and the goal will never be realized.

Perhaps the key to exemplary on-time delivery performance in this latter scenerio lies in the last condition—**"at no lost opportunity cost."** No organization, no matter how well managed, can be all things to all people, but few exercise restraint in declining opportunity or the discipline subsequently required in focusing their resources.

Nature and Scope of the Problem

In a survey conducted in our own company, peoples' opinions on the causes of poor on-time delivery performance fell into the following categories:

Organization
Lack of communication
Too many different product specifications
Too many different process flows
Culture
Conflicting goals
Management direction
Lack of resources
Attitude
Yield unpredictability
Too long cycle-times—(the window of uncertainty)

It is the nature of the beast that there is almost certainly a degree of truth in all of these. **On-time delivery performance is in fact a function of everything and everyone in an organization—affected by so many highly dispersed, but interdependent factors, that no one person or function is normally willing, or able, to accept exclusive ownership. As such, of all of the performance parameters by which an organization can be measured and judged—this may be the singularly most informative and important—since all other competencies (and incompetencies)—from the way a new product is managed during the development phase, all the way to shipping it in high volume, at high quality, low cost, and on time—are captured in this measurement.**

Good on-time delivery performance is the output of the process of dynamically reconciling aggregate supply and demand at the macro level, with all of the attendant specific product variables at the micro level. How these variables change in relation to each other is reflected in lead-time elasticity—increasing as demand exceeds supply and decreasing as supply recovers, sending signals to the market place accordingly.

The Scheduler's Dilemma

In the face of uncertainty, with perhaps no prerogative or flexibility to adjust either CRD or FSD from the initial commitment as the situation changes over time, the scheduler is obliged to call it right first time at the time of order entry. If he errs on the side of caution and schedules a lead time sufficiently far out for there to be high confidence of it being met, he risks losing an order. (If the product becomes available sooner than the FSD scheduled, the scheduler faces a further dilemma to deny the customer the product until the FSD arrives, after the CRD initially requested, or service the customer by shipping and taking an early to FSD delivery penalty.) Also, if the product is not specific to a customer, there is the risk it will be used to satisfy an earlier requirement—robbing Peter to pay Paul. On the other hand, being too optimistic runs the risk of a delinquency and a late delivery penalty. What are some of the factors which make calling it right first time difficult to achieve?

The scheduler must understand both the demand and supply situation in detail. The amount of capacity already committed out into the future must be known. The delta between what is available in total and that portion which is already committed is what is available to support new orders. Knowing with any degree of precision, what the existing capacity is, especially if mix is a factor, is usually the first problem encountered. A further complication is that situation in which capacity is expected to change in the future—perhaps due to additional capital equipment or forecasted productivity improvements—which may or may not occur on schedule. On this one is entirely dependent on one's colleagues in manufacturing. A reliable forecast of demand is usually the second, for which one is equally dependent on product marketing.

At one extreme, mature, standard commodity product is a relatively easy situation to deal with. If the unit weekly capacity is known (and it should be), then the supply run rate can be accurately established. Reconciling this with the demand backlog run rate determines the amount of this capacity already committed, the delta remaining being that capacity, regulated by lead time, available to support future business. If demand exceeds supply, these lead times will increase until more capacity is brought on stream. In this scenario, no product lot is unique and therefore continuity of supply is not noticeably affected if one lot, for whatever reason, encounters difficulty. There are always others to replace it. It is simply the rate of flow which matters from a customer service point of view. Cycle-time will only have a bearing on the cost of funding the inventory in the system and on quality feedback response time. (It is these expanding and contracting lead times which, perhaps more than any other factor, give rise to the boom or bust perturbations in the semiconductor industry. As lead times increase, customers can become apprehensive about continuity of supply out into the future and place orders for longer-term delivery against a forecasted rather than real demand in their own business. In some cases, this apprehension results in double or triple bookings with different vendors). On semi-custom or full-custom product, however, or uniquely engineered product, each lot becomes at some point in the manufacturing cycle unique to a specific customer. As such, it must be tracked specifically in order to detect any deviation as soon as it occurs so that immediate corrective action can be taken.

Treatment—There is No Quick Fix Panacea

Since on-time delivery performance is determined by these competencies which reside at the very core of a business, it is a function of the degree to which the principles determining these competencies are satisfied:

1. Perception of Relative Importance

On-time delivery must be a sacrosanct and inviolate, primary, business performance parameter as perceived by the customer. Measurement systems and management expectations predetermine behavior and if on-time delivery is not perceived from top management through all rank and file in the organization as being at least as important as other parameters, then it will be operationally relegated to secondary importance. It will be treated as a derived and dependent, rather than as an inviolate, independent variable. If making or exceeding the monthly or quarterly sales forecast, for example, is a culturally ingrained management preoccupation, then decisions will almost certainly be made which in maximizing this, may compromise on-time delivery. If on the other hand, quality, cost, and on-time delivery are the primary focus, if in fact the customer needs take precedence to the extent that these parameters are sacrosanct, then the sales value associated with this prescribed delivery profile will be accepted as the dependent variable.

2. Organizational Structure

In order to consolidate acceptance of the principles of ownership and control, the organization must be structured for highest possible degree of self sufficiency. If on-time delivery is to be considered of strategic, rather than tactical importance, the structure of the organization must be consistent with this. Structure, after all, should follow strategy.

3. Rationalization

No organization can be all things to all people. To attempt to do so it can only result in doing everything badly and nothing well. The boundaries of uncertainty (and opportunity) must be deliberately limited by accepting the need for:

a. Customer Differentiation
  (1) Where opportunity is not a limiting factor, it is only good business sense to offer different "tiers of service." But care must be taken to ensure that labels for these categories of customers are chosen not to offend.
  (2) Criteria for deciding chosen few.
    (a) Bookings forecast
    (b) Billings history
    (c) Current backlog
    (d) Strategic importance

b. Market Segment Differentiation
  (1) Some market segments are more important than others to any business. It makes no sense to attempt to maximize opportunity by serving all and doing it badly at the expense of serving a few well.

c. Product Differentiation
  (1) A vigorous, lively, product portfolio does not mean that some products should not be allowed to "gracefully, fade away," or even be "assisted" on their way.

4. Realistic Goal Setting

a. Reconcile corporate/sector/group/division/SBU goals.

5. **Managing Capacity**
   a. Only schedule 85 percent of capacity.
   b. Know at all times what capacity is available and what is already committed.
   c. Measure factories and factories within factories on cycle-time and output to linear mix.
   d. Manage lead times judiciously.
   e. Management consistency—avoid hula hoops.
   f. Practice restraint—have discipline to say no when it hurts least before a commitment which will probably not be honored is made.
   g. Bottleneck capacity is factory capacity—real cost of a bottleneck operation—contrary to conventional accounting "wisdom" is the forgone opportunity cost.
      (1) Linearity of supply and demand—avoid if possible, peaks and troughs in both.
      (2) Set up SC numbers for OEMs.
      (3) Standard product—inventory used on a first come, first serve basis—replenish with short cycle-time.
      (4) Avoid need for manual intervention in Auto Pick Systems.
      (5) Orders on credit hold?—do they affect on-time delivery measurement?
      (6) Interdependence/statistical fluctuations.

6. **Continue to Hone Forecasting Competence**
   a. Refine forecasting skills.
   b. IBIS—visibility/execution/control—processing information cycle before processing product. Good intentions and sense of urgency are not enough. The tools to communicate what should be done, when, how, and by whom must be available.

7. **Operational Competence**
   a. Run to desired WIP profile—minimum thresholds.
   b. Streamline product flow/clerical transactions and geographic logistics.
   c. Deal with uncertainty with greater responsiveness/flexibility JIT and SCM—rather than with inventory—JIC.

8. **Educate—All Functions—Rank and File**
   a. Consistency of external internal measurement.
   b. Change PMC measurement criteria—measure what customer measures.

9. **Design for Manufacturability—Predictable/Zero Defect Manufacturing**

10. **Ship to Preferred Customer OEMs from Test—Not Warehouse**

IMPLEMENTING IBIS

Linearity and On-Time Delivery

Before IBIS and modules, our factory performance with respect to linearity of bookings, billings, and shipments from the final test area to the finished goods warehouse followed the very typical "hockey stick" pattern. (The 80/20 percent rule applies here too!) In any given month, we would usually ship, from the final test area to the warehouse and from the warehouse to the customer base, 20 percent of the product forecast in the first three weeks of a four-week fiscal month and the remaining 80 percent of the product in the last week, with an equally disproportionate amount on the last day—if we were lucky. It was part of our culture to refer to this frantic fiasco as ''billings week'' and ''billings Saturday.'' (The situation was perpetuated from month to month by sucking inventory out of the system at the end of the month to the extent of imbalancing the production lines and because, after such a physical and emotional trauma, most people lacked ''vigor'' the first few days of the subsequent month.) Obviously, such an activity profile had many other undesirable side effects in terms of factory loading and quality. Intervention to correct this addressed both sides of the supply/demand equation.

An analysis of our backlog profile for any given month showed that customer CRDs were concentrated around Fridays and Saturdays, the first and fifteenth of the month. Even if product were available to ship against these orders, it resulted in a very serious peak loading problem for our finished goods warehouse and shipping people, with very little activity being asked of them for ten- or twelve-day intervals and then huge surges concentrated in two days or so, with a frequently overwhelming peak on the last two or three days. (More typically, with our functional, push system of manufacturing, we would have inventory/backlog mismatch.) So accommodating were we, not only did we stoically accept this customer-induced and self-imposed erratic behavior, we scheduled FSDs in exact conformance, making no attempt to smooth the load. This customer demand pattern and these factory scheduling and shipping practices were fairly universal across all of our business units.

Even when the factories were able to ship linearly, which wasn't often, the propensity was to ship units for units sake and absorb overhead recovery and certainly not therefore, to the correct mix. (Actual before and after performance in this respect is shown in the attached figure.) While IBIS provided the required degree of visibility and control, the modular organization of our resources permitted successful execution in shipping linearly to the correct mix. The terms ''billings week'' and ''billings Saturday'' are no longer part of our vocabulary. Now, **every day is billings day** with linearity of all of these parameters planned and tracked daily.

While on-time delivery is still measured to FSD, this will be replaced by CRD as our ability in this respect improves. To achieve high performance to this criteria, our interaction with customers in linearizing their aggregate demand, will certainly need to increase significantly, persuading them that our collective behavior is not in our mutual best interest.

Running a business successfully can be considered analogous to nature's many parallels of **maintaining a state of dynamic equilibrium at a desired level**. See Figure 12-4.

Dynamic equilibrium in business is profitable conciliation of sales and manufacturing (and/or purchases) through inventory management.

Knowledge is currently the **most decisive element** required in running a successful business.

It is important to make the **distinction** between **data** and **knowledge**. Bits of data are analogous to **pieces of a jigsaw puzzle**; only when the pieces are **assembled** does it **illustrate a picture** and **convey an idea**.

A picture is worth a thousand words.
(An idea is worth a thousand pictures.)

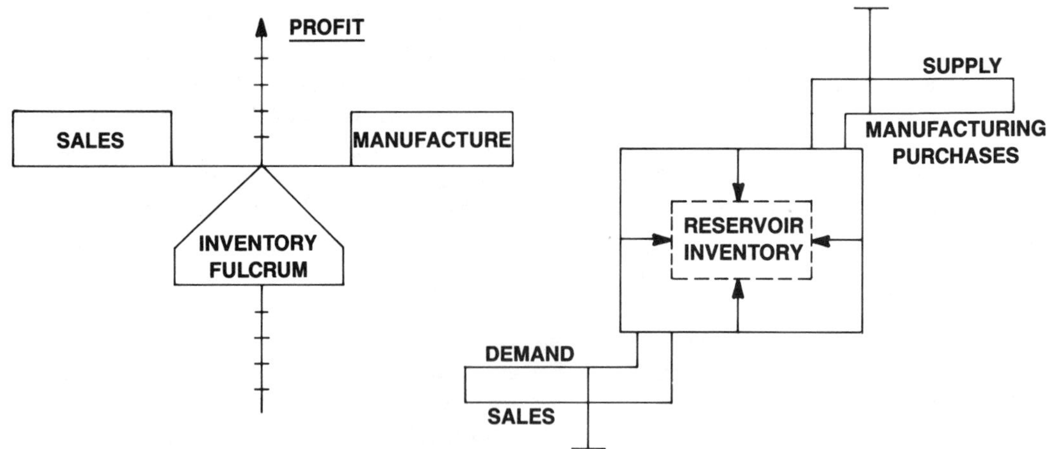

Figure 12-4 Dynamic Equilibrium

Data are raw material, like all raw material they need to be:

1. **Acquired** (and maintained)
2. **Treated (processed)**—it may then emerge in the form of an end product as knowledge
3. Utilized (**applied to decision making**)

With **manual methods** (pencil, paper, calculator) in such a complex business as ours, far **too much time is spent on (1) and (2)** and **not enough on (3).** Three is the management and application of knowledge—**decision making and implementation.**

That is why IBIS (or its equivalent) needs to be created. See Figure 12-5.

- Current status of business information management (data).
  - Acquisition
  - Manipulation
  - Analysis
  - Presentation
  - **Mainly manual**—slow/inefficient/costly.
- Self-help automation efforts in various groups tends to be:
  - Parochial
  - Unstructured
  - Uncoordinated
- Parallel group needs are usually the same/similar, independent approaches are different/wasteful.

IBIS

- **Objective** —To provide business P&L forecast/actual comparisons and any associated data required for business management
  Speedily
  Accurately
  Meaningfully
  Productively

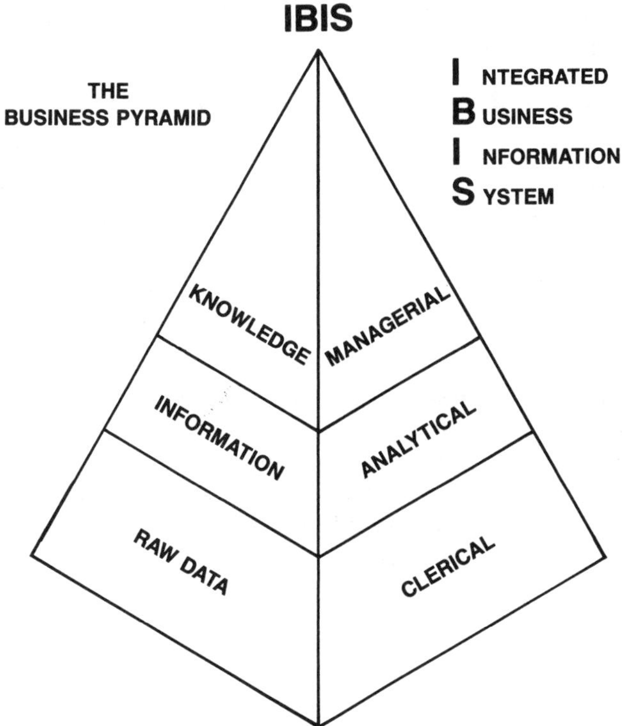

Figure 12-5 The Business Pyramid

- **How?** —By **automating** product marketing, production control, engineering, manufacturing, and financial **number crunching**—in the MIS environment.
- **Resources** —Optimization of existing physical and human resources through a **coordinated cooperative effort** between operations/MIS.
- **Time scale** —**Incremental return** by using structured/systematic approach.

SYSTEM GOALS

System goals are to **enhance what is currently provided by MIS** to **meet the unique needs of each business** without the **traditional disadvantages of universal solutions**.

1. Obtaining appropriate reports in which attributes are contained
2. Visually scanning report for information
3. Extracting and recording manually
4. Processing by calculator
5. Recording and reporting manually
6. Transcribing by typing onto foils
7. Transmitting results by conventional mail (foil)

It will simply be a matter of **running or writing a utility code**. Actions **(1) to (7)** will be **executed automatically**.

Main Data Base Arrays Are:	**Main Utility Arrays Are:**
On-Line	**Off-Line**
1. Sales—Order Book	1. Order Book Analysis
2. Inventory—Area, Stage of Completion	2. Inventory Analysis
3. Manufacturing—Technical Attributes	3. Manufacturing and Technical Reports
4. Financial—Standards/Actual/TPs	4. Product Costs/P&Ls

Because of **variation significance** of device attributes **management of every aspect of the business must be at device level.**

Compensating errors cannot be assumed to permit use of averages.

With each data base array there will be a suite of utility programs to create utility arrays. There will also be a suite of utility programs that operate on device attributes contained in more than one array.

UTILITY PROGRAM SUITES

Sales Data Base	**Inventory Data Base**	**Manufacturing Data Base**	**Financial Data Base**
Backlog Profile	Inventory	Production Reports	FG WWS
Will Advise	By Product By	Line Balancing	RS WWS
Customer to Advise	Stage of Completion	Probe Yields	DIE WWS
Delinquency	By Manufacturing	Final Test Yields	FG TP
MSD	Area	Product Information	RS TP
CRD	By Device Total Inv.	Summary	DIE TP
Credits	By Process Step	Mask Status Chart	FG Local Std
RMR Status		Bill of Materials	RS Local Std
Samples		Specifications	DIE Local Std
% Technology		Throughput	Margins
% Purchases		Moves	
% Segment Sales			
% Region Sales			
% Customer Sales			
% Distribution			
% External			
% Internal			
% Turns			

SYSTEMS USERS

Document Central	Product Engineering
Marketing	Assembly Engineering
Production Control	Production Test
Finance	Quality Assurance
Manufacturing—Wafer Fab	Shipping
Production Test	Management
Assembly	Administration (Secretarial)

SYSTEM IMPLEMENTATION

Upon the broadest backs shall fall the heaviest burdens. Even withstanding the fact the typical MIS organization is not in a position to provide this quickly and independently because of other commitments, the time taken to complete a program of this nature is, among other things, a function of the difficulties which arise. The user, or **users**, are **unable to define what is required** in terms that can be easily implemented, **due to lack of EDP systems knowledge** and conversely, the **MIS organization** fails to understand what the user wants, due to **lack of operations knowledge.**

There is a language barrier. See Figures 12-6 and 12-7.

SYSTEM DEVELOPMENT GUIDELINES

- Appoint a **project leader** (MIS).
- Appoint **team member** from each **user group** as a group leader.
- MIS create **data base structure in host environment**.
- MIS establish **rules of custodianship**.
- MIS establish **communications protocol**.
- **Systems/product engineering** establish **peripheral interfacing**.
- Team member from each **user group defines utility program requirements.**
- **User groups provide** and **maintain data base device attributes.**
- **User groups** provide or **acquire means** to **write own utility programs**.
- All **user files** should be—**Structured**
  —**Modularly independent**
- **Utility programs** should be **matrix equations**.
- **MRP (material requirements planning)**—is only a small **part of the solution**.
- Using **proprietary PCs as MIS terminals accommodates IBIS** and gives user **access to stand alone applications software libraries**.
- User should define **exact format** and **frequency** of **output data** required.
- Data base should be modularly structural by SBU.
- Data base should be designed to allow comparison of:
  1. Forecast to Budget
  2. Forecast to Forecast
  3. Actual to Budget
  4. Actual to Forecast
  5. Actual to Estimate
- Start with manufacturing plan.

MIS ENVIRONMENT
UNIVERSAL PROBLEMS—
UNIVERSAL SOLUTIONS

USER ENVIRONMENT
UNIQUE PROBLEMS—
SPECIFIC SOLUTIONS

DATA BASE ARRAYS

EDAC

IRAB

TANDEM

EXCORCISER

EXCORMACS

WORD PROCESSOR

UTILITY ARRAYS

TERMINAL

RSX-11 OR VAX

TEST SYSTEM

IBM XC PEANUT

GRAPHICS TERMINAL (TELEGRAPH)

RAINBOW

LISA

LINE PLOTTER

INTERCONNECTS VIA MODEMS
AND DIRECT DATA LINKS WHERE
APPROPRIATE

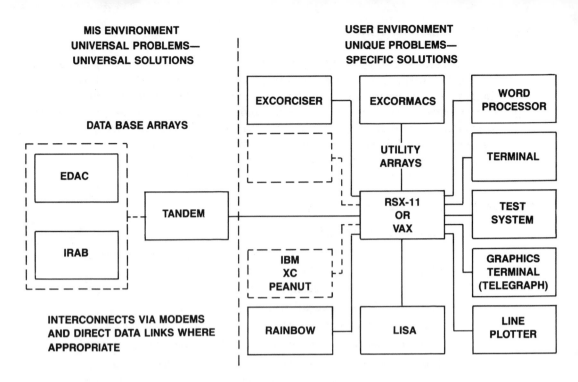

Figure 12-6 MIS, User Environment

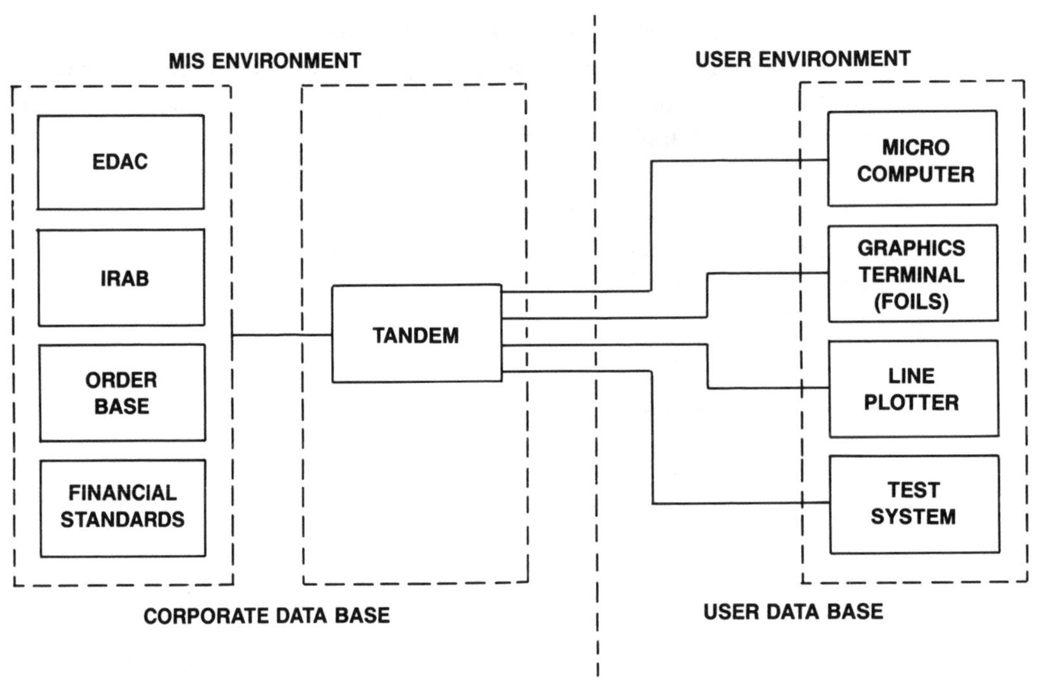

Figure 12-7 IBIS

FILE RESPONSIBILITY

1. Order Base/Backlog Data	MIS/Production Control
2. Inventory Data	MIS/Production Control
3. Engineering Data	MIS/Product/Device Engineering
4. Financial Standards Data	MIS/Finance
5. Aged Bookings Forecast	Product Marketing
6. Aged Book Fcst by Device	Product Marketing/Product. Cont.
7. Aggregate Billings Forecast	Production Control
8. Sales Plan by Device	Production Control
9. Month to Date Billings	Production Control
10. Month to Date Forced Bookings	Product Marketing
11. Backlog Utility Files	Production Control
12. Capacity/Cycle Time Matrices	
a. Wafer Fab	Fab Manufacturing Mgmt.
b. Unit Probe	Test Manufacturing Mgmt.
c. Assembly	Production Control
d. Final Test	Test Manufacturing Mgmt.
13. Manufacturing Plan/Act.	
a. Wafer Fab	Production Control/Manuf. Mgmt.
b. Unit Probe	Production Control/Manuf. Mgmt.
c. Assembly	Production Control/Manuf. Mgmt.
d. Final Test	Production Control/Manuf. Mgmt.
14. Linearity Charts Plan/Act	
A. Wafer Fab	Production Control/Manuf. Mgmt.
B. Unit Probe	Production Control/Manuf. Mgmt.
C. Assembly	Production Control/Manuf. Mgmt.
D. Final Test	Production Control/Manuf. Mgmt.
15. Probe Yield Analysis	Product/Device Engineering
16. Probe Yield Forecast	Product/Device Engineering
17. Final Test Yield Analysis	Product/Test Engineering
18. Final Test Yield Forecast	Product/Test Engineering
19. ASP/Margin Analysis	Finance
20. ASP/Margin Forecast	Production Control
21. Purchases Plan	Production Control
22. Manufacturing Plan Utility Files	Production Control
23. Inventory Forecast/Actuals	
a. Wafer Fab	Production Control/Manuf. Mgmt.
b. Unit Probe	Production Control/Manuf. Mgmt.
c. Assembly	Production Control/Manuf. Mgmt.
d. Final Test	Production Control/Manuf. Mgmt.
24. P&L Forecast	Finance/Ops. Magr.

13

Managing For Profit/ Business Strategy

Being a capital intensive industry with very high fixed costs in the form of depreciation on facilities, capital equipment, and so on, **realization of market share is an essential prerequisite to profitability**. The greater the **volume** of product over which these costs can be absorbed, the lower the proportion that each unit of product need carry and, therefore, **the lower the ASP at which it can be profitable**.

There are basically two ways to increase market share:

1. By **forcing** existing products down the learning curve such that the **reduced product cost** realized permits **greater penetration** into existing applications and into new applications that were previously not cost effective, by being able to accept a **lower price** than the competition (see Note 1).

2. By **new product introduction**. In this industry, new products are the life's blood, even in good times, and there are many examples of **distinctive competence** in this respect giving rise to **pre-eminence** in **market share** and **profitability**.

Note 1: Learning curves or experience curves, where reductions in product cost are associated with increases in volume, do not cause these reductions in product cost to occur automatically. What they do is provide **opportunity** and **incentive** to bring about a reduction in costs by being more **productive**.

The means (resources) to reduce product costs must then be applied.

WAFER FABRICATION

This function is particularly **capital intensive** with high fixed cost; i.e., **high cost of doing nothing**. Circumstances need to be created such that this can always run at or near the limits of its **absolute** capacity in order that these costs can be absorbed over high volume. The distinction is made between **absolute** capacity that the facility is resourced to do in terms of **capital equipment** and its **effective** capacity that it is resourced to do in terms of **direct operator** staffing. Effective capacity can also be a function of the **product mix** that the facility is required to run since the number of **process steps** required to build a wafer can vary **by product or by process technology**. Essentially, however, **wafer cost** can be considered to be **common to all products** and it is the responsibility of wafer fabrication management to reduce this to its lowest possible value by various means: **controlling expenses, maximizing mechanical yield, increasing productivity, reducing cycle-time and inventory**, for example. Final accountability of this function is not the production of low cost wafers but of die. This is where individual product differences begin to emerge and give rise to **distinct product costs**. This aspect has been dealt with in Chapter 8.

Given that **demand** and **manufacturing base** (the number of different products which the area can make) permit the facility to be run at or near the limit of its **absolute** capacity, then **control** is the key to the contribution to profit required of this function. Process parameters such as critical dimensions and voltage thresholds must be **optimized** via final test and unit probe correlation for **maximum yield** to **prime** as well as **standard** product specifications. Having determined the best **recipe**, the task then takes the form of minimizing the amount of necessary **resources** consumed. These constitute **variable costs** (costs which, unlike fixed costs, would not be incurred if the product was not made, as a function of volume). They cannot be eliminated but they can be minimized.

Inventory, as **work in process (WIP)**, should also be minimized since inventory

1. **is cash** that is being held in an unproductive form,
2. **extends manufacturing cycle times** which increases the period of uncertainty between taking an order and servicing it,
3. **increases risk** due to the unknown acceptability of the product, and
4. **delays feedback** on product performance.

The next task is to minimize the time taken to arrange the **ingredients** in conformance to the **recipe**—the **cycle-time**. This is very much a function of

1. **inventory**—by stage of completion,
2. **activity level**—in terms of volume,
3. **duration and number**—of steps in the processing cycle, and
4. **proliferation**—the mix of products required to be run.

Because of the **complexity** and **inertia** of this operation, every effort must be made to provide **stability** so the preceding steps can be achieved. Changes can be avoidable or unavoidable. In the case of unavoidable changes, attempts must be made to **insulate** any manufacturing activity, but particularly this one, from the full effects of these. They are not particularly good at accommodating change and operate most effectively in stable conditions. It takes a great deal of time and effort to **ramp up** a wafer fabrication area and an equally great amount to wind it down. For this reason **long-term visibility** into the expected activity level is extremely essential.

The **strategy** to be pursued in respect of the **wafer fab area** should be as follows:

1. **Load the area at or near limit of absolute capacity**
2. **Increase width of manufacturable product base**
3. **Optimize product mix for maximum contribution (ASP – cost)—see Note 2**
4. **Optimize product/process recipe**
5. **Maximize good die per wafer at probe (gross die per wafer/yield)**
6. **Develop and apply rigorous control**

7. **Provide long-term activity level visibility**
8. **Minimize cycle time and work in process**
9. **Minimize variety of technologies required**

Note 2: An ideal business strategy from a wafer fabrication loading point of view is one in which 60–70 percent of the product mix is high volume, commodity products, priced perhaps at break even margin to ensure the volume required to consume capacity and absorb costs, the remaining capacity being used for products carrying higher margins.

Although wafer fabrication has been dealt with separately, most of what has been said also applies in general terms to all of the manufacturing functions. The common denominator of these must be **relentless pursuit** of **reduced cost**. The functions that are able to make the next most significant contribution in this respect are test and assembly, both of which fall under the jurisdiction of the product engineer in addition to his obligations in helping to reduce die cost by pursuing mask shrinks, yield enhancements, and so on. These functions both lend themselves to **increased productivity** and **reduced product cost** by **increased automation**.

PRICING STRATEGY

At the outset of this section, it was stated that **market share** is a prerequisite to **profitability** and the two main methods of increasing market share were identified. Obviously **price** has a particularly important bearing on both of these. The relationship between **volume** and **product cost was also emphasized. But where do we break the vicious circle**?

In a competitive environment, especially one in which **supply exceeds demand**, were we to use actual **product costs** incurred by an underutilized facility as a basis for price setting, it is highly improbable that those prices would permit a sufficient level of factory loading to be attained to permit **product cost reduction** to take place. The strategy which must therefore be employed is to establish as accurately as possible what the **product costs would be** if the factory were effectively loaded.

These **product costs** must then be reconciled with the **market ASP**, in the knowledge that **market ASP** is given and cannot be significantly affected. This is especially true in a **product family** with **low market share**. If potential buyers do not like your prices they can go elsewhere. This is less true the higher the market share any one vendor has since the customer has less alternatives in source of supply. In this way, all else being equal among competition, price as the **independent variable** will hopefully give rise to the **desired volume** which, as the **dependent variable**, will permit forecasted **product costs** to be achieved which make the ASP/cost relationship economically viable.

In a situation where demand exceeds supply, a different strategy would be employed since the price the customer is willing to pay to secure a source of supply may well be higher. In this situation, opportunity costing/pricing would be appropriate.

FOREGONE OPPORTUNITY

If wafer starts required exceed capacity available, then those products which contribute most win the silicon, and the price which the purchaser is requested to pay must be looked at in the context of this.

In summary then,

1.	Supply	>	Demand	Buyer's Market	Marginal Costing
2.	Demand	>	Supply	Seller's Market	Opportunity Costing

In either set of circumstances, a strategy must be employed which is **self-fulfilling** in creating **the desired scenario**.

POINT OF SALE BUYING CRITERIA

A customer's decision criteria is based on an evaluation of the following between vendors:

1. Product Specification (Utility)
2. Price
3. Availability
4. Quality/Reliability
5. Track Record/Service

The **hierarchy** of these criteria is likely to be **dynamic** in that it also will reflect the **prevailing supply/demand conditions**. The astute vendor will manage this to most closely conform to what he believes the purchaser hierarchy will be at any point in time.

STRATEGY

An analysis of all of the preceding factors should give rise to a **business strategy** which, against the background that has been drawn in previous sections, should reflect the following questions:

1. Where do we want to get to?
2. Where are we now?
3. What do we have to do to get there?

This **strategy** should address **goals** which are **quantifiable** such as **market share, profitability, and quality**. In this case of **microcomponents**, for example, the total portfolio is considered to be **three main categories** of product for each of which there is a **distinct strategy**:

1. Standard Product
2. Customized Single Chip
3. 16-Bit Products

There are aspects which are common to all categories, and these are embraced in a **common strategy**: that is, **quality**. Aspects of each category in which **distinctive competence** is considered to be essential to success are articulated in a **specific strategy**. These are as shown in Figure 13-1. Broadly speaking, however, in today's competitive environment and the **Japanese presence**, any strategy which is not predicated on **superior** marketing, engineering, and manufacturing is unlikely to succeed.

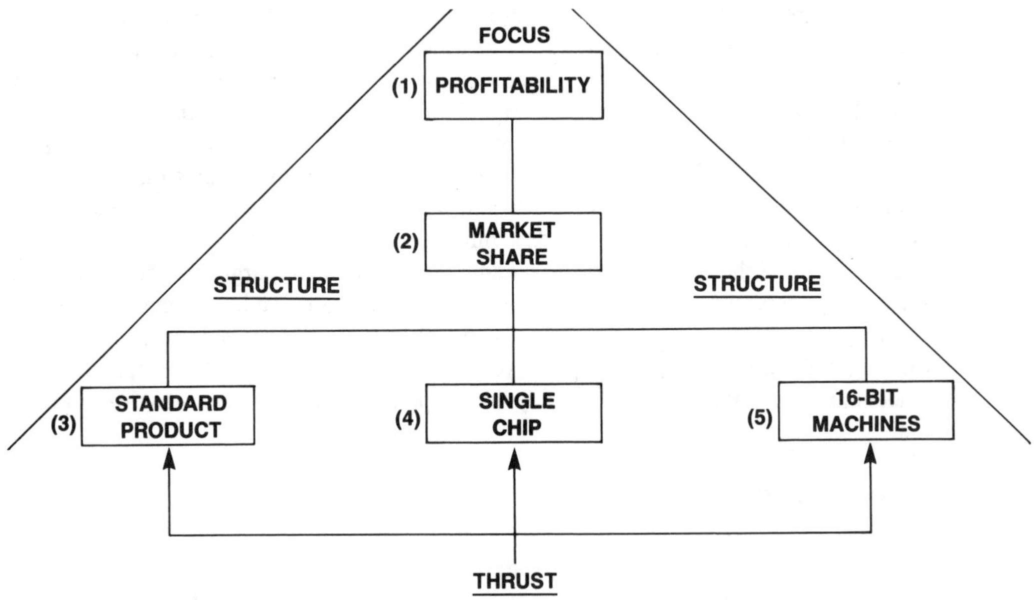

Figure 13-1 Strategic Hierarchy Microcomponents

STRATEGY—A DEFINITION

Strategy is the determination of the basic long-term goals and objectives of an organization. It encompasses the adoption of courses of action and allocation of resources necessary for accomplishing goals by segregating those aspects that are enduring and unchanging over relatively long periods of time from those that are, of necessity, more responsive to changes in the marketplace and the pressures of other environmental forces.

Strategy and Leadership

Why, over the course of time, do some businesses continue to grow and prosper while others stagnate, perhaps even atrophy and die? Why do some organizations, flush from some past success, with large reserves of funds at their disposal, or access to the best technology available, find it difficult to repeat past success while others, not so technically or financially well endowed, thrive and flourish, ostensibly it would sometimes appear, on no more than a shoestring? There are as many explanations of course as there are examples of both extremes: beginner's luck, the temporarily monopolistic benefit of an innovative new product or manufacturing process, a particularly benevolent market or other circumstantial observations explaining success, on the one hand, to the apathy or complacency usually associated with failure on the other. Are these same conclusions as convincing in explaining exemplary performance over time, or one organization's performance relative to another where all things in the operating environment are apparently equal, such as might be the case for similar enterprises, of equal maturity, comparably resourced, participating in the same market place with essentially similar product portfolios? Do they explain the differences in corporate vitality separating success from failure?

If, in rejecting these explanations, we of necessity must then continue our search to identify the most significant factor behind success of an enduring nature, we might do so by applying a process of elimination, identifying these common factors, which in being universal, can be considered to have little or no bearing on relative performance. Such things as access to the same technology, or labor force, or the same pool of MBAs and other professionals, the cost of capital, all of the ingredients in fact which any enterprise may have equal access to in common with all others. This process having run its full course, it is more than likely that we would conclude that strategy, both its conceptual quality and the manner in which it is implemented, more than any other factor, is what distinguishes companies and determines their relative performance. Since strategy is at least one of the more significant parameters of leadership, arguably the primary and ultimately essential contribution, we might further conclude that in the final analysis, the caliber of leadership of an enterprise is the ultimately distinguishing, critical factor. Starting with strategy then, although in practice it may appear virtually inseparable from leadership, since they are so mutually interdependent, let's review what we know of both.

What Is Strategy?

So elusive is a satisfactory definition of strategy, and to an even greater extent, leadership, that a great range and variety of attempts abound from the so uninformative as to be useless, to the so misconceived as to be dangerously misleading. But while the kernel of truth may elude our grasp, we can at least identify, and hopefully safely discard, those definitions and perceptions which are patently not true.

Strategy is not, for example, the inevitable product of a formal strategic planning process. This may well be the intent of such efforts, but it is not necessarily the result. Institutionalizing its creation cannot guarantee its production. All too often, the efforts expended by this approach become mechanistic and ritualistic, with the creation of numbers for number's sake. Neither is it portfolio management. This is a management technique, a tool, to help in managing cash flow, in guiding investment decisions requiring the allocation of scarce resources. It is almost exclusively a clinical and analytical process. Nowhere does it call for the creative contribution so essential to sound strategic thinking. Strategy is not the product of a long-term financial plan. This is an if-then exercise in hypothetical scenario models determining probable profitability, human resources and capital equipment funding required to support the hypothetical sales scenarios. It does not in any way address the critical issue in the strategic process—how these sales are to be generated, only what will be required in the way of resources, and the probable financial outcome, if they are. Neither can the need for strategy be satisfied by management edict or anecdotes. There is little the management autocrat or the fireside philosopher can contribute to the process with mandates, benign platitudes, or rules of thumb. If strategy is none of these things, what then is it? (Yet another definition, I'm afraid.)

Strategy: The process of realizing quantified objectives through competitive advantage by conceiving, developing, implementing, leveraging, and sustaining a critical distinctive competence in a collaborative manner; to articulate and then communicate the end product of this process to all concerned with its implementation.

Like any process, if we know its components, it can be approached in a structured and systematic manner.

Components of the Strategic Process

- **Definition of objectives (the vision)**
- **Data acquisition (fact finding)**
- **Data analysis (applying intelligence)**
- **Perception process (creative insight)**
- **Collaborative development (more than participation)**
- **Organizational commitment**
- **People commitment**
- **Perceptions of reality (including acknowledging cultural beliefs)**
- **Articulation (mission statement)**
- **Communication**
- **Execution and control**

The essence of strategy is its theme, its golden thread. It is the glue which binds together all else into a cohesive, focused entity.

Much of what we know about strategy and leadership was developed in a military context, if for no other reason than there are plenty of case studies, well documented by military historians, available to us for study. In both contexts, the military and the commercial, the general objectives and processes are very similar—how to retain possession of territory (market share) already held while attempting to wrest ownership of more from the opposition. Only the means are different: in the one case munitions, in the other, products or services. All else is the same, or at least very similar. In both contexts, the initial process consists of first asking and then finding the answers to appropriate questions—which positions should be defended, which should be attacked, where is the opposition's weakest link, when is it advisable or prudent to retreat or capitulate? How should resources be deployed, in what mix, where and when? How much will it take? Can we afford it? In preparation for battle how are the armies to be trained, how are they to be equipped, how is discipline to be established and enforced, how is the equipment and ammunition (product), to be funded, sourced, manufactured, distributed to the field? Is the terrain well understood? What do we know, what do we not know but need to know, what can we know and how so, about our adversary—his resource strength, his deployment of these resources, his strategy in the use of them? When the battle begins, how are resources in the field to be coordinated, what communication systems will be required? How is morale to be maintained at the highest possible level?

From such studies, the practice of OST—objectives, strategy, and tactics—popularized in the mid-1970s, evolved. The objective is the desired end result. Strategy addresses the how of implementation, developed prior to the actual confrontation and tactics—the mechanics of real-time execution in the field. This development brought some structure, if not substance, to our understanding of the strategic process. Because all else was held to be more or less equal—the same battlefield, equal access to men and equipment, and so on—strategy and leadership were held to be the decisive factors in determining which battles, and wars, were won and lost. Many examples of numerically superior forces being defeated by an interior one, but brilliantly led, served to reinforce this view. In the industrial battlefield, the customer decides victorious and vanquished.

In this context, the process must begin by defining the objective, with a search for the answer to the question, "what business are we in?" Only in this way can we be sure that we focus our resources on the appropriate tasks, which positions to defend and which to attack. This in turn leads to the next question, "what distinctive competence or competencies are required to be successful in this business?" While customer oriented, the thrust arising from this process must be calibrated against strengths and weaknesses, absolute in the case of self and relative in terms of the competition, assessing status quo in order to measure the competence gap. Only by developing and implementing a strategy to close this gap can the objectives be realized.

The process calls for the bringing to bear, first analytical skills, those competencies residing predominantly in the left hand side of the human brain and then in turn, the creative skills of the right hemisphere, analyzing the data available to separate the essence from the elixir, to find the kernel of truth, the course through the storm. This warrants a willingness, a respectful eagerness, to be prepared to challenge conventional wisdom in the search for innovative leverage. (A fuller treatment of these aspects is presented in Chapter 2.)

The quality of any strategy produced by such a process will obviously be a function of all the components of that process, but just as strategy and leadership are held to be the critical factors in determining the quality of an organization, the most critical factors in the strategic process are those of perception and creativity. Clearly defining reach-out, but realistically attainable objectives, gathering, collating, and analyzing all of the pertinent data—about customer preferences and behavior, competitor's strengths, weaknesses, and perceived strategies, regional market idiosyncrasies and so forth—all of course are important, but these primarily analytical tasks lie well within our general competence. Just as in computing, while garbage into the strategic mill will ensure that what emerges is no more useful, providing accurate, comprehensive, pertinent, high quality input is not of itself sufficient to produce the desired, high quality end result. This is also a function of the inference engine in the applications program and the algorithms driven by it in the strategist's mind. Perception in the strategic context is the art of seeing what is not immediately obvious, the ability to identify some meaningful pattern or theme from a jumble of data in disarray. It is the process of producing knowledge or intelligence from simply information or data.

As in the overall strategic process, each component can in turn be described as a subprocess, including those of perception and creativity, albeit less definitively since they are less well understood than the other, more analytical skills. Perception and creativity take us into the realms of the human intellect residing predominantly in the conceptually creative and holistic right hemisphere of the brain. While we are far removed from being able to understand this process in detail, any more than we are able to understand how we reason, or learn, or memorize information, we are able to identify its major components. Four stages have been identified and as in most tasks, the grunt work of gathering, absorbing, and beginning to assimilate the information in the mind takes place in stage 1. This is followed in stage 2 by the process of immersing oneself in the information, allowing it to percolate through and incubate in the mind, reflecting and refining it, both consciously and subconsciously, for meaning. The third stage, if it occurs at all, is when the idea is illuminated, the eureka stage as it were. Stage 4 then consists of testing and validating the end result.

Returning to the main strategic process flow, the implementation stage following conception always requires commitment and patience, sometimes courage. This is why strategy and leadership are inseparable. Brilliant strategy can neither be conceptualized nor implemented without the leader giving strategy its first breath of life and then nourishing it to fruition. This is not part of the management task which can be delegated to subordinates, or contracted exclusively to consultants, both of which would be unacceptable forms of abdication.

Perhaps one of the derived benefits of the work being done in artificial intelligence and expert systems will be a better understanding of the structure and mechanics of this process. Who knows, perhaps some day we might even have expert systems in strategy. Until then, however, we must be content with making best possible use of the naturally occurring variety.

SOME IMPORTANT ASPECTS OF STRATEGIC THINKING

Mental Attitude

- Establish correct frame of mind! Don't **hide** behind **excuses**.

Excuses:

- Strength of dollar
- Lack of **defensive** government intervention—(consumer pays tariff surcharge/ complacency is encouraged)
- Japanese import tariffs/other barriers to market penetration
- Unfair trading practices
- Japanese (Asian) work ethic
- Japanese business trinity—industry/government/education (society)
- No/small defense budget—more funding for R&D/industry
- Cultural group synergism/not individual
- Low wage rates
- Lower capital costs
- Undervalued currency

Positive thinking doesn't always achieve results
but negative thinking never does

BE COMMITTED TO WINNING

Set Objectives

- Set winning as an objective.
- Develop strategy to achieve objective. Objectives must be quantitative (winning/ won hard to measure).
- Set up structural hierarchy of subordinate, **quantitative** objectives.
  - Market share percent—now/future
  - New product definition/introduction
  - Quality objective—now/future
  - Price/cost objective—now/future
  - On-time delivery—now/future
  - Well-defined/controlled cost reduction programs
- Break ultimate objective (5/10 years out) into intermediate objectives—3 months/ 1 year/2 years.

"The mind to imagine, the skill to do.
The **determination** to **follow through**!"
Quality of **execution** is as important as the plan!

Develop Strategy

How to Achieve Objectives

- Worship at the altar of **customer sovereignty**.
  The world does not owe **anyone/any society** a living.
- Work to understand **customer expectations** both now and in the future.
  Accept that expectations become more demanding with time.
- Identify where **distinctive competence** is **imperative** in servicing these expectations.
- Fully understand relative strengths/weaknesses of self/competition.

KNOW YOUR ADVERSARY

Why Is Japan So Successful?

- Japan imports 90 percent of its energy, 70 percent of its food.
  It is not an indigenously rich island. They **must be successful** in **exporting** to maintain/improve standard of living.

Know thyself
Why is Western Hemisphere not winning?

- Historical legacy—post-Second World War—pent-up demand/ruined economies.

  U.S. could market anything it manufactured—**complacency!**
- Focus on short term results—"fast tracker/whiz kid"—MBA factories.
- Focus on management—not on **leadership!**
- Mountains of WIP take care of uncertainty.

WHAT DO WE HAVE TO WORK WITH?

- Land
- Labor
- Capital
- Knowledge
- **Leadership**—the **catalyst!** to **synergism**

- Leadership—What is it?
  The ability to **inspire** "ordinary"1 people to achieve **extraordinary** (distinctive) **results**

  "Managers do things right. Leaders do the right things."2 (Nothing is so futile as to do well that which should not be done at all.)

  The **difference** between **efficiency** and **effectiveness**.

1. "Ordinary" people are usually **stultified**. Leaders release **latent** potential—usually by having more faith in people than they have in themselves.
2. From *"Leaders—The Strategies of Taking Charge."* Bennis & Burt.

- Managers solve/**react** to problems already **visible**; leaders seek/anticipate those which are not (see Kepner Tregoe action sequence attached).
- Leadership—How does it work?
- A leader
  1. Carries a **vision** (of the future) in his mind's eye—a **goal**, a **destination**, an **end result** (high expectations precede high performance)
  2. Quantifies/understands **status quo**
  3. Communicates/earns collective commitment to the **"vision"**
  4. By eliciting **participation** in goals/alternatives/strategy **formulation** and **execution** in getting from status quo to desired end result (see TACK common objective chart, Maslow's Hierarchy of Needs, and Johari Window)

  Definition of:
  1. Goal—A quantified desired end result/objective
  2. Strategy—Analagous to planning/preparing a military campaign
  3. Tactics—Execution on the field of battle
- Leadership—What **climate** does it need to **flourish** in/or **create**?
  - **Passion** for excellence
  - **Compassion** for/**understanding** of self/others (people want to be **LED**/not **managed**—motivation—self-fulfillment—carrot, not stick—ask any horse)
  - Commitment/determination/tenacity to **task**
  - Relentless pursuit of **knowledge/innovation** (A **picture** is worth a **thousand words**—an **idea** is worth a **thousand pictures**)
  - Interdependence → dependence → predictability—trust
  - Using **management** tools and techniques to **release** human potential

LEADERSHIP MYTHS

- Leaders are **born**, not **bred**
- Leadership is a **scarce commodity**
- Leaders are **charismatic**
  (Charisma is an effect, not a cause of leadership)
- A leader is a **"puppeteer"**
  (Leaders lead from the front, "managers" drive from behind)
- Leaders are needed/found **only** in most senior positions

COMMITMENT

Public Agenda Forum 2 undertook a major survey of the American nonmanagerial work-force not long ago, with the following disturbing results:

- Fewer than one out of every four job holders say that they are currently working at full potential.
- One half said they do not put effort into their job over and above what is required to hold onto it.
- The overwhelming majority, 75 percent, said that they could be significantly more effective than they presently are.
- Close to six out of ten Americans on the job believe that they "do not work as hard as they used to." (This may or may not be true, but it's their perception.)

Even more troubling is the possibility that the tendency to withhold effort from the job may be increasing. A number of observers pointed out that a considerable gap exists between the number of hours people are paid for working and the number of hours spent in productive labor. There is evidence that this gap is widening. A University of Michigan survey shows the difference between paid hours and actual working hours grew by 10 percent during the 1970s.

EXAMPLES OF IMPORTANT LEADERSHIP STUDIES

Do I:

1. Set the task of the team?

2. Make leaders accountable for teams of 4–18; give all leaders instruction in the **three circles**?

3. Plan the work, pace its progress, and design jobs to encourage the commitment of individuals and teams?

4. Set individual targets after consulting and discussing progress with each person regularly, at least once a year?

5. Delegate decisions to individuals? Where I make decisions do I first consult those affected or their representatives?

6. Communicate the importance of each person's job; explain decisions to help people apply them; brief team monthly on progress, policy, and people?

7. Train and develop people, especially those under 25; gain support for the rules and procedures; set an example and "have a go" at those who break them?

8. Care about the well-being of people in the team; improve working conditions; deal with grievances and attend functions?

9. Monitor action; learn from successes and mistakes; regularly walk about each person's place of work, observe, listen and praise?

The Industrial Society, London (England).

THEORY X/THEORY Y
Douglas McGregor

Theory X: Employees dislike work and will avoid it if they can. They cannot be trusted and need close control. They always prefer security, avoid responsibility, and are anti-organization.
None of this applies to managers.

Theory Y: Employees see work as a part of life, as natural as sleep or recreation. Under the right circumstances, they can be trusted to achieve objectives. In the right climate, they will accept, even seek, responsibilities and identify with company objectives.

BRINGING STRUCTURE TO STRATEGY

In the belief that a picture is worth a thousand words, the following charts attempt to show in graphic form how some of the more important topics already dealt with individually in previous chapters, are **integrated into a cohesive whole**. See Figures 13-2 through 13-6 and Table 13-1.

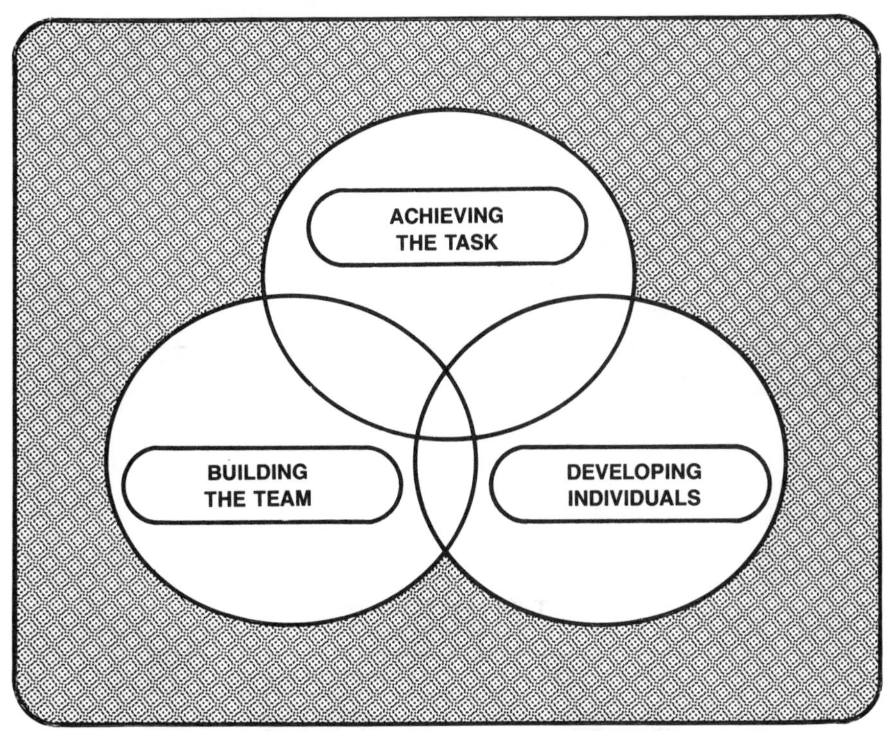

Figure 13-2 Action-Centered Leadership

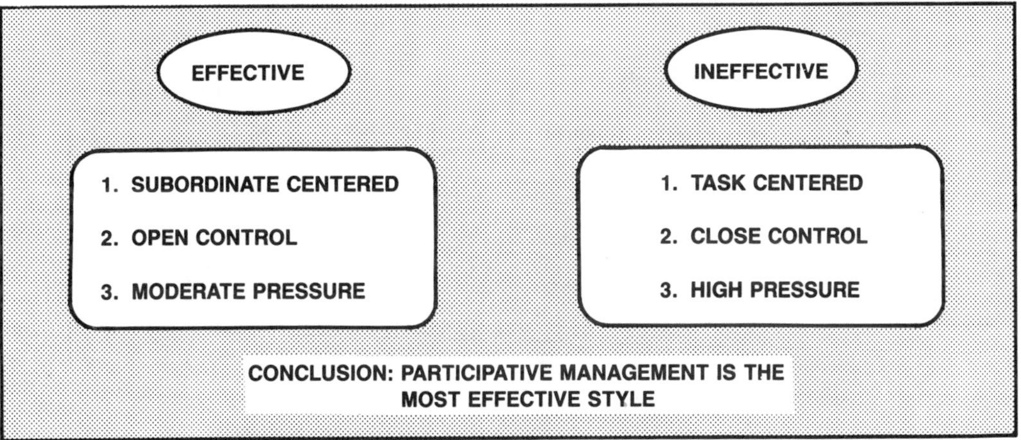

Figure 13-3 Effective Leadership
Rensis Linkert

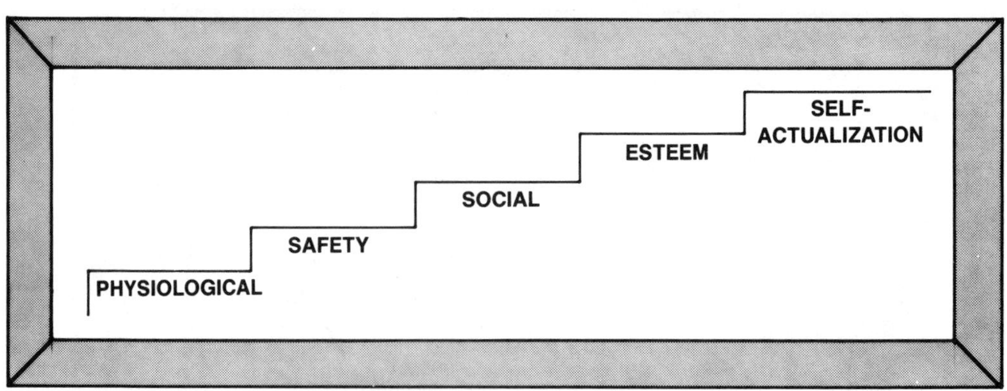

Figure 13-4 Hierarchy Of Needs
Abraham Maslow

Table 13-1 Motivation
Frederik Herzberg

Hygiene Factors	**Motivation Factors**
Dissatisfaction	**Satisfaction**
Company Policy	Challenge
Supervision	Job Interest
Personal Relationships	Feedback
Renumeration	Responsibility
Job Security	Personal Development
Physical Conditions	
Status Symbols	
←—— Environment	Job Itself ——→

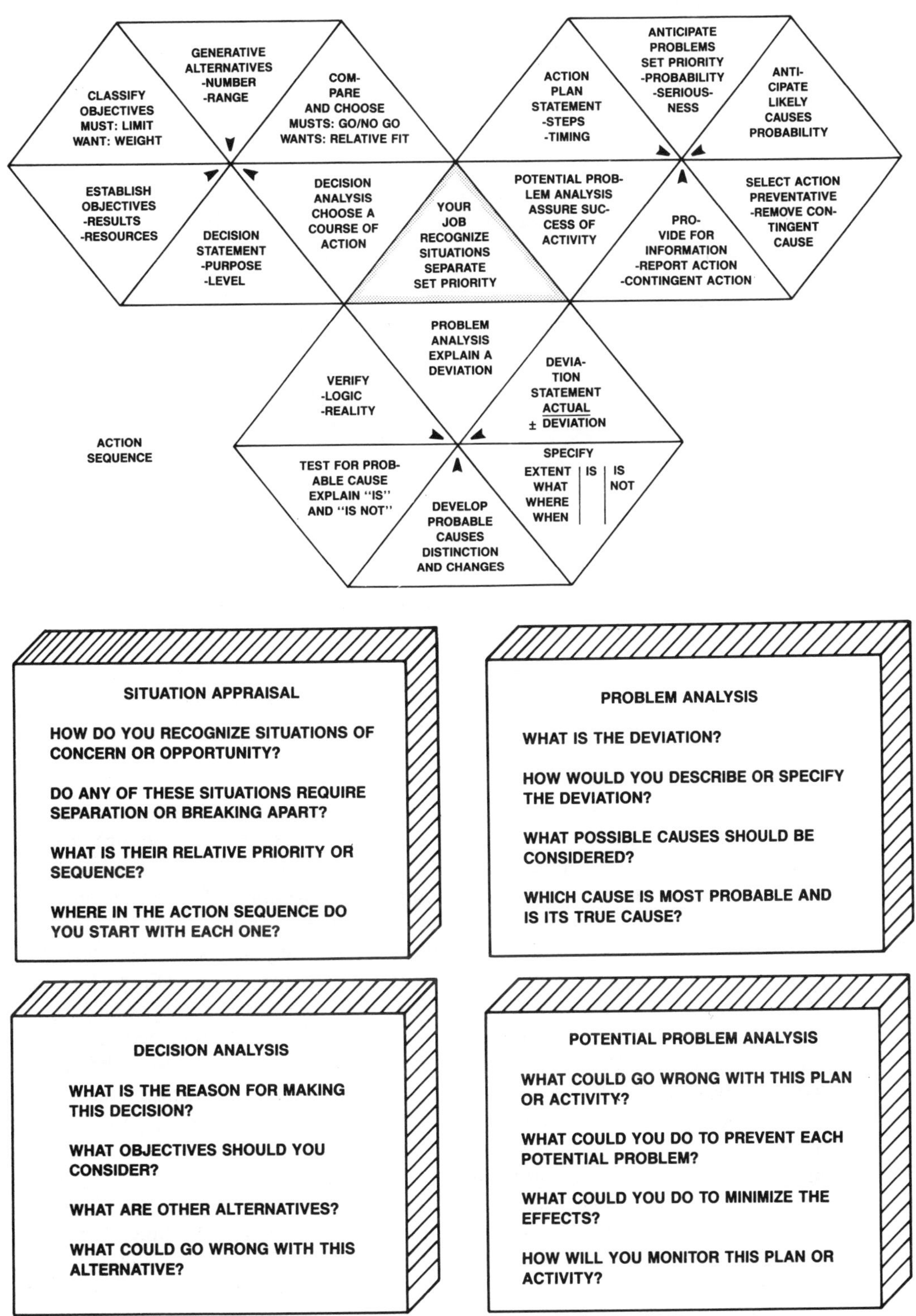

Figure 13-5 An Example of Structured Thought Process in Problem and Potential Problem Analysis

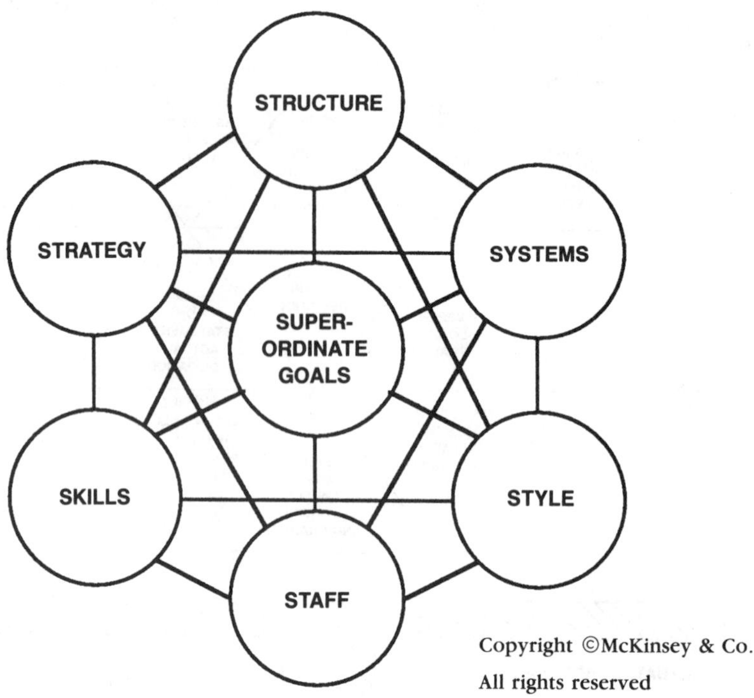

Figure 13-6

In its rightful place at the top of this strategic, hierarchical structure, is **profit—the superordinate goal of all businesses**—regardless of their product or service, market, whether publicly or privately owned, or any number of other distinguishing features. (How these profits are distributed between internal and external uses is outside the scope of this text. Only its creation has been addressed here.) The way in which profit has historically been measured in **the standard cost accounting system** has been dealt with at some length in Chapters 4 through 9. More importantly perhaps, how the performance of a manufacturing business should be measured—in terms of **process accounting** and **RONA**—**r**eturn **o**n **n**et **a**ssets rather than just as **PBT**—**p**rofit **b**efore **t**ax on sales—has also been discussed. This modified approach is particularly appropriate in the modern world as businesses migrate to **short cycle-time manufacturing**, requiring much lower levels of inventory, and as they become, with increasing automation, less direct labor, but more indirect labor and capital intensive. We concluded in fact, that **world-class manufacturing demands world-class accounting**—that being able to measure, quickly and accurately, those things within the factory which must be measured—rather than can be measured—is at least as important as measuring inventory and fulfilling the external reporting requirement. The importance of understanding not only the accounting but also the **fundamental economics** of the business and the industry of which it is part has also been treated in some depth.

From our study of the work on "learning" curves, "experience" curves, "opportunity" curves—call them what you will—in Chapters 7 and 12, we have learned that in a business such as semiconductors, for example, with such a **high fixed cost infrastructure** in proportion to total cost, that **market share**, the next level down in the hierarchy, **is a prerequisite to profit**. (We also learned that market share should be **measured in units** as well as dollars.) We confirmed that only with high volume, captured by **aggressive, future cost based pricing**, can the opportunity and incentive to minimize fixed cost per unit be won—but that **the means to drive these product costs down**, in the form of product and process engineering resources, **must then be provided**. We also learned that the lower our **break-even fixed cost**, the more successful we were likely to be in this respect. Another important observation of our study of learning curves was that of cycle-time, that to minimize cycle-time (**the period**) and thus **maximize** the number of **cycles of learning** in a given time (**the frequency**) was at least as important as applying the folklore in its classic sense.

We convinced ourselves that market share can only be won and held by providing **total customer satisfaction**. What this means—its composition in terms of essential, **nonmutually exclusive ingredients**, varying only according to the nature of the product, is shown in the next level down and consists of **(1) product functionality, (2) quality/reliability, (3) price/cost, (4) on-time delivery, and (5) total service.**

Product Functionality—the task of defining and designing these new products with which to create and sustain a living product portfolio, each designed for **zero defect manufacture** as well as for **high product performance**, has been treated at length in Chapters 1 and 2, again in the context of the new product life cycle. (The need for shortest possible cycle-times here is at least as great as for that in manufacturing.) The point was made that **distinctive competence in phase 1** of this cycle—the product introduction stage, where **product innovation** is at a premium—**creates opportunity in the marketplace**. However, **only with distinctive competence in phase 2—in process innovation and manufacturing excellence—can this opportunity be converted into positive cash flow and profit**. So critical in fact are these competencies, that the opinion was expressed that the battles currently being fought around these between East and West will determine who will be the ultimate victors in the industrial war currently being waged. The point was emphasized that product functionality was of paramount importance during the first phase of the new product life cycle—that to have less than distinctive competence in this rendered all other ingredients academic. We further concluded that to provide all of these ingredients over a broad product portfolio, to a wide customer base, we needed to rise to the challenge of **managing mix**. We discussed how to provide these ingredients in a nonmutually exclusive way, using **group technology** and **focused factories** to avoid the historical precedent of having to trade off one against the other, at the expense of customer satisfaction.

Pricing strategy, again in the context of the lessons learned in understanding the relationship of our fixed and variable costs with volume, was also discussed. Designing a pricing strategy based on future, projected costs, in order to give rise to a **desired end result, self-fulfilling scenario** in terms of high volume loading was described. Some of the major components of these product costs are shown in Figures 13-7 and 13-8. In a global context, where **product transfer price can be regarded as a cost** to the intermediate buyer, a discussion of the management of these costs was included in Chapter 8.

Manufacturing's role in contributing to total customer satisfaction by **accepting ownership for the quality, cost, and on-time delivery ingredients, and in assuming the mantle of the primary agent of change** has also been discussed. The need to apply manufacturing as a **strategic** rather than as a **tactical** weapon was stressed. That any

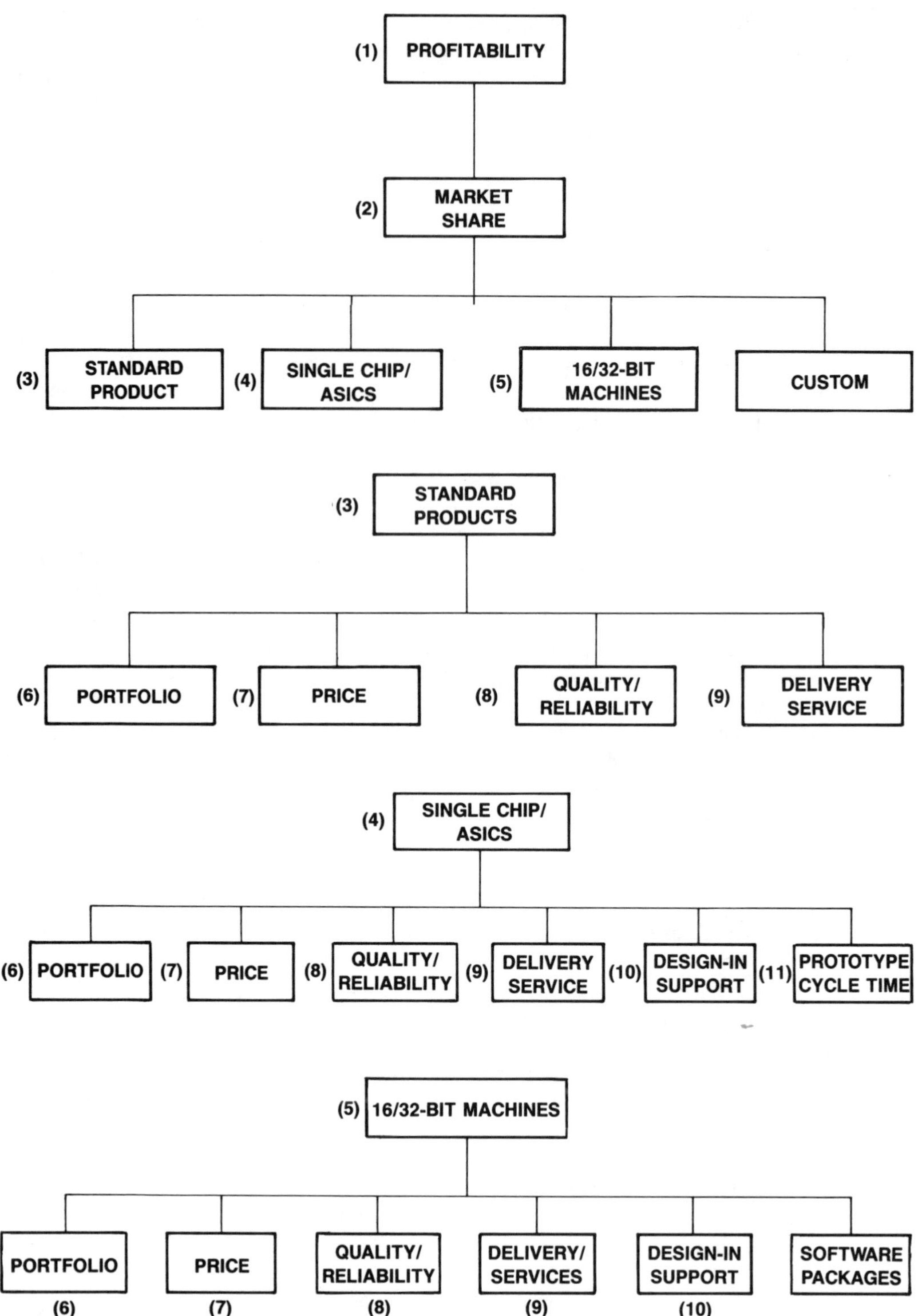

Figure 13-7 Strategic Hierarchy

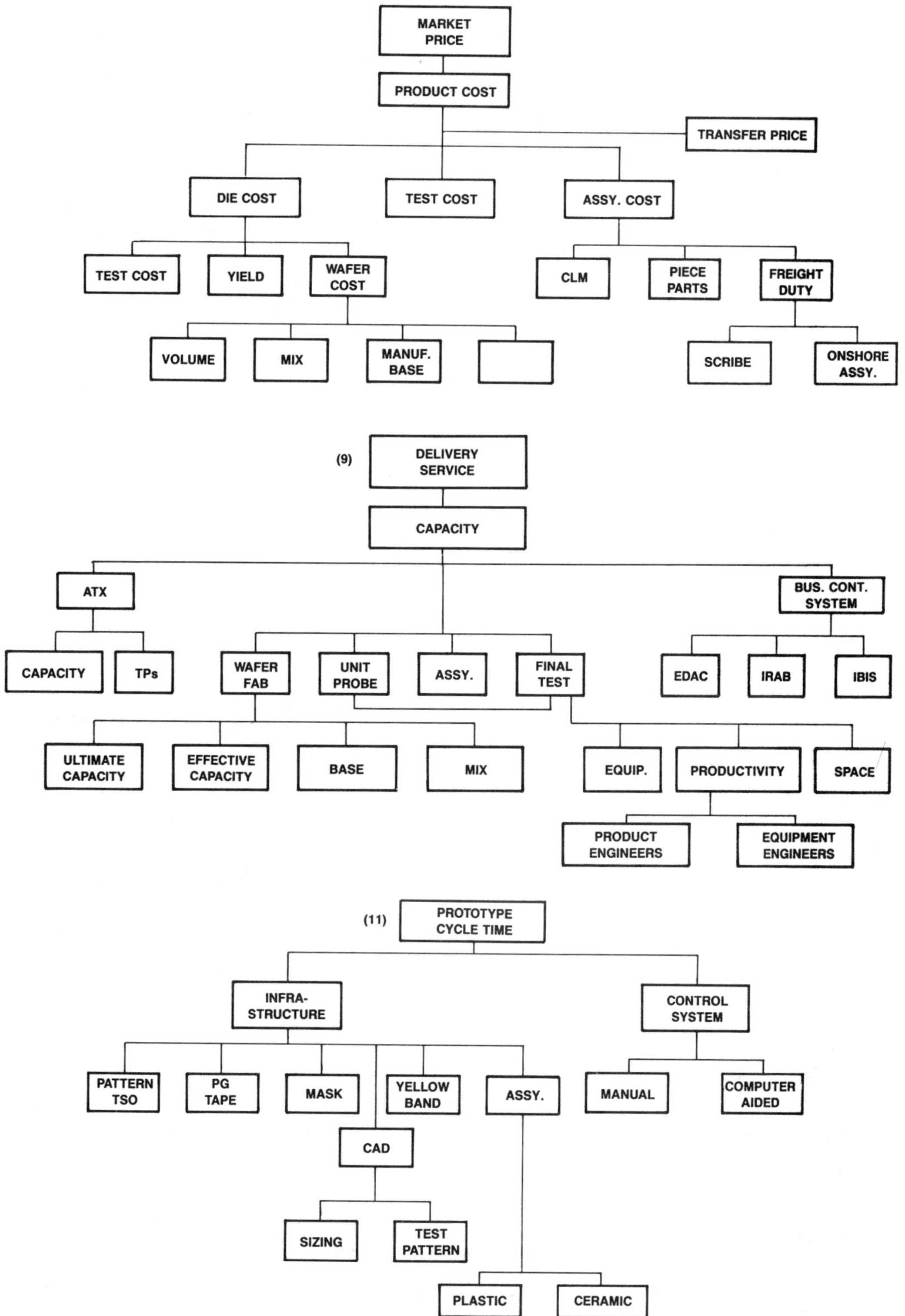

Figure 13-7 (continued)

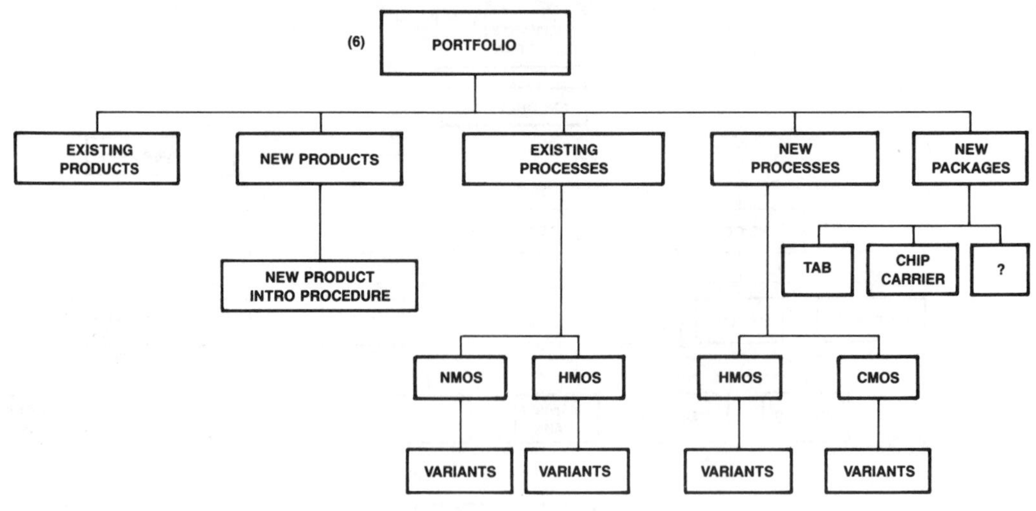

Figure 13-7 (continued)

PRODUCTION PLANNING AND CONTROL—INVENTORY CONTROL

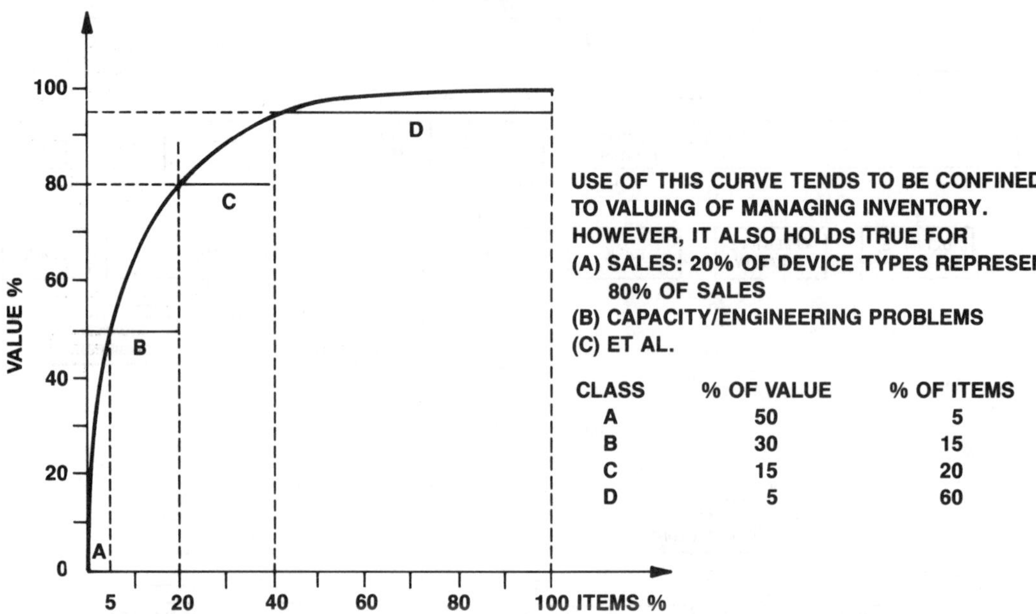

USE OF THIS CURVE TENDS TO BE CONFINED TO VALUING OF MANAGING INVENTORY. HOWEVER, IT ALSO HOLDS TRUE FOR
(A) SALES: 20% OF DEVICE TYPES REPRESENT 80% OF SALES
(B) CAPACITY/ENGINEERING PROBLEMS
(C) ET AL.

CLASS	% OF VALUE	% OF ITEMS
A	50	5
B	30	15
C	15	20
D	5	60

In 1897 Wilfred Pareto, an economist, demonstrated the lognormal pattern of distribution of wealth. This pattern appears in nature in any group of activities or articles representing a certain total amount of time or value.

Mathematicians refer to the Lorenz rather than the Pareto curve, though both are the same.

In the example above as applied to inventory control, 5% of the total items in any inventory represent 50% of the total value. 20% of the total items represent 80% of the value; 40% of the total items represent 95% of the value. The remaining 60% of the items represent only 5% of the total value. It is from this distribution that the so-called 80/20 rule originates. 80% of the value of inventory is reprsented by 20% of the items. Thus, an "A.B.C." classification of inventory can be built up as a basis for control.

Figure 13-8 Pareto or Lorenz Curve—A.B.C. Classification —80/20 Rule

such manufacturing based strategy should address **dealing with uncertainty** of customer demand, of supplier delivery and quality, and of factory execution by using **modern manufacturing approaches such as SCM and JIT**. The need to deal with uncertainty by **reducing cycle-time** and **increasing flexibility** and **responsiveness**; by organizing our resources into focused factories within a factory rather than by depending on forecasts and by building inventory; and then **using the money saved in inventory carrying cost to fund the evolution of automated flexible manufacturing systems**, was described in Chapter 6.

We discussed the major components of any successful manufacturing strategy—those of **visibility, execution, and control** of what needs to be done, when, by whom, and how. All of these components are needed in order to ship high quality products at lost cost and on-time. There is a need to deal with the problems of **"islands of information"** in the factory office before attempting to deal with the problems of **"islands of automation"** on the factory floor. In this respect, there is an absolutely indispensible need for a system such as **IBIS (described in Chapter 12).**

At the next level down, we begin to diffuse into the complexities of the manufacturing infrastructure itself, where the "war on waste" can begin to be fought in earnest. We saw that this process must begin, contrary to the arms length relationships of the past, with **close collaboration** between the many functionally specialized groups involved in the design and manufacture of new products, and by managing these resources and this process as a **totally integrated system**. As was stated earlier, we concluded that this process requires that the design community must design quality in using the **DFM techniques** described in Chapter 3 and that the manufacturing community must complement this by providing operations capability under **statistical process control**, as described in Chapter 14. In effect, that quality should be designed and built into the product rather than the traditional approach of designing and manufacturing the product in virtual isolation and then inspecting rejects out using lot sampling plans. We deal with the issue of identifying where, on the **manufacturing continuum**, our operation lies, where it needs to be, what needs to be changed to get there, and how these changes should be introduced by **building layers of competence**.

The kind of new **molecular organization structures** required to support this kind of approach, instead of the old, **functional hierarchies** of the past, were discussed in Chapter 6.

In Chapters 15 and 16, we develop the argument that the **process of renewal** must begin with **people and existing systems first** and with automation later—in effect, by making best use of what you already have. That becoming world class does not necessarily mean replacing what already exists by state of the art automation—that a manual system which does not work is not likely to be replaceable with an automated one which does. We argued the case that robots should be used for tasks which humans cannot or should not do—not as a mechanical facimile of a human being. Much work still remains to be done in facilitating communication, much less cooperation, between machines across CIM networks. Good product and process engineering will bring more immediate, less costly, more lasting benefits, than investment in new equipment—or in trying to escape to some low cost labor region of the world—a reminder that **there is more to competing than direct labor cost**. There is a place for **artificial intelligence**, but at its very embrionic stage of its evolution, any activity in this should for the time being, be regarded as **part of the learning process for the future** and **not as a practical solution to the problems of the present**. Suffice it to say that blessed are those who have the will to be world class but are too poor to make the mistake of thinking that plunging into automation or delegating/abdicating to consultants is the panacea. There is **no substitute for self-help and hard work**.

Finally, knowing what it takes to become world class is now fairly common knowledge. The desire to be so is equally popular. But proceeding beyond this point, converting vision and desire into reality, is what distinguishes the few from the many, action from rhetoric. The transition is usually one involving enormous change—and **change** is **almost always resisted by the inertia of the prevailing system**. It is here that bold, extremely resolute, and patient leadership in manufacturing, is indispensible. There are a thousand frustrations, many of them self-imposed by the system itself according to its coefficient of diffusion—the degree to which change is accepted by, and transmitted through, the infrastructure—to daunt all but the very determined. In such an environment, **without passion, there will be no excellence**. There might not even be any self-imposed change for the better at all, only the **perpetuation of mediocrity** until external events, manifesting themselves in lost market share and deteriorating financial performance, demand to be acknowledged. Senior management may well articulate the need for change, and even how it is to be implemented but only through zealous commitment in the manufacturing leadership ranks will this be carried beyond simple lip service. Managing change means understanding needs not only of the task but of the individual and of the group of which he or she is part. As managers we must **earn commitment** by making these needs concentric and overlapping by developing mutually beneficial goals, and then **testing any such change for efficacy and permanency by applying the pressure test**.

In any manufacturing business, marketing is the ship's pilot and navigator; design and engineering are her artificers; management represents the captain and complement of officers on the bridge; the factory is the ship's engine. To those with an ear for its music, much can be told from its tune. The manufacturing manager, the conductor of the great orchestra of manufacturing, is a member of a profession historically held in low esteem because the work was considered to be neither important nor challenging. Now hopefully, we know otherwise. As we have come to realize that manufacturing to us is a tactically employed, necessary evil. To the Japanese, it is a strategic weapon. In the final analysis, it is simply this perception of relative worth of manufacturing which, above all else in the grand scheme of business, will determine who is or will be world class and those who aren't—and never will be.

PRODUCTION PLANNING AND CONTROL—INVENTORY CONTROL

FACTORY OF THE FUTURE

14

Quality and Statistical Process Control in Integrated Circuit Manufacturing

A GENERAL DISCUSSION AND SPECIFIC APPLICATIONS EXAMPLE

Introduction

This chapter reviews conventional lot-sampling technique quality-measurement systems with particular emphasis on their tendency to misdirect an organization's resources in its quality thrust. The chapter then expands into exploring the merits of statistical process control (SPC) as an alternative approach by attempting to develop a universal model of the SPC concept and then discussing the application of SPC to a specific example operation.

QUALITY CONFORMANCE

Definitions/Measurement Systems

Product Quality—Conformance to Specification
Product Reliability—Quality over Time

AQL—Acceptable Quality Level (Sampling Plan). An AQL sampling plan measures that quality level which is considered acceptable as a process average. It is most commonly expressed as percent defective. The sample must be of sufficient size to guarantee that a product lot will be acceptable 95 percent of the time. (AQL is usually specified with a 95 percent "confidence level.") For example, an AQL of 0.4 percent means that the producer has a 95 percent confidence level (out of 1,000 units delivered, no more than four are defective). The producer also has reason to expect that 19 out of every 20 lots shipped will be accepted by a customer testing to the same AQL.

Producer's risk is the probability that a lot with an acceptable quality level will be rejected by the customer's sampling plan. Using the previous example, the customer could pull a 20-unit sample which happened to contain four defective units. The customer would fail this lot and return it to the supplier, even though the other 995 units were good.

Consumer risk is the probability that a "reject" lot will be accepted by the customer sampling plan.

LTPD—Lot Tolerance Percent Defective (Sampling Plan). An LTPD sampling plan relates to quality levels which the customer would regard as unacceptable. This approach assures that each lot of units with an unacceptable percentage of defects will be rejected. A confidence level of 90 percent (or customer risk of 10 percent) is commonly used. For example, if LTPD is specified at 2, then 90 percent of the time, a lot with more than 2 percent defective units will be rejected.

While for a given lot size and sample size an AQL and LTPD can be chosen which are equivalent, the AQL will change if the lot size changes significantly. LTPD is based on a statistically large enough sample size that increasing it would only increase the confidence level by approximately 5 percent. The decrease in confidence level from the AQL's 95 percent to the LTPD's 90 percent is partly explained by this phenomenon.

AOQ—Average Outgoing Quality. AOQ can be expressed as a fraction (e.g., 0.1) or as a percentage (e.g., 10 percent) defective. It is important to make the distinction here between outgoing quality, from QA gate and incoming quality to QA gate. If lots rejected at QA gate are rescreened, defective units being replaced by known good units, then the overall AOQ will improve. The best overall AOQ will be realized when either all of the lots submitted to the quality control gate are perfect (that is, there are no rejects) or when all lots are bad. Each lot that fails the gate criteria will be 100 percent rescreened with defective units being replaced with good units. The worst case will be when the defect lot distribution lies somewhere in between. AOQ will then be determined as a function of incoming lot quality, and the probability is that a lot will be accepted by the inspection procedure.

AOQ and AQL are sometimes confused. They are not the same thing.

An AQL of 0.1 percent does not assure an AOQ of 0.1 percent. In general, AQL is a set goal which can be met with a statistical probability by a sampling plan inspection. The equation relating AOQ to AQL is not simple since it includes the number of lots failing the AQL gate as well as the number of lots passing. Normally the AQL result is better than the AOQ.

PPM—Parts Per Million. PPM is used to express very small reject levels in easily understood terms: e.g., 100 PPM = 0.01% defective. Distinction is usually made as to the category of failure, i.e., whether a defect category is a combined electrical and cosmetic (visual) failure or whether each is measured separately. PPM values are difficult to guarantee in the same way that an AQL is guaranteed since the number of units which must be tested to accurately measure PPM is high.

PDA—Percent Defective Allowable. Prior to the emergence of SPC, which will be described later, all of the above have been most commonly applied to screening operations such as production test/QA gate or incoming inspection and are conventionally understood to be quality indices rather than reliability indices, although there are no theoretical limitations preventing their use in this context. The volumes normally associated with these operations have warranted the use of probability assurances based on the statistical evaluation of a sample, drawn from and considered to be representative of the total population sampled. Pre and post burn-in test data, which addresses reliability rather than just quality, is more usually expressed in terms of PDA since 100 percent of the population is being "sampled." PDA is the reciprocal of yield through an operation.

The burn-in operation is an accelerated life simulation, the data from which are used to extrapolate the probable defect profile (the bath tub). Early failures in this profile are due to "infant mortality," later failures to "wear out."

Historically, quality and reliability attributes have tended to be narrowly defined or at least measured only with respect to the product itself. Quality and reliability, in the broadest sense, can equally well be applied to the total output or end product of an enterprise. In this context, it is the quality and reliability of the total process of converting customer need to customer satisfaction which is important.

These requirements are to a large extent addressed in MIL-M-38510F and MIL-STD-883C. The need for conformance is not only confined to the product, measured on an independent lot-by-lot basis, but also to the process by which these products are manufactured. Product quality is, after all, a function of the quality of this process. These requirements can only be fulfilled by means of a total quality system (TQS), not just by concentrating the specialist QC/QA resources at gate prior to shipping the product, but by dispersing them to guide the application of the principle of building in quality at every step. Within this total quality system, SPC should be applied from product and process design through shipping, to at least the critical operations in this process. Many a product has failed conformance or has shipped delinquent due to a "quality" problem introduced much earlier in the process, including order entry.

SPC—Statistical Process Control. SPC represents a departure from measuring quality exclusively in terms of product attributes to one of measuring, analyzing, controlling and improving the attributes of the process by which the product is manufactured. Measuring product attributes can be regarded as a direct quality measurement. Measuring process attributes can be regarded as indirect. The relationship can be considered analogous to cause and effect. Statistics (state arithmetic) are simply a means of quantification (the technique of presenting measurement data) and will be dealt with only briefly by way of completeness. Some basic concepts and terms are described later.

The main theme of SPC has to be the second part of the expression, process control, with the emphasis on real time. A more appropriate acronym therefore might be RTPC (real time process control), safeguarding the unwary against a possible preoccupation with the statistics at the expense of engineering and controlling the process. Again, the emphasis must be on cause rather than on effect. A conventional quality system attempts to control a process or sequence of processes by measuring the output of that process or processes. This is obviously after the fact, especially if, as is usually the case, the product attributes are measured long after the product has been processed. This is entirely typical of the traditional gating system. The best that can be achieved with this kind of approach is that most, but not all, of the defective product will be prevented from appearing in the field, with costly and disruptive rework being undertaken on the defective population within the factory. At worst, the defects will not be correctable, resulting in low process yield, costly scrap rates and delinquent deliveries. Some may even elude our grasp and escape into the field.

SPC means many things to many people, but surely its value lies in it being pre-emptive and proactive rather than reactive. Process control means controlling the process rather than controlling the end product of that process. Control is usually and should be applied at the input of a system, not at the output. SPC addresses cause rather than effect. This approach is graphically depicted in Figures 14-1 to 14-16 which can universally represent any process. As before, output parameters are still measured and monitored, but so are process input variables. Even more importantly, the output is linked to the input via a correlation and feedback mechanism. Engineers will recognize this as a

EXAMPLES OF CHARTS USED IN CHARACTERIZING AND CONTROLLING PROCESSES

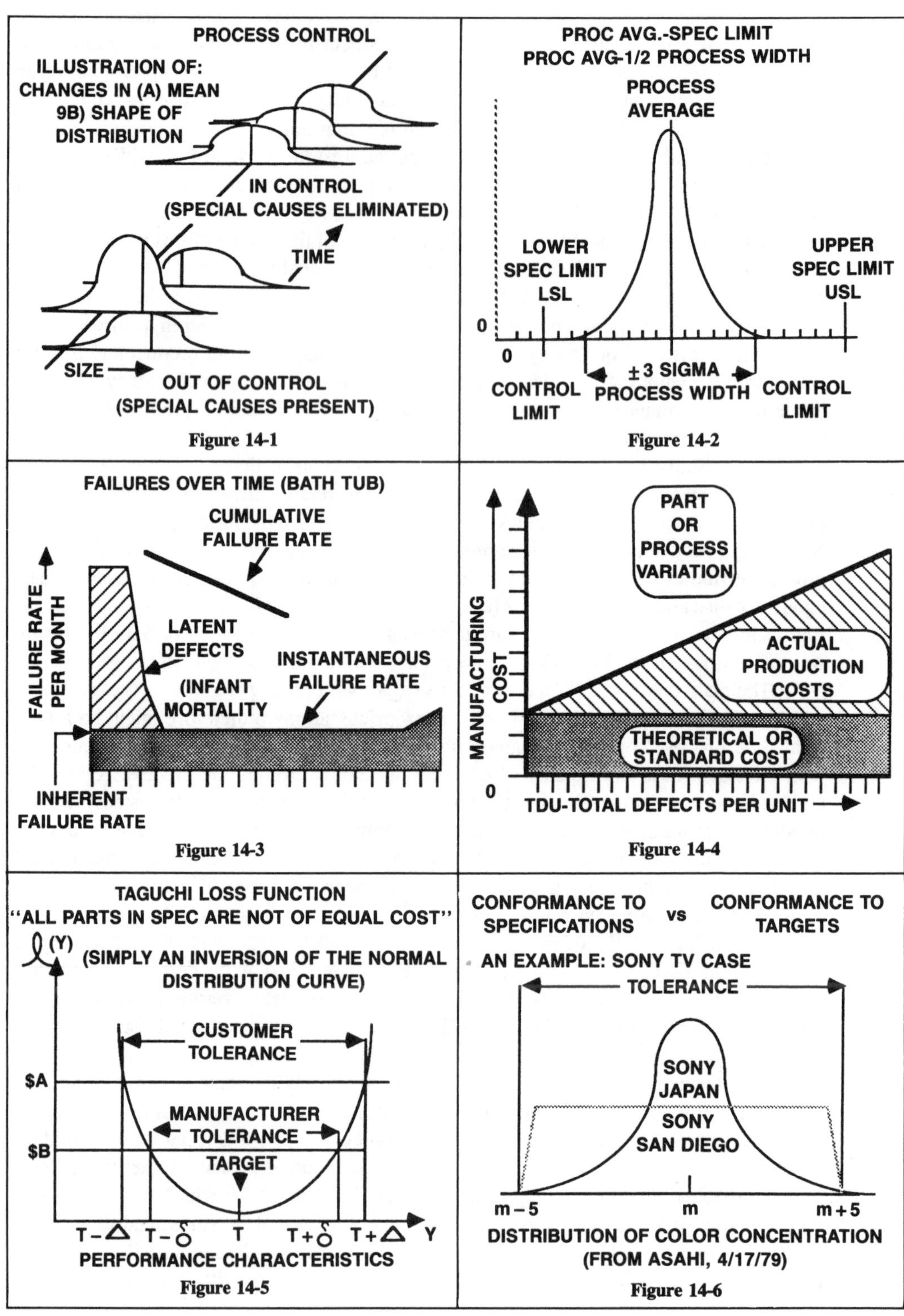

Figure 14-1

Figure 14-2

Figure 14-3

Figure 14-4

Figure 14-5

Figure 14-6

EXAMPLES OF CHARTS USED IN CHARACTERIZING AND CONTROLLING PROCESSES

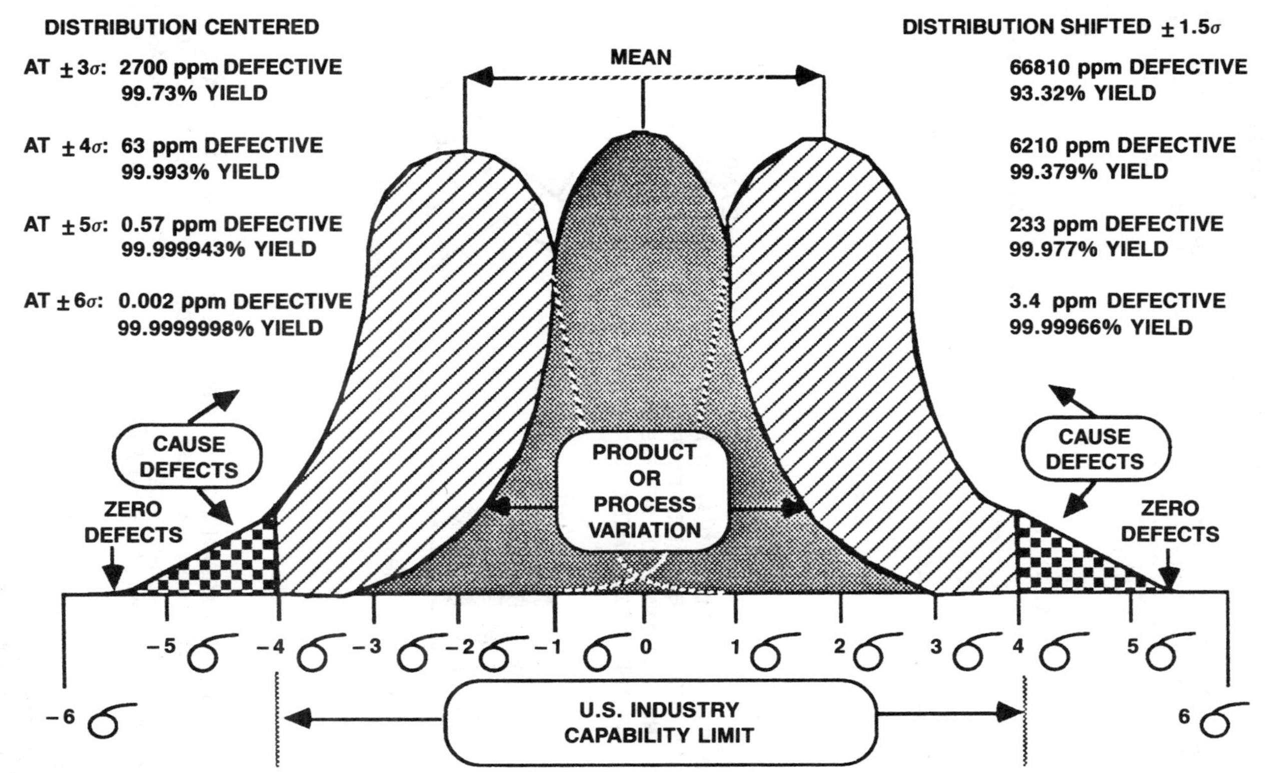

Figure 14-7

EXAMPLES OF CHARTS USED IN CHARACTERIZING AND CONTROLLING PROCESSES

THE CONTROL CHART IS THE BASIC TOOL OF SPC AND IS A GRAPH OF SOME CHARACTERISTICS OF THE PRODUCT PERCENT DEFECTIVE AS IT VARIES WITH TIME. IT USUALLY HAS CONTROL LIMITS ON THE GRAPH FOR GUIDANCE AS TO TOLERANCE LIMITS.

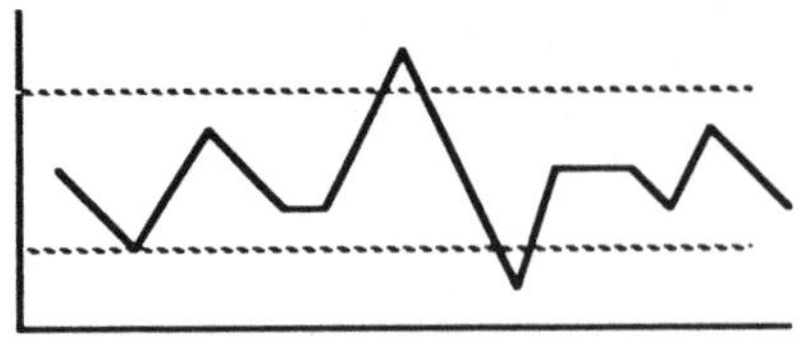

Figure 14-8 Control Chart

FLOW CHARTS DEPICT HOW A STREAM OF MATERIALS MOVE THROUGH A PROCESS. THEY ALLOW EASY UNDERSTANDING OF FLOWS AND ARE USEFUL FOR PICKING PLACES TO RECORD DATA.

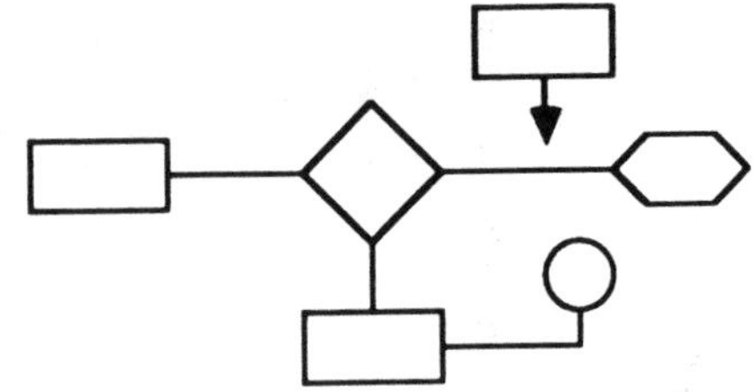

Figure 14-9 Flow Chart

A BAR GRAPH OF DATA THAT, AT A GLANCE, SHOWS THE SHAPE, CENTRAL VALUE, AND THE MANNER OF DISPERSION OF THE MEASUREMENT

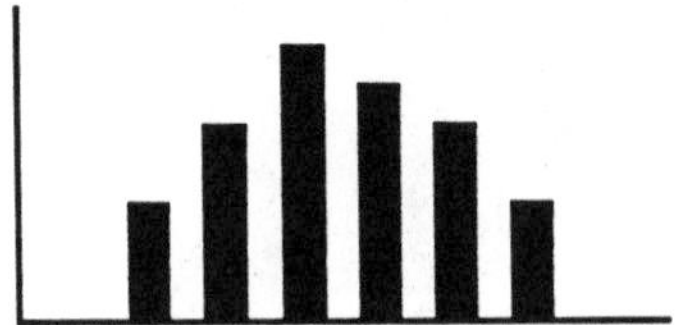

Figure 14-10 Histogram

THE CAUSE AND EFFECT DIAGRAM IS USED TO COLLECT AND LIST THE MANY FACTORS THAT AFFECT THE FINAL PRODUCT

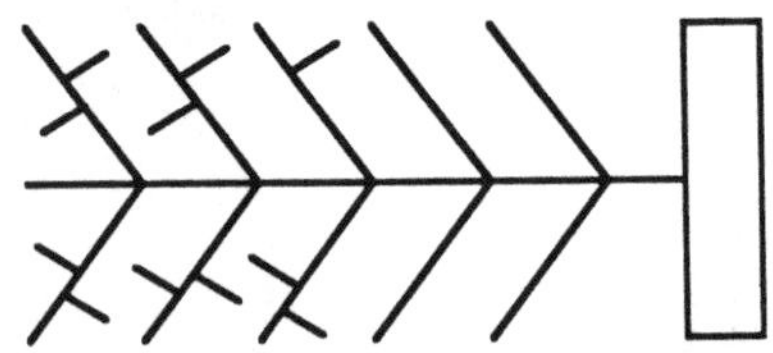

Figure 14-11 Fish Bone (Ishikawa) Diagram

A BAR GRAPH OF DATA ARRANGED TO SHOW THE LARGEST AND MOST IMPORTANT FACTORS IN DESCENDING ORDER. IT ILLUSTRATES THE MAJOR PROBLEM AREAS.

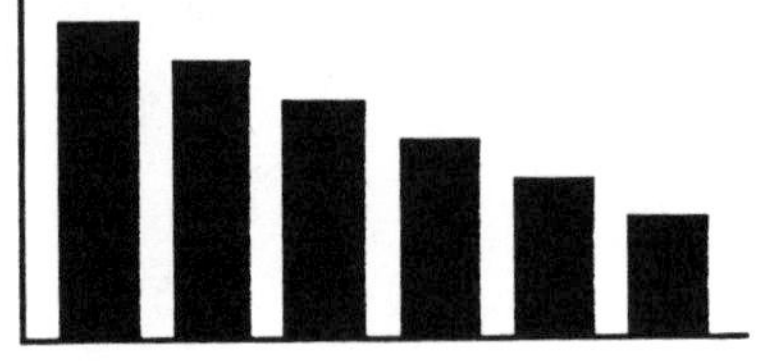

Figure 14-12 Pereto Diagram

ONE MEASUREMENT OF DATA DISPERSION IS THE DIFFERENCE BETWEEN THE MINIMUM AND MAXIMUM VALUES OF AN ATTRIBUTE IN ANY POPULATION

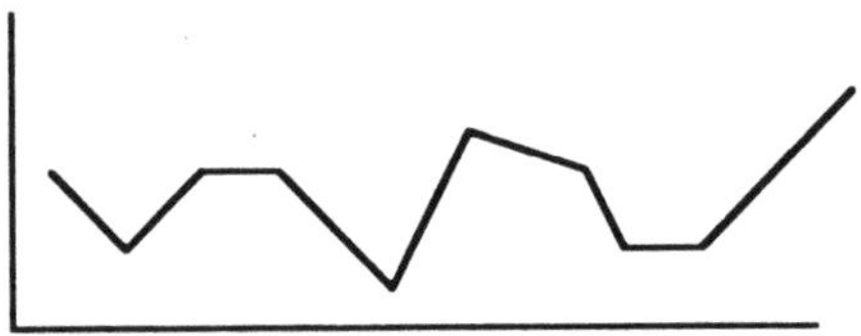

Figure 14-13 Range Chart

EXAMPLES OF CHARTS USED IN CHARACTERIZING AND CONTROLLING PROCESSES

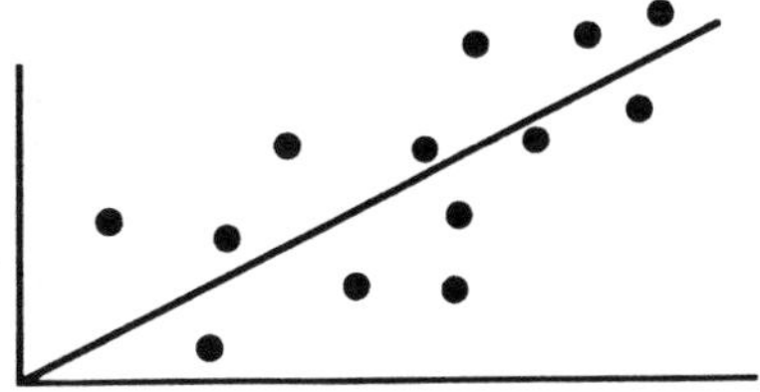

THE SCATTER DIAGRAM IS USED TO
ILLUSTRATE DISPERSION (SCATTER)
ABOUT A COMMON VALUE

Figure 14-14 Scatter Diagram

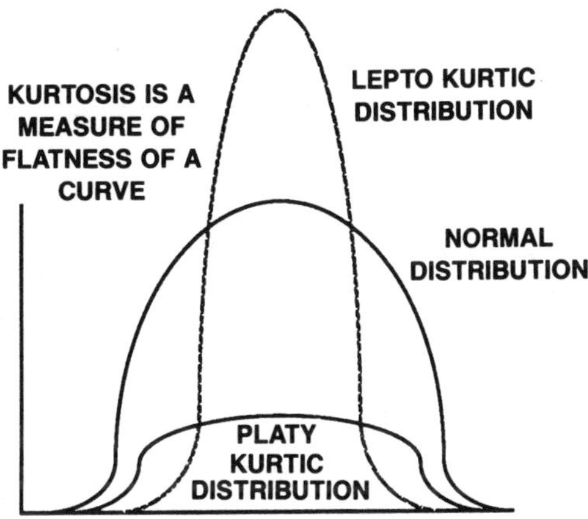

Figure 14-15

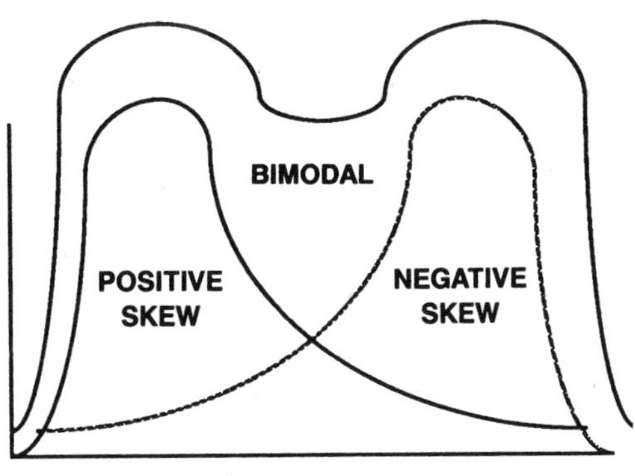

Figure 14-16

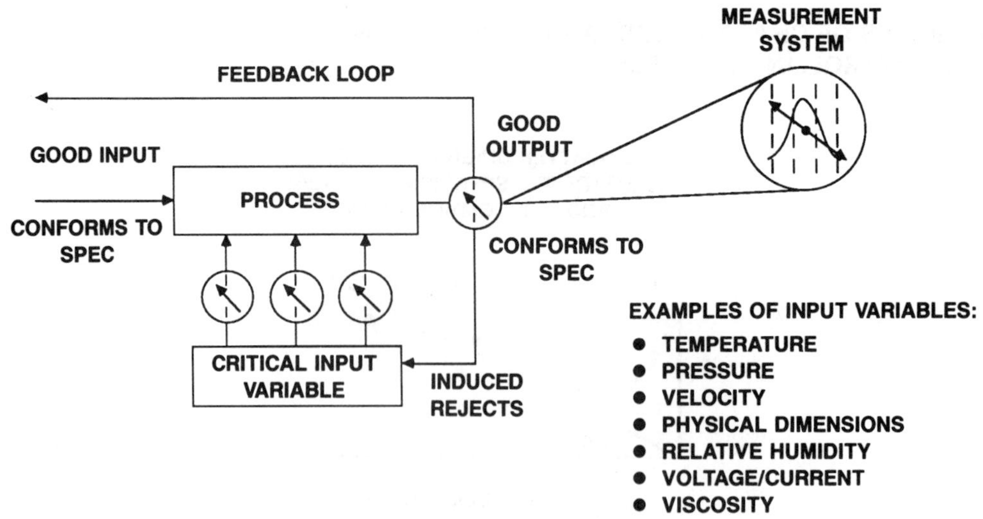

Figure 14-17 SPC Process Model

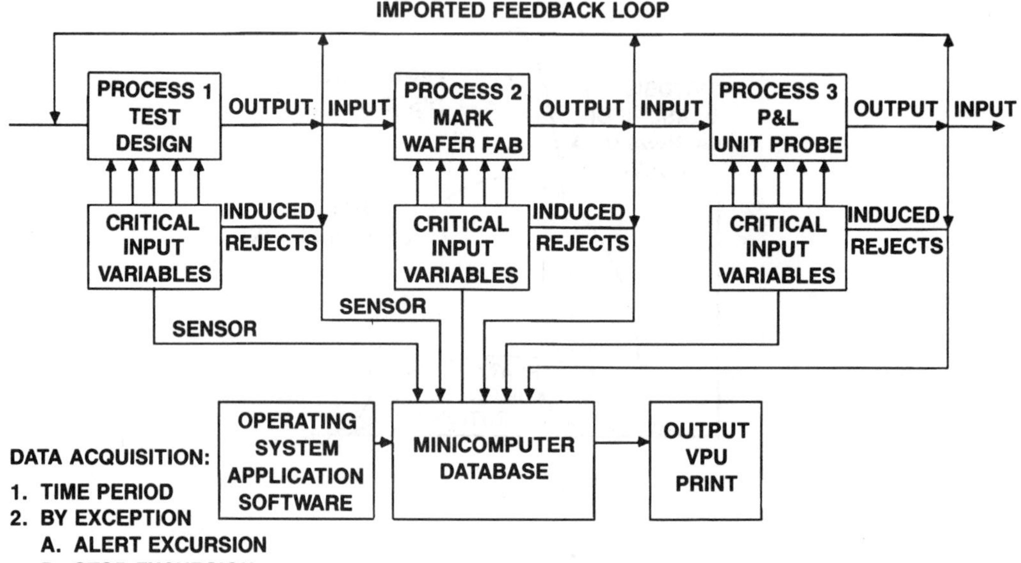

Figure 14-18 SPC Network

servomechanism based on the self-regulating feedback loop principle. The real essence of SPC then is real-time feedback: prevention is better than cure. If product attributes have been correctly correlated with the input variables of a process and monitoring of these variables show them to have remained within tolerance, then the output of this process, the product, will be within tolerance and conformant to specifications.

As the diagram in Figure 14-17 shows, rejects can be induced by the process under consideration, as well as being imported from up-stream sources, and it should be apparent that SPC can and should be applied to address this. In the case of the imported rejects, the feedback loop for the recipient operation would not only close back within itself but would also extend back to the output and input of the preceding operation or operations. (See Figure 14-18.) The feedback loop need not be confined to value added manufacturing operations; screening operations such as unit probe and final test are also legitimate candidates to be included in the network. For the really ambitious, design, sales, and marketing can also be included at the cutting-edge of the system. How else can one claim to have a total quality system?

Practical Implementation of SPC

General Approach

- **Identify critical operations in the process**
- **Identify critical/sensitive parameters in each operation**
- **Characterize these parameters—correlate output to input**
- **Define standard deviation limits—up to 6 sigma (standard deviations)**
- **Define technique/frequency of measurement**
- **Design and implement data acquisition and storage system**
- **Produce statistical analysis application software**
- **Develop data base structure and control chart format**
- **Define parameter drift/excursion alert threshold**
- **Define parameter drift/excursion stop threshold**
- **Identify sources/causes of variation (deviation)**
- **Define/provide resources to correct/improve deviation**
- **Close the feedback loop**

Product and Process Capability

Quality is free . . . but only if you pay your dues up front!

In a conventional lot sampling system of measuring and controlling quality, product is manufactured, assembled, and then 100 percent screened by comparing product attributes against pass/fail limits. Lots which pass this operation are then submitted to some form of quality control gating operation, usually an exactly equivalent operation with relaxed pass/fail limits, but tighter than those to which the product is specified to allow for machine to machine, or time dependent correlation differences. Samples are then pulled and the lot population from which they were drawn is dispositioned in one of five ways, depending on the results of the gating operation as follows:

1. **Sample OK (Population OK): Ship product**
2. **Sample Not OK: Place on hold pending engineering disposition: (a) rework, (b) rescreen, (c) scrap**
3. **Sample OK (Population not OK): Ship product (escape)**

Since conclusions about the population from which these samples are drawn are based on statistical probabilities, the lack of certainty inherent in this approach demands acceptance of the fact that, since there is a finite probability that in all disposition options, some varying proportion of the population will inevitably be reject product, this therefore, must be considered to be unavoidable, leading to the notion of consumer's risk. (Not surprisingly, this notion itself is becoming increasingly less acceptable to customers.) Producer's risk, the rescreening or reworking of a lot which the sample results may precipitate, but which the total population post-rescreen results may or may not subsequently confirm, is a manufacturing inefficiency accepted with equal stoicism. Not only does this approach not achieve consistently high levels of quality, the time involved and capacity consumed in dispositioning of lots to engineering hold or rescreen adversely effect on-time delivery and cost, creating much waste in the form of nonconformant product in the process of doing so. Also, since information feedback is not immediate, all work in process in a manufacturing system relying on this quality control approach is, until tested, of unknown quality and therefore, in jeopardy.

As we stated earlier, SPC is a radical departure from this discontinuous, toss-it-over-the-wall approach, so radical in fact that any transition from lot samplng to SPC should begin, first with a review of the shortcomings of the lot sampling approach, followed by an effort to develop a thorough conceptual understanding of SPC—not, as is so often the case, with a flurry of activity in creating control charts and developing training programs in statistics. (There are lies, damned lies, and statistics.) Such over-zealous, but premature and misguided efforts may produce nothing more than the busy work of recording history and the real potential of SPC may not be realized. SPC is not simply a change in technique—it is a change in culture—and such changes tend not to be effective if simply superficially cosmetic, but must permeate deeply into an organization's infrastructure, at all levels and to every function, if they are to be successful.

Step 1—Create receptivity to the need for change by reviewing limitations of lot sampling approach.

Step 1 in any transition to SPC, therefore, must be to review the lot sampling system, in order to reaffirm, communicate and convince all concerned that no matter how well refined, this approach alone can never deliver the new levels of quality performance required in today's fiercely competitive world; that only SPC, properly applied in enhancing sampling methodology, has this potential.

Step 2—Develop, based on the following principles, a complete conceptual understanding of SPC—not just the statistics!

1. Quality of the product is a function of the quality of the process by which it is designed and manufactured.

2. The design, engineering, and manufacturing organizations are responsible for quality—not the formal organization of that name.

3. Strategic thrust must be on:

a. Building in quality—not inspecting out rejects.
b. Emphasis must be on proactive prevention—not reactive correction.
c. Resource concentration must be on earliest cause—not on latest effect (symptoms).

4. Product must be designed for manufacturability, within tolerance (target)—not just for highest product performance. Yield, cost, and on-time delivery must not be compromised.

5. The process must be characterized and process potential index Cp and process performance index Cpk must be established; process output (product parameters) must be correlated to process input parameters.

6. Real-time feedback control is mandatory—automated if possible.

7. Excursions outwith alert/stop thresholds must precipitate immediate appropriate action, preferably under automatic control.

8. Maximum benefit is realized in a just-in-time (zero or low inventory) environment (no WIP jeopardy).

9. Materials delivered to each operation, both from preceding operations and external sources, must be controlled by SPC.

10. Complete process, from start to finish, must be flow charted including clerical transactions as well as physical movement of material. Any activity-adding cost, but not value, should be eliminated.

(Test screening is an obvious exception. This activity adds value to the product in the accounting convention sense, but obviously does not change the physical composition. As stated earlier, its purpose is either 100 percent production test screening or for purposes of measurement and analysis.)

Statistical Process Control—A Definition

Based on these principles then, a satisfactory definition of SPC might be as follows:

> Product quality is a function of the quality of the process (or system) by which it is designed and produced. Statistical process control represents a departure from the reactive—after the event—traditional lot sampling approach to measuring and controlling product quality, with its emphasis on inspecting out rejects—to the proactive approach of building quality into the product. This is done by **controlling the variability of critical input parameters of operations within a process**. This, within statistically derived and controlled, predefined alert/stop limits, correlated and linked with process output parameters, in a real-time feedback mode such that the values of means and scatter of the output population, and distribution profile, is also controlled within predefined limits.

This is a very comprehensive, but also very cumbersome definition. A much more succint definition is simply **to eliminate waste by controlling variability**. (A process in this context is considered to be a series of individual, but related, operations.)

Step 3—Define desired end result—for each critical operation and for the cumulative process.

While all of the aforementioned principles are important for successful implementation of SPC, one of the most fundamental is that of process capability. Not surprisingly, process capability must be judged in relation to the desired end result the process is expected to produce. Our goal must be to consistently produce populations of product whose attribute distribution profile lies within predefined tolerances defined in terms of standard deviations. (See Figure 14-1.) This raises the need to reconsider what, as perceived by the customer, is quality. Several definitions have been offered as follows:

- Fitness for use—Juran
- Conformance to requirements—Crosby
- Meeting expectations of the customer—Feigenbaum
- Meeting conformance to target (not specification) and the reduction of variability of all key characteristics of a process or product—Taguchi

These definitions apply to product quality, not quality in its broadest sense, that of total satisfaction to the customer. Feigenbaum's definition is the most complete in this latter respect but Taguchi's is the most pertinent with respect to product quality alone. (Issues other than product quality are discussed elsewhere.) With respect to product quality, we must then define for every critical product parameter, what is and is not an acceptable limit in relation to some PPM criteria required. (The ideal of zero defects, with high process yield, can only be approached incrementally over time.) Ideally, we would prefer all of the values for each of these parameters to fall within a very narrow, bell shaped or normal, Gaussian shaped curve whose mean is precisely located within narrow limits. To do so, both the variance of the location of the means and the scatter of the distributions for each specified attribute population needs to be precisely controlled as shown in Figure 14-2. (The relationship between process tolerance in terms of standard deviation and rejects in parts per million is illustrated in Figure 14-7.) The basis of the statistical treatment of different kind of parameters is provided in the appendix at the end of this section.

The Relevance of Standard Deviation—As a general rule, we already know from our basic statistics training, that in any curve of attribute distribution which is both unimodal and reasonably symmetrical about its average, we can, with little error, assume that approximately 66 percent of the attribute population occur within ± 1 standard deviation, 95 percent within ± 2 standard deviations and that less than 1 percent of the population occur outwith ± 3 standard deviations. (Curves encountered in real life on the factory floor are not of course normally so obliging. Part of the objective in characterizing a process is to engineer it such that the output is in fact normal.) We shall discuss later why even this apparently insignificant 1 percent is too much. Even a distirubiton centered at 5 sigma contains 57 parts per million defective. To even approach zero (0.002 ppm – 2 parts per billion) 6 sigma capability is required.

Step 4—Characterize process and establish process potential index (Cp) and process performance index (Cpk).

This involves establishing the degree to which the process is (or is not), capable of producing that predefined, desired end result in terms of its potential and actual performance. (It is implicit in our definition of SPC that some processes will not be capable of producing the desired end result and will require extensive process engineering treatment, perhaps even total replacement of the process. This can be the real test of the commitment to SPC, extending beyond simply lip service.)

Process performance index Cp is a measure of the natural or intrinsic capability of a process to produce the required characteristic. It makes no statement about the actual centering of the process.

Process performance index Cpk is a measure of the process performance index Cp adjusted for k to take into account any difference between the design nominal and the actual process where:

$$Cp = \frac{\text{Specification Width (design tolerance)}}{\text{Process Capability (total process variation)}}$$

$$= \frac{\text{USL} - \text{LSL}}{6\ \text{sigma}}$$

Cpk = Cp(1 – k) where;

$$k = \frac{\text{(Target nominal mean point – Actual process mean point)}}{\text{(USL – LSL)/2}}$$

USL = Upper specification limit of the parameter

LSL = Lower specification limit of the parameter

Both indices measure the relationship between product and process in unitless terms. (See Figure 14-1.)

Consider a design characteristic whose nominal value is specified at 10.00 mm with a tolerance of ± 0.1 mm. Assume that when we measure the output of the manufacturing process, we find the actual value of the mean to be 10.00 mm with a standard deviation of 0.05 mm.

A typical example of Cp and Cpk calculations in the semiconductor industry environment is the measurement of Tad (timing address delay) at 150°C. For this example, the design specification calls for a target delay of 90 ± 30 ns. A measurement sample yields a mean of 103.90 with a standard deviation of 1.97. The process limits are the mean value $\pm 3\sigma$ or 103.90 ± 5.91, i.e., a minimum of 97.99 and a maximum of 109.81.

With this information, we can now calculate Cp and Cpk.

$$S = 60 \qquad P = 6\sigma$$

$$Cp = S/P = 60/11.82 = 5.08$$

This illustrates that while process variability is under good control, the process is not well centered as shown by a relatively low Cpk as follows:

$$\overline{X} = 103.90; \text{ Design Target} = 90$$

Therefore

$$K = \frac{\overline{X} - D}{S/2} = \frac{103.90 - 90}{60/2} = \frac{13.90}{30} = 0.463$$

$$Cpk = (1 - k)Cp = (1 - 0.4633)/5.08 = 2.726$$

Process potential then is a measure of the natural ability of a process to produce output within tolerance (target) when only inherent or intrinsic variations are present; in other words, when environmental and imported variables are excluded from the system. (Some treatments of SPC advocate classifying the variables into two categories, assignable and random, with only the assignable causes being attacked. This can prove to be a less than complete approach.) As a general rule, the greater the value of this number, the tighter the tolerance the process is capable of maintaining. Cpk is a measure of the degree to which the process is performing to its inherent potential. Capability indices allow the information contained in a histogram to be represented by a single number. While this is convenient, it should be noted that since it deals primarily with the location of the mean of a population and not dispersion, it is not a totally comprehensive measure. This does not however detract from its usefulness in being able to predict the proportion of defects which any process so characterized will produce. Characterizing process capability, unlike pass/fail testing, requires that the complete operating profile of both product and process be quantified. The interface and interaction between device parameters and process parameters can only be characterized by a series of controlled iterations to establish the relationship of changes in the values of output with changes in the values of input parameters. This can be a very time consuming process. Not to do so does not prevent the shipping of product and is, therefore, most regrettably, often done badly, or not at all, resulting in low quality product being produced by an equally low yielding process. The cost incurred in characterizing a process can not be avoided—only deferred, usually in a dramatically escalating manner.

Step 5—Assuring stability of operation—micro managing change (variables).

Having established that both product and process, insulated from both environmental and imported variables, are indeed inherently capable of consistently producing the desired end result, how is the stability of each operation in the process to be assured? How can each individual operation in the process be insulated from these variables which would, if transmitted through into the system, cause excursions in the output outside of the process tolerance limits? It helps in this respect to classify these variables and attributes, which all operations have in common, into three broad categories:

Environmental	Imported	Inherent or Intrinsic
Ambient temperature	Incoming materials from:	Degree of precision
Relative humidity	1. Preceding operations	Stability/drift
Dust	2. External sources	Controllability
Vibration		Degree of difficulty
		Accuracy
		Reliablity
		Repeatability
		Tolerance

We can further classify these variables into:

Avoidable or unavoidable
Predictable or unpredictable
Gradual or immediate in their effect
Cyclically recurrent or sporadic and spontaneous
Constant or intermittent
Universal or specific
Controllable or uncontrollable

Test Screening versus Value Added Operations

Unlike value added operations, the desired output of a test screening operation such as unit probe or final test, or QA gate for that matter; is to classify a population, with highest possible confidence, into good and reject categories. A major input variable affecting this confidence is test equipment set-up integrity. RFT has been developed to address controlling this variable. (This discipline is an indispensible prerequisite to SPC for any equipment which is reconfigured to accommodate product changes.)

The Real Potential of SPC

To regard SPC as nothing more than simply yet another way to measure and control quality is to risk missing an enormous opportunity. It may well be in fact the single most important source of manufacturing productivity improvement which our industries so desperately need to regain competitiveness. Our predominantly functional approach to manufacturing of building inventory with quality controlled by lot sampling techniques, refined over the course of the years to a statistician's fine art, is extremely wasteful of material, human effort, capacity, time, customer goodwill, tolerance, and repeat patronage. SPC in conjunction with JIT, SCM, and some degree of automation, on the other hand, is an extremely economic approach to manufacturing, which the Japanese were quick to realize and perfect. This combination offers the greatest potential to optimize quality, on-time delivery, and cost in a nonmutually exclusive way by attacking variability induced waste. But while the returns are great, so too is the investment—not necessarily in money, but in commitment of time, effort, and determination. It can be a very traumatic experience to take an organization, which for years has focused on effects, through a transition to focus on causes. Prevention, as the doctor said, is better than cure, but to convince people, even intellectually, that what they have been doing since time immemorial is wrong, or at least no longer adequate is difficult enough; to change work habits ingrained over the years, is quite another matter. The propensity to defend status quo, continuing to deal with symptoms, rather than causes, will be quite institutionalized.

In addition to this, life has now become so complex, it is easy to lose sight of that which is fundamentally important as opposed to simply being a time trap or busy work. Very simply, it is to bring new products to the market, of high quality, at acceptable cost in a timely fashion. With much shorter product life cycles, the Japanese are in no less of a rush to get there than we are, but where they are systematic and thorough, we are too casual and wasteful. They do not relinquish the principle of doing it right first time as readily as we seem to be willing to do. A product rushed prematurely to market, not adequately engineered, built with an unworthy manufacturing process can create damaging, and very enduring, first impressions. There is a relationship between rework in the factory and rejects in the field which only appropriate resources, timely applied—up front during phase 1 and very early in phase 2 of a new product introduction cycle—can eliminate. The alternative, field retrofits and subsequent reiterations, is both wasteful and harmful. (Would you fly in new aircraft still being engineered after its maiden flight? The aircraft industry have found ways to avoid requiring us to do that. The same kind of approach is surely possible in other industries.) The greatest concentration of effort by the Japanese is during these early phases. Our way is to tend not to react until we are "overwhelmed by opportunity" in the form of a large, possibly delinquent backlog of orders, late in phase two, using "direct labor" to sift through the debris. We love a cavalry charge—the Japanese prefer to avoid the need for one. This is why their cumulative yields, in the case of our particular industry—finished goods per wafer started—can be two, three, and even four times greater than ours. The "insignificant" 1 percent defects per operation in a process consisting of upwards of 100 such operations has a very significant cumulative effect. The message is very clear. If we really want to compete, we must: **Eliminate waste! Do it right first time! Start now!**

Summary

1. Create receptivity to the need for change; review lot sampling technique limitations.

2. Develop conceptual understanding of SPC.

3. Flow chart the complete sequence of operations in the process (both material movements and clerical transactions)—apply SPC at earliest point for greatest benefit.

4. Develop training and implementation plan.

5. Define desired end result for each operation and cumulative process.

6. Characterize critical operations of the process and define process capability indices—(redesign if necessary).

7. Characterize product and define product capability—design for manufacture—(redesign if necessary).

8. Provide required process capability—develop/document/enforce best methods. Standardize operating procedures.

9. Ensure stability of the operation (controlling the process); establish a comprehensive, preventative maintenance program.

10. Apply the 80/20 rule to environmental/imported and intrinsic variables. Those due to the "system" are almost certainly more significant than the human operator.

NOTE

Relevance of 1.5 sigma. This number is arbitrarily chosen. This process is not allowed to shift more than this before corrective action is taken.

In applying SPC, we should bear in mind that it was developed for continuous flow processes such as petrochemicals—how do you separate misprocessed product for rework? That does not mean that it cannot be applied to a batch production process. In a manufacturing process in which the equipment of any operation is frequently reconfigured to accommodate product changes, for example, there is no point applying SPC to monitor the test operation on the specific product lot per se, unless all possible steps have been taken to ensure that the equipment has been correctly set up and is functioning properly prior to testing. This requirement can be fulfilled by developing, documenting and enforcing the disciplined procedure shown in the following flow charts. (See Figures 14-19 to 14-23 and Tables 14-1 to 14-4.) In any operation, there is an almost infinite number of both output and input parameters involved. The key to successful implementation is to select the output parameter most sensitive to most input variables. In this way, any deviation from tolerance will be detected.

On the subject of data acquisition, this can range from reading measurements from gauges and manually entering into the SPC data base through a keyboard, to the most elegant, where data acquisition is fulfilled automatically via temperature and pressure sensors, and electronically downloaded into the data base. It is the latter approach which is discussed in this example. The form in which data base storage is accommodated is open to choice. This can take the form of onboard machine memory or locally situated personal computers (islands of SPC), but problems of data exchange between operations and integration of the total data base are more difficult to overcome than with a common centralized data base. Even this approach is not without difficulty in machine-to-machine communications due to lack of network protocol standardization at all levels. Again, it is the latter approach which is considered in this example.

Recall that our ultimate goal is to achieve continuous process flow, with no discontinuity and disruption of either product or data due to unnecessary handling. SPC works best in a JIT environment where the benefit of feedback is immediate and the amount of defective WIP is minimized. It can work in the more traditional functional push system JIC provided the system is first flushed of all defective WIP. SPC is not, of itself, a panacea for high quality—it is the icing on the cake, but only if the infrastructure required to support it has been well engineered in the first place.

Nothing worthwhile is easily achieved but the reward for this effort will be an operation which builds quality into the product rather than have to depend on inspecting rejects out.

MEDIAN: MIDDLE VALUE.
MODE: MOST COMMONLY OCCURRING (MODAL) VALUE.

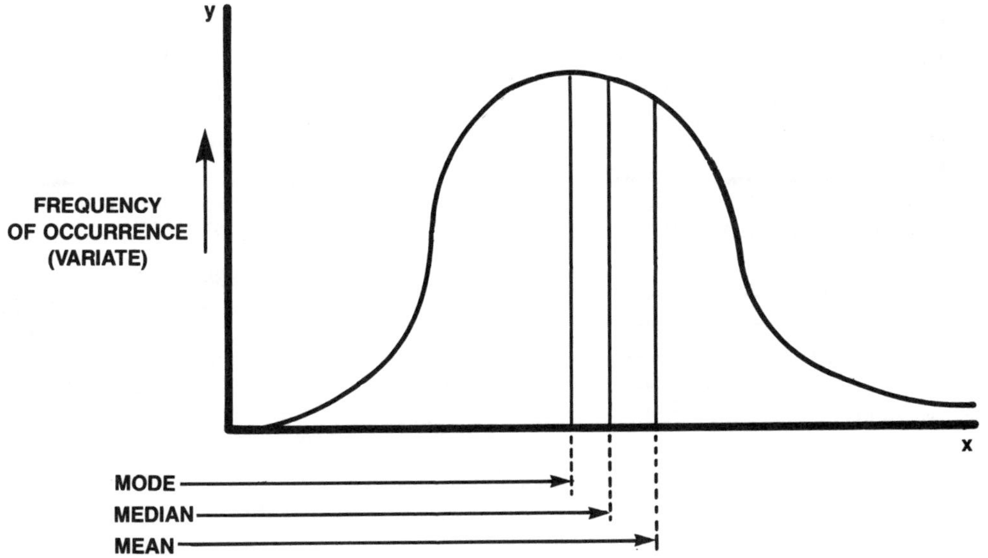

SCATTER (VARIANCE): A MEASURE OF VARIABILITY ABOUT THE MEAN VALUE.

UPPER QUARTILE: VALUE ABOVE WHICH 25% OF THE POPULATION APPEARS.

INTER QUARTILE: VALUE BETWEEN WHICH 50% OF THE POPULATION APPEARS.

LOWER QUARTILE: VALUE BELOW WHICH 25% OF THE POPULATION APPEARS.

DEVIATION: A MEASURE OF DISPERSION.

MEAN DEVIATION: $\frac{\Sigma|x-\bar{x}|}{n}$

VARIANCE: $\frac{\Sigma(x-\bar{x})^2}{n}$ (ROOT MEAN SQUARE)

STANDARD DEVIATION:

$$\sigma = \sqrt{\frac{\Sigma(x-\bar{x})^2}{n}}$$

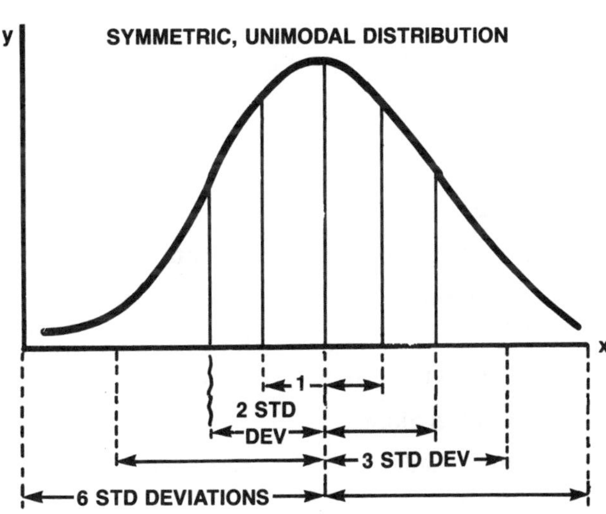

Figure 14-19 Frequency (of Occurrence) Distribution

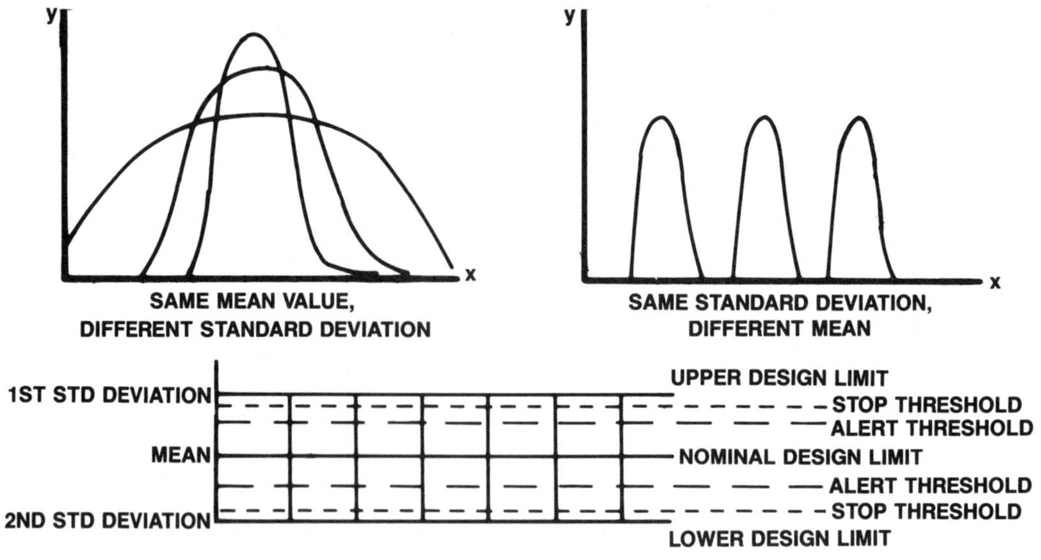

Figure 14-19 (continued)

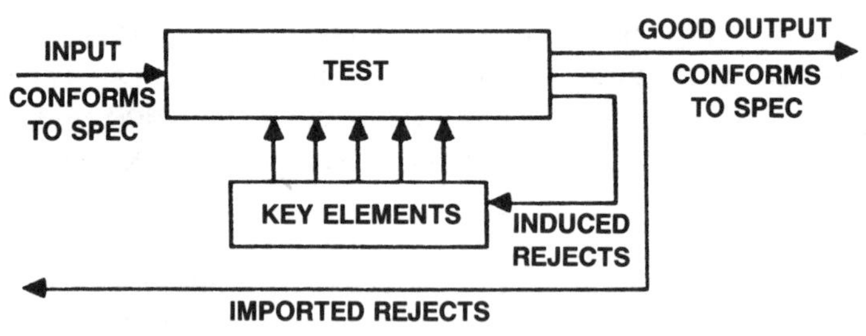

Figure 14-20

Table 14-1

Key Elements	Data Type	Comments
Test Site Temperature	Measurement	Constant readout to be read periodically
Contact Resistance	Measurement	Beginning of each set up
Pin/Pin Skew	Measurement	Once a week or board change
Bin Results 5% Sample	Attribute	By device type
Bin Results Total Lot	Attribute	By device type
Load BD/Handler/ Test Head	Attribute	By device type

Table 14-2

Action	Responsibility	Status
Complete standard operating procedures	Training Production Equipment Eng.	4/30
Establish standard set-up procedures	Training Production Equipment Eng.	4/30
Identify and implement additional key variable instrumentation requirements	Equipment Eng.	5/16
Set up initial measurement and attribute data bases	Equipment Eng.	5/16

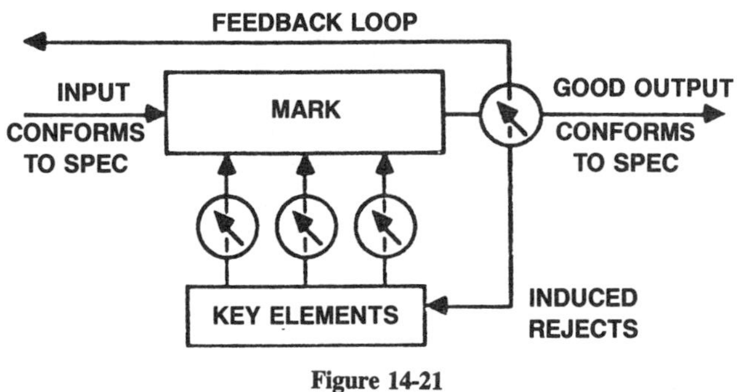

Figure 14-21

Table 14-3

Key Elements	Data Type	Comments
Heater Temperature	Measurement	Constant readout to be read periodically
Belt Speed	Measurement	Constant Readout to be read periodically
Ink	Measurement	Verify type and expiration
Permanency Results	Attribute	Each lot
Visual Results	Attribute	Each lot

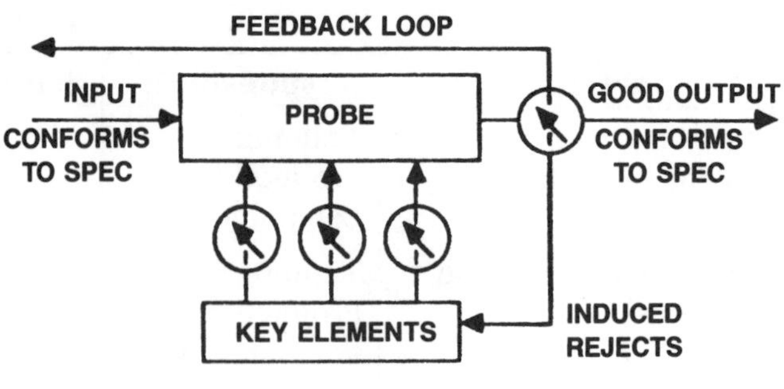

Figure 14-22

Table 14-4

Key Elements	Data Type	Comments
Probe Planarity	Measurement	Overdrive to chuck continuity
Chuck Temperature	Measurement	Periodically by device by prober
Opens	Attribute	By probe card by device
Yield %	Attribute	By test head by load board by device

BASIC STATISTICS

AVERAGE: Measure of the central tendency (mean).

ARITHMETIC MEAN: $\frac{\text{Sum of the measurements}}{\text{\# of measurements}}$

$$\underline{X} = \frac{X_1 + X_2 + X_3 + \ldots + X_n}{n} = \frac{\Sigma X}{n}$$

HARMONIC MEAN: $\frac{1}{\text{Arithmetic mean of the reciprocals of the values}}$

$$H = \frac{n}{\Sigma \frac{1}{X}}$$

GEOMETRIC MEAN: $G = \sqrt[n]{X_1 \bullet X_2 \bullet X_3 \bullet \ldots \bullet X_n}$

Averages are intended to be representative of the population. The nature/shape of the distribution determine which average is appropriate, e.g., avoiding distortions caused by extreme values.

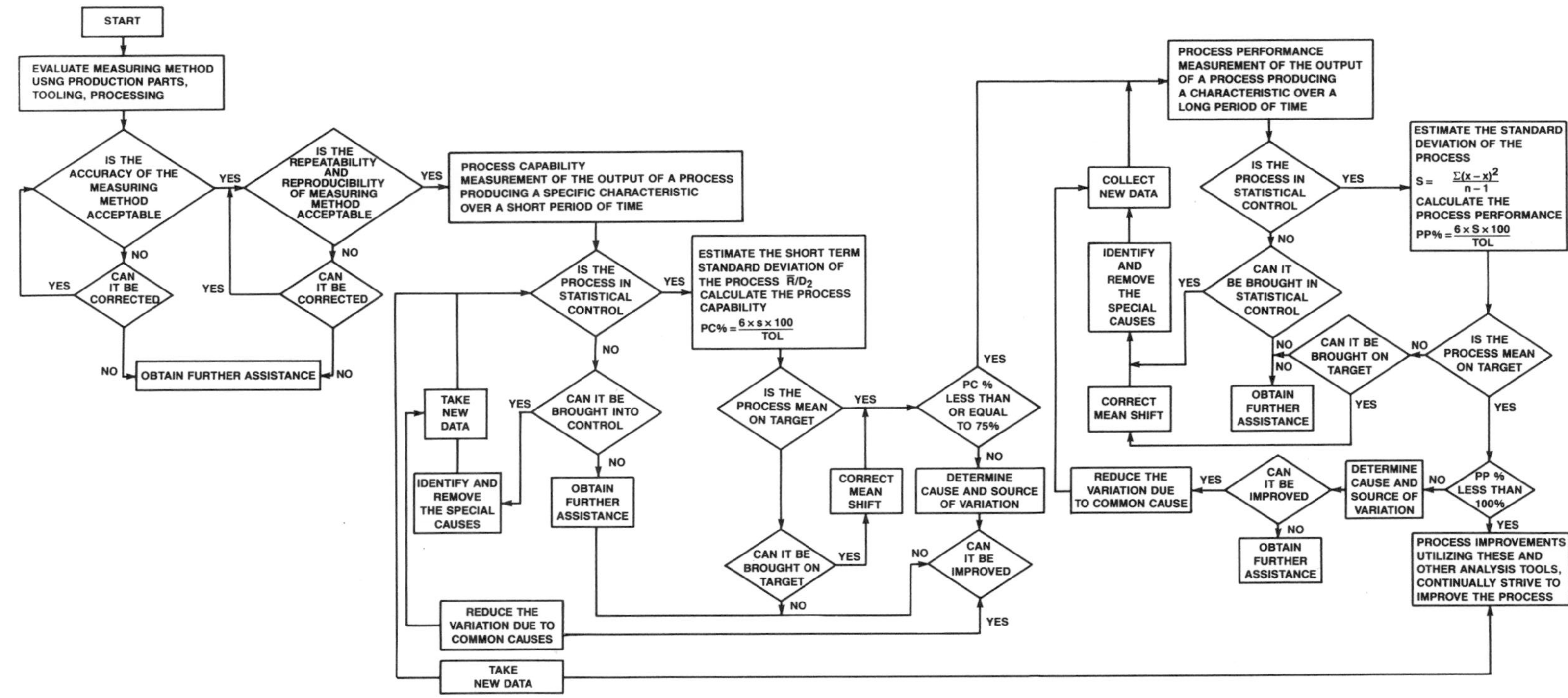

Figure 14-23 Process Analysis Flowchart

15

Computer Integrated Manufacturing

Most manufacturing processes, especially those which are labor intensive, are still organized according to the principle of the division of labor, first articulated by Adam Smith in his book, *The Wealth of Nations*, in 1776. Using pin making as an example, Smith argued that the total output for a given group of people will be greater if each person concentrated on only one task in the whole series of tasks involved in producing pins, rather than each person fulfilling all of the tasks involved in making a complete pin, on the assumption that practice (repetition) makes perfect. That there is at least some merit in this form of organization would seem to be self-evident in that it is still in use today more than 200 years later. In contrast to more contemporary approaches to manufacturing such as JIT, SCM, FMS (flexible manufacturing systems) and focused factories, this method has come to be described as the functional approach to manufacturing.

However, while the basic principle has survived the passage of time, other things have obviously changed. Products and manufacturing processes have become much more complex than in the days of pin making in 18th century Britain, as technology evolved and became much more sophisticated. This has had the effect of placing ever increasing reliance on the need for communication systems to maintain the cohesiveness of the multidiscipline functional unit. That which in the past was simple enough to be memorized, has now become so complex as to warrant documentation. Bills of material, assembly shop order instructions, product design drawings, process flows and methods are but a few of the more obvious examples. Until very recently the most obvious and widely used medium to fulfill these documentation requirements was paper (papyrus), invented circa 2000 B.C. by the Babylonians. Its proliferation is evident in almost every office and workplace.

In addition to this, dividing the total sequence of operations into specialized tasks created the need to coordinate and reintegrate the individual tasks back into a cohesive, balanced unit. This need incidentally, precipitated the emergence of scientific management in general and work study, or more fashionably, industrial engineering in particular. Over the course of time, these trends continued, with progressively more and more sophisticated efforts to improve the productivity of the direct manufacturing operator function being applied. Human physical effort was at first enhanced with primitive technology hand tools, then power assisted tools, until almost total replacement of the human operator physical contribution was achieved with fixed function mechanization.

With the advent of semiconductors, principally minute, low cost, high reliability microprocessors and dynamic RAM memories, the process of being able to progressively enhance the contribution made by the human intellect began, leading to various forms of automation (quasi ''intelligent'' mechanization) and ultimately to robotics. Unlike physical effort, the need for direct human intellectual effort in the manufacturing function cannot be completely eliminated until expert systems and artificial intelligence systems are perfected (this will be discussed with more detail in Chapter 17). Concurrent with these trends, increasing availability and pervasiveness of use of cheaper and more reliable storage media, such as magnetic tape, discs, and semiconductor memory created the possibility of electronic data bases as a commercially viable and technically feasible alternative to paper as a documentation medium.

But despite replacing the human being with machines, the basic principle of organization, of dividing up the total task into a series of smaller tasks, and then applying resources to each of these tasks in a specialized manner, remained. This in fact is the situation which is most prevalent today and has been aptly described as ''islands of automation.'' Not surprisingly then perhaps the problem of reintegrating these specialized resources, of having them communicate and cooperate with each other as a cohesive unit, also remains. We have to some degree been successful in replacing people with machines, but only at the cost of exacerbating the communication difficulty. People could at least be reasonably safely assumed to posses the most rudimentary prerequisites of communication, a common language. This is far from being the case—especially if supplied from different vendors—with machines. The people equivalent would be a multi-lingual workforce with no universal language.

The assumption that these problems can and will be solved, and we shall inquire into this in more detail later, has led at least one school of thought to extrapolate these trends to their ''ultimate conclusion,'' industrial utopia, frequently if not optimistically described as ''factories of the future, lights out factories, peopleless and paperless factories.'' To such visionaries, these trends tend to be perceived synonomously, but at least in this writer's opinion, prematurely, with CIM. See Figure 15-1.

While there is nothing wrong of itself in conceptualizing the top of the pyramid as a focus in the mind's eye, so wide is the gap between what is theoretically conceivable and that which is practically realizable, that it is much safer to regard CIM as a challenge or a problem to be solved, rather than as a solution to be implemented, as many pioneers, with the courage of their convictions, have found to their cost. CIM as it stands is a process, a means to an end, not an end in its own right. It is also dangerous to assume that CIM can be designed and developed in a vacuum, isolated from shop floor reality, and installed as a turnkey operation, totally replacing all that has gone before. Again, using the pyramid as an analogy, the top may well be the objective, but if it is to materialize, it must be painstakingly built, layer by layer, from the bottom, with each layer of competence as it were being systematically set in place before the next is attempted.

It took decades, if not centuries, for systems to evolve which facilitated cooperation and integration between people in industrial environments. Hopefully it will not take as long to develop the infrastructure required to fully support CIM, formidable though it may be; but the fact remains, it does not exist in full today and it will take time, no matter how fervently we wish it into existence to complete its evolution. With this in mind, we might now propose a formal, universally applicable and acceptable definition of CIM.

The CIM "Wheel"

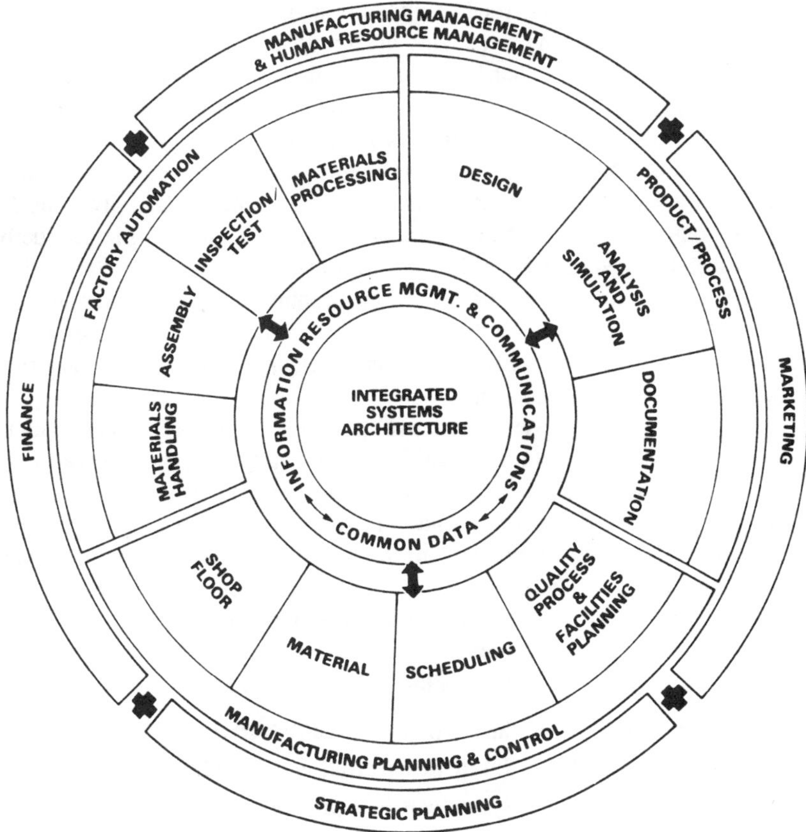

Figure 15-1 The CIM "Wheel"
Developed by the Technical, Computer and Automated System Association of SME (CASE, SME)

CIM is the process of replacing the human physical and intellectual contribution to individual manufacturing operations, in any sequence of such operations, by machines, in a common electronic data base environment.

The question of scope arises here as to the sequence of operations. To some the range is confined strictly to manufacturing operations. To the more ambitious it extends from customer data bases such as a custom product design or product mix demand profile, through to shipping.

WHY DO WE NEED CIM?

CIM is perceived to be an appropriate response, perhaps the only potentially adequate response, to ever intensifying competitive pressure. In the global environment, particularly in the face of the Oriental onslaught, the criteria for success have changed dramatically. Customer expectations in product utility, quality, on-time delivery, cost, and service responsiveness are escalating rapidly. It is no longer adequate to respond by being world class in only one of these parameters and simply adequate in all the others, on the historically based assumption that manufacturing operations cannot be all things to all men and must be optimized to excel in only one (see Wickham Skinner footnote). These parameters must now be regarded as mutually inclusive rather than exclusive and ways of organizing manufacturing to provide them must be developed. At the same time that the criteria for success are changing, the difficulties in being able to meet these criteria are becoming greater. As mentioned earlier, products and processes are becoming innately more complex, the demand for variety is increasing, leading to problems of mix management, the ultimate challenge being to support lot sizes of one, with no penalty in cost, quality, or service. All of this at a time when industrial productivity is declining. The current average annual rate of improvement for U.S. manufacturing productivity is 1.8 percent. This has declined from 3.0 percent during the 1950s, 1960s, and 1970s. We must not digress into a dissertation on macroeconomics but this apparently numerically insignificant decline can be the difference between budget and balance of trade deficits and surpluses at the national level, between stagnant and increasing disposable income at the individual and family level.

Generically, CIM is an alternative approach to the traditional, labor intensive functional form of manufacturing organization. It is a general framework, a set of guidelines, a process which attempts to reconcile supply and demand in the most optimal manner, at their current respective stages of evolutionary complexity: escalating customer expectations, increasing complexity of products and processes, product and process proliferation, and mix management, and so on. It is being developed and applied in practice to a variety of different and apparently unrelated criteria, all of which in fact are really elements of overall competitive competence, the relative importance of which may vary according to the specific situation being addressed:

Replacement of direct-labor physical contribution
Replacement of direct-labor intellectual contribution
Improvements in quality—(statistical process control)
Improvements in responsiveness to fluctuations in demand
To improve ability to manage mix
To create a "universal" data base
To integrate "islands" of automation (and information)
To eliminate use of paper
To build a cumulative and enduring knowledge data base
To locate factories where the markets are
To be first
To be the same (equal)
To integrate external business parameters with internal operations parameters in a common electronic data base environment
To facilitate improvements in customer/supplier data exchange dialogs
To reduce cost of direct labor and material
To reduce new product introduction cycle-time

Perhaps herein lies the key to successful implementation of CIM. All too often these things are pursued as independent objectives, the problem of reconciling them with the other, equally important objectives, remaining unsolved.

It is all too easy to make gigantic leaps of the imagination and confuse what is theoretically conceivable with what is practically realizable. It is important to define in the mind's eye, the ultimate destination, the specific end result being sought. But this capability cannot be conceived, designed, and developed in a vacuum and installed as a turnkey solution. It is equally important to define status quo, in order that the gap may be quantified and an appropriate strategy to close the gap be developed and implemented in a controlled manner. CIM can only be implemented successfully as part of a process of continuous evolution in industrial methods and technology, not as many pioneering goliaths have found to their cost, as a revolution (see noble experiments). It has to be developed and implemented systematically in a sequential fashion, with each layer of competence being laid down prior to the next one being attempted. We must be very careful of biting off in our zeal, more than we can chew at one sitting. Remember the pelican: a wonderful bird is the pelican; his beak can hold more than his belly can.

Since part of our task is to integrate, we shall need a vehicle which allows us to see both detail and big picture simultaneously. This being the case, the best possible foundation on which to begin building a CIM superstructure is a flow chart of the existing (or planned if the venture is new) sequence of operations. This flow chart should represent status quo totally comprehensively with every operation—and material movement transaction associated with each operation—represented. This in itself can lead to improvements quite independently of CIM. Are the operations in the correct sequence; are there any redundant operations or material transactions; does each operation add value—or cost; is there a predefined path for every foreseeable outcome; are there any work in process banks which can be eliminated? If the flow chart has been created in an electronic data base, and there are many excellent personal computer application programs for this kind of work, then modifications can be done quickly and easily. It may even be desirable, if not essential, to maintain two flow charts, the first representing status quo, the second the planned end result if different from the existing. This will allow intended changes in procedure to be easily assessed, quantified, and communicated. This is an extremely pedestrian task and may seem far removed from CIM, but it is an absolutely indispensible prerequisite. The flow chart is the skeletal framework around which, and by which, all of the other functions will be established and supported; the local area network, the material movement routing and storage if necessary, quality control monitoring and feedback stations, and so on, especially if the intention is to use SPC. It should also indicate the expected cycle-time for each operation, the cumulative cycle-time, the throughput per hour, and total capacity of each operation. This information will be essential for line balancing and cycle-time planning and control. The method specification for each operation should also be referenced here. In this fashion, the complete sequence of events, how long each should take and how each should be executed can be represented in a comprehensible and easily communicable manner. If we cannot make our factory work on paper (or simulate it in an electronic data base) then we will not be able to make it work in practice.

The next step is to then examine each operation, developing and documenting the best possible method of execution, ranging from manual all the way through to artificial intelligence. There is no shame in applying a manual method which is known to work, albeit as an intermediate solution, rather than some esoteric method which is as yet untried and tested. Remember, this is an evolutionary process, not a revolutionary one. Any radically different way of executing an operation, especially if the operation is in any way critical, should always be supported by some known, workable contingency method, until the new approach is proven. It is a very frequent occurrence for a piece of equipment, intended to mechanize or automate some operation previously undertaken by a human being, to require in situ engineering to reach an acceptable level of operating performance. There are many reasons for this, but some surprisingly common ones are due to perhaps obvious, but invalid assumptions. Some of these assumptions follow in bold text with counter explanations following.

"Mass production" means homogeneous populations of material. Like people, no two products, material pieceparts, or machines for that matter are absolutely identical. They may be very close, but they are each unique in some way. Even the best controlled processes can only guarantee values of parameters within tolerance and while we nevertheless continue to strive for perfection, these tolerances are not zero.

Another assumption is that a machine replaces, in total, the human contribution. This is often the objective, and belief, but not the reality. All too often the human contribution is underestimated or taken for granted; some sublety is overlooked. For example, conventional, and widely used figures of merit in specifying the acceptance criteria of capital equipment is mean time between failure (MTBF) and mean time before repair (MTBR). An equally, perhaps even more important but overlooked figure of merit, is mean time between assist (MTBA); in effect tweaks, nudges, and pokes by the human operator, none of which are in the formal job specificaiton, from which many replacement machine specifications are initially drawn, to "encourage" some temporarily malfunctioning mechanism to resume normal operation. Integrated circuit test handlers are classic examples of this, the ability to accommodate this rarely being engineered into the initial design of the equipment and at best, is usually a second generation retrofit and at worst, a spit, a prayer, and a piece of string "band aid" solution. Where, with a slight out of tolerance part, a human operator might just "jiggle it in," an automatic handling machine will force fit, usually unsuccessfully and do much damage in the process. This has been a particularly endemic problem associated with the recent trend to automatic insertion of integrated circuits in printed circuit boards, mandating the need for product populations with physical dimensions confined to limits within a few thousands of an inch.

Equipment vendors have a thorough understanding of the specific user need for which the equipment is purchased and of the environment in which it is expected to operate.

The aforementioned are offered by way of example only, the point being that unless a mechanized or automated operation can be repetitive and predictable, unless the piece of equipment has inherent capability to deal with every conceivable scenario which may arise, no matter how slight the variation, it is unlikely that it can operate in concert with many other interdependent operations for any meaningful length of time. Cases where a "state of the art" machine to replace a humble direct operator has defied the combined skills of several highly qualified technicians, engineers, and managers, are not infrequent. They are the rule, rather than the exception. This does not mean that we should not try new, potentially better ways. It simply means that in situ engineering is to be expected and foreseen, that the new method should be supported by a known, workable contingency until perfected. If "people and paperless" factories are indeed worthwhile objectives, then we best remain cognizant of the fact that nothing worthwhile is easily, or quickly, achieved.

All of the aforementioned, such as computer aided test (CAT), computer aided engineering (CAE), and so on fall into the realms of computer aided (as opposed to integrated) manufacturing (CAM), and each can present a formidable challenge in its own right, but they are the nuts and bolts of CIM, not the chassis. CIM is the process of integrating these "nuts and bolts." Integration, first and foremost, means communications.

With such a Pandora's box of high tech toys at our disposal, we could perhaps be forgiven for focusing exclusively on the problems of machine-to-machine communication in their own right. But that would be myopic. Even if we are totally successful in replacing all human participation in the manufacturing process—not likely in our lifetime—we would still have human participation at the extremes of this sequence of events, however we define its range. We would still have customers, suppliers, and support vendors with a need to communicate using machines, among other communication mediums. For reasons we have already described, the kind of communication need we are addressing is far removed from a simple, face-to-face dialogue between two people. We are talking about ultra heavy traffic communication. Communication which will require a very well designed traffic system to carry it. So let's begin to build our data traffic system now, brick by brick, beginning with an understanding of the communication characteristics of our fundamental electronic building brick, the integrated circuit (IC). We shall then examine how these bricks are glued together to make bigger structures and how these structures in turn are glued together to make communication superstructures, CIM networks and finally, how human beings interface with these networks in making them serve their communication purposes.

This task will embrace many specialized disciplines: semiconductor physics, computer science, electronic hardware and software, data communications principles, human value systems—their hopes, fears, and attitudes, each of which is a complex study in itself. This is one of the main reasons why CIM challenges should not be undertaken lightly, why trailblazing efforts tend until now to have been confined to those with the skills and financial resources in sufficient measure to be able to stumble, sometimes frequently, and yet still stay the course. If we are to integrate these resources, we need at least an appreciation of all of them, especially their interfacing characteristics. We shall now attempt to give a cursory picture of these characteristics. Pursuit of a more in-depth understanding of any of the related disciplines, be it out of curiosity or necessity, is left to the discretion of the individual reader but can perhaps be guided, at least as a first step, by the bibliography included at the end of this text. Collectively, we shall try and confine ourselves to reaching no more than the minimum level of understanding required to be able to perceive how the pieces of our jigsaw puzzle can be assembled together.

BITS, BYTES, AND BLOCKS

On-Chip Communication

Microprocessors and computers, the engines of electronic communication systems, are credited with having extravagant capabilities and they are indeed truly remarkable, but they are much less intimidating and awe inspiring than the high priests of electronic wizardry would have us believe with their cult deifying jargon. Perhaps their most remarkable characteristic is that they are capable of complex, heavy traffic communication using only a two character (digit) alphabet, 24 less than the 26 used in the English language and 6,998 less than approximately 7,000 used in Japanese Kanji. All digital integrated circuits, no matter how complex, are simply configurations of switches. This is true of microprocessors, dynamic and static RAMs, ROMs, EPROMs, and EEPROMs, and so on. The switches employed may have varying characteristics and be configured in a seemingly infinite variety of arrangements, depending on their specific application, but they are nevertheless still only switches. A switch is capable of assuming only two states—ON or OFF. A popular convention is to represent the ON state by the number 1, the OFF state by the number 0 (high and low are almost equally popular conventions, representing signal levels which turn a transistor switch ON or OFF—more on this later). See Figure 15-2.

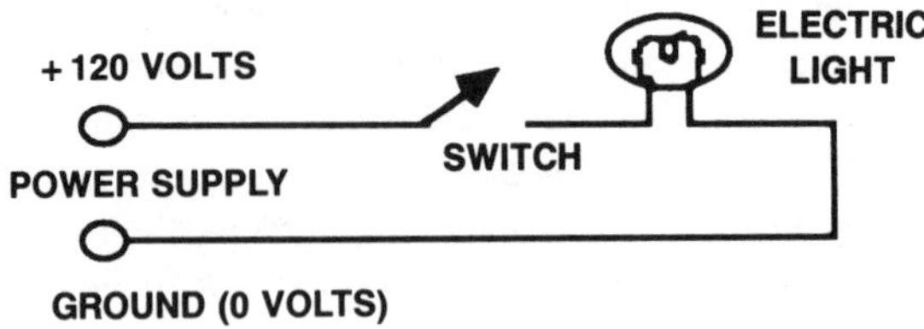

Figure 15-2

Before we proceed too far in developing our understanding of how these switching properties can be made to do useful work in satisfying our communication needs, let's take a few minutes to try and equip the nonelectrical engineers among us with an understanding of some basic principles of electricity they will need before we continue. Most people have at least heard the term voltage or volts, probably in a domestic appliance context, but are less familiar with the terms current and resistance. We shall need a basic understanding of these terms and their relationship to each other if we are ever to feel comfortable with data communication networks. To aid our understanding, let's consider an analogy with which almost everyone is familiar, a domestic water supply. See Figure 15-3.

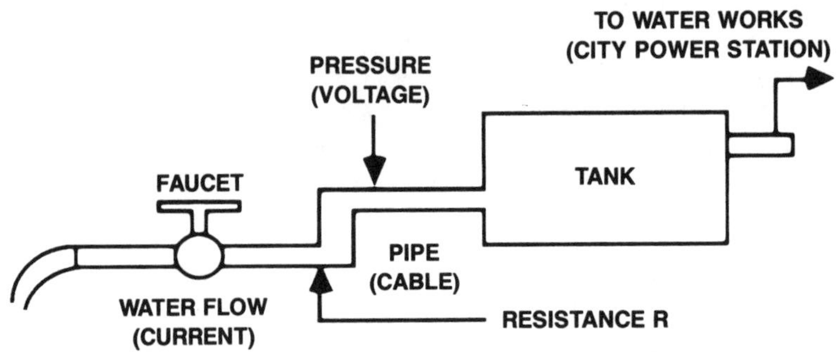

Figure 15-3

If we want to increase the rate at which water flows from the pipe, we can do several things. We can raise the water tank higher. This will increase the water pressure (voltage). We could also increase the diameter of the pipe. This in effect reduces the resistance to the flow of water between the tank and the faucet. Imagine the water molecules in turbulence. The electronic equivalent of water molecules flowing in the pipe are electrons flowing in the cable. We could also reduce resistance to the flow of water by reducing the length of the pipe.

We can now see the relationship between rate of flow of water and pressure and resistance:

$$\text{Rate of flow} = \frac{\text{Pressure}}{\text{Resistance}}$$

In our electronic equivalent circuit:

$$\text{Current (I)} = \frac{\text{Voltage (V)}}{\text{Resistance (R)}}$$

So, if we double the voltage, we shall double the current which flows. We can also achieve the same effect by halving the resistance.

We are primarily concerned with how we can control the flow of data (information) in our communication network. Since currents will be used to represent our information, if we can control these currents, manipulate them and route them using switches, then we can achieve our purpose. The way this is done is by configuring our switches in various ways to create control functions called logic elements. In a way we are playing a game of true or false based on the coincidence or noncoincidence of electrical signals. We represent all of the possible states of these elements with tables, called truth tables. These logic functions are then, in turn, configured together in various ways to create higher order functions such as microprocessors and memories, integrated in one piece of silicon (monolithic ICs).

Consider one of the simplest logic elements. Suppose we want a signal of some description to appear, only if two conditions exist coincidentally. A real-life example of the need for this condition would be to control an elevator. The signal to the motor to start raising or lowering the elevator should only be transmitted if: (1) the elevator door is completely closed and (2) a floor button is pressed. This could be represented as follows (see Figure 15-4). Since we have a choice of floors, we would need to add more logic elements in order to be more specific.

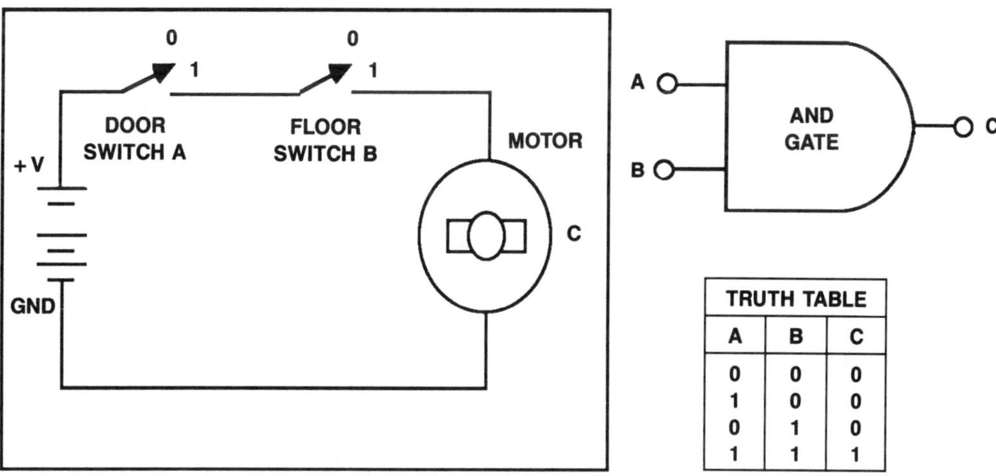

TRUTH TABLE		
A	B	C
0	0	0
1	0	0
0	1	0
1	1	1

Figure 15-4

This process is sometimes referred to as "gating," since signals are in effect controlled by gating them through to a subsequent stage or not according to predetermined conditions, coincidence of signals at the input of the gate, being satisfied. Since switches A and B must both be closed for a signal to appear at the motor, this is called, not surprisingly, an AND gate. Its Boolean algebra symbol is shown in Figure 15-4. This is a very simple example, but it is simply this principle which is employed in all digital integrated circuits. Some other basic configurations of logic elements are shown in Figures 15-5 through 15-14. The other main class of integrated circuits is analog. Unlike the digital switch, which has only two, well-defined stable states, **on** and **off**, an analog switch as an "infinite" number of states within its fully **on**, fully **off** range.

These **on/off** conditions, represented by convention, by 1s or 0s, **highs** or **lows**, are the language of digital integrated circuits—their two character alphabet. This is the only language the chips (ICs) understand. Their vocabulary is expanded by using patterns of these 1 and 0 states to represent letters of the alphabet, numbers, and other characters, etc.

Suppose we flick the switch in Figure 15-2 **on** then **off**. We would see, at the output terminal, a low voltage state, followed by a high voltage state, followed by a low voltage state. We call this a bit. If we did this eight times in quick succession, we would see eight bits—called a byte. If we define a bit as a time window, rather than a high or low state, then even if we operate the switch in a nonalternate pattern of 1s and 0s, we could still consider this to be eight bits or one byte. We could achieve the same thing if we had eight switches at the input, each capable of being switched on and off independently. Sending several eight-bit bytes in succession would represent a block of data. What these patterns of bits represent is called coding. There are several standard codes but in all of them each character of the alphabet, each digit from one to nine, symbols such as periods and commas, have predefined bit patterns. Some of the most widely used standards are shown in Figure 15-15.

2's Complement Arithmetic

Probably for no other reason than that we have ten fingers, the number system that we as humans are most familiar with is the decimal system. Using only ten characters—0 through 9—we can represent any number, positive and negative, no matter how large. When we reach the number 9, and have exhausted all characters in the units or one's column, we simply start again to the left of this column and use the same characters again, only with a different weighting or "base" in the ten's column. The number 19 for example, tells us that we have one (1) ten's unit and nine (9) one's units. Decimal numbers then are said to be represented in relation to the base ten—in effect, ten discrete states.

While very conveninent for us as humans, the decimal number system is not so convenient for computers—which do not have ten fingers—their nearest equivalent are switches—which have only two discrete states—assuming either a one or a zero—on or off state. As such, a number system which could represent any possible number—positive or negative—using only two states—that is, to the base 2, would be very desirable. There is such a system—called the binary system.

As before, when we have exhausted all of our characters in the one's column, in this system—either 0 or 1, we simply move to the left to continue.

(a)

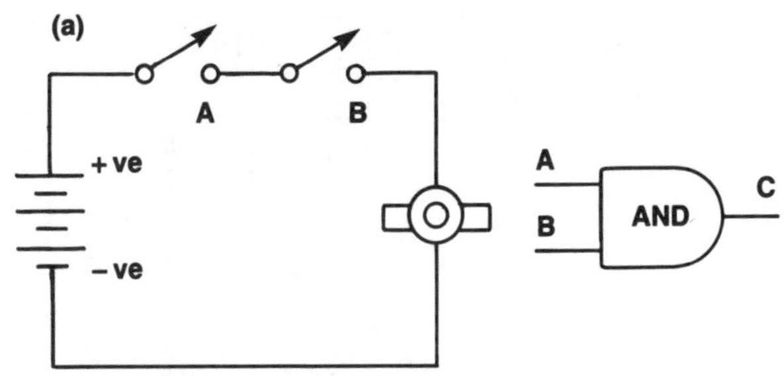

TRUTH TABLE		
A	B	C
0	0	0
1	0	0
0	0	0
1	1	1

(b)

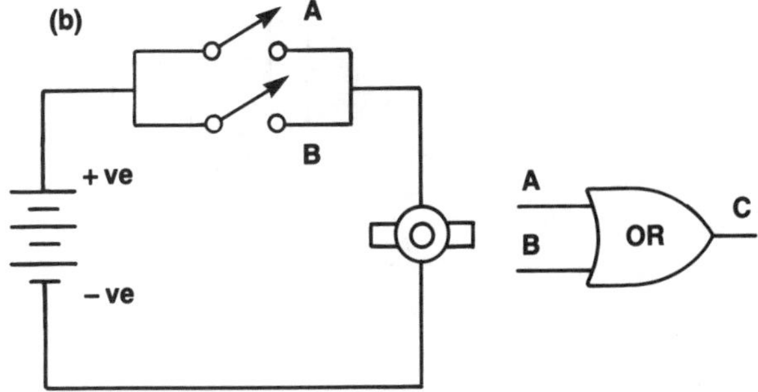

TRUTH TABLE		
A	B	C
0	0	0
1	0	1
0	0	0
1	1	1

(c)

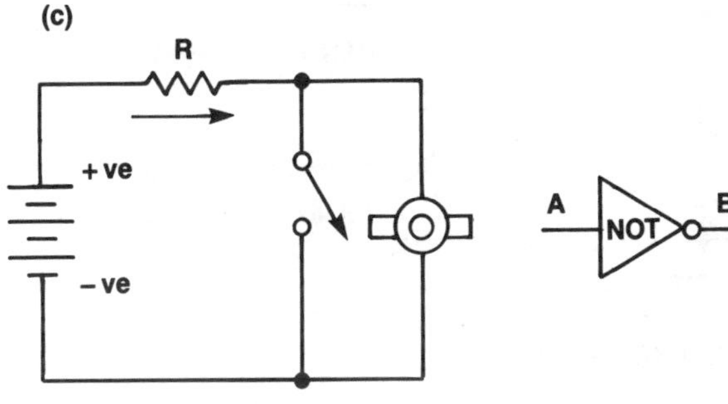

TRUTH TABLE	
A	B
0	1
1	0

(d)

A
B
OR
C
D

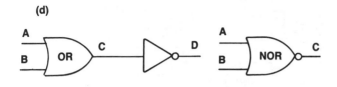

A
B
NOR
C

TRUTH TABLE			
A	B	C	D
0	0	0	1
1	0	1	0
0	1	1	0
1	1	1	0

Figure 15-5

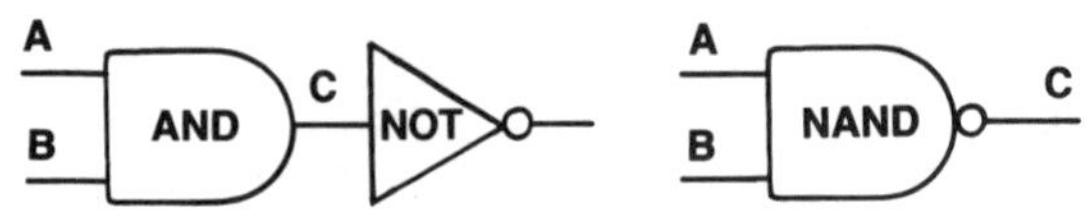

TRUTH TABLE			
A	B	C	D
0	0	0	1
1	0	0	1
0	1	0	1
1	1	1	0

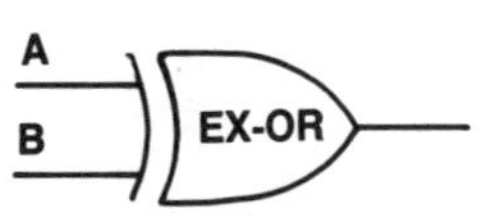

TRUTH TABLE		
A	B	C
0	0	0
1	0	1
0	1	1
1	1	0

Figure 15-6

SET-RESET (SR) FLIP-FLOP

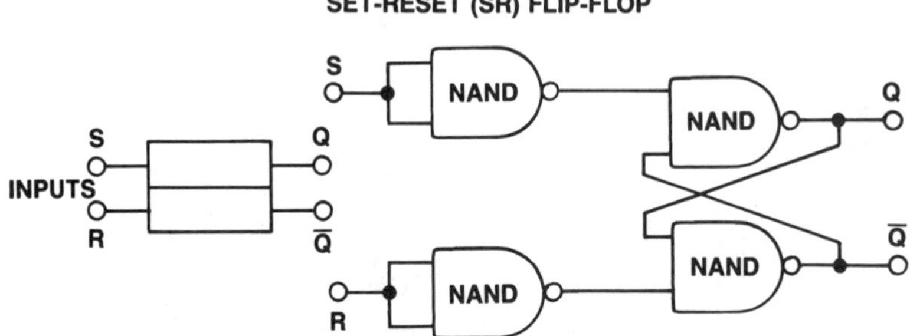

CLOCKED SR FLIP-FLOP

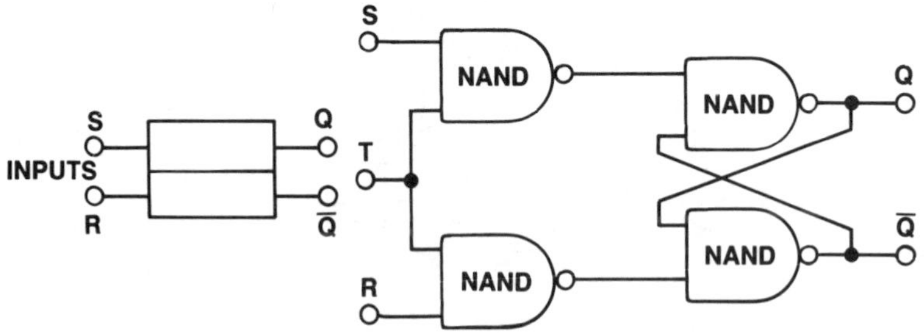

Figure 15-7

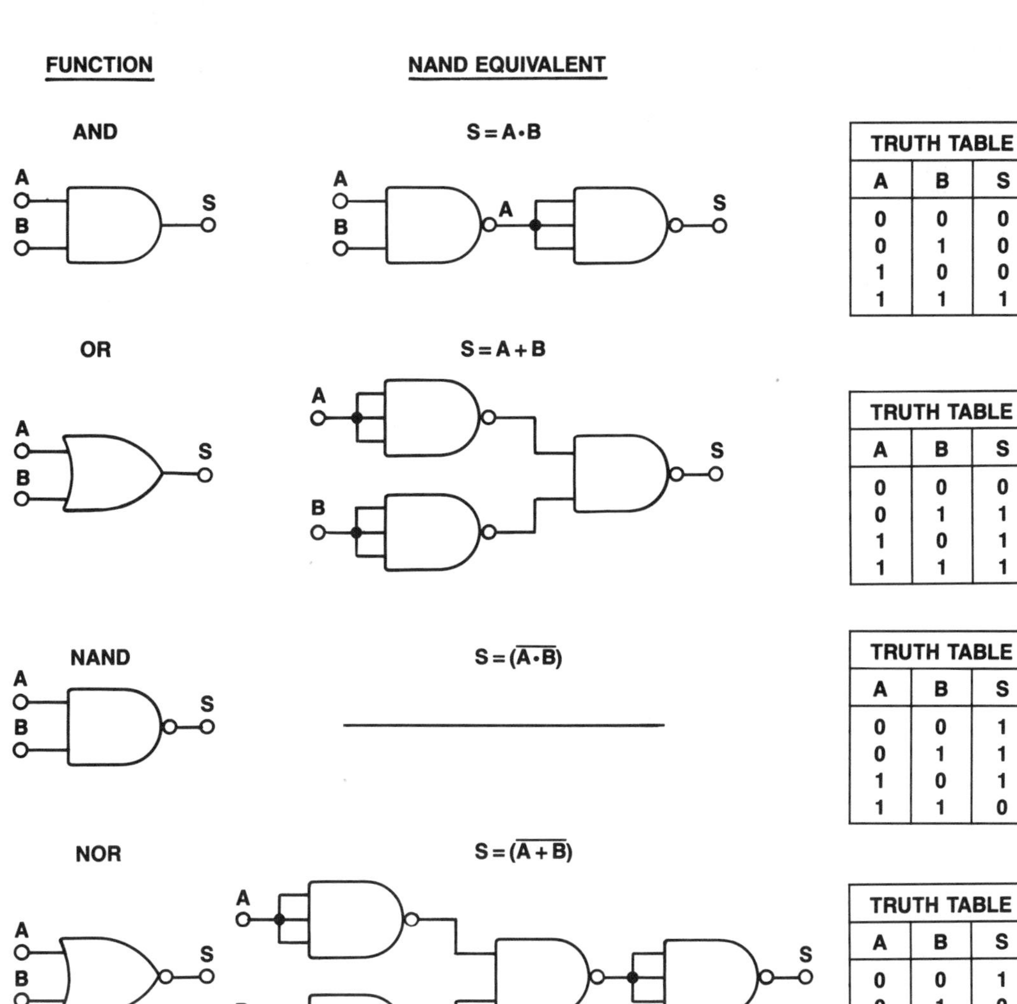

TRUTH TABLE		
A	B	S
0	0	0
0	1	0
1	0	0
1	1	1

TRUTH TABLE		
A	B	S
0	0	0
0	1	1
1	0	1
1	1	1

TRUTH TABLE		
A	B	S
0	0	1
0	1	1
1	0	1
1	1	0

TRUTH TABLE		
A	B	S
0	0	1
0	1	0
1	0	0
1	1	0

INVERTER

S = $\overline{A}$

A S

A S

TRUTH TABLE	
A	S
0	0
0	0

Figure 15-8 Basic Logic Functions Implemented Using Only NAND Gates

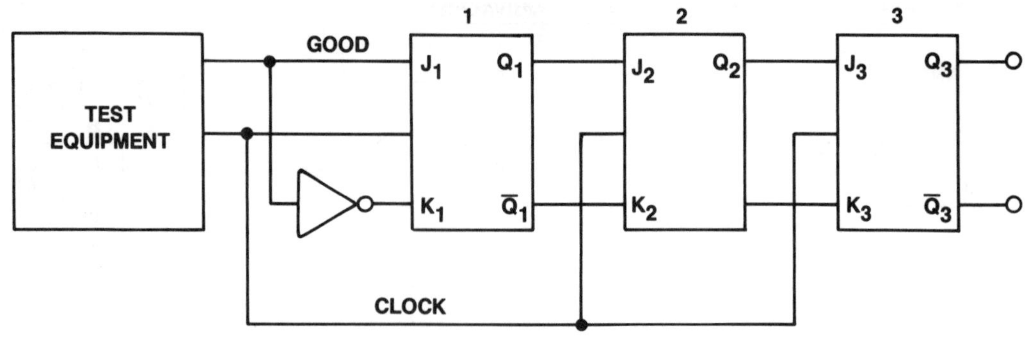

Figure 15-9 Simple Three-Stage Shift Register

FLIP-FLOP STATES Q_3	Q_2	Q_1		ALARM S
0	0	0	ALL POSSIBLE STATES	1
0	0	1		1
0	1	0		1
0	1	1		0
1	0	0		1
1	0	1		0
1	1	0		0
1	1	1		0

Figure 15-10

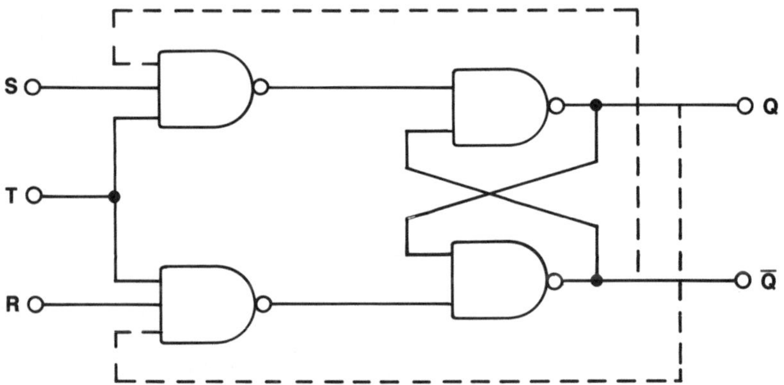

Figure 15-11 Clocked SR Flip-Flop with Additional Feedback

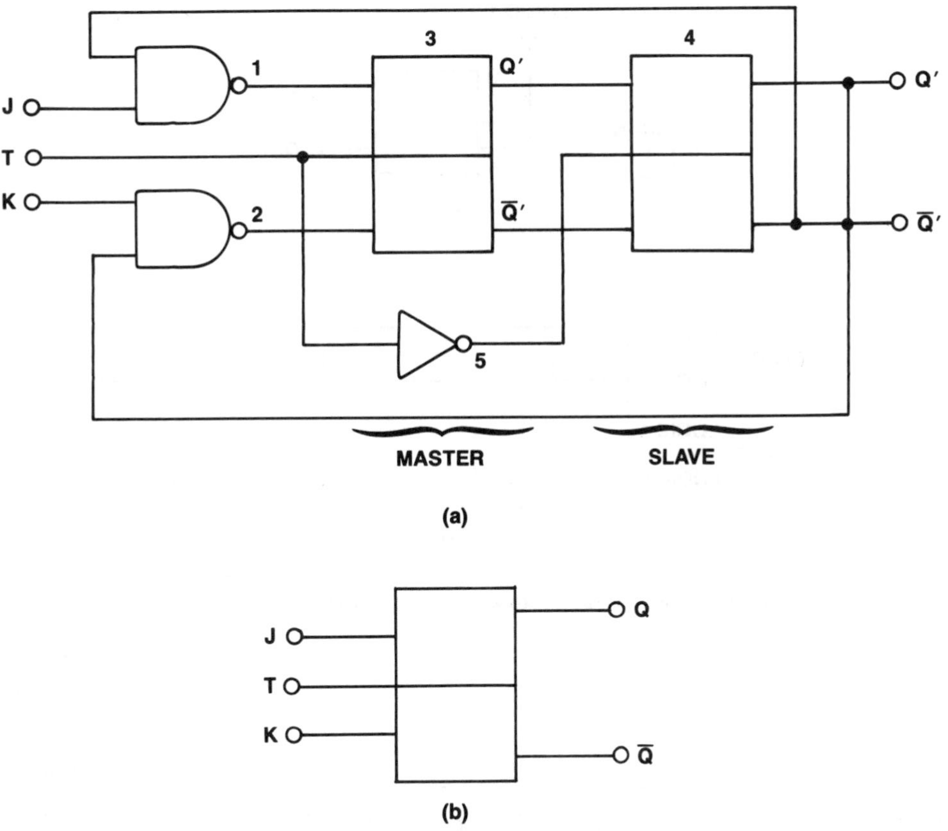

Figure 15-12 JK Master Slave Flip-Flop

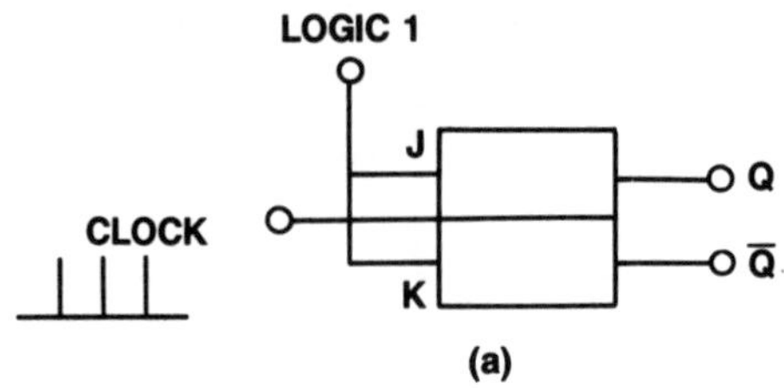

(a)

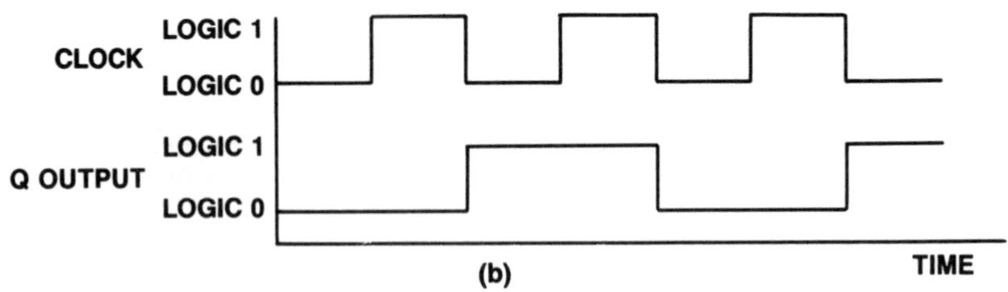

(b)

Figure 15-13 Relationship Beetween Input and Output Signals of a JK Flip-Flop

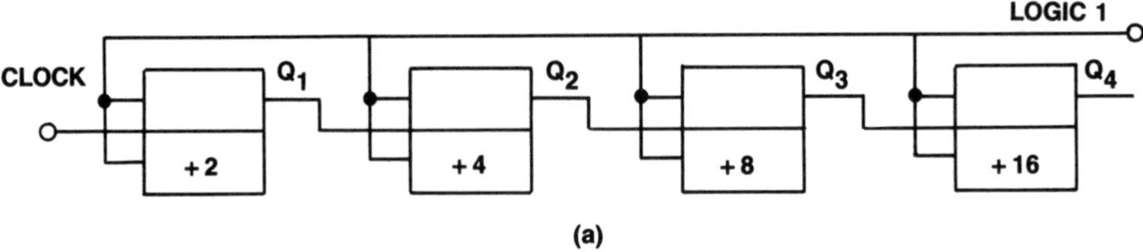

(a)

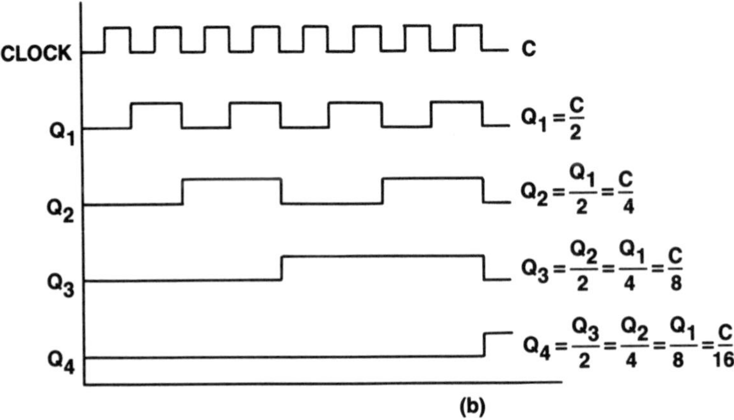

(b)

Figure 15-14 Ripple-Through Binary Counter

DECIMAL	SIGNED BINARY	1's COMPLEMENT	2's COMPLEMENT
15	01111	01111	01111
14	01110	01110	01110
13	01101	01101	01101
12	01100	01100	01100
11	01011	01011	01011
10	01010	01010	01010
9	01001	01001	01001
8	01000	01000	01000
7	00111	00111	00111
6	00110	00110	00110
5	00101	00101	00101
4	00100	00100	00100
3	00011	00011	00011
2	00010	00010	00010
1	00001	00001	00001
0	00000	00000	00000
−1	10001	11111	11110
−2	10010	11110	11101
−3	10011	11101	11100
−4	10100	11100	11011
−5	10101	11011	11010
−6	10110	11010	11001
−7	10111	11001	11000
−8	11000	11000	10111
−9	11001	10111	10110
−10	11010	10110	10101
−11	11011	10101	10100
−12	11100	10100	10011
−13	11101	10011	10010
−14	11110	10010	10001
−15	11111	10001	10000

Figure 15-15

The general case for a number system of base b follows. We can see that the successive positions of the digits, from left to right, are weighted as shown:

$$\ldots\ldots\ldots\ b^3\ b^2\ b^1\ b^0,\ b^{-1}\ b^{-2}\ b^{-3}\ \ldots\ldots\ldots$$

(The radix point, (:) separates the integral and fractional part of the numbers.)

There are basically three forms of the binary number system. They are: (1) signed binary in which negative numbers are notated with an extra bit to the left of the most significant bit, (2) 1's complement, and (3) 2's complement. Because of its unique properties, there is a unique code for every number and all numbers can be similarly treated in all arithmetic operations. The 2's complement form has become the most commonly used version in general purpose digital computers.

Many excellent treatments of this topic are available. Computers function by using strings of these 1s and 0s to represent alphabetic, numeric, and symbolic characters.

In our example, we are using electromechanical switches such as those used to control lights in a room, to construct our logic elements or gates. A room light controlled by two switches in different locations, a two-way switch, is in fact a logic circuit.

Obviously if we have to depend on the human hand to control our switching activity, the complexity, and speed of the functions we shall be able to design, will be very limited—enter the transistor. The transistor is a three terminal electronic switch whose state can be switched between on and off by an electronic signal. Now we can use signals to control our information signals, i.e., switch the switches. There are many forms of transistors, each optimized in a particular way, high-speed for fast switching applications, low-power consumption for battery applications, high-drive currrent for power-hungry applications, very small geometry for high-density memory storage, but they are still basically switches and all digital ICs are arrays of interconnected transistors on the same piece of silicon.

NETWORKS

Machine-to-Machine Communication

This is where the real task of creating our CIM network begins. Physically linking our machines together and developing the infrastructure required to allow our data traffic to flow speedily, safely, and interactively in order to integrate our "islands of automation" (and information) into a cohesive unit. Until now we have remained within the confines of the individual pieces of equipment, learning how to create specific task-oriented machines with the inherent ability to control such tasks by following explicit instructions. We began to develop our understanding of this process at the most fundamental level, with a basic review of semiconductor physics, exploring how the physics of a semiconductor material can be employed to create switches, how these switches can in turn be configured to create logic functions, and how these in turn can be configured to create higher order functions such as microprocessors and semiconductor memories. We learned how to communicate with these machines using software to translate from our 26 character based alphabet to their two binary digit 1s and 0s alphabet, with much of the translation task being fulfilled by the machines themselves. This provided us with all of the ingredients we needed to create our "islands of automation;" a machine with a memory to store task oriented instructions and a "reasoning" mechanism, a microprocessor or minicomputer with which to interpret these instructions and control the execution of the task.

We have successfully forged one of the links in our communications chain, human being to individual machine and vice versa. This in itself is a significant achievement, but the human master is not satisfied in having the silicon slave simply do his bidding on purely menial tasks. He wants to go further and have the slaves collectively take responsibility for their own supervision, to undertake some of the tasks of management as well as execution. To do so, the machines need to be able to communicate, not just with the human master, but with each other. This would be much easier to achieve if all vendors of equipment agreed upon a common, universal language. This is not the case and is not ever likely to be the case for the same reasons that human beings of different nationalities have not yet done so—not because it is not technically feasible, nor even because it is practically difficult, though by no means impossible, but because, for reasons of self-interest, it is politically unacceptable. (Does anyone remember Esperanto?) So despite having a common two binary digit alphabet we will find that like humans, who also share the same alphabet but apply it differently to different languages such as German, French, Italian, or Swahili, our machines will have to deal with each other's grammar if they are to communicate successfully. The extent to which we shall be successful in overcoming these challenges will depend very largely on the degree of "intelligence" of the equipment we are required to interface to the network.

Equipment IQs, Dumb, Smart, and Intelligent. This broad rule of thumb classification has usually been confined to terminals only but is equally applicable in describing the degree of self-sufficiency of any kind of equipment being interfaced to a network.

A Dumb Machine. The cheapest, lowest performance end of the spectrum, usually employing low-speed, asynchronous, single-wire digital communication, each character of data being transmitted individually. Such machines generally have no inherent message acknowledging (ACK/NACK) capability or error detection and correction. They are the most basic form of transmitter/receiver, usually connected to network nodes where keyboard entry of data is the limiting factor. A typical example is the teletype machine—the forerunner of the modern electric/electronic typewriter and PC based word processor. Since the machine has no on-board memory, it cannot be directly addressable by the network, although indirect addressing schemes called multiplexing (polling) can be devised.

A Smart Machine. The middle to high end of the spectrum, these machines will usually employ high-speed, synchronous communication of blocks of data in the half-duplex but more often in the full-duplex mode of operation. In synchronous communication, the data bits are synchronized by a system clock to predefined time windows. In asynchronous communication, the bits of data can occur sporadically and randomly with respect to events taking place elsewhere in the system. This type of machine is likely to have local memory, and can be addressable on the network, will be capable of automatic error detection/correcton and retransmit on error, but will likely be fixed in terms of its function.

The Intelligent Machine. The upper extreme of the range, it will almost certainly have local instruction processing capability in addition to local memory, and will be multifunctional in that its use can be modified under software control. This equipment will be highly self-sufficient and place the lowest burden on the network in not having to depend on the central host computer for control of most of its activity. A typical example of a smart terminal would be a personal computer interfaced, either as a discrete entity or integrated into some piece of equipment, to a network data base. Our difficulties, as if we did not already have enough, will be further exacerbated in that networks, capable of hosting machines with different languages, are not, and indeed can not be universal in their structure. A network design, like that of a transistor switch, or a logic element, or a microprocessor, must of necessity, given current state of the art, be optimized for the purpose for which it is intended according to application specific environments. (See Figure 15-16.) These application environments can be broadly classified into five major categories which determine the relative importance of the network's characteristics.

General Office. The typical word processor predominant environment, personal computer proliferation, copy machines, printers, and perhaps corporate network data terminal equipment (DTE). The work is generally clerical or administrative in nature with much keyboard entry of data. A network for such an environment, a so called front end local area network (LAN) is required to readily accept the interfacing of a relatively large proliferation and quantity of equipment from many vendors, at relatively low cost. Since human beings are the data transaction speed, and to some extent volume limiting factors in this environment, they are not required to support particularly fast, heavy duty

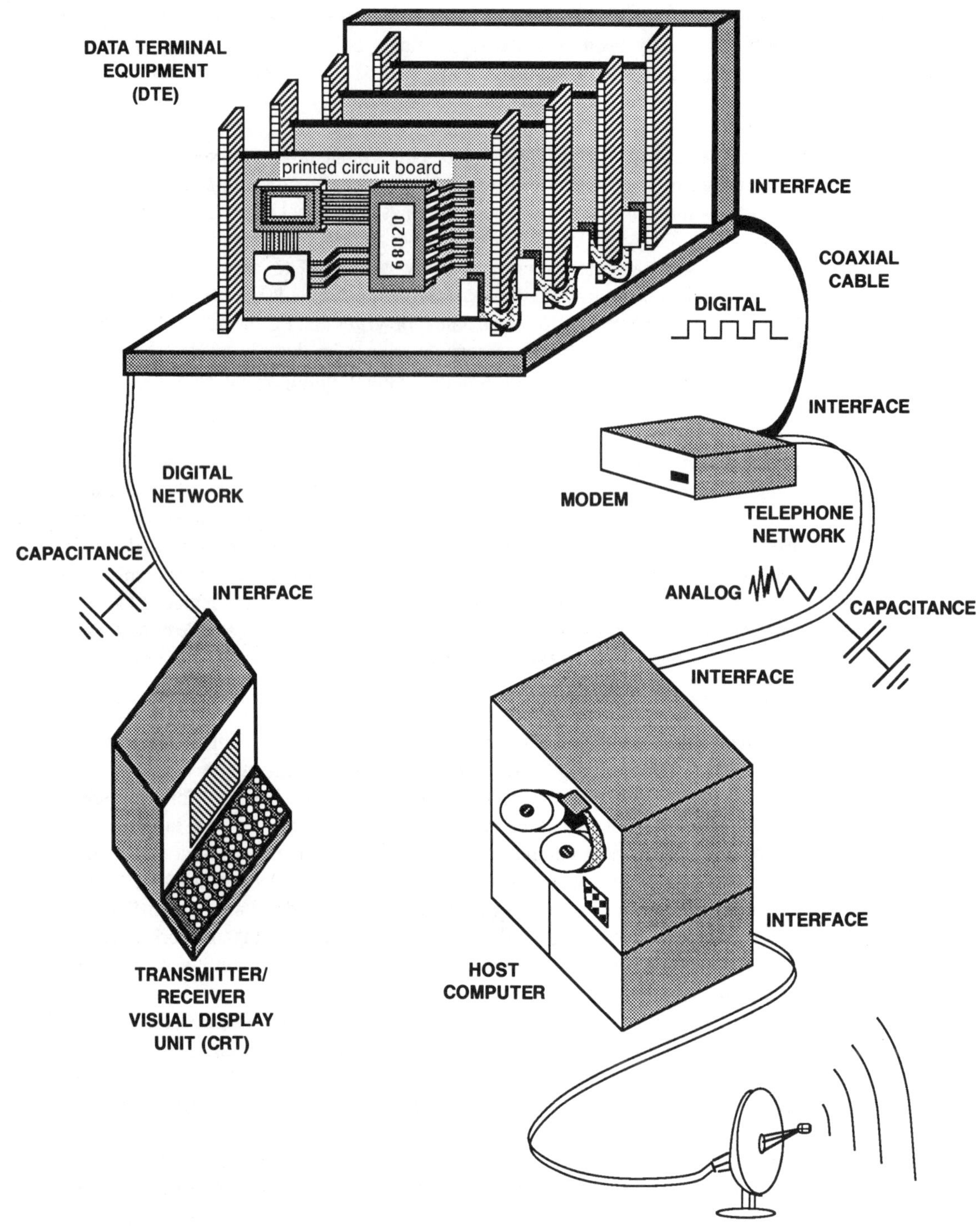

Figure 15-16 A Typical Network

traffic. There are a variety of proprietary LANs which have been developed to address these needs. As a general rule, equipment in this environment will be "dumb," or at best "smart" terminals rather than "intelligent."

Engineering Office. This may well be a micro and mini computer intensive environment with computer aided design and computer aided engineering work stations, line plotting equipment, graphics terminals and corporate data base terminals. Fast, heavy traffic data block (file) transactions are likely to be the norm in this environment. Like bankers, these folks tend to work nine till five during which time network up-time will be important. Unfortunately, no one has yet succeeded in designing equipment which respects these hours and agrees to go down only after everyone has gone home. Equipment in this environment is likely to be smart to intelligent.

The Computer Room. This is where the concentration of large, expensive mainframe machines and peripherals will be greatest. Like the engineering environment, ultra fast, heavy duty traffic will be the norm but equipment proliferation is not likely to be as great and it will not be highly geographically dispersed. This function may well be a global service supporting continuous factory operations as well as communication transactions taking place in other international time zones. As such, its uptime, loading, responsiveness, and productivity will be crucially important.

Factory Floor. By far the most demanding environment in terms of proliferation. You will almost certainly find at least one of everything that anyone ever wanted to hang on a network. There will also be physical constraints imposed by the imperatives and logistics of the manufacturing process itself. This environment may well be required to operate 24 hours per day, perhaps seven days per week (producing lot sizes of one, at zero cost, with zero defects delivered on-time with zero lead-time, staffed by demotivated, unskilled operators and maintained by inadequately trained, over-worked technicians, engineers, and supervisors—just joking—I think? This situation never arises in real life, only in text books).

The Campus. Networks required to integrate LANs together, frequently with different structures or over large geographic distances are described as wide area networks as shown in Figure 15-17. (For some reason the acronym—WAN, unlike LAN, has not been adopted for common usage). The individual LANs are connected together by means of **bridges**, if the network interface characteristics are similar and by **gateways** if they are not. There are three board classes of generic networks designed to meet these needs, each optimized according to the characteristics mentioned earlier, each in consequence having their relative advantages and disadvantages. (See Figure 15-18.) Deciding which architecture is most appropriate for a given environment requires consideration of the following:

Cost	Lowest cost, highest performance tradeoff
Number of nodes	Few, moderate, or many
Geographic dispersion	Campus, regional, national, or international
Data rate	Slow, medium, or high speed
Volume	Low, medium, or heavy traffic
Physical reliability	

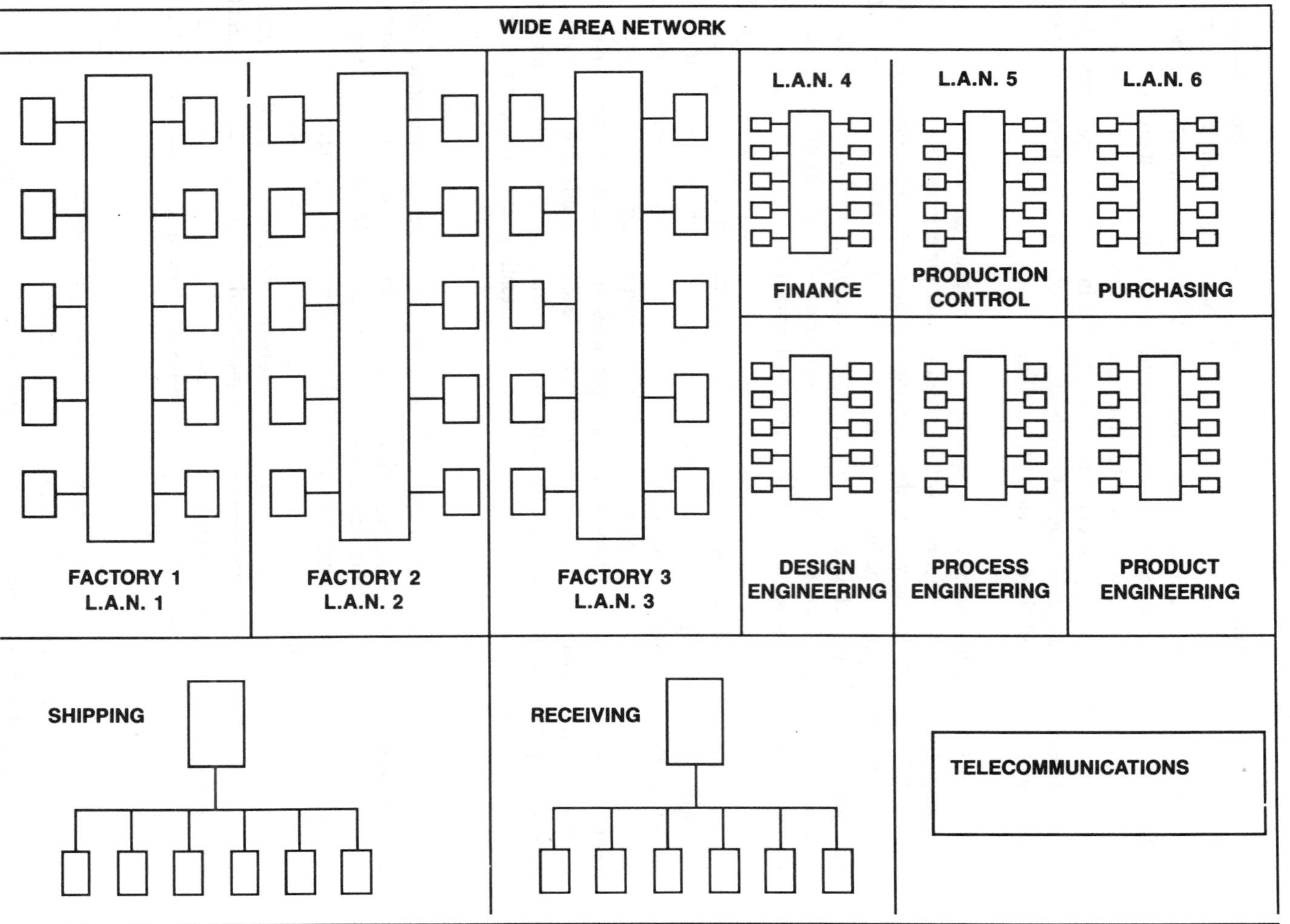

Figure 15-17 Typical Wide Area Network

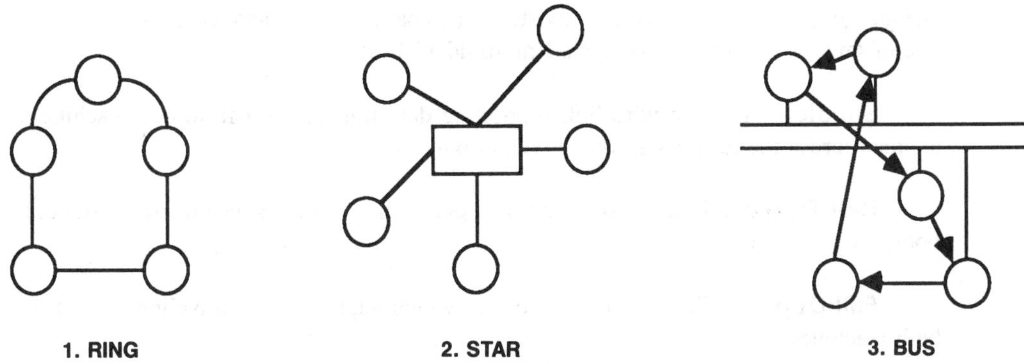

Figure 15-18 Network Architectures

Connectability	Cost/effect on rest of system
Data integrity	Need for automatic error detection, correction, and retransmit
Data security	Need for encryption/decryption
Flexibility	Ease of expansion/modification/integration

Let's pause at this point and take stock of where we are again before we are overwhelmed by the bewildering number of variables we are required to comprehend.

We now know that there are five main classes of environments, each with different requirements, which we need to consider in addressing our network needs:

> **General office, engineering office, computer room, factory, and campus.**
>
> **That these environments utilize different proliferations of equipment whose performance ranges from dumb to intelligent.**
>
> **That there are three generic network architectures, each with different advantages and disadvantages.**
>
> **That there is a range of criteria which needs to be considered in matching these network architectures to user environments.**
>
> **That a choice also exists as to the form of the physical interconnect of the network:** twisted pair, flat ribbon cable, coaxial cable or fibre optic cable (see physical links), existing telephone network land lines, and of course satellites.

Assuming we can rationalize all of these and feel confident that we have made a good decision, that the outcome is the best possible one for our needs, let's now address how the individual pieces of equipment in our labyrinth communicate with each other. (Even if we have not reached that happy peace of mind state, we cannot stop here, so let us proceed on the assumption that we have and get back to our less intimidating 1s and 0s).

The information passing between machines across the network will, as we have already established, be encoded in strings of 1s and 0s called bytes (eight bits). We are not restricted to transmitting only one byte of information at a time. Many contiguous bytes, called a block of data, can be sent, with each byte representing a different alphabetic or numeric character. This data can be transmitted and received across the physical channel linking the two machines (twisted pair, coax, or fibre optic cable, and so on) in one of three ways. (More decisions I'm afraid.) These are:

Simplex. A single wire link supporting data transmission from one machine to another across the network in one direction only.

Half-Duplex. This is also a one wire only link but allows data traffic to travel in both directions alternately.

Full-Duplex. This is a two wire link which supports data traveling to or from both machines simultaneously.

The speed at which these data streams travel across the link is measured in terms of **bit rate**—the number of **bits per second**, but more often as **baud rate** (not the same as bit rate)—the number of **signal transitions per period of time**.

All too often, because of differences in equipment and signal-line speed characteristics, **transmission rate** mismatches occur on networks to which a wide proliferation of equipment is connected. Signal speed on an **HCMOS** chip for example can be in the order of 50 MHz (Mega Hertz, 50 million switching transitions per second), faster in the case of a bipolar chip, but few networks and much peripheral equipment, can match these speeds due to capacitance, line losses, and electromagnetically induced switching noise. **Buffers**, large configurations of semiconductor dynamic or static RAM memories, are used to deal with these mismatches by allowing the rate at which data an input to the buffer to vary from the output rate or vice versa. (Capacitance—if we return to our water supply system analogy, capacitance can be compared to intermediate reservoirs in the system, or leaks in the pipe; one sometimes desirable, the other never, but both of which have the effect of reducing pressure and slowing down the rate of flow of water.) (See Figure 15-16.)

Transmission Codes. These codes are analogous to different languages. They use the same fundamental alphabet, but the rules of grammar, the structure of the words and sentences, the meaning of bit arrangements, are different. Obviously, two machines, like two humans who wish to communicate, must first agree upon the use of a common language. Some commonly used codes are as follows:

ASCII. American standard code for information interchange is a widely used code in both telecommunications and data transmission. The teletype machine is the most familiar example of the use of this code. (See Figure 15-19.)

Baudot. Also used in teletype applications where transmission speed is a function of keyboard entry, this is a five-level code capable of representing 58 different characters.

EBCDIC. External binary coded decimal interchange code. Developed by IBM, this code allows 256 characters to be represented using eight-bit bytes (binary coded decimal).

Protocol. Transmission codes are analogous to the rules governing the structure of any given language, with syntax governing the meaning of arrangement of symbols. Protocol is analogous to the rules governing the use of language, etiquette if you will: listening without interrupting while another speaks for example, or timing an interruption

ASCII CODES (7-BIT)			
CHARACTER	ASCII CODE	CHARACTER	ASCII CODE
@	1000000	FORM FEED	0001100
A	1000001	CARRIAGE RETURN	0001101
B	1000010	RUBOUT	1111111
C	1000011	SPACE	0100000
D	1000100	!	0100001
E	1000101	"	0100010
F	1000110	#	0100011
G	1000111	$	0100100
H	1001000	%	0100101
I	1001001	&	0100110
J	1001010	'	0100111
K	1001011	(	0101000
L	1001100	)	0101001
M	1001101	*	0101010
N	1001110	+	0101011
O	1001111	,	0101100
P	1010000	–	0101101
Q	1010001	.	0101110
R	1010010	/	0101111
S	1010011	0	0110000
T	1010100	1	0110001
U	1010101	2	0110010
V	1010110	3	0110011
W	1010111	4	0110100
X	1011000	5	0110101
Y	1011001	6	0110110
Z	1011010	7	0110111
[	1011011	8	0111000
\	1011100	9	0111001
]	1011101	:	0111010
	1011110	;	0111011
NULL	0000000	<	0111100
HORIZ TAB	0001001	=	0111101
LINE FEED	0001010	>	0111110
VERT TAB	0001011	?	0111111

Figure 15-19 ASCII Codes (7-Bit)

to coincide with a natural break when the listener wishes to become the speaker without being rude or colliding with the previous speaker's unfinished transmission.

Asynchronous Transmission. Used frequently in low volume, sporadic transmission situations such as with "dumb" terminals, where the transmission usually in itself only constitutes a small load on the network but since each transmission arises sporadically and there may be many such stations, it must be synchronized with everything else which can occur on the network by transmitting a start and stop bit to the receiving equipment before and after the data to be sent.

Synchronous Transmission. Unlike free-running asynchronous equipment, stations using synchronous transmission are each locked into a common timing signal regulating their behavior. Usually employed in block rather than character by character transfer of data, synchronous transmission supports much higher transmission speeds, sophisticated error detection, error correction, and automatic retransmission of data if required. Buffers, mentioned earlier, are usually interspersed between the transmitting and receiving equipment to permit high volume, high-speed bursts of data blocks.

Bysynch. Binary synchronous communication protocol, developed by IBM, is the most commonly used synchronous protocol. A half-duplex, character-oriented protocol which can be used with a variety of transmission codes, it is frequently used in applications where polling, interrogating the network for active stations, is employed.

HDLC. High level data link control procedures represent attempts by major manufacturers to improve on bisynch protocols. Used more in Europe than in the United States, they are bit-oriented protocols.

Parity. This is a technique which is employed to ensure that the data received correspond exactly to that which were transmitted. For a variety of reasons, electromagnetically induced interference, power transients, and so on, bits of data can be erroneously dropped or added to a transmission on a network. Various parity techniques can be applied to not only detect but also correct this should it occur. Parity can be **odd, even, vertical**, or **horizontal**. Odd or even parity simply means adding one or more bits to the data being transmitted to ensure that the 1s bits of each character add up to an odd or even number upon arrival.

Vertical Parity. With vertical parity, the system simply counts the number of 1 bits contained in each character prior to the transmission and then compares this with what is received for an odd or even number as predetermined. Any bit gained or loss during transmission, a 1 bit becoming a 0 or vice versa will be detected. However, if an even number of bits are corrupted, the bits total will still add up to an odd or even number and errors of this kind would pass undetected. This problem can be dealt with by using **horizontal** parity, also known as **longitudinal redundancy check (LRC)**. Unlike vertical parity, which only examines each character of a block of data by character only, horizontal parity examines each individual bit. Obviously, this approach lends itself to synchronous rather than asynchronous transmission where blocks rather than bits or bytes of data are being transmitted en masse. A refinement of this technique, called **cyclic redundancy check (CRC)**, employs statistical algorithms in conjunction with block check characters added to the data to check the integrity of every bit in every character. Correct transmission is acknowledged with a handshake signal from receiver to transmitter called ACK. In the event of an error, handshake consists of a NAK signal which can automatically initiate retransmission of the previously corrupted data.

Linespeed and Bandwidth

As we discussed earlier, transmission lines, the physical interconnect between pieces of equipment or from an equipment station to the network can take several forms. This, in conjunction with the speed characteristics of the equipment and any modems interspersed in the line will determine the linespeed (bits-per-second) and the bandwidth (the frequency range) of the line. Within a business complex, equipment in close physical proximity is likely to be interconnected using a medium which supports digital signal traffic only. (In the digital only domain, where only short distances are involved, linespeed and bandwidth can be very much higher than even the most superior analog transmission line.) As distance between nodes increases, progressively more use of the existing telephone network is made, both within and especially outside of the physical boundaries of the complex, especially where geographic dispersion of the nodes is great. In this analog domain, transmission lines tend to be classified into three general categories in terms of bandwidth and linespeed.

1. **Subvoice or narrowband.** This category offers a bandwidth of less than 300 Hz (Hertz) and can support data speeds up to 180 bps (bits-per-second) only. As such, it is usually only suitable for direct, short distance connection of low-speed (dumb) equipment. (Generally speaking, data rate is inversely proportional to transmission line length. This is true of all grades of transmission.)
2. **Voice-grade band.** In this category, bandwidth extends from 300 Hz to 3000 Hz and data speed can range from 300 bps to 14,400 and in some cases beyond.
3. **Wideband or broadband.** This category includes transmission lines with bandwidths greater than 2,700 Hz and can support data rates of 64,000 bps and above. Of particular interest in networking environments, this scheme allows voice, digital date, and video signals to coexist on the same line.

Still within the analog domain, these lines can be **metallic, dial, dual dial**, or **lease**.

Metallic. This is usually a short, direct, four-wire, dedicated telecommunications link between two stations. As such, quality of the line, and therefore transmission speed, will be high, but since the line is dedicated, the link will be vulnerable in the event of line-down unless a backup contingency has been provided.

Dial. This is normally a two-wire, half-duplex, pay as you go, public telephone network line with its own telephone number. It has therefore, all of the advantages, and disadvantages, of this system.

Dual Dial. This involves the use of two pairs of lines in order to support full-duplex communication and therefore improve on the response time of the single dial approach.

Lease. These are, normally four wire, full-duplex, private lines, leased from the telecommunications authority. Always a direct, permanent link between two stations, this approach provides short response time and high transmission speed, but cost is fixed independent of use.

Bus Arbitration. Since the network itself is a common resource shared by a wide proliferation of equipment, any one of which will have occasion to use the network for communication purposes, some means must be employed to manage access to and resolve potential conflict in the use of this resource by all equipment stations or nodes. There are several approaches, the main ones being token ring or bus and carrier sense multiple detect (CSMA) with or without collision detection (CD).

Token Ring. With this approach, each station on the network is given the opportunity to gain access by means of a special packet of information, the token, which circulates on the network behind the last block of data transmitted by a station. A station which requires access to the network asserts this need by "capturing" the token. This station then transmits its block of data and issues a new token which is then available for capture by another station. Using this approach, access priority, access periodic—

the token rotation time—and the amount of data which can be sent during any capture period can be regulated. The maximum time any station must wait for access to the network is controlled and station response time, therefore, can be assured within a predictable time.

CSMA/CD—Carrier Sense Multiple Access. This approach relies on each station on the network "listening" for the presence of a carrier to confirm whether or not another station is using the network. When this is not the case, any station can then commandeer the network for its own use but must still listen to detect the possibility that another station may be coincidentally attempting to do the same. Should this be so, a "collision" is said to have occurred and all stations involved must cease transmission immediately until the network is again free. This is an adequate approach where data traffic consists of short, sporadic bursts, such as in a general office environment, but as network loading increases, overall performance rapidly degrades beyond a network dependent threshold. On a heavily loaded network, since several attempts to gain access may be necessary, the length of time for a device to response to a control signal cannot be predicted. Fast, real-time response to a control signal therefore, cannot be assured. Since factory applications are typically of the consistently heavy, large data block traffic variety, CSMA is considered to be less suitable for this environment than is token ring or bus.

As was mentioned earlier, there are three broad classes of generic network architectures, each with their relative advantages and disadvantages.

In a ring formation, the serial structure requires that information to or from any station be routed through all other stations, the address of the target station being carried with the transmitted message. This can result in considerable redundant traffic on the network since each station can be called upon to simply relay information not intended for it to another station in the chain. Also, due to its serial structure, the failure of any one station will most probably pull down the whole network. This will also be the effect in adding or deleting stations. The star configuration represents a much less vulnerable arrangement since each station can be managed to operate independently of all others. The existence of a central node, however, optionally available as an active node or merely as a central connection point, may require longer cable runs than that required by either a ring or bus approach. The additional cost of this will vary according to the form of physical interconnect employed, twisted pair, coaxial cable, and so on.

For industrial environments, the bus topology would appear to be the most suitable architecture. Stations associated with manufacturing cells, for example, may be tapped into the bus at any point, stations may be added or deleted, which is a frequent requirement in a manufacturing process, with little or no impact on the rest of the system, and control can be established at any time from any point on the bus, permitting distributed control capability. Yet another important aspect of the bus structure's attractiveness is the opportunity to establish a reconfigurable logical ring structure to support token passing (see bus arbitration).

In addition to physical configuration, another important network characteristic requiring further selection is that of the physical interconnect. This too must be decided according to the network characteristics criteria established earlier. Twisted pair is by far the cheapest but is by far the most limited in performance in terms of data transfer speed and distances attainable, limited to approximately one or two Mbps and about one kilometer maximum distance respectively. Equally limited, although aesthetically more pleasing, is flat ribbon cable. Coaxial cable, perhaps the most widely used interconnect, can be good up to about 10 Mbps and over distances up to about two and one-half kilometers. Fiberoptic cable offers by far the best performance of any physical linking medium (satellites are obviously unsurpassable for vast distance) being lighter than coaxial cable, much less susceptible to extraneously induced electromagnetic or electrostatic interference and is capable of supporting data rates of 100 Mbps and more with little signal attenuation, but being a still relatively new technology, is still somewhat more expensive. With such a wide spread in cost/performance ratio, it makes sense to employ these solutions selectively in a mix and match mode as appropriate.

Standardization

With such a wealth of choice in architecture, protocol, physical links, transmission codes, and so on, it is perhaps not surprising that there is no universally accepted ''one best way'' of designing a network suitable for every application environment into which any piece of equipment, from any vendor anywhere in the world, can be easily interfaced. Until now, the absence of any clearly favored popular consensus solution has resulted in a proliferation of proprietary solutions from major vendors—Ethernet, PC-Net, AppleTalk, Starlan, Omninet, Arcnet, Telenet, Tynet, and so on, each hoping, but lacking the influence, to establish a de facto standard by default. Being able to integrate these diverse partial solutions into a cohesive total application requirement solution has precipitated much activity in the design and development of bridges and gateway products as unifying links. While these approaches are likely to continue unabated, it would seem that in the light of General Motors' very strong declaration in favor of manufacturing automation protocol (MAP) that this will provide some unifying influence by being widely accepted as the common underlying infrastructure in future network design, at least those in industry applications oriented toward supporting ''factory of the future'' manufacturing concepts. These efforts are being orchestrated by various International Standards Organization (ISO) committees in which GM is playing a vigorous leading role. (See Figure 15-20.) These proceedings bring structure to the task of creating order out of what is, on first impression at least, chaos by using the ISO model as a core upon which to build solutions to each element of network hierarchy. Standards activity addressing networks up to 50 Mbps are being led by the IEEE organization, those above this by ANSI Committee X3t9.5.

Based on the Open System Interconnect Model (OSI)

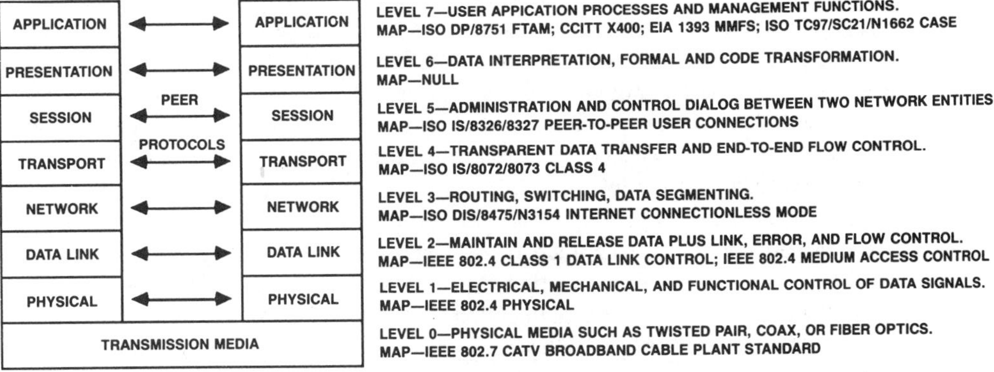

Figure 15-20 ISO Standards Activity

Allan Bradley Application Level Model

Machinery Process Level. The first level where the cutting edge of the tool in a manufacturing process interfaces with the product, sensing input parameters such as speed, temperature, pressure, and physical dimensions, on the one hand and outputting control signals to various functions on the other. In a SPC application, for example, output parameters of the process would be measured and using an appropriate servo-loop feedback mechanism, input signals regulating the process would be generated to provide real-time process control.

Station Level. Continuing with our SPC example, decisions based on the values of the output parameters of the process would be taken at this level (microprocessor level).

Cell Level. The level at which several operations in a multitask work cell or module would be integrated and coordinated (microcomputer level).

Manufacturing Center. The level at which supply and demand would be reconciled—demand schedules, shop orders, bills of materials, process specifications, machine loading and status to plan schedules, and so on.

Plant Level. The level at which overall planning and coordination, material requirements planning, parts ordering and payroll, and so on, would be controlled.

Corporate Level (X.25). The level at which corporate strategic planning, the coordination and a collection of multi-strategic business units operating statements would occur.

GM-MAP Manufacturing Automation Protocol

MAP represents General Motor's approach to solving the problem of integrating a wide proliferation of electronically controlled equipment, from a variety of different vendors, to a common network. Based on the ISO open systems interconnect model shown in Figure 15-21, it is a non-proprietary, ten megabit-per-second, broadband, token bus controlled communication standard in the process of being developed by a task force led by GM's Manufacturing Engineering and Development Group.

Consistent with the ISO model shown, the first four layers deal with issues common to devices connected to the same network such as would be the case for equipment in a cell configuration perhaps on the factory floor. Level zero, the transmission media layer, defines these standards pertaining to the physical interconnect aspects of hardware—the type of cable (twisted pair, coaxial, and so on), data transmission rate, network access method. Level 1, the physical layer, deals with mechanical interfacing standards—primary dialogue protocol and the levels and timing of electrical interface signals. Level 2, the data link level, establishes the communication protocol—odd or even parity, the error detection and correction technique to be employed, the structure of the data frames (blocks), which are to be transmitted. Level 3, called the network layer, controls the signal routing, switching, and segmenting of the data blocks. So important are these levels in an automated industrial environment, where rapid communication at a machine to machine level is required for such things as real-time process control, that a subset

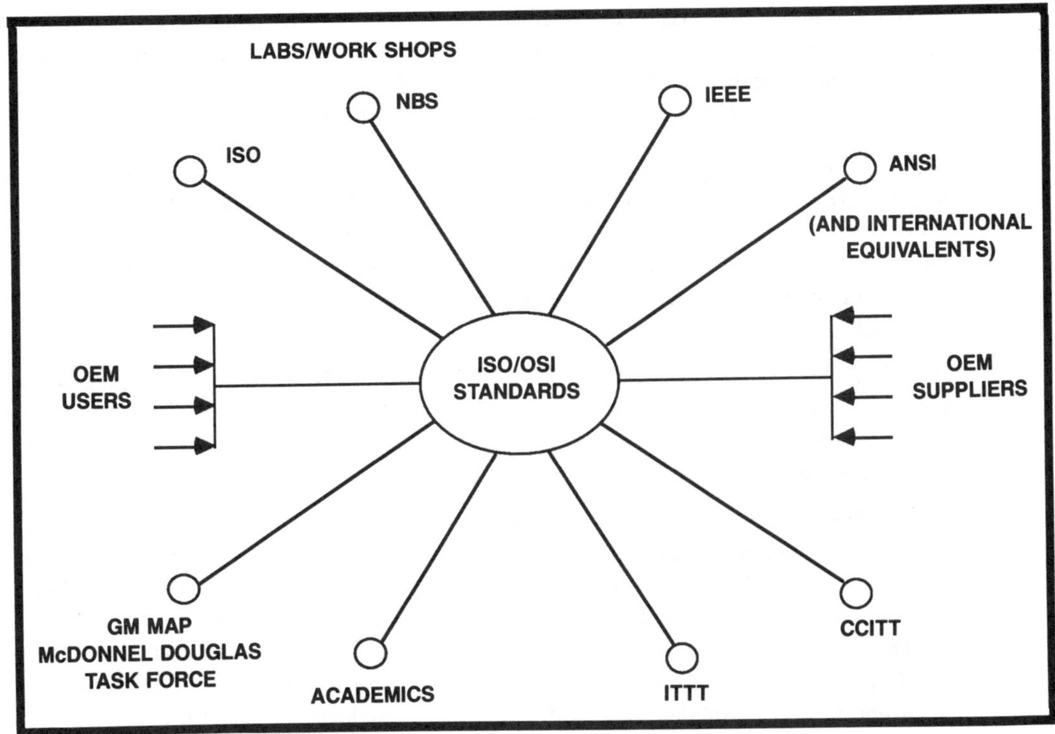

Figure 15-21 A Simplified Explanation of the 7 + Layer Model and MAP Standards

of MAP, called Mini MAP, is being developed. Mini MAP is a single channel, five mega-bits-per-second baseband rather than broadband standard.

Layers 5 to 7 of MAP, like these of the ISO model, address the standardizing of interconnectability attributes of different networks as might be the case in expanding communications beyond the factory floor to the factory level itself. Integrating order entry information with machine loading and execution control would be a typical example of this need. Layer 5, the session layer, facilitates communication between different application programs running on different stations. Layer 6, the application layer, ensures that any application program, running on any station, will interface successfully with any display terminal connected to the network. Layer 7, the application level, ensures file transportability from station to station.

Support for this approach is very broadbased with many OEM equipment manufacturers committed to including MAP compatibility in their products with the service sector supporting these OEM suppliers committed to developing and making available board, and eventually chip level, interface solutions in order to expand connectability at lower cost. Even so, to develop and implement a MAP network can still be a lengthy and costly process since much of the equipment already in use and therefore not intrinsically compatible, will require custom solutions to the interfacing problem. Much of this existing capital equipment may already in fact be networked using more proprietary working standard networking solutions such as Ethernet or Decnet. Intended for general and engineering office environments rather than the factory floor, Ethernet is designed to handle sporadic, but infrequent, large data block transfers, not the typically short, frequent bursts demanding real-time control encountered in a work station or cell environment. As such, it is only a single channel, broadband network utilizing CSMA/CD, making token and transmission management simpler but less powerful and flexible. While less costly to implement, it is not comparable to the complex, but more powerful broadband transmission capability of MAP. Being incomparable does not necessarily mean incompatible, however, and it is likely that coexistence will be supported.

Note 1: Since learning through the elbow is a function of frequency—the number of learning cycles in a given period—and frequency is a function of each individual operation cycle time and complexity, designing each task to require the least amount of skill minimizes learning time. The other side of the coin however, confirmed by many studies in job enrichment, is that boredom can prevent the rapid early progress from being sustained.

Note 2: A basic law of electronics is that "like repels, unlike attracts." For example, a north pole and south pole of two magnets will attract each other, two north or two south poles will repel. In a similar way, negatively charged electrons will repel each other but will be attracted, physically drawn, to a positive electrical charge.

Note 3: Wickham Skinner's message is simple but of fundamental importance—it is that a company's manufacturing policies must be consistent with the way it is competing in the marketplace. No factory, Skinner argues, can achieve every objective—low cost, perfect consistency, high quality, short lead times, wide product range, high flexibility—but any factory can be designed to achieve just one of these things. *The Good Book Guide for Business* (Wickham Skinner). Wickham Skinner is the James E. Robinson Professor of Business Administration at Harvard University's Graduate School of Business. These are the historical mutually exclusive imperatives of manufacturing. This is no longer acceptable in the modern competitive environment.

BUSINESS AND STRATEGIC MANAGEMENT

16

Software and CIM

INTRODUCTION—WHY CIM?

> **"The time has come" the walrus said.**
> **"To talk of many things.**
> **Of shoes—and ships—and sealing wax—**
> **Of cabbages and kings—**
> **And why the sea is boiling hot—**
> **And whether pigs have wings."**
>
> *Lewis Carroll—Alice Through the Looking Glass*

In a way, the acronym CIM (computer integrated manufacturing) is unfortunate since **it implies that the need to integrate computers, or computer backed systems, is limited to the factory floor**. In many manufacturing businesses, the problem is not so much that the equipment on the factory floor is not integrated and needs to be, but that the "front end" of the business is not, or that there is a major disconnect between what goes on in the front office or the design department and the shop floor. After new product introduction, where computer aided design (CAD) and computer aided manufacturing (CAM) are often integrated to reduce the design/development cycle-time, one of the next principal justifications in embarking on a CIM project is **to reduce the cycle-time from receipt of a customer's order to delivery on products already released to production**. That the cycle-time is longer than one would wish is usually assumed to be because of long cycle-times in manufacturing. Analysis usually shows however that it is at least in part due to the methods used in entering the order into the company's system, processing the information, communicating it to the factory floor and then transferring product and ownership across the organizational interfaces between functionally specialized departments as the product proceeds through the manufacturing process. This is not to say that the cycle-time on the factory floor is not also too long or that efforts be spared to reduce it, or that the individual pieces of equipment which make up the manufacturing system do not need to be integrated; but rather that **the scope of CIM should be considered to be from order entry to shipping, and not simply limited to manufacturing**. Computer integrated business (CIB), or computer integrated enterprise (CIE), or even computer integrated organization (CIO) might be a more appropriate description but somehow these acronyms are not as catchy for purveyors of automation to peddle. (In our particular case, this problem was addressed by means of IBIS discussed more fully in Chapter 12. Also see Figure 16-1. For our purposes here however, we shall stick with the popular convention.

Even with the correct perspective on scope, many well-intentioned CIM efforts have subsequently proven to be abortive. There are many reasons for this, but one of the most frequent is a result of **picking the wrong place to start**. It is not atypical for a CIM project to begin by attempting to integrate miscellaneous pieces of equipment which already exist on the factory floor, so called "islands of automation," migrating outwards from this point to progressively "absorb" other pieces with an assortment of hardware and software "patches." This is rather like trying to build a jigsaw from the miscellaneous pieces in a child's toy box: one does not have a vision of the desired end result (the jigsaw puzzle picture), does not know if all of the pieces are available, or if the pieces available will fit.

DEFINING THE SYSTEM—THE DESIRED END RESULT

The correct place to start a CIM program is not deep in the bowels of the factory, but:

1. **With a clear definition of the desired end result in terms of the business (not technology) parameters, that such an integration is expected to produce,**
2. **With a detailed understanding of the process currently employed,**
3. **With an appreciation of what is currently technically feasible—and what is not—in terms of CIM, and then**
4. **To migrate, from this desired end result, back into the infrastructure of the system with an understanding of the attributes that will be required of the system.**

In general terms, a business exists to satisfy customer needs. Assuming that the new product definition and marketing efforts have been successful, these needs are made known to the enterprise in the form of an order for a product or service, the specification of which is predetermined or agreed. It is at least part of the business function then to process the information received in order to interpret the requirement, to communicate the appropriate instructions to those concerned in satisfying it, and then to process these instructions on the factory floor prior to delivering the product. In summary, **a business must process information about the order before processing the product to satisfy the order**. This then is the answer to the question posed at the beginning: **if we cannot manage our data, we cannot possibly expect to manage our factory or our business**. The earlier this information can be converted into a form suitable for electronic processing, the shorter the delivery cycle-time will be. To actually receive the information from the customer in this form is the most ideal. It is good to remember, however, that CIM communication is not confined exclusively to machines but includes human communication needs as well. Unlike computers, humans do not cope well with electronic 1s and 0s whizzing around a network.

The expected output of the system, to deliver a product or service, will be defined in general, in terms of product functionality, quality, cost, on-time delivery, and service related parameters—the ingredients of total customer satisfaction—**and the nature and scope of this expected output will determine the attributes required by the system being integrated**. A single, standard product, single process, perhaps even single customer enterprise, will only require CIM, if at all, in its simplest form—a system whose data traffic will be a homogeneous stream, varying only in volume and modulated perhaps

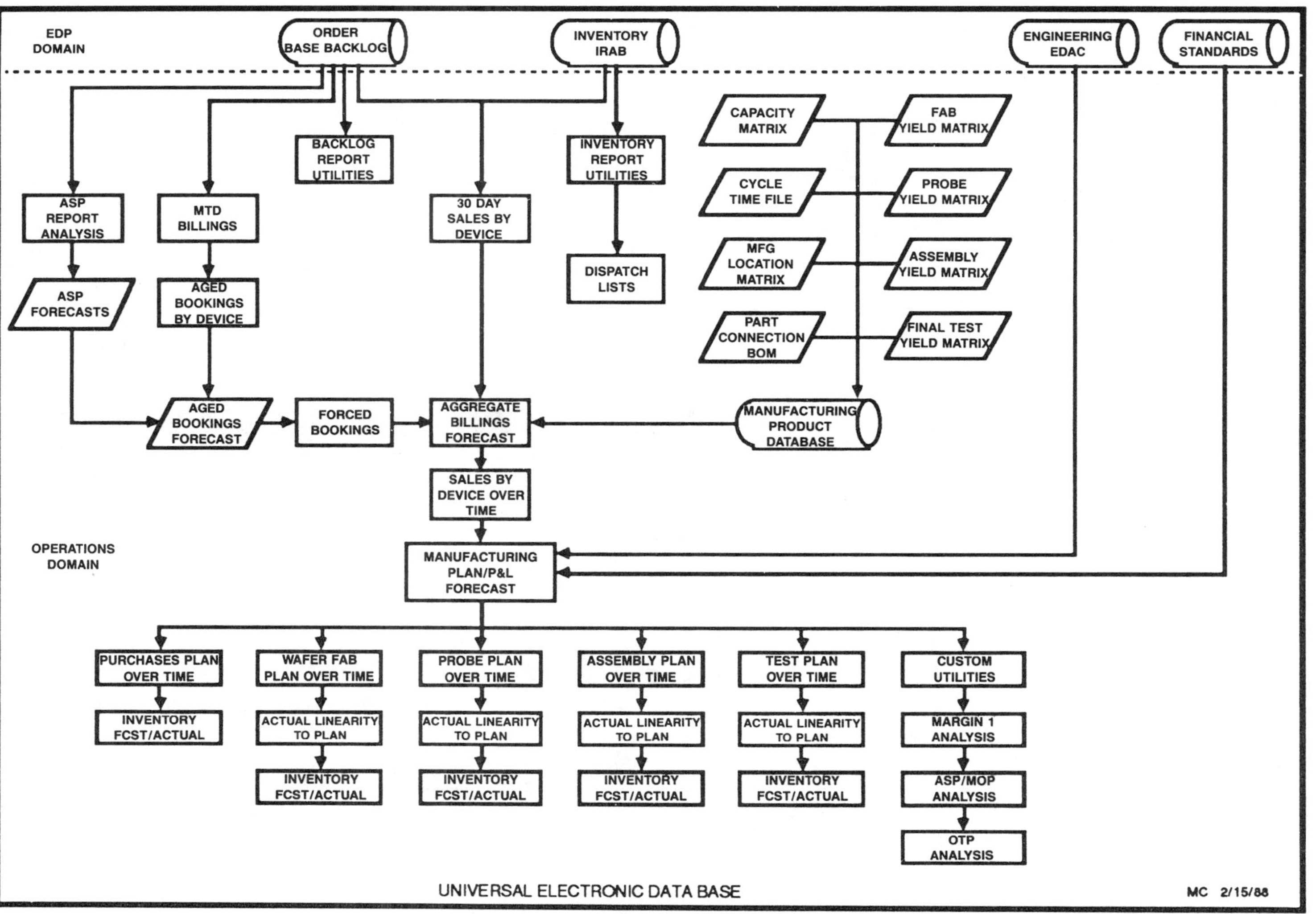

Figure 16-1 Integrated Business Information System

only by the complexity of the product itself. The other extreme, a multiproduct, multiprocess, multicustomer base enterprise, with perhaps varying lot sizes, offering standard, semi-custom and full-custom products, will require something quite different in which the data traffic will consist of **"packets of information"** associated with each customer order or factory tracking lot, only part of which may be generic, the remainder being specific or **unique to each customer or product**. The former, in dealing with a much less complex situation, may achieve the desired end result by any one of a variety of means other than CIM, thus avoiding all of the time, effort, and cost involved. The latter will almost certainly find it to be indispensible. (ASICs, single chip MCUs, customized standard products are examples of the kind of businesses in the semiconductor industry which require this kind of CIM infrastructure.) Among all of the rationales used to justify embarking on such a time consuming and costly effort, there is in fact only one which is universally valid; that is:

The need to meet escalating customer requirements of quality, cost, and on-time delivery—across a wide product portfolio, to a wide customer base, in varying lot sizes—despite ever increasing complexity of products and processes—by processing the information associated with processing the product . . . in electronic form. That is . . . to **integrate "islands of information"** . . . and then **"islands of automation" . . . in that order!** More pragmatically, if the MIS department has the charter to orchestrate CIM, what would their internal "customers" define as total satisfaction? More than likely it would include the following:

1. **Real-time, universal access to specific information**
2. **The elimination of nonelectronic data transfers**
3. **A portfolio of self-help, user tools**
4. **A paperless environment**
5. **Any node to any other node(s) transactions**

Generally speaking, there are three broad directions which a CIM implementation might follow, two of which are intercompany, the third being intracompany:

1. **Top to bottom**, linking the vertical hierarchy within the organization.

2. **Product beginning to end**—the new product design/development/manufacture and ship cycle—CAD to CIM—linking horizontally through individual organizations as it were. This in fact, is the direction required by a comprehensive statistical process control system.

3. **Inside to outside**, linking both supplier and customer data bases to that of the enterprise. The most ambitious challenge is to attempt all of this simultaneously. This is probably not a good strategy.

BUILDING THE SYSTEM—HOW CIM?

As in the internal combustion engine, where the hardware design determines the ultimate operating potential, the software is the fuel which makes computers productive and determines the degree to which this potential is realized. It is to the design and realization of this potential which we now turn. The hardware subcomponents of the system, the building blocks as it were, linked together by coaxial or fiber optic cable in a network, have already been discussed. We now turn our attention from these "hard," physical components to the "soft" ones. **While the overall system design must be top down, the actual building of the system, as in building the hardware, will be from the bottom up**. We shall start at this level, at one of the application nodes of the system, explaining how software development has evolved to the point it is at today and expand outwards and upwards through the infrastructure as the integration process proceeds, finally arriving at the overall, system software level. As we saw, there were many incompatibility problems with hardware due to equipment proliferation and lack of standards. We find the same thing in software to an even greater extent.

A TYPICAL APPLICATION

Let's consider a very typical application on a CIM network: **business or technical report writing**. Imagine that one of our engineers has to write a product lot report, including a statistical process control history for a population of product being manufactured for a very important, overseas customer, who requires the report to be shipped with the product. To do so, our engineer will need access to information possibly contained in several, nonuniversally accessible, geographically dispersed data base domains within the company, as well as various software programs to assist in preparing his report. The report is to contain a record of the product's manufacturing history, the process yields at various operations, a statistical analysis of the population at each critical step in the process and a correlation of the parameters measured in the wafer fabrication area with the electrical parameters measured in final package form at test. The product movement history through the factory or factories, consisting of quantities and dates in to and out of the various operations, will almost certainly be stored on the company's corporate mainframe computer, perhaps an IBM 9370 for example. (The reader will recall this as one of the first applications of computers in industry. This usually proves to be a most cumbersome legacy.) Since IBM has 70 percent of the mainframe computer market, this is not an improbable scenario. If this is a typical system, our user will have these data made available to him embedded in a paper printout—along with the data of all other users.

Being short of time, and not inclined to such menial work anyway, he will persuade the department secretary to visually search the file for the information he needs and have her record it on another piece of paper. If he is fortunate, he can avoid this tedious process if his company has granted nonelectronic data processing types access to the corporate archives and made a search tool such as structured query language (SQL) available to the user community. Armed with this tool, and provided he has learned how to use it, or can persuade someone to do it for him, he can use this to search the corporate data base for the information he seeks. If he is extremely fortunate, the word processor application program he intends to use to write the text of his report, or the spreadsheet he intends to use to tabulate his data, will have this capability embedded in it already. By whatever means, and a great deal of time and determination, he now has his data—already in his personal computer data base if he is lucky—or on a sheet of paper if he isn't—in which case he then faces a keyboard load of these data into his PC.

Having reached this point, he then uses the operating system on his machine to call in the spreadsheet program he now needs to organize, process, and tabulate his data in the format he needs. But at this point he has only dealt with the inventory data. The quality data, which he needs for the process analysis part of the report, is in the manufacturing department's Digital Equipment Corporation minicomputer, having been downloaded from individual machine cells using a program which he himself wrote sometime before. The process of getting these data from the mini into his PC will be similar to that involved with the mainframe. In addition to this, the SPC data needs to be processed—to compute means and standard deviations of the product lot for example—using a software application program which only runs on the design department's Sun or Apollo engineering work stations, since some of the data have to be made available to the customer in graphic form. All of this he then has to assemble into a single, cohesive report—most probably using cut and paste if his machine is not capable, which it almost certainly isn't, of this degree of integration. He then has to distribute the report to several geographically dispersed locations in order to get internal management approval prior to releasing it to the field sales manager in Munich, who will then pass it on to the customer. Again, if he is fortunate, there will be an internal, electronic mail system running on the corporate mainframe available to do this. If not, he reaches for his supply of envelopes and mail drop codes.

PRODUCTIVITY AND CYCLE-TIME

To summarize then, the tools our engineer needed—the software application programs—were: (1) structured query language—to interrogate the various data bases; (2) word processor—with which to write the report text; (3) graphics software—for the treatment of data required to be presented in this form; (4) spreadsheet—to tabulate, process arithmetically and format data; (5) machine control download software; (6) statistical process control data acquisition and analysis software; (7) CAD; (8) CAM; and finally (9) electronic mail. With a fully integrated CIM network, with all of the application program data bases compatible, he can do this task in a few hours. Without it, it will take patience, tenacity, and much legwork over several days or even weeks. If the report has to be modified—and supervisors almost always require that they do, don't they?—he can do so quickly and easily with the system. Without it he will probably quit. The task we set our engineer called upon all of the resources of the CIM network. If we can satisfy his needs, almost certainly we can satisfy the needs of any and every other user. It is to this challenge we now turn.

THE EVOLUTION OF CIM—WHERE IT BEGAN! WHERE IT'S GOING! WHERE IT'S AT!

CIM cannot by any means be considered to be a mature technology. The fact that it is not, that it is still very much in an evolutionary mode, makes it very difficult to measure where it is at on the development scale. From the outside looking in, it looks like chaos. How does one bring order out of this chaos? Although the transitionary phase we are currently in is indeed cluttered, the start and end points can be fairly well defined, however, allowing us to set at least rough limits on the scale. Intermediate graduation points, described in terms of phases, help to establish how much progress has been made already, assisting then to some extent in quantifying what remains to be done. Also, although there is a bewildering proliferation of hardware and software products available, from a vast range of suppliers, we shall find that **there is a common nucleus of software** (as is also the case for hardware), **around which much else is built**.

The upper limit on the scale, the desired end result described in our engineering task at the beginning, is easiest to define. It will only be reached when:

1. Real-time, universal access to all data banks is realized—the elimination of "islands of information" prior to integrated automation.

2. **Electronic transfer of all data is realized.**
3. **Software is fully integrated or "transportable."**

These end objectives can only be realized when **the standardization process has reached the point where universal interoperability is possible . . . if ever.**

This then defines the end of the scale. The origin of the scale lies back somewhere in the late 1950s, early 1960s. Prior to this period, computers were so big, unreliable and expensive, that their use was confined to heavily funded, scientific research work. As they became less expensive, more reliable and more generally available, they were then used in industry to handle such "islands of information" as inventory and payroll. **Like the functionally specialized organizations they serviced, they too became isolated and territorially protected**. Only in the mid-1960s did computers begin to be applied to the actual **wealth-creating process** on the factory floor, initially in the form of automatic test equipment, where the "expected" desired end result of the manufacturing subcomponent of the total organization system could be relatively easily and unambiguously defined in terms of the product operating specification. Then came machines with processing power and memory, as we discussed earlier, which were applied to the actual, **value-adding operations** in the manufacturing process. Then of course, individual personal computers and engineering work stations began to appear in both office and on the factory floor to serve the indirect categories of employees. **It was the obvious merit of having these "intelligent" tools communicate with each other in a cooperative way which led to the evolution of CIM. The problem which CIM efforts face today in addition to these organizational legacies from the past is that these machines were not designed to be integrated**. (In a way, we are asking machines to do what we as humans have only been partially successful in doing.) Even efforts to integrate within one narrowly defined domain, such as a personal computer, where attempts to integrate the data base software with the word processor and spread sheet for example, have proved to be extremely difficult. Unlike the until recently, highly regulated telephone industry, where the network came first and then the telephones themselves, forcing models from different vendors to be compatible with it, in the very open market computer industry, the machines themselves came first, each with their unique software, and then the networks.

The need for CIM emerged as a result of both divergent and convergent forces. In the beginning, there was IBM and AT&T. Each dominated what were then two very distinct, stand-alone industries—data processing and telecommunications, respectively. Although in many cases, each shared customers in common with the other, **the data processing and telecommunication needs of these customers were seen to be distinct and were serviced separately**. (This is the practice of market segmentation and customer differentiation advocated in marketing text books. Could it be the CIM players of today are making the same mistake by segmenting the market into (1) office automation, (2) factory automation, (3) software automation, and (4) vertical integration?) The machines available for data processing then were large, expensive, and had substantial capacity—more than could be typically consumed by one task. The cost and capacity of these machines mandated that customers who could either not justify the capacity or the cost of owning their own equipment, would subcontract their inventory or payroll runs to IBM for batch processing at some central location. Those with larger workloads and budgets could lease the hardware and software from IBM. The really rich and powerful could even persuade them to sell them a machine and to customize, at a price, some software for them. The data would be physically shuttled to and from these locations to be manually transposed onto punched cards or paper tape prior to being ingested by the computer for processing. (The use of punched cards is still a widespread practice even today.) Output was provided on paper printouts and again physically transported back to the owner or user.

Perhaps lulled into a sense of false security behind patent protection, this privileged position inculcated in IBM the belief that it was in the high margin, data processing service business—not the business of taking care of customer information management needs in the most cost effective and least inconvenient way to the customer, no doubt leading to the arrogance and complacency of which IBM has occasionally been accused. AT&T, on the other hand, saw themselves as being in the telephone rather than the data communication business. With networks and telephones, they serviced the analogue communication needs, but not the digital data processing and communication needs, of people separated geographically.

THE DIGITAL AND ANALOG WORLDS START TO CONVERGE

Up to this point, data transfer—from machine to machine, or person to machine, and vice versa—was by physical transportation means. Remote terminals did appear, but relying on digital transmission as they did then, their distance was very limited. The technology which made greater distance possible for transmission of digital data, the link to unite the digital and analog worlds, until then entirely separate domains, was the modem. Initially nonintegrated in silicon, and therefore expensive, their use was limited. (Communication integration can be achieved in hardware which is fast, reliable but inflexible, or software which is flexible, but slower and less reliable.) Over the course of time, the semiconductor industry brought low cost and high quality and reliability to this technology and made more widespread use possible. At first, only mainframes were interconnected by this means. Over the course of time, mainframe machines began to be used for order entry—a very simple but repetitive, high volume task, and then product design—an infrequent but massive number crunching task. Whatever the task, **data processing was very much a highly centralized activity**.

Life was much simpler then. Products and processes were much less complex and customer expectations much less demanding. The divergent force came with the arrival of the ever pervasive personal computer, making real-time, decentralized processing—albeit confined to unique local data bases—possible for the first time. At first, these machines were little more than toys. Indeed the highest volume markets were for games, but over the course of time, they have evolved into the highly sophisticated business tools they are today.

THE EVOLUTION OF THE PERSONAL COMPUTER

1. **Stand-alone** (Toys/Games)
2. **Business application software** (Word processor/spreadsheet—the de facto "standards" become established)
3. **Linked to mainframes** (Dual Role—PC/Network Terminal)
4. **Linked to other PCs** (Local Area Networks)
5. **Multitask** (Integration)
6. **The portable PC arrives on the scene**
7. **Metamorphosis to network terminal/engineering workstation—triple role** (32-bit architectures)

This created an explosive demand for lots of cheap software and led to the creation of many small, independent software firms. (There are some 25,000 software companies in the United States alone. The biggest of these, Computer Associates, has sales in the region of $600 million. IBM sales by comparison, are in the order of $60 billion per year.) In the future, this proliferation will almost certainly decrease as more and more mergers take place. According to Broadview Associates, the leading merger-broker in the software industry, the average take-over price of such firms is in the order of $7 to $10 million.

THE TRANSITION PERIOD—TODAY AND BEYOND

At this point, in the early 1980s, we have all of the ingredients necessary for the integration process to begin—including user need. Phase 1 of this evaluation process was completely counterproductive, a false start as it were. **Motivated by what was subsequently seen to be misguided parochial self-interest, vendors tried to defend their own particular cabbage patches by asserting their own de facto standards on users.** Cooperation was most certainly not the name of the game and vendors designed their machines without any regard whatsoever of the need to communicate with equipment from another vendor. That was the customer's problem. **The second phase was a user driven attempt to achieve the desired end result, using customized and therefore expensive, ad hoc hardware and software patches.** This fueled the creation and growth of these many small software companies and consultants. Success on a small scale was all that could ever be possible with this approach. **It is one which of necessity, is still very much in vogue.** (The worst of these would be called kludges—the most derogatory term for a piece of work in the engineering vernacular.) The third, emergent phase of **cooperative standardization on the part of suppliers** still has a very long way to run. This cooperative effort is formally supported by organizations such as the Corporation for Open Systems (COS), McLean, Virginia, a nonprofit international research and development consortium of more than 65 computer and communication companies, founded in 1986 to promote the development and acceptance of open standards interconnect (OSI) and integrated services digital network (ISDN) standards. In reality of course, these phases are not so distinct but overlap to a large extent. It is in this context of ostensibly "cooperating" on standardization in which each player's strategy should be examined. Few if any, are without "ulterior" motive. **Because of software's particular role in making the integration of all of the independent pieces of hardware assets productive as a complete entity, it is here that the battle for market share is being fought.** It is here where future profit potential is seen, in the main, to reside. Software is a much more open field than hardware, with no supplier in a dominant position, although as we shall see, there are, just as in hardware, a few key players able to influence future direction and outcome. This they are attempting to do by **gaining control of the very process of integration itself**. The specific issues of this integration process on which they are locking horns are **multitasking operating systems, data-base control, networking capability, and interoperability**. We shall briefly look at each of these in turn.

The software employed in a CIM network can be considered in terms of two broad categories. There is the **task specific application software**—the cutting-edge tools the engineer in our example needed. Then there is the **system operating software**, without which the applications software could neither be run nor produced. Included in the operating systems libraries are such general utilities as translators, editors, debuggers, compilers for creating application software, and networking control software. These are described in more detail later.

APPLICATION SOFTWARE

For obvious reasons, this is where we encounter the greatest proliferation. This in itself of course, is no bad thing, giving users plenty of choice. **It is more than annoying, however, when the application of interest to you does not run on the particular piece of equipment you happen to own or under the operating system you happen to have.** For most of the preceding tasks, our engineer would have used commercially available versions of these application programs on his personal computer. By far the most popular of these, the nucleus around which many other application programs are designed, each optimizing one feature or another, are: **LOTUS 1-2-3** spreadsheet, developed by Mick Kapor and Jonathan Sachs, accounting for fully two-thirds of all spread sheet programs in use today. **EXCEL** from Microsoft—running on Macintosh PCs and **Visicalc**, from Visicorp, developed by Dan Bricklin.

OPERATING SYSTEMS

The operating system software is the resource manager. It is the common operating environment for both program and programmer. It deals with generic, universal things, leaving the application program to deal only with these things which are application specific. It knows where everything is and what its status is. It can detect and interpret signals coming in from the keyboard, to call an application program perhaps. It knows where the line printer is and how to send data to it. The hardware of the system determines the speed at which the machine can process data, but the operating system determines the flexibility of the machine in handling a variety of tasks. Unfortunately, **in a typical CIM system, not all application nodes will be operating under the same operating system software, making internode communication difficult if not impossible**. The most popular operating systems by far currently being used are: **MICROSOFT Disc Operating System (MS-DOS)** for IBM and IBM Clone Personal Computers (Bill Gates), UNIX and Digital Equipment Corporation's VMS.

A recent major innovation in this field, although not due to be fully released until late 1988, is Microsoft's new OS/2 Operating System. Developed jointly with IBM, this operating system is designed to facilitate the implementation of IBM's Systems Application Architecture (SAA) standards on IBM's PS/2 microcomputers and mainframe machines. OS/2 will support a technique called multitasking—the execution of several programs or tasks at the same time—a capability without which the task of getting programs to cooperate with each other—a mandatory requirement in the integration process—can be extremely difficult and frustrating. Its predecessor DOS, in which the vast majority of personal computer programs are written, can only support one program at a time. IBM obviously hopes that this will prove to be an attractive vehicle for independent software houses to use in bringing up new software for IBM's machines.

Such improvements as multitasking lead to increased user productivity and of course, lower frustration in not having to wait for the machine. Existing multitasking operating systems normally multiplex between programs or tasks, spending a few milliseconds on each. To do so, the operating system must be in complete control of all of the system resources at all times in order to avoid data collision and conflict in the use of common resources. Time-sharing is really multiplexing. To the user, it looks as if the system is entirely dedicated to his task alone. In reality, the central processor is multiplexing across two or more tasks, spending a few milliseconds on each. Since machines normally only have one central processor, a common resource required by all tasks and applications,

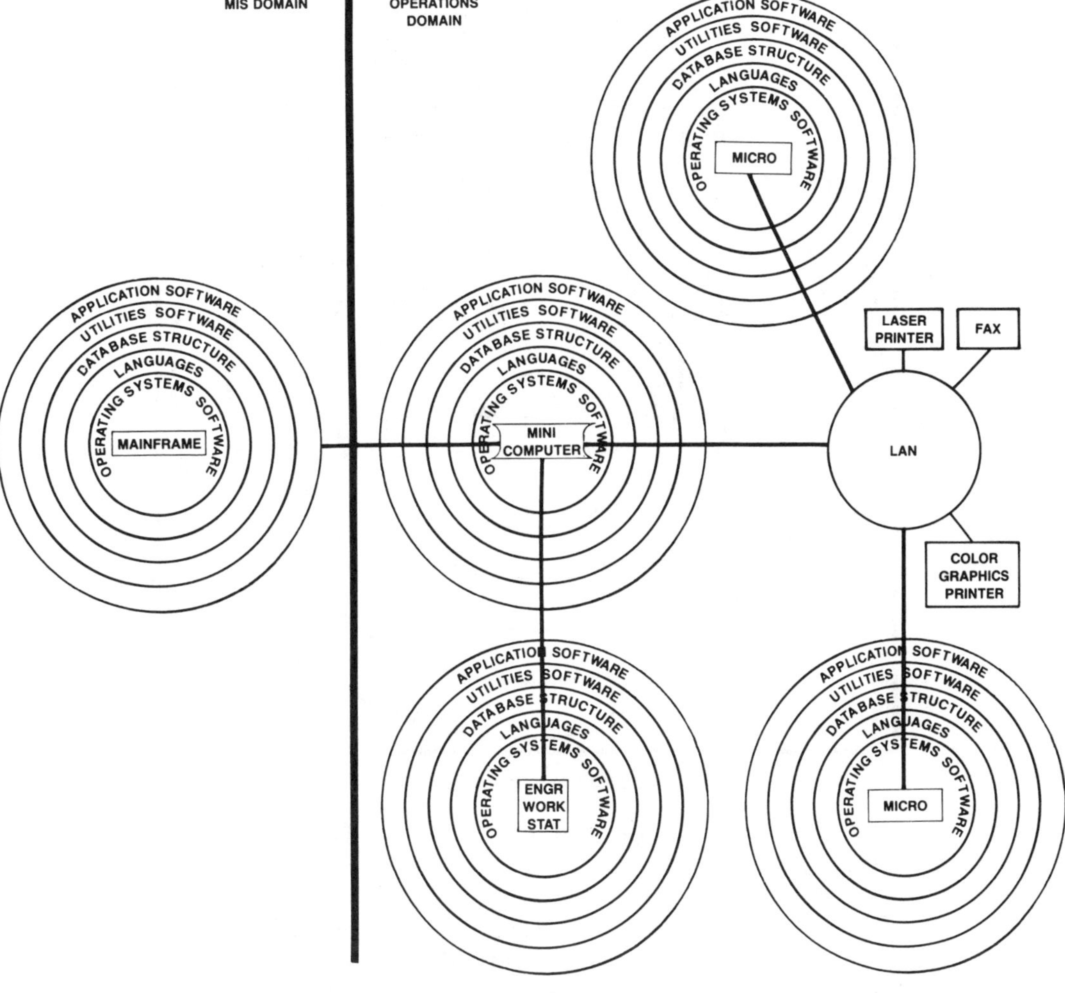

Figure 16-2

this requires a great deal of sophistication in an operating system. In order to switch from one task to another, the operating system must know the exact status, in detail, of the program it is about to exit in order to save this status on the "stack" registers of the machine, ready for subsequent restoration on returning from the next task.

Recognizing that an operating system cannot possibly be all things to all people, Microsoft is providing a feature called "dynamic linking" which allows programmers to integrate their own code into the operating systems on an equal footing with the OS code. Two application programs provided by Microsoft and IBM (Presentation Manager—their version of Macintosh's Graphical User Interface and LAN Manager—which extends the system to manage communications with other machines over local area networks) will be among the first programs to use this feature. A third program, due sometime in the future, will allow the operating system to access databases on behalf of application programs running under its control. See Figures 16-2 and 16-3. Microchannel, a feature incorporated in IBM's Personal System 2 (PS/2) to make networking easier, will be discussed in the network section.

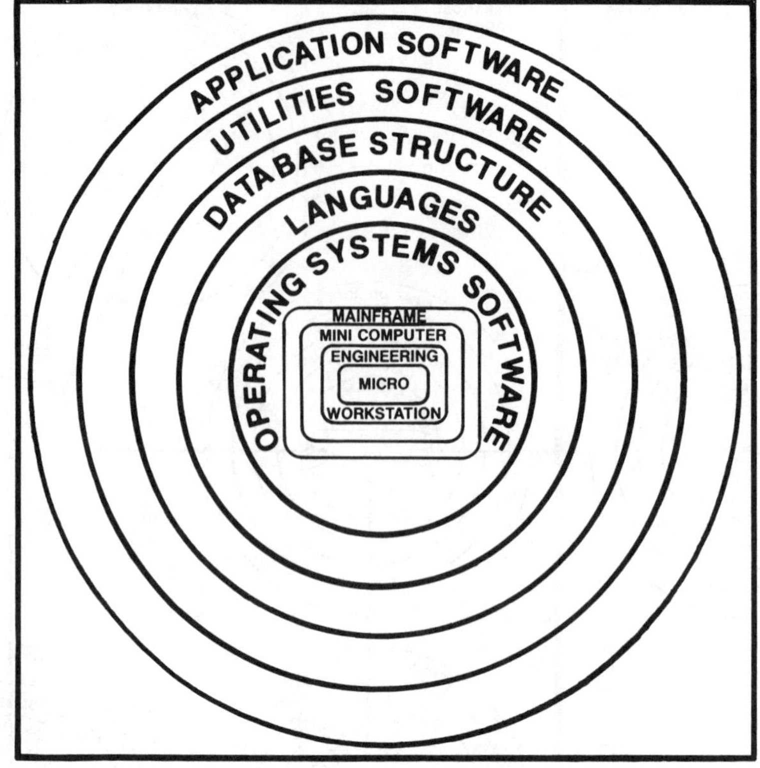

Figure 16-3 The Integrated System

The major alternative operating system to OS/2 is UNIX. (Macintosh uses its own proprietary operating system and as such, it is not available for general use.) Created out of dissatisfaction with existing offerings in the 1970s by Ken Thomson and Dennis Ritchie of AT&T Bell Labs, UNIX is perhaps the most innovative commercial software product ever made available—and the most badly managed. (When UNIX first became available, AT&T was still a government regulated monopoly, and so were unable to fully exploit UNIX commercially.) It already offers what other operating systems, including OS/2, can only promise—a fast, flexible environment supporting multitasking and data sharing. Supported on all Unisys machines for example, it permits a degree of application program portability that IBM can only envy. Programs written under DOS can already coexist in versions of UNIX from Locus and Microport. As a direct result of various engineering communities customizing it to their own particular needs, there are now several incompatible versions in which application programs written in one will not run in the other. Such "enhancement" (some would say pollution), is very common in the software industry. There are now some 600,000 copies in use in a various forms. In an attempt to revert back to a universally standard version of UNIX, AT&T entered an agreement with Sun Microsystems and Microsoft to develop a version optimized for Sun's architecture. (With OS/2 to offer as an alternative, Microsoft cannot exactly have a strong vested interest in the success of this or any other version of UNIX.) Not all application programs, however, are capable of multitasking even with OS/2. A newer verison of OS/2, promised for 1990 and running on Intel's 80386 microprocessor, will allow programs written under DOS to run together.

DESIGNING THE DATA BASE STRUCTURE—THE FOUNDATION UPON WHICH ALL ELSE IS BUILT

This is a vast topic in its own right, with much development work currently underway. The size of the effort reflects its importance, however. We shall present a cursory introduction only, with a discussion on the theory of the data model included at the end of this chapter. Further study of this very important subject must be left at the readers discretion. Recall that if we cannot manage our data, we cannot manage our factory and **the data base structure is the foundation upon which all else, beginning with our ability to manage our data, rests.** If storing massive amounts of data were all that we were concerned with, this could easily be accommodated by entering raw data elements or records contiguously as they occur on a variety of memory storage mediums. For data accessed infrequently, this storage will be provided in ROM, magnetic tape, or disc form. (Software which does not change, but may be accessed frequently, such as the operating system, is also stored in ROM.) For data accessed more frequently, where rapid retrieval is important, this will almost certainly be stored in semiconductor static or dynamic memory. If we could store all of our information in this form there would be less need for efficient data base management systems (DBMS) but this approach would prove to be inordinately expensive and impractical and so we must concern ourselves with the efficiency of our data base management system.

Storage capacity is only one attribute of our ideal data base. If this were all it were capable of, the best return we could expect out of it would be to simply regurgitate the data—still in their original, raw unstructured state. If one were to design an ideal data base structure, the following attributes would be required.

1. **Store a large amount of data**
2. **Allow fast retrieval of data**
3. **Find any specific data quickly and easily**
4. **Arrange and process specific data**
5. **Support a multiuser environment**
6. **Security and access control**
7. **Ensure data integrity**—read only/read/write access
8. **Allow easy update**—without having to shut down the system
9. **"User friendliness"**—user oriented rather than machine oriented
10. **Efficient use of memory**

These attributes cannot all be achieved on a mutually inclusive basis with existing data base technology but can be optimized according to some alternative basic generic structures. Each has its relative advantages and disadvantages. One need of particular interest to us as users, rather than EDP professionals, is to be able to find any specific data, quick and easily. We have a need to arrange it and process it, to format, communicate, and present it. Our need in fact is **to convert raw data into useful information**. A raw data bank is like a stream one knows contains gold dust. Finding the gold dust—the information as opposed to the raw data in a vast corporate data base—using pot-luck and panning, will almost certainly be a long laborious task, **unless one has a clue as to where to start the search, and has an efficient search and extraction method**. With clues however, direction signposts as it were, the search process can be made much less arbitrary.

These clues or direction signpost will only be available if the data are **stored in a rigorously structured fashion**. A search for data will be much quicker if there is some pattern to key off. This is made possible through the use of the record model, the basis of most traditional data base structures, in which data are first arranged and then stored in **a fixed linear sequence of field values** and by using **information about the structure of the data base itself, so-called metaknowledge, to find and manipulate the data**. This structure is very much machine rather than user oriented. The task in data base design, as in all software, is to enable the user to communicate as far as possible, in his own natural language, rather than that of the machine. The degree to which this is successful is a function of the **design of the user interface**.

THE MECHANICS OF THE SEARCH PROCESS

Structure query
Search
Find
Process
Format
Present
Communicate

There are basically two ways of building this bridge between raw data and information. First is the use of powerful **semantic data models**. The rigor and complexity required of this approach results, at best, in only partial implementation. This is the approach taken with current state-of-the-art data base management systems. Second, is the building of a high level, **conceptual data base** on top of the conventional data base. This is the approach currently being taken by many data base researchers.

Conventional data base structures—the hierarchical, the network, the relational, the distributed—each of which are described in some detail, differ mainly in the way in which the data are organized. This in turn, determines the utility and flexibility of information retrieval and the **query range**, that is, the structure of the data base predetermines the range and kinds of questions which can be asked of it. This in turn will predetermine what can and cannot be done by all subsequent software. There are several approaches which can be taken with regard to how the data are structured.

Hierarchical Data Base

In this model (see Figure 16-4), data are organized in simple "tree" structures with collections of trees called "forests." This requires that some records be subordinated to others. The main disadvantage of this approach is that any specific record can only take its full meaning when seen in comlete hierarchical context. The user's view of the data implies a knowledge of the hierarchical structure. This kind of architecture does not allow updating without denying access to all users while this is being done.

Network Data Base

In this approach, the data are organized in ad hoc groups, with members of each group linked to each other or to other groups. In this way, a data search can trace through these links. The disadvantage is the need to maintain the complex linkages. Also, no clue can

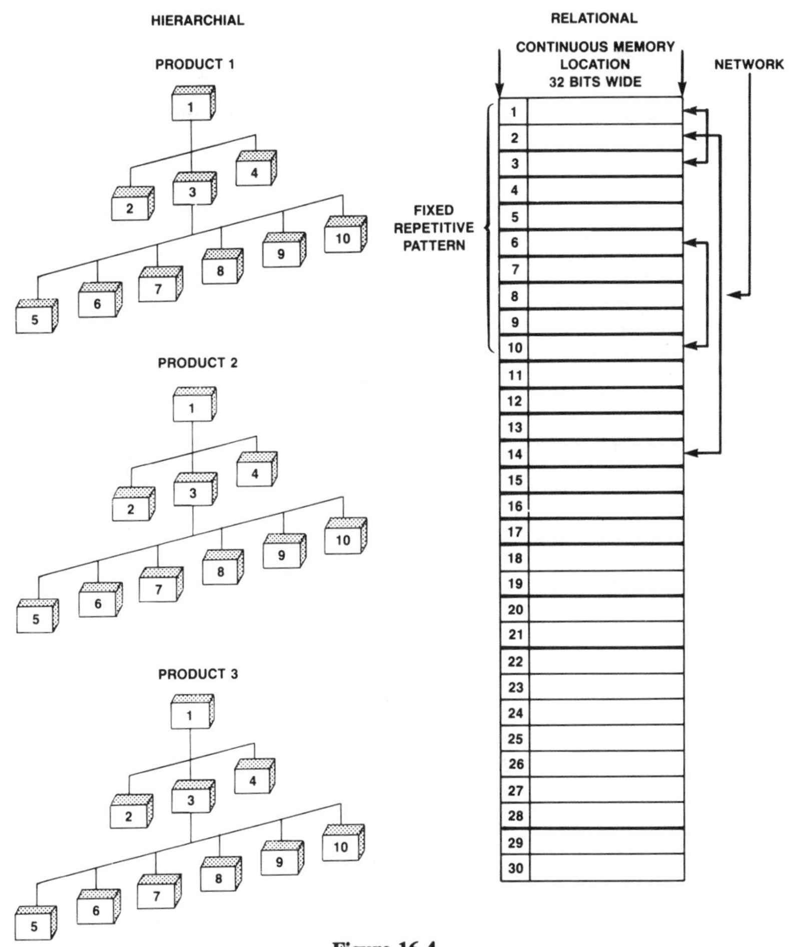

Figure 16-4

be provided from the linkages as to the best search strategy. The updating limitations apply here too.

Distributed Data Base

These are data bases which may reside in more than one physical location. They appear to the user as having the same structure. This is not necessarily the case in practice. Such data bases may reside in different locations on a network. In a relational distributed data base, different tables may be stored on different computer systems but be related by joins or unions. A major design objective of a distributed data base is that the user need not be concerned with where the data resides. This is a matter for the data base designer. The data definition should be independent of location.

Relational Data Base

This is by far the most important, practically available data base technology and as such, we look at this in some detail. **Due to its ability to support high level, nonprocedural languages, the relational approach has the highest "user friendly" potential.** A nonprocedural language frees the user to some extent from having to know and conform to the rules of syntax, allowing the formulation of queries in terms of properties of the resulting set, that is, the resulting set, rather than in terms of the structure of the data base itself. Compared to a general purpose programming language, a simple query language is relatively easy to learn. The relational approach to data base design attempts to overcome the disadvantages of the other approaches: the need to understand the hierarchical structure, the need to understand and maintain a network of links, avoid shutting down the data base to do updates, by:

1. **allowing all data to be considered more or less equal and**
2. **establishing relationships between data bases using location coordinates.**

In this way, the user can regard his data as simply tables from which derived views, in the form of other tables, can be produced using relational operators. For example, one operator allows the user to extract a subset of rows from a given table, another a subset of columns, to produce a derived table. These tables are constructed according to strict rules, including an unambiguous index for each piece of data based on the relationship between data. (See Figures 16-5 and 16-6.) In this way, the user can develop views over large expanses of data by employing "joins." The user does not need to understand the structure of records and how they are stored in the data base memory bank. The DBMS attends to all of this. (This is discussed more fully at the end of this chapter.)

AN EXAMPLE OF A COMMERCIALLY AVAILABLE RELATIONAL DATA BASE MANAGEMENT SYSTEM

The most commonly used commercially available data base management systems, one of which will be briefly discussed as an example, are: **ADR**—Datacom, **ADABUS**—Software AG, **IDMS**—Cullinet, **IMS/DB2**—IBM, **dBASE**—from Ashton Tate, developed by Wayne Ratcliffe, **ORACLE, INFORMIX, INGRES** from Relational Technologies Inc., and **UNICENTRE**—from Computer Associates. Not all of these are relational data bases.

DB2 (IBM Database 2) is a subset of IBM's MVS operating system which allows any number of users to access any number of relatonal data bases using the relational language SQL. There are over 2,000 installations on IBM systems and less than full implementations are available on IBM PCs. A key component in IBM's SAA strategy, transaction speeds are not as fast as IMS. IMS is a hierarchical data base system and Oracle/Ingres compatible. It does not require the unique "primary" key concept and can run in interactive or host language mode. It guarantees that one user's update activity will not cause an incorrect result in anothers.

Data base vendors are in the process of defining a standard way of retrieving data—structured query language (SQL)—dividing the data base market into two parts:

1. **Information retrieval engines and**
2. **Software programs for converting queries into SQL.**

SQL is one example of a data base management tool language. While extremely powerful, it can however **only access those portions of the corporate information data base which are included in the SQL data dictionary**. Further, users of SQL need a high level of understanding concerning the specific items of interest and the relationships

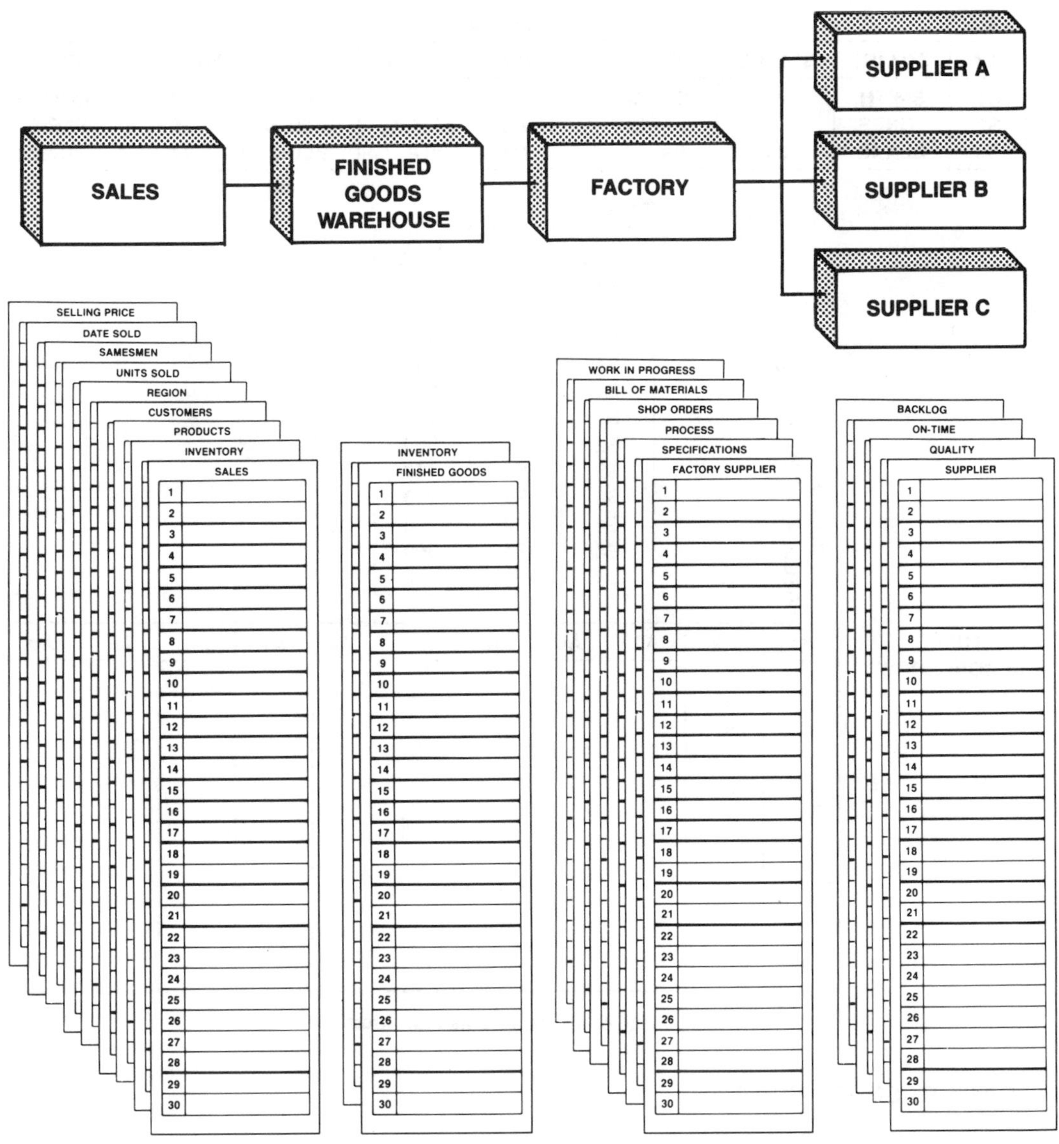

Figure 16-5

between those items and other information items to effectively make queries of the data base. So while fourth level languages do indeed facilitate easier interrogation, their power is not without restrictions. (In our paperless integrated manufacturing system (PIMS) development, we intend to make a certain subset of information accessible with only limited understanding of the entire subset.) The idea of any army of analysts accessing widely variant sections of an entire corporate information base, assuming an in-depth understanding of the contents of that data, and drawing speculative conclusions, should always be a major concern in a CIM system design.

TABLE 1

S #	SNAME	STATUS	CITY
S1	SMITH	20	LONDON
S2	JONES	10	PARIS
S3	BLAKE	30	PARIS

TABLE 2

P #	PNAME	COLOR	WEIGHT	CITY
P1	NUT	RED	17	LONDON
P2	SCREW	GREEN	12	PARIS
P3	BOLT	BLUE	17	ROME

TABLE 3

S #	P #	QTY
S1	P1	300
S1	P2	200
S1	P3	400
S1	P4	200
S1	P5	100
S1	P6	100
S2	P1	300
S2	P2	400
S3	P2	200
S4	P2	200
S4	P4	300
S4	P5	400

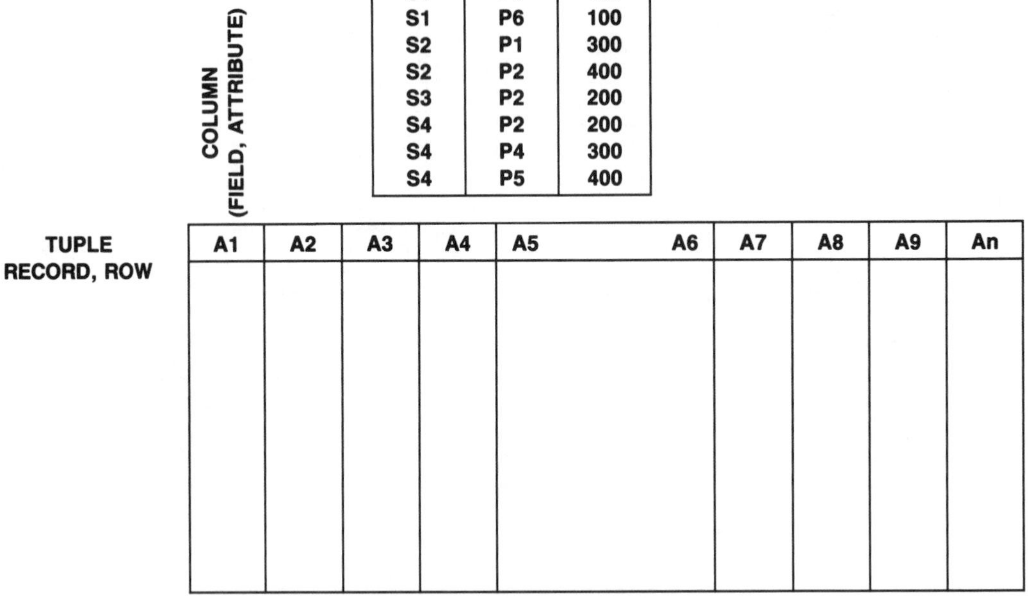

COLUMN (FIELD, ATTRIBUTE)

TUPLE RECORD, ROW

A1	A2	A3	A4	A5	A6	A7	A8	A9	An

Figure 16-6 Relational Data Base Structure

DATA BASE STANDARDS

Complementing all of this activity in data base management systems development, is the development of standards dealing with the structure of data closer to the user level. Examples of these are:

Initial Graphics Exchange Specification (IGES). IGES is an IEEE standard dealing with product geometric data. It does not deal with nongeometric data such as dimensions and tolerances. These are addressed by means of: **product data exchange specification (PDES)**—National Bureau of Standards. **Product definition data interface (PDDI)**, a standard sponsored by the U.S. Air Force, defines the interface between engineering and manufacturing in which product attributes are grouped in one of five categories: **(1) geometry, (2) topology, (3) tolerances, (4) features, and (5) part control information**. These are the kind of attributes which a data base used to store bills of material or parts specifications would have to handle. These are contained within the higher level, system standards.

Integrated Digital Data Services Network (ISDN). This is, or will be when it exists, the Rolls Royce of wide area networks (WAN) in which the simultaneous transmission of voice, data, and video signals can be transmitted over a simple, twisted-pair, telephone line. Partial implementation has begun in the form of two services: 2B + D and 23B + D. The characters describing these services indicate the manner in which information is transmitted. The basic service (2B + D) will facilitate transmission over two B channels carrying voice and data at 64 kbps (kilo bits per second) and one D channel carrying video signal information at 16 kbps, for a total capacity of 144 kbps. The primary service (23B + D) will support transmission over 23 B channels and one D channel, each with a capacity of 64 kbps, for a total capacity of 1.544 megabits per second.

CIM STRATEGIES—ORDER OUT OF CHAOS

For reasons we now understand, most corporations do not have the luxury of starting a CIM project with a clean slate. It is more typical that the task involves the integration of an already existing proliferation of equipment and software from many different vendors. It is also the nature of CIM that it will cross many functional boundaries and involve both internal and external specialists: the MIS department, many user departments, all levels of management, systems analysts, programmers, hardware and software suppliers. How does one address the integration process in a practical way? If we apply our old faithful 80/20 rule, we find that 20 percent of the players—and the products—form 80 percent of the problem—and probably the solution.

Like any good strategy, the process should include a vision of the designed result, an assessment of the existing situation, and an implementation game plan. It can be summarized in three questions:

1. Where do we want to be?
2. Where are we now?
3. How can we get there from here?

The first step requires vision. "The clear definition of the desired end result" we discussed earlier. Most members of existing organization are so familiar with and conditioned by **"the way we've always done it" that they cannot envision how it might be done better or in an entirely different "best" way**. Many times the most valuable results from a new system whose development has been driven by such a solid and cohesive vision were never in fact predicted. Rather, the most valuable results were the serendipitous effect of a fundamentally good design, derived from a seasoned, astute vision. To answer the question, "where do we want to be?" most effectively, we must allow ourselves to be unfettered by the answer to the second question, "where are we now?", which is why this particular order is recommended. It is also important to stress that this vision is defined in terms of a business, rather than a technology first framework. The latter carries a great risk of technologically elegant but inappropriate solutions.

Bearing in mind that CIM is an evolutionary process of building on what one already has as opposed to a revolutionary one of replacing everything with something new, the second step is to assess what resources are currently available, what procedures, protocols, and feedback loops are in effect, and most importantly, what is currently working well which we can build upon. One does not want to throw out the baby with the bath water.

The emphasis here must be on discovering what the current reality is: not only how the existing system is supposed to work, but what specific and undocumented adaptations have evolved; what implicit protocols have evolved over time as safe and predictable ways to use the system.

The third step is mapping a strategy to get from where we are to where we want to be. This is the most demanding aspect of the challenge of introducing change into an organization. The fundamental truth about change in an existing organization, and CIM implies very significant change, is that it must be done incrementally. It is probably not a good strategy to bite off more than one can chew at one sitting. There is a danger, of course, that in breaking down the vision into manageable components capable of integration into the existing system, the integrity of the vision suffers. To avoid this loss of vision, the best strategy is not to attempt to rigorously predefine answers to "how do we get there from here?", but to carry a continual awareness of the current reality as it evolves with respect to the desired end result and, guided by this awareness, to make decisions along the way that always move us toward rather than away from our vision. So, the third question changes from "how do we get there from here?" to "does each proposed change move us toward our goal or away from it?" Or put another way: "what is the next small step we can take that moves us closer to our goal?"

THE ESSENTIAL COMPONENTS OF CIM— THE BUILDING BLOCKS

The remainder of this paper takes the view that surveys of available products or discussions of the history of program development can be done in an illustrative manner rather than exhaustively. A list of all available programs that handle spreadsheets or data bases will easily exceed a hundered entries. It would be more effective to limit the list to several well-known programs in each category and to use common principles to build on that nucleus. The pareto rule also applies to computer software.

RULES FOR SELECTING SOFTWARE

There are two sets of rules concerning selecting appropriate software tools for use by members of organizations. One concerns selecting software that affects the entire organization: this is the charter of the management information systems (MIS) or electronic data processing (EDP) group. The other concerns end-users of information drawn from the corporate data base. This dicotomy revolves around the general versus the specific; the needs of the many versus the responsibilities of the few.

The programs managed by the MIS group—the custodians of the corporate data base—are typically large production systems that run on a continual basis. They produce reports on predictable schedules, maintain the major corporate data bases, and typically run on large mainframes. The solutions appropriate in this context will almost certainly range from adequate to mediocre because they have to satisfy a broad set of needs and potential uses. Analysts and other end-users, on the other hand, use software tools tailored for specific applications or that are capable of generating applications. Many of these programs are so-called 4GLs (fourth generation languages). They include spreadsheets, data base manipulation tools, modeling and simulation systems, statistical analysis packages, graphics programs, word processing programs, and, for more computer-literate users, programming development environments that include standards tools like editors and compilers. Solutions to these needs and problems can be selected based on specific applicability to the needs of the project and their personal preference and workstyle of the user.

The MIS group must make decisions that are safe, conservative, and viable in the long term. End-users on the other hand may be more adventurous on an ad hoc basis, secure in the knowledge that the models, programs, spreadsheets, and data bases will not impinge on the integrity of the overall system and may even be discarded after one use. It would be foolish to try to consolidate these two phenomena into a single set of rules. Trying to apply rules appropriate to one group to the other group will result in poor decisions.

There is, however, a rather simple strategy that allows these two different user types to work together effectively. If the manufacturing systems developed and maintained by the MIS group have a consistent and well-defined ''export'' methodology that is accessible by the ''import'' methodologies of end-user tools, then analysts are free to develop their tools using information from a variety of corporate information sources without relying on MIS resources on an ongoing basis or waiting for MIS support. The presupposition of compatible data interfaces ensures that the information users will have access to the information sources without requiring extensive definitions of standards, formats, and protocols.

THE SOFTWARE DEVELOPMENT PROCESS

Why is software so expensive to develop? One reason is that while engineering is considered a science, programming is still considered an art. The traditional approach, to ''think like a computer'' works for problems usually too small to matter. For his manufacturing cell program, our engineer would almost certainly have written it himself. Alternatively, he could have submitted a request to his friendly, but seriously backlogged EDP or MIS department, but could not afford to wait the two years involved. (Besides, they only market what their particular ''factories'' can build, don't they? Rather than learn to ''build'' what their customer wants.) Self-help requires more effort—but is usually much quicker. Regardless of who does it, the main steps in this process are as follows:

1. **Define the application task.**
2. **Develop solution methodology** (flow charts/algorithms).
3. **Write source code.**
4. **Type.**
5. **Compile** (translate from user language to machine language).
6. **Edit** (correct errors in user language source).
7. **Compile.**
8. **Debug.**
9. **Repeat steps 4 through 8.**
10. **Test and characterize.**
11. **Document and update at all steps.**

Steps 4 through 10 would all be conducted under control of the operating system, successively calling in each of the utility programs specific to each task in producing the program, as would the running of the application program itself.

At step 3 above, the programmer would program the machine in one of the following ways:

1. **Pure binary:** In the late 1950s to mid-1960s, it was common practice to program machines directly in binary code, requiring the human programmer to know not only the machine's language and vocabulary precisely in order to program 1s and 0s directly into the machine, but also its architecture; that is, its internal structure and how it operated. Holes punched in paper tape or cards by an off-line machine was the typical communication medium between human and machine. Obviously an extremely tedious and error prone process, this was replaced by BCD programming.

2. **Binary coded decimal (BCD):** In BCD programming, the programmer uses a conversion table in which symbols are used to represent groups of "bits." These symbols are then translated and encoded into machine language, usually by the machine itself, initially by means of hardware but then by software. The subsequent enhancement of this software conversion or "translation" process by the machine then led to the development of assembly level language programming.

3. **Assembly level language (mnemonics) translator:** In assembly level language programming, the programmer again used a cross reference list of quasi English, shorthand mnemonics to represent data and instructions to be executed by his machine. LOAD ACC BA for example, instructed the machine to **fetch** data from two specified memory locations and then to **execute** the add instruction on the contents of these memory locations. These instructions were "translated" to machine code 1s and 0s by the machine itself using a program called an assembler or translator. By this time, magnetic tape was beginning to replace paper and cards. (The fetch and execute instructions, measured in number of system clock cycles, is a typical measure of a computer's speed of operation.)

4. **High level language compiler:** Being able to instruct our machines in English words, using a choice of programming languages such as **(a) BASIC**—Beginner's All Purpose Symbolic Instruction Code; **(b) FORTRAN**—Formula Translation, particularly suited to handling mathematical problems; **(c) COBOL**—Common Business Oriented Language; **(d) PASCAL**; **(e) ADA**; **(f) C** language.

5. **Fourth generation language:** English statements and expressions—NOMAD, FOCUS, IDEAL, SQL. As software engineering evolves, we get closer and closer to being able to communicate with our machines in our language rather than having to translate into theirs, with the machine itself taking on more and more of the translation task. We are still very far removed from being able to communicate in conversational English. Some machines have indeed been programmed to respond to spoken commands. This is not understanding but simply noise pattern recognition and has nothing at all to do with comprehension. They all represent a trend to improving the programmer's productivity at the expense of trading off the systems productivity. The common theme is to reduce the amount the programmer has to remember.

6. **Modular software:** One approach being taken to solve the problems of the software development process to is assemble ever larger building blocks into systems which satisfy specific needs. This approach is necessarily less efficient in both speed and physical resources, but it does allow for rapid and effective development. In this way, each software module is refined over the course of time and used as a commonly available building block.

The modern approach:

a. **Black box system requirement documentation.**

b. **Design modular structure—each module is a "black box."**

c. **Write a formal "block box" specification for each module.**

d. **Use formal methods for process documentation.**

e. **Design real-time systems as a set of cooperating sequential processes, each with a specified period and deadline.**

If the expected output from the system cannot be precisely defined, the system can hardly be expected to provide it.

7. Automatic code generation: The theory behind automatic code generation holds that it is possible to define a system, or system subcomponent, in terms of the required output only—a "black box" as it were, in which the internal workings need not be specified, the computer itself dealing with this in writing the program. What we mean by "automatic" programming is a matter of definition. We have had automatic programming for many years, ever since the first translator was written, in the sense that the machine itself converts user mnemonics to binary code. The degree of automation has increased to the point that a fourth level language compiler can take language very close to the source of our natural language and convert it to code. This is not the same however as generating a sequence of instructions to deal with an original problem automatically. If the solution to a problem can be defined by an algorithm, then the computer can indeed generate the code required to execute that algorithm. Few problems in the real world can be defined in this way.

BUGS, VIRUSES, AND LOGIC BOMBS

The software has not yet been written which can be guaranteed to be free of errors. In more cases than not, the computer gets the blame! However, computers do what you tell them to do via the software. That is not necessarily the same as what you want them to do. This is a function of the shortcomings of the human thought process and inability to precisely define all of the conditions likely to be encountered in a program—not of the computer. Developing software is a complex process involving the joint effort of the user community, the systems analyst, the programmer. The user community does not always define its needs in a clear, comprehensive, and concise way. The systems analyst is the architect who has to understand these user needs, what is possible from a system hardware and software point of view, and how to reconcile these. The programmer's task is to codify the instruction of the solution. Left alone, most programmers usually just jump in and start writing code, find that it does not work, then begin a process of trial and error, tweak and patch. Most lack adequate formal training, especially in the mathematical tools that are available.

Structural or errors of logic can be detected and corrected fairly easily. The more invidious data errors, which can be due to either hardware or software, are much more difficult to detect. It is impossible for example to test every microprocessor for every data combination at every node. The fact that the software development process still involves much trial and error leads to many software revisions. Most software carries a disclaimer. Software is not withheld from sale until it is known to be error free but is released when the rate of error detection has diminished to what is considered to be acceptable levels. A bug is simply an error in the software. A virus is a contagious bug. For a variety of reasons, the state of the art software differs from that of other engineering disciplines. Engineering functions fall into three categories. The first of these is **analog**. These are functions which, **within a broad range, exhibit an infinite number of stable states**. The semiconductor diode is such a function. Its behavior can be described by continuous functions where the mathematics are well understood. Such a system, since its behavior can be confirmed by mathematical modeling and by testing, should contain no unpredictable behavior.

Digital or **discrete** functions, the category which software falls into, **contain a finite** (but usually huge), **number of stable states**. Systems containing such functions are designed in such a way that the behavior of the system when not in a stable state is not significant, or referred to as the don't care state. Software programs are discrete state systems with little or no repetitive structure. Since the human programmer is not capable of comprehending all of the interactive conditions which can and do arise, attempts to deal with this problem include the use of mathematical logic to replace continuous mathematics.

STRATEGIC ALLIANCES AND PARTNERSHIPS

No vendor, not even the mighty IBM, can bring all of the ingredients to a CIM party and many strategic alliances and partnerships have been formed in order to be able to offer complete product portfolios to customers. Some of the more important of these alliances and the major planks in each vendor's strategy are now addressed.

IBM (International Business Machines)

With some 35 to 40 thousand IBM mainframes in the world and perhaps over 10 million IBM and IBM clone PCs, they are obviously a major player. Unlike DEC machines, however, their equipment is not compatible. (Could this be one of the reasons why IBM's profits declined from $6.6 billion in 1985 to $4.8 billion in 1986 as their overall market share declined from 60 percent in 1985 to 27 percent in 1987?) The overall framework of their strategy to address this is through **systems application architecture (SAA)**—a proprietary "standard" intended to increase the compatibility between IBM equipment. SAA consists of three standards:

1. **Common Programming Interface:** This standard is designed to allow programs to run on a variety of machines, called "transportability" in computer jargon. Programs conforming to these standards, written in IBM defined versions of some of the more commonly used general purpose languages such as COBOL, C, and FORTRAN, will run on IBM9370 mainframes and PS/2 PCs for examples.
2. **Common Communications Support:** Deals with protocol structure allowing programs to swap data across networks. User commands displayed in graphical user interface (GUI) menus which will, as far as possible, have the same function in every program.
3. **Common User Access:** To address "user friendliness" by using GUI screens instead of keyboard commands.

The first product is intended to be a version of OS/2, a new operating system for PCs developed jointly by IBM and Microsoft. This software is intended to be upward compatible allowing programs written under DOS to operate in OS/2. This approach, contrary to IBM's practice in the past, will be open to all users in order to encourage the vast army of "camp followers" in the industry to write software for IBM machines. An agreement with Lotus to develop spreadsheet for its mainframe machines, is an early example of this. (If you can't beat them, join them?)

Strategically, IBM is developing a new attitude: in IBM's words "a new openness to customers' needs." Another major plank in IBM's strategy is **PS/2** (Personal System 2) with the microchannel hardware expansion bus, designed to accommodate two processors, one of which might for example manage communications on a network while the main chip handles primary user interactive tasks. Other hardware can also be accommodated on this bus. With microchannel, which IBM hopes will kill the clone business by being difficult to copy, the PS/2 should be better suited to network environments. At the time of this writing the new software to take advantage of this feature is not yet available and users, confused about the benefits of microchannel, are reluctant to migrate to the new machine. IBM also intended to rely even more heavily on patent protection, with much of the internal technology of the new machine protected by patents. Legitimate cloners will be required to pay a 5 percent of sales license fee. Another new product from IBM, a minicomputer called Olympia Silverlake, is designed to protect their position in this part of the market by running their Systems 36 and 38 software.

DB2, discussed earlier, is also a major component in IBM's strategy, also supporting the belief that he who controls the data base and access to it controls the integration process. A potential weakness in IBM's strategy is users reluctance to change from a large installed base of "standard" machines. PS/2 is not upward compatible with this previous generation of machines and there is no guarantee it will become the new standard. For customers, the potential benefit must justify the substantial change involved. While people are willing to leave hardware by the wayside, switching to better and cheaper hardware as it becomes available as they progress forward, software is a different matter. It is expensive, and becoming even more expensive. New software is usually difficult and time consuming to learn. It can be very troublesome, especially in the beginning, so users are reluctant to part with something in which they have developed trust. IBM is also supporting manufacturing automation protocol (MAP) as part of their thrust in the factory automation business.

DEC (Digital Equipment Corporation)

Founded in 1957, DEC's president and founder, Mr. Carl Olsen holds the view that **"the real problem is how to make the customer's whole enterprise productive."** In other words, it is the company-wide network and not the performance of any individual machine, which is important. Consistent with this philosophy, DEC offers a portfolio of products of similar architecture regardless of the size and power. As such, these machines can be easily integrated into a network. An example of this is DEC's own Easynet, a company-wide network of 27,000 machines across 26 countries, accessible to 75,000 of DEC's 118,000 employees. The fact that DEC's sales more than doubled from 1984 to $9.4 billion in 1987, with most of this growth coming from the increasing acceptance of its VAX series of minicomputers—long successful in the technical and scientific community—in the much broader commercial market, lends support to the validity of this vision. The VMS operating system of the VAX, common to all machines and considered in some quarters to be superior to UNIX in terms of user security, is well equipped to handle time-sharing and networking tasks. Although just to be safe perhaps, DEC has a significant effort underway developing their own version of UNIX called ULTRIX.

As for the future, DEC is publicly keeping faith with the past, perpetuating their "the network is the system" strategy by designing more VAXs, including ones equipped with multiple processors to improve cost effectiveness and improve their already considerable networking capability. These products include Argonaut, the most powerful VAX ever built, and a personal VAX, targeted to sell at less than $4,000. These machines, however, will only run under VMS. The questions against which DEC and others must test their strategies are: will the customer base continue to favor companies with integrated portfolios such as DEC in the future as they continue experiencing the real difficulties of integrating a proliferation of equipment, including IBM products, or will PCs replace minicomputers? (Surely the ratio of PCs/engineering workstations/minis and mainframes will continue to change. I do not know the real numbers, but I imagine that for every mainframe in the world, there are 100 minis, and for every 100 minis, 100 PCs.) A question more specific to DEC: will their faith in the VT 100 workstation in preference to PCs be seen to be a blind spot? (DEC's excursion into the PC market with their Rainbow machine failed.)

More of a business strategy issue, will DEC continue to be vulnerable to attack from hungry, more cost effective competitors in the high end PC and engineering workstation business coming up from below as they try to preserve high margins in their "captive" customer base? Have they got it wrong in believing that new products based on the new reduced instruction set chips (RISC) such as SUN's SPARC or Motorola's 88000, will not be a threat due to the software lag? (These new chips are special purpose microprocessors in which most frequently used instructions are highly optimized for greater speed. These instructions as well as data are stored in very fast, on chip "cache" memory.)

Mr. Olsen has already proved himself and DEC to be very astute campaigners. What is said in public and practiced in private behind the scenes, may not be the same!

DEC/Apple

Neither company can by itself offer a complete solution to its customers' networking needs anymore than IBM can. Together they hope to form what may transpire to be a very powerful alliance. DEC's strength in networking and its ability to offer a fully integrated line of VAX computers which in conjunction with Apple's PCs may allow them to capture a bigger share of the office automation market of which DEC, who estimates that 40 percent of its customers have Macintoshes, has only 10 percent. The network will also accept IBM PCs.

AT&T (American Telephone and Telegraph)/SUN (Stanford University Network)

They are working together to produce a standard version of UNIX in order to attack the PC and workstation network market. Competitors, including IBM, Hewlett Packard, Apollo, and others, fearing that AT&T and SUN would steal an early lead in the development of software under this new "standard," have formed an alternative group to define yet another version. Both are collaborating in a joint effort to produce Graphical

User Interface—Open Look—to make UNIX more user friendly—running under UNIX on AT&T 6386 PC. (Olivetti, 22 percent of which is owned by AT&T, develops and manufactures PCs and workstations for AT&T.) GUI was originated by Xerox on a computer called Alto and made a commercial success by Macintosh. Apple is now suing Microsoft, charging that Presentation Manager violates Macintosh's patented technology, Road Runner. UNIX has the best software development tools; new operating systems require ten times more memory. Lotus is planning a UNIX version of the 1-2-3 spreadsheet. Emerald Bay from Wayne Radcliff is taking on dBase and can funnel the same information simultaneously to several PCs on a network. Analysts speculate that AT&T may try to bolster its strength in computers through acquisitions.

Ashton-Tate

The leading supplier of PC data bases since 1982, their original product dBase is the foundation upon which many microprocessor application programs are built. Ashton-Tate no doubt hope that he who controls the data base can control the process of integration itself. A major plank in their strategy is dBase IV, designed to serve several different computers and programs on a network and by providing a data base language called dBase SQL, in which programs can communicate with it and each other.

Microsoft

With absolute control of OS/2, the central nucleus, Microsoft is developing a language to allow programs written in it to time-share under it. This may be a version of BASIC which is not popular with users. They are also pursuing aggressive diversification into the applications software side of the business. Since they are self-sufficient in software development, they are in a strong position to be able to integrate their products. Already they offer the operating system for the Macintosh, and its Exel spreadsheet as well as Word and Multi-plan on IBM PCs.

These are but a few of the major players. There are many others and the reader would be well advised to conduct the same kind of analysis with any of them with whom they do or intend to do business.

CONCLUSION

The first step in a CIM project is to **confirm that CIM is needed in the first place**. It is all too easy to become ensnared because it is fashionable, or because the technocrats think it is neat, not that it is needed. There are plenty of people out there who will be glad to take your money selling you something you might not really need. (They may also take your money for something that will not work.) Given that one is convinced, however, the next step is to **decide its form**. This process begins by **defining the expected output** of the system, followed by **a comprehensive analysis of the way the existing system operates**. Only then, guided by **an inviolate vision of the desired end result**, should the system design phase begin. Without this vision, the unwary can easily stray from the virtuous path up technologically blind alleys. Success in CIM is becoming much less a function of choice of hardware and more a function of **system** and **software design** and **choice of strategic partners**—and their **"camp followers."** With integration in mind, people are no longer buying stand-alone pieces of equipment and life is now too complex for the arm's length relationships of the past. With improving interconnectability of hardware and greater transportability of software—called interoperability in the parlance of the industry—the question is not whether CIM is feasible anymore but how, although this must never be taken for granted or the difficulties underestimated.

Neither can "turnkey" CIM solutions be bought off the shelf. The environment is usually so dynamic that it has changed before the software to control it has been completed. Even a "standard" integration package will almost certainly need to be customized to a user's specific environment. Because universal interoperability is still a very long way off, customized **patching remains the order of the day** and such **software is very expensive** and **not always reliable**. For this reason, **the architecture must be modular, open ended** and the **development in-house**, although the topic is so strategically important and complex, that the use of dedicated internal specialists, supported by external specialists, is highly recommended. **Pick partners carefully for the long haul.** Know their **strategies, strengths, and weaknesses. Beware of false prophets.** The system definition and implementation stage will require **multidisciplined, cross-functional teams**. With such a technically and politically complex topic, and such diversity of personalities, skills and backgrounds, territorial disputes are likely. This kind of situation, in which there will be many forays into long cherished domains and fiefdoms, can only be managed **by clearly delineating the EDP and user community domains and responsibilities**. Give careful thought to who should lead such a motley crew. It will prove to be a leadership challenge of the highest order. **Without top-down management commitment, it will not be possible at all.**

The data base structure is the foundation upon which all else is built. The design of this determines what can and cannot be done with the stored data; what kind of questions can be asked and how they are formulated; the kind of reports which can be produced; how updates are managed by the data base management system. The data base is the common core around which a great diversity of user community needs must be serviced.

Know your standards: Standards, whether by concensus or de facto, make it possible for one program to interact and cooperate with another. These are obviously very useful and helpful in virtually all contexts. Where would we be without agreement on red lights, railway tracks, electrical outlets? The absence of accepted standards during the early proliferation of personal computers allowed thousands of individuals to take a shot at implementing their ideas. Had rigid standards been in place right from the outset, integration would not be fraught with the difficulties it has today. However, many breakthrough products would never have been developed, with a consequent loss to state of the art computer usage.

CIM currently suffers from the other side of this issue. We now have many areas where **three, four, five, or more standards are competing for acceptance**. This makes the systems analyst's job much harder. All of the activity currently underway is ostensibly designed to promote the acceptance of the idea of vendor independence in which customers can develop applications that may later be ported to other hardware and other operating systems with relative ease. This approach has no doubt been undertaken for well-researched marketing advantages rather than altrusium. Even IBM, the company that brought planned obsolescence to the computer industry, has recently announced a strategy to make software developed for IBM machines portable across IBM product line boundaries by means of SAA.

Will the open systems standardization effort succeed or will politics impede progress? POSIX is an Institute of Electrical and Electronic Engineering (IEEE) sponsored alternative to OS architecture under development, the intention of which is to establish a standard interface between the operating system and the application program. In theory, it could be added to any operating system, including UNIX. There are indications that this is likely to be the direction favored by the Hamilton group. So already, there seems to be two major camps forming.

As products and processes become more complex, they soon exceed traditional analysis methods and **computer simulation of the manufacturing process becomes inevitable**. This provides a formal way of defining the desired end result and defining, testing, and maintaining the manufacturing methodology in detail. **Remember . . . if we cannot make our factory work on paper, we cannot expect to make it work in practice.** By using a computer generated model of the manufacturing system, simulation allows us to create, plan, implement, analyze, and modify in a risk minimizing, potential maximizing environment. The simulation approach consists of (1) **model construction—** using software to construct a model of the manufacturing system, (2) **manipulation—** changing inputs and measuring outputs—characterization—overlaid on the data base management system, and (3) **presentation—**graphics/animation/pie charts, and so on. Sixteen-bit PCs may be suitable for small local jobs but a 32-bit engineering workstation, mini, or mainframe will almost certainly be needed for more comprehensive representations. (A 16-bit machine can only construct slightly more than 65,000 (2^{16}) unique memory addresses. A 32-bit machine on the other hand, is usually much faster and can manage 4.3 billion (2^{32}) unique locations in memory. The choice of tools depends on the job. (Animated graphics using Easel software from Interactive Graphics is an example of such a package.)

To introduce CIM into an organization is as much of a political as a technical challenge, encroaching as it does on functional territory likely to be fiercely defended. During and after the transition, bear in mind that **the system should serve the people and not vice versa**. The end result is not simply new technology but **a new culture in the enterprise**. This will have **far reaching ramifications on organizational structure and the roles of the many functionally specialized departments if the benefits are to be realized in full**.

There must be a cherished and inviolate vision of the desired end result. Without this to test every step of the way, the unwary can be all too easily duped into a very elegant but totally inappropriate technology. CIM may be required, perhaps even indispensible, for your business. But don't ever imagine that it will be easy to make the transition!

APPENDIX—THE RELATIONAL DATA MODEL

The data model employed in this approach is based on an abstract theory of data, the principles of which were first postulated by Dr. E. F. Codd in 1969/70, at that time a researcher with IBM. He first realized that the discipline of mathematics could be applied to inject some principles into a field—data base management—very much deficient in such qualities. (This, as we have seen, is very much the case for software in general.) The relational model deals with three aspects of data: **structure, integrity, and manipulation**. We discuss each of these in turn. In the definitions which follow, commonly used informal equivalents of the formal terms are provided in brackets.

Atomic. The smallest indivisible unit of data. In every row and column position in every table, there is always exactly one data value.

Attributes [Field, Column]. The columns of a table.

Tuples [Record, Row]. The rows of a table.

Domain. The set of all possible data values of some particular type. The pools of values used to obtain the actual values which appear in the columns. Domains are primarily conceptual in nature. They need not necessarily be stored in the data base as actual sets of values, but they should be specified as part of the data base definition.

Significance of Domain. If two attributes draw their values from the same domain, then comparisons—and hence joins/unions, and so on—involving these two attributes probably are meaningful because they compare like with like. Conversely, if the two attributes draw their values from different domains, any comparisons are not likely to be meaningful. For example, a department number and a machine number might be drawn from the domain of positive integers less than 1000, but relating the two via a join would probably be meaningless.

Relation [Table]. A relation on domains D1, D2, . . . Dn, consists of a **heading** and a **body**.

Heading. A fixed set of attributes A1, A2, . . . An, such that there is a one to one correspondence between the attributes Ai and the underlying domains Di (i = 1,2, . . . n).

Body. A time varying set of tuples where each tuple in turn consists of a set of attribute value-pairs (Ai:vi)(i = 1,2, . . . n). For any given attribute value-pair (Ai:vi), vi is a value from the unique domain Di which is associated with the attribute Ai.

A table and a relation are assumed to be the same thing. Strictly speaking, this is not the case. The rows of a table have an order from top to bottom whereas the tuples of a relation do not. (The body of a relation is a mathematical set and as such, does not have any order in mathematics. The same is true of columns.) Codd initially laid down 12, but some of these criteria are nice to have rather than absolutely essential.

Relational Schema. A relation name with its set of attribute names.

Relational Data Base. A collection of relational schemas.

Degree of the Relation. The value n—the number of attributes in the relation or equivalently, the number of underlying domains. A relation of degree 1 is said to be unary; degree 2 is binary; degree 3 is tenary; and of degree n, n-ary.

Cardinality. The number of tuples in the relation.

Integrity

For relation R, with attributes A1, A2, . . . An, the key K is the set of attributes K = (Ai, Aj, . . . Ak).

Uniqueness. The key K is unique if at any given time no two distinct tuples of R have the same value for Ai, and the same value for Aj, . . . and the same value for Ak.

Minimality. None of the Ai, Aj, . . . Ak can be discarded without destroying the uniqueness property.

Candidate Keys. A set of attributes is said to be a candidate key if it satisfies the properties of uniqueness and minimality. Any one candidate key can be assigned as the primary key, the other candidate keys are called alternates.

Alternate Keys. Any candidate key not chosen as the candidate key.

Primary Key (Unique Identifier). By defining structure as it was in the previous section, every relation has a primary key. Since the body of the relation is a set and sets, by definition, cannot contain duplicate elements at any given time, no two tuples of a relation can be duplicates of each other.

For example, suppose a relation contains an employee number and a social security number. Both are unique identifiers for each employee and each is a candidate key. If we choose the employee number as the primary key, then the social security number is the alternate key.

Foreign Keys. A foreign key is an attribute (or attribute combination) of one relation R2 whose values are required to match these of the primary key of some relation R1 (R1 and R2 not necessarily distinct). Note that a foreign key and the corresponding primary key should be defined on the same underlying domain.

Entity Integrity. No attribute participating the primary key of a base relation is allowed to contain nulls.

Referential Integrity. If base relation R2 includes a foreign key Fk matching the primary key Pk of some base relation R1, then any values of Fk in R2 must either be (1) equal to the value of Pk in some tuple of R1 or (2) be wholly null (i.e., each attribute value participating in that Fk value must be null). R1 and R2 are not necessarily distinct. For referential integrity, it is clear that a given foreign key value must have a matching primary key in some tuple of the referenced relation if that foreign key value is not null. For example, if we have a department file which has the department number as the primary key, then we can have department number as a foreign key in an employee file. Any department number in the employee file must be found in the department file or be null. It could be possible that the employee has not yet been assigned to a department in which case their department is legitimately null.

Base Relation. A relation or table that really exists, i.e., is stored as opposed to a view.

Manipulation

Relational Algebra. A set of operators and a relational assignment operator which assigns the value of some arbitrary expression of the algebra to another relation.

NOBLE EXPERIMENTS—A CASE STUDY IN CIM

Article from the *Wall Street Journal*, Tuesday, May 13, 1986.

Auto Makers Discover "Factory of the Future" is headache right now
Robots misfire and scanners misread at a GM Plant; Ford has to alter a van
But firms are still believers

Detroit

General Motors Corporation's new $600 million assembly plant in Hamtramck, Mich., on Detroit's east side, was designed to be a showcase for industrial high technology. The plant has 260 robots for welding, assembling and painting cars, 50 automated guide vehicles to ferry parts to the assembly line and a battery of cameras and computers that use laser beams to inspect and control the manufacturing process. GM has splashed pictures of the plant across its new annual report and produced a pamphlet describing the facility as a "passage to the future." But so far, the Hamtramck plant, instead of a showcase, looks more like a basket case. Though the plant has been open for several months, the automated guided vehicles are sitting idle while technicians try to debug the software that controls their movements. In the ultra modern paint shop, robots at times have spray painted each other instead of the cars, some cars have been painted so badly that GM had to ship them to a 57-year-old plant to be repainted. Hamtramck is turning out only 30 to 35 cars an hour, far less than the 60 an hour it was designed to build.

Real World

The problems at Hamtramck (pronounced Ham-TRAM-ick) are unusual only in degree. Detroit's auto makers—especially GM and Ford—are spending billions to automate their plants, hoping to cut production costs and thus better compete with Asian rivals. But they are finding that the myriad of technologies that worked well in isolated pilot projects aren't easily coordinated in the real world of high volume manufacturing. Their experience has implications for a wide range of manufacturing industries, which often adapt for their own use techniques pioneered by car makers. "We underestimated the magnitude of the task," acknowledges GMs Jan Tannehill, who oversees Hamtramck and several other GM assembly plants. "We are making progress, but it has been very slow." So slow, in fact, that GM is rethinking its plans to put even more high-tech gear into its plants. The company has shelved for at least a year plans to equip Hamtramck with equipment that would automatically install wheels and tires. And it has cancelled several robot orders for the plants that will build its new generation of mid-size cars to appear in 1988. "We're going to phase in automation slower than we had planned," a GM spokesman says.

Easy Does It

If GM does scale back its automation plans, it will be concluding what many experts already believe: high technology, like strong medicine, must be taken in carefully measured doses. Auto makers are having enormous problems both in coordinating sophisticated machinery and in training their workers to handle it. ''New technologies haven't made any massive improvement in (the auto industry's) productivity,'' say James Harbour, an auto industry consultant whom GM recently hired to help solve its technology problems. ''So far, they have turned out to be more show than substance.'' Auto makers could make bigger gains, he says, by scrapping outmoded work rules, managing their work forces better and handling their parts inventories more efficiently. Some think—and executives at the auto companies acknowledge—that the domestic auto industry, having made record profits in the last few years in a market protected by quotas on Japanese car imports, went on a spending spree to try new technology. Contends Maryann Keller, an auto analyst at the New York brokerage firm of Furman, Selz, Mager, Dietz & Birney Inc., ''The goal of all the technology push has been to get rid of hourly workers. GM thought in terms of automation rather than replacing the current system with a better system.'' The Japanese these days are emphasizing new technology more in the cars themselves than in car plants. Despite the yen's recent rise, U.S. auto makers are still spending $1,200 more to build a car than the Japanese are. But at Honda Motor Company's U.S. assembly plant in Marysville, Ohio, costs are about the same as at Honda's Japanese plants. The Marysville plant has just two automated guided vehicles.

GM Went First

Mazda Motor Company's plant just south of Detroit, which begins production next fall, will cost about 25 percent less to build than GM's Hamtramck plant because it won't have such sophisticated and expensive equipment. Yet the plant is to produce 240,000 cars a year with 3,500 workers, while Hamtramck has 5,000 workers and is aiming for 220,000 cars a year at full production. ''It's clear that Honda and Mazda get a lot more capacity for much lower investment,'' says Martin Anderson, an auto industry consultant. ''If you have just the right amount of technology, you end up with lower investment and yet high productivity.'' GM built the first high-tech assembly plant in Lake Orion, Michigan, an hour north of Detroit, in 1983. Since then the big three auto makers have spent billions of dollars on plants and equipment, some on entirely new plants and some on existing ones that were revamped and crammed full of advanced machinery. Five such ''factories of the future'' have been opened in the last year alone—three by Ford, two by GM—with problems as complex and as costly as their equipment.

When the first Ford Aerostar minivan rolled off the assembly line at the company's revamped St. Louis plant last July, for example, it arrived seven months later then planned. First Ford had to struggle to get computer-controlled machinery from two dozen different suppliers to communicate, instead of producing an industrial Tower of Babel. Then the company realized that its equipment was so sophisticated that workers couldn't properly operate it, even after months of training. After production began, Ford had to make a substantial and unwanted change in the minivan to accommodate the machinery. The high-strength, low alloy steel used for the floor pan was too light to trigger the machine that assembles the van's under body. So Ford had to switch to a heavier, but less strong, gauge of steel and then reinforce it. The vehicle itself now is heavier than planned.

A system that uses robot vision and lasers to inspect critical points of the van's under body at the St. Louis plant hasn't been used at all since it was installed a year ago. And a multimillion-dollar computer system to monitor machine functions and warn about trouble spots in the manufacturing process is hardly being used. ''The device is not beneficial,'' says James L. Adams, the manager of the plant's body-assembly area. ''Even now while we are in full (production) speed, way past launch, we still have new problems every day,'' says Mr. Adams. ''It's just part of installing significant automation.'' He adds, ''the mistake we made is putting in all these technologies at once. It really has strained our resources.''

In high-tech car plants, delayed launches and missed targets are common as robots. Introduction of Ford's Taurus and Sable mid-size cars was delayed for three months because of problems at the highly automated Atlanta plant that builds them. GM's revamped Buick City complex in Flint, Michigan, started production but at this time is building only 45 cars an hour, instead of the planned 75. One problem plaguing Buick City was the vision-equipped robots that install windshields were breaking some of them. Sometimes the robots, after grasping a windshield with their suction-equipped arms, would push too hard while putting the glass in place because their vision systems lacked proper depth perception. GM says the problem has largely been corrected.

Although such foul-ups may slow Detroit's headlong rush into high-tech, they won't halt it. U.S. auto makers are convinced that automation will cut costs and increase quality in the long run, and also provide the flexibility to build several models on the same production line. That way they can respond quickly to changing tastes and produce more models aimed at specific market niches. ''We absolutely have to make our cars have more specifics and differentiation than we have in the past,'' says GM Chairman Roger B. Smith. ''The key to that is the intelligent systems of robots that can say, uh oh, here comes an Oldsmobile that's got to be welded differently than the Buick that just went by.'' That is what is supposed to happen at the Hamtramck plant. It produces four GM luxury cars that sell in the $20,000 to $30,000 range—the Cadillac Eldorado and Seville, the Buick Riviera, and the Oldsmobile Toronado. Besides being the world's newest and most modern auto assembly plant, Hamtramck is an intermediate step toward the much-touted $33.5 billion Saturn manufacturing complex being built in Spring Hill, Tennessee. Saturn is supposed to revolutionize the auto manufacturing process. As each car's frame starts down the Hamtramck assembly line, a worker attaches a programmable ''box'' about the size of a recipe card, replacing the stacks of ''specification sheets'' used in older plants. The box specifies the car's make, model color, and equipment. Electronic scanners ''read'' the box all along the line. They tell the robots and other machines how to build that particular car and flash information on display monitors telling workers which parts to add by hand but sometimes ''when the car stops in front of me, the computer flashes the code for the wrong bumper,'' says a worker at the plant. ''So what am I supposed to do? I report the problem to the team leader. But by the time the technicians fix the problem I have bolted on 50 wrong bumpers—a Cadillac on an Olds, an Olds on a Buick, a Buick on a Cadillac.'' Similar problems plague an innovative system that uses cameras and laser beams to guide robots in applying sealants to a car's joints. The robot often misses the right places, and then drips the glue-like sealant on the floor. So now workers are doing the job manually. ''It's a low-priority item for us to fix now,'' says Mr. Tannehill, the GM executive who oversees the plant. It is obvious why other priorities exist. Watching the cars being built at Hamtramck is like viewing a film in slow motion, even when the assembly line is moving—which it often isn't. During a recent tour of the plant with GM officials, the line broke in two places.

At one point a robot in the sophisticated robogate system—where several sections of the car body meet and receive more than 100 welds in 27 seconds—smashed into a car body and stopped the line. Farther down the line a futuristic machine that uses cameras and laser beams to measure the openings of each car body wasn't working, and cars were backed up behind it. Some workers, meanwhile, read newspapers to pass the time until the line restarted. The machine breakdowns are taking a toll on human beings too; Hamtramck's plant manager, Earl Harper, took what GM terms an indefinite "medical leave" for ailments that were aggravated by the pressure of the job. Mr. Harper, 60, says he had expected the plant to reach normal production much faster than it has, and now he wants to "get away and relax." He says he is retiring.

The biggest of Hamtramck's problems are the plant's paint shop, the most expensive part of the facility. In ordinary setups, car bodies pass through one long paint booth on a continuously moving line, and workers spray-paint them with semi-automated equipment. But at Hamtramck, the main assembly line splits up and directs each car into one of eight separate—and unmanned—paint booths. Robots in each booth bend, twist and turn to spray-paint the bodies. Ironically, GM designed this system to be simpler than the one it put in the Lake Orion plant three years ago. There, painting robots move alongside the moving assembly line, making coordination tricky. At Hamtramck the robots in each booth are stationary, but the problems are worse. Initially, the robots' paint hoses would break because of the constant arm bending; that problem was solved through reinforcement. But the paint booths still frequently come to a standstill. As the plant attempts to increase production speed, the robots must bend, twist and turn much faster, and the stress produces breakdowns. Cars often emerge from the booths painted unevenly, resulting in long lines at the two booths that are designated for redoing already painted cars. The ultimate indignity has been shipping several hundred cars to a nearby Cadillac plant built in 1929 to be repainted with old-fashioned hand-held spray guns. "The modular robot paint system is the hardest part of the plant to get going," says Lynn Minger, Hantramck's new manager. For each of the 19 colors the plant uses, he says, the robots must make different adjustments to regulate the pressure of fluid into the paint gun, the rate at which paint is sprayed from the gun, and other "parameters" he adds, "it's complex."

Mr. Minger, 42 years old, became manager of the Hamtramck plant. The plant, he predicts, will resolve its major problems and reach full production in July, eight months behind the original schedule. But getting up to speed won't be easy. Mr. Minger recently called a meeting of Hamtramck's salaried employees to tell them that the plant's poor performance was "putting their jobs and reputations on the line," says one person who was present. Mr. Minger says he "wasn't that tough." But he adds: "I simply laid out the facts of life, which is that we're behind schedule."

FROM CRAFTSMAN'S GUILD TO CIM—OLD HABITS DIE HARD

The opportunity and ingredients necessary to become world class are available to all. Some of these components, such as CIM, Expert Systems, SPC, are still in the evolutionary stage of development, but then only some of these are needed in all situations and not all are needed in every situation. Where they are required, they present a very formidable challenge to reduce to working practice, but to a great extent this is not really the issue anyway. Their nonavailability, or difficulty of implementation, or immaturity are not the primary impediments to world-class status. Whether or not these powerful new concepts are required to restore competitiveness, or as is more often the case, we simply need to make better use of what we have, at least in the short term, the biggest common impediment is usually ourselves—in our willingness and ability to deal with change, either externally or self-imposed. Our attitude to change—our receptivity to the need for it, how adeptly we manage (or mismanage) it—is to some extent shaped by the fact that time for us has a different intellectual and emotional impact in terms of past, present, and future. As mere humans, we cannot forecast the future. We have an intellectual notion of the future in the context of events we expect to occur—our next meeting or birthday, our next mortgage payment, our summer vacation, losing our job—but since these events are yet to occur, we can have no direct experience of them; we can only relate to them indirectly through previous, similar experiences. If we have no such previous experience, then we can only speculate as to its effect in the future. Our intellectual awareness, responding to the signals we receive in the present, complements our past experience and shapes our emotional attitude to the future—optimism, pessimism, anxiety, fear, apprehension, eager anticipation—emotions which relate to events which may or may not occur. When we are faced with uncertainty in the future, with impending change or the need for change, we can choose to ignore it, deny its existence, resist it, passively await its arrival, or reach out and try to shape it in the image of our preferred or desired end result.

The past, on the other hand, we are much more comfortable with, particularly in times of uncertainty. We tend to cling to it, to retreat to what we know best in times of adversity. Unlike the future, whose effects we can only imagine, we have actually experienced its pleasures and pains, intellectually and emotionally. They leave their mark on us. It makes us what we are. Without these past experiences in fact, we can have no sense of time in the future. We revere the past because it has stood us in good stead, at least until now.

We do not, as do some cultures, revere the past to the extent that we idolize it, but we do institutionalize it. We try to preserve that which we found by trial and error, these values, beliefs, rules of thumb, value judgments supported and perpetuated by systems we found to have worked.

But we cannot reach out and shape the future, while we still cling to the past. We risk becoming caught in a time trap—reluctant because of its associated uncertainty, to push ahead into the future—at the same time, impeding our potential progress by wanting to haul our heritage from the past on our journey. To reinforce our sense of security, to bring order out of uncertainty, we institutionalize what is, and is not, acceptable behavior, work practices, compensation policies, job classification schemes, the way we organize ourselves, our approach to solving problems and resolving issues, the way we account for inventory, how we measure and track costs, the way we account for overhead recovery—rules and systems based on these rules which set the boundaries of the playing field. When circumstances change, solutions which are appropriate in these new circumstances are disallowed because of the rules restricting corrective action to what was "acceptable" in the past rather than most appropriate for the present. The rules outlive their usefulness and prevent or delay appropriate corrective action. The "establishment" in any organization is what it is because of these rules—and its natural instinct for self-preservation would have these rules respected, not challenged. The advocacy of change can too readily be misconstrued as "rocking the boat." These are the early symptoms of the "British disease"—resisting the future by trying to perpetuate status quo—which can at best only degrade to mediocrity. It is contagious! It can have a long incubation period. It can be economically fatal! But it is treatable, sometimes curable!

The proof that the impediments to being world class are not availability or maturity of technology, or the rules of the international game, or a "sullen, lazy workforce," but simply facets of human nature and how we manage (or mismanage) them is evident throughout our industrial history. If, for the sake of argument, we divide the history of industrial evolution into major phases, we will see ample evidence that the transition from one phase to the next was always resisted. We can also observe that those organizations, industries, and nations who resisted it least, who made change work for them rather than against them, in the long run fared best.

Major Phases in the Evolution of Manufacturing

- Self-sufficient craftsman
- Labor intensive, functionally specialized mass production
- Mechanized, functionally specialized mass production
- Automated mass production
- Just-in-time mass production
- Computer integrated manufacturing

Self-Sufficient Craftsman

Manufacturing first appeared as a specialized profession when our prehistoric tribal predecessors reached the point in their societal development where they were able to support a tools and weapons specialist. (No doubt even then there was resistance to change and impediments to the transition.) While by far the least significant method of production now, this has survived to the present day in the form of the independent craftsman, producing the complete article, by virtue of his or her own efforts and skill, for local markets, without the need for an elaborate supporting infrastructure. This endured as the only form of manufacturing well into the sixteenth and seventeenth centuries. The institutionalizing process ran its course then with the establishment of craft guilds, controlling supply by restricting access to the trade through apprenticeships and by applying restrictive trade practices in the market place.

Labor Intensive, Functionally Specialized Mass Production

The first transition, from craft guilds to industrialization, with its printing presses and steam engines, we also know was resisted, most notably by the Luddites. Mass production as we know it, in accordance with Smith's principle of the division of labor and specialization, was first applied, on a grand scale at least, by Henry Ford—a single product, conveyor belt, bring the work to the person configuration. Hugely successful for many years, Ford's refusal to accept that the business had grown in scale and complexity beyond his ability to control it autocratically brought a dramatic change of fortune to the company which took the subsequently appointed management team many years to correct.

So successful has been this approach to manufacturing—what we have described as functionally specialized mass production—that its practice has become very widespread and it is still the predominantly used approach today. Obviously it has served us well and we have continued to refine both it and the underlying infrastructure necessary to support it over the years. Its greatest attribute is its ability to support high volume at potentially low cost by maximizing overhead recovery, consistent with the principle of economies of scale. To support its huge appetite for material, we have developed policies, procedures, and systems consistent with that need—economic order quantity purchasing, inventory stockpiling, multisupplier sourcing, and so on. This property has also directed other major policies—in marketing what the factory can build, in cost accounting—developing systems to track physical and clerical material transactions, in personnel policies—classification of labor into direct and indirect, according to whether this resource contributed by adding value directly to the product or was employed indirectly in manufacturing support functions. The large quantities of inventory, defined by accounting convention, at least for balance sheet purposes, as an asset rather than a liability, had to be accounted for. This of course gave rise to the need for elaborate computer systems to account for it. Personnel policies followed a similar path, focusing on direct labor job classification, compensation policies, training, and so on.

Since adding value to the product using this approach was directly, and almost exclusively, a function of the human operator contribution in physical effort and skill, we classified this resource by accounting convention into two categories—direct and indirect. Direct was defined as that which added value to the product, further subdivided, since inventory was considered to be an asset rather than a liability, into inventoriable and noninventoriable. While direct labor costs, as a significant proportion of the total costs, were rigorously measured, monitored, and controlled, adding direct labor to an organization—implying an increase in a wealth creating resource—could usually be justified by an increase in volume alone. This was not the case for indirect resources, considered, again by accounting convention, to be a nonproductive overhead burden. Any improvements in quality and productivity were expected to come primarily from the direct labor source, leading to growth in the management "sciences" of work study and industrial engineering who attempted, among other things, to develop the notion of a "standard" operator, possessing a "standard" level of skill, applied with a "standard" degree of motivation, the combined effect of which was measured in Therbligs (Gilbreth spelled backwards). With hindsight, this may now appear ridiculous, but such was the state of the art then, and to some extent, even now.

Many of the inventory and cost accounting systems still in use today originated in and evolved in this environment. Such was the significance of direct labor that it became a yardstick for the measurement of other parameters. Overhead recovery for example, was then, as now, absorbed in relation to the direct labor base. Overhead costs were considered to be fixed and therefore "uncontrollable." To simply account for them rather than control them was considered acceptable; to find someone to accept undisputed ownership of them, was difficult.

An Example of Overhead Recovery

Fixed overhead per month (rent, utilities, equipment depreciation)	500K$
Standard labor cost per hour	5$
Standard operation rate per hour	100 units
Unit volume per month (capacity base used for overhead recovery)	500 K#
Standard hours required	500,000/100 = 5000 hours
Total standard direct labor cost	5000 × 5 = 25,000 K$
Overhead absorption rate	20:1
Actual units produced	550 K
Earned overhead	550 K$
Actual direct labor cost	27,500 K$
Overhead variation	50 K favorable

With this method, in a capital rather than labor intensive environment, it is difficult to separate capital productivity issues, or that of any other factor for that matter, from those of direct labor. Volume, mix, machine, and labor efficiency variations and perturbations distort the measurement in ways difficult to comprehend when trying to associate cause and effect. Ratios of the relative proportions of these resources, such as direct to indirect and inventoriable to noninventoriable burden were tracked. Scrap and rework were considered inevitable and the measurement systems also included the means to capture these costs, in effect encouraging the addressing of symptoms rather than causes, institutionalizing not only competence but incompetence.

Mechanized, Functionally Specialized Mass Production

The next major phase was the replacement of this direct labor physical contribution to the value added process by fixed function mechanization—machines designed to fulfill a specific, narrowly defined task, as was that of the operator it replaced, but capable of fulfilling only that task. This too was resisted, most obviously by those being displaced. With fixed function mechanization, direct labor as classically defined is reduced, even eliminated. As such, the value-added contribution no longer comes from direct labor but from machines. Throughput rates are those which the machine is capable of, not the human operator. Capital equipment in itself is not productive. It requires other resources, traditionally considered to be indirect or burden to make it so. By definition, the need for these resources will be opposed since, due to the reduction in direct labor, the direct to indirect ratio will deteriorate. There are many other consequences of this apparently one for one substitution of resources.

As the work load across a series of tasks fluctuates—a typical occurrence in a functional system in which balancing across operations is not normally controlled—human operators, provided they have the necessary skills, can be redeployed accordingly. This is obviously not possible with fixed function, dedicated machines. With reduced flexibility, stable loading assumes critical importance. With regard to quality, a person can detect and respond approrpiately to unacceptable excursions to tolerance in the material being processed. Unless otherwise equipped, a fixed function machine will trundle on regardless. This is still by far the most predominantly used approach today, although we are already into the next phase, that of automation—multifunction mechanization. As we know, there are but a few pioneers in the next and latest phase, CIM.

Automated, Functionally Specialized Mass Production

This constitutes a significant improvement on merely mechanized production lines with each task being brought under greater control, sometimes with improved flexibility, as the equipment is provided with more electronic "intelligence," but the problem of integrating these resources—islands of automation—remains largely unsolved, at least in a uniformly consistent way.

While we continued to refine this basic approach, we never really questioned its continuing validity. It does indeed have much merit but it also has major shortcomings, no longer tolerable in today's environment in which customer expectations have escalated beyond the potential of this system's ability to satisfy them, no matter how much we continue to refine it. The functional approach cannot readily support product proliferation in the form of mix—with mix comes complexity, with complexity comes longer lead time and higher costs due to changeovers. It cannot handle small lot sizes—low cost only comes with full loading. If volume drops, costs increase—the more capital intensive the system, the higher the cost of doing less. It cannot support demand above its finite, fixed capacity. Additional capacity only comes in large increments. When it is running fully loaded and well, it has enormous momentum—but with momentum comes high inertia, it cannot accommodate change easily or quickly.

To accommodate scenarios other than simply the need for high volume at low cost—high quality, cost sizes of one or few, the ability to support product proliferation, short cycle-time, and so on—we have devised variations on this theme. But with all of these, there are inevitable tradeoffs.

- **Continuous process, homogeneous product.** Capable of high quality at low cost—but single product only.
- **Continuous process, batch product.** Improved capability to handle mix—but quality, cost, and cycle time are invariably compromised to some degree.
- **Job shop—many, small different product lots.** A hybrid combination of the best attributes of continuous process, batch, and project—but none are optimized.
- **Project—lot size of one.** Extreme cost (and cycle-time) penalty.

Today's reality is that we need manufacturing systems which combine the relative strengths of each of these approaches without compromise in order to satisfy the requirement of high quality, low cost, and short cycle-time for small lot sizes. So enamoured of these systems have we become that like our predecessors before us, we too have institutionalized what we know best.

Just-In-Time Automated Mass Production

This approach, more than any other, begins to challenge the precepts upon which many of our supporting infrastructure systems are predicated. With little or no inventory or direct labor, much of the provisions of these systems become redundant.

Modular Mass Production and Computer Integrated Manufacturing

The modular approach, using existing manufacturing technology to reduce work-in-process zig/zag, represents an intermediate step between just-in-time functionally specialized and fully fledged, computer integrated manufacturing.

Planning for CIM

In today's fiercely competitive environment, it takes nothing less than manufacturing excellence, not just to win, but to even stay with the pack. This excellence cannot be achieved by perpetuating status quo. Neither can it be achieved with more of the same, applied with renewed vigor. A radically new approach employing CIM is required. CIM is in fact, such a radically different approach to manufacturing from what we have known in the past, that to use the term revolution rather than evolution to describe its effects is probably not an overstatement. This particular transition in manufacturing systems may take 10 or 20 years to run its full course, but in the perspective of the last 200 years, when change occurred so slowly and gradually as to be virtually imperceptible, this will be by comparison, a period of rapid and tumultuous change. Whether riding on its crest, swept aside in its path, or drowned in its wake, its effects, at least for some, will be traumatic.

So far reaching are the changes which CIM brings, the need for planning its introduction and adjusting to its consequences are not by any means confined to the factory floor. These changes pervade every facet of an organization's existing structure and culture, bringing with them the need to review, revise, and in some cases, even discard some of our most sacred tenets, refined and reinforced by custom and practice over the years to become part of our accepted "conventional wisdom." In its most highly refined form, CIM in conjunction with expert systems, means little or no direct labor. With just-in-time materials control, it means little or no inventory. With statistical process control, it means little or no scrap and rework. If applied in its broadest scope, from customer interface to shipping the product, its networks and data bases transcend functional boundaries and encroach on every little fiefdom. To serve the needs of such a multiuser community, its objectives need be broad and its economic justification must be measured in the context of these total needs. Traditional accounting policies and procedures will be vigorously challenged: return on investment formula will be required to be modified to comprehend factors historically not included due to benefit quantification difficulties; reduction in inventory carrying cost made possible by shorter manufacturing cycle-times; increased revenue due to the improved mix management capability; the shift in associated resources from direct to indirect; the benefits of being able to process information faster and more reliably; reconciling the cash flow consequencies of higher up front capital equipment and development costs against improved competence rather than reduced sustaining costs; reconciling both external and internal reporting accounting needs. Knowledge, the fourth factor of production, assumes dominance in this scenario, integrated with land, labor, and capital, and the greater the degree of integration—of data, machines, and organizational functions, the more effective CIM will be.

As with any new technology, CIM will mean great good fortune for some, for others the end of an era. The deciding factor, as always, will be our attitude to change, separating those who reach out and embrace it from those who resist it with the rewards and penances of the marketplace respectively. Time is of the essence. There is none available to rest on one's laurels. The rapid implementation of CIM does not sustain a competitive lead, it closes an uncompetitive gap.

The Imperatives of Technology

1. There is an increasing amount of time separating the beginning of a task from its completion. Knowledge is applied to a minute fraction of the task, then on that in combination with some other fraction and thus on to final completion. The more thorough the application of technology, the more sophisticated the production process, the further back the application of knowledge will be carried.

2. There is an increase in the amount of capital that is committed to production independent of increase of output. We are irrevocably committed it seems, on the path of every intensifying automation. Systematic, regular tasks tend to be capitalized and automated.

3. With increasing technology, the commitment of time and money tend to be made every more inflexibly to the performance of a particular task. That task must be precisely defined before it is divided and subdivided into its component parts. Knowledge and equipment are then brought to bear on these fractions and they are useful only for that task as it was initially defined. If the task is changed, new knowledge and probably new equipment need to be brought to bear.

4. Technology requires specialized manpower. Not surprisingly, it can be applied only by those who possess it and neither is it confined, as one might initially imagine, to technologists or engineers. Technological imperatives demand the same degree of organized, systematic application of knowledge across the total spectrum of business activity.

5. The division of labor, or more fashionably specialization, needs to be re-integrated. This calls for organization. Indeed, this task may be so complex as to require the attention of a specialist in organization.

6. The magnitude of the time scales of capital commitment, the inflexibility of this commitment, the needs of large and complex organization and the problems of market performance under constraints imposed by advanced technology, intensifies the need for planning.

17

Artificial Intelligence and Expert Systems

"The analytical engine has no pretensions whatever to originate anything. It can do whatever we know how to perform. It can follow analysis, but it has no power of anticipating any analytical relations or truths. Its province is to assist us in making available what we are already acquainted with."

The above quotation, articulated by Ada, Countess of Lovelace in critiquing Babbage's analytical engine circa 1882 is with respect to computer capability, especially those based on the Von Neumann architecture, as valid now as it was then. Despite what we read in the popular press and some of our technical and scientific journals, artificial intelligence, which seeks to develop solutions to the kinds of problems currently beyond the scope of conventional computer architectures (and the human brain), is still more wishful thinking than reality. Where much progress is being made is in expert systems, and it would help to make the pursuit of artificial intelligence much less intimidating if this less emotive term describing the real fruits of this activity in all but research laboratories were used. In fact, it may be more appropriate to refer to these systems as advisory rather than expert since few are exclusively relied upon in practical applications.

These systems, using the conventional Von Neumann architecture, are already commercially available though still confined to automating very narrow, highly specialized segments of knowledge-intensive tasks; some fields of medical diagnosis, specific tasks in engineering design and development (semiconductor logic and systems design simulation, analysis, layout, mask set, and test pattern generation), in manufacturing management in the form of process control, numerical machine control, in equipment maintenance and diagnostics, in financial investment and portfolio analysis, in oil field exploration, and so on. These are areas where our knowledge of the subject is at least reasonably comprehensive and can be applied to the task in hand in a well-defined, highly structured fashion. At the present time, there are an estimated 1,000 expert system applications in the United States alone in various stages of development, up to and including commercial application. (A reference of some of the commercially available products in this field is provided at the end of this chapter.) Many of these masquerade, somewhat pretensiously, under the guise of artificial intelligence. While some of these achievements are indeed impressive, if this very specific element of the much broader concept of artificial intelligence were all we could hope to aspire to, we would still have little more than silicon parrots, systems capable only of behavior within the range of what they have been taught, not capable of solving anything but the simplest of tasks by computer standards and almost certainly, completely incapable of solving those outside the boundaries of their existing knowledge base.

Artificial intelligence aspires to go beyond this, marshaling all that we know (and there is much that we don't), about computer science and the human brain to solve problems and execute tasks which currently exceed the memory capacity and reasoning capability of both. A familiar if controversial example of such a task is illustrated by the kinds of problems which would have to be solved in creating, assuming it is even possible, the kind of system required to make Mr. Reagan's Strategic Defense Initiative (SDI) a reality. This epitomizes the characteristics of the problem an ideal artificial intelligence system has to address.

It is massively complex in terms of hardware, software, and scale.

It must work first time—no dry runs.

It must deal with situations and problems it has never before encountered.

As anyone who has written computer programs will confirm, if we consider that the probability of a software code working right the first time diminishes rapidly beyond the first ten instructions, this I think you will agree, is a very formidable, if not impossible, task.

A much more down to earth and less controversial example (no pun intended) which serves our illustration purpose most aptly, is that of the traveling salesman problem, stated as follows: given that a salesman has to make a call in each of n cities, what is his shortest possible route? The way a conventional computer based on Von Neumann architecture would tackle this would be to sequentially compute every possible chain of city to city links and then identify the shortest. This would be the very best solution according to that criterion, distance, but the time required to arrive at this answer would escalate exponentially as n, the number of cities in the chain, increased. A chain of 10 cities can be linked in 181,440 ways $((n-1)!)/2$, a few seconds perhaps of central processor time, but a chain of 30 cities for example, can be linked together in a mind boggling one trillion billion billion different ways. Even a superfast conventional architecture computer would require somewhere in the order of one hour of CPU time for this task. Obviously, if we wanted to play variations on this theme, identifying the fastest or least costly route for example, we would soon run up our processing bill. This is almost entirely a function of the limitations imposed by the architecture of a conventional Von Neumann machine.

Data, parameters describing the problem, are entered through the keyboard. Don't let the magnetic tape fool you; at some point in the process, someone, possibly in Taiwan, laboriously entered these data by hand.

The analysis of the data is limited to this given, preprogrammed "universe" of knowledge. In the parlance of the knowledge engineers who develop these expert systems, this is called the "domain."

All data manipulation, fetching from and storing to memory, is executed sequentially.

The system hardware, the functional elements of the system such as central processor, memory, and peripherals are connected in a fixed and inflexible configuration with respect to each other.

Communication with the system, at least initially, will be via some slow, error prone, and tedious mode which compromises the power and convenience of con-

versational English.

The speed, memory capacity, and algorithmic "reasoning power" of the system will have very finite limits.

Consequently, much of the time consumed in problem solving is not productive but is used to manage overhead functions such as computing addresses and moving data to and from memory. In our traveling salesman example, if we assume that each city to city iteration requires five software instructions, that each instruction requires five machine cycles and that the system bus speed is 1 MHz (one million cycles per second), then our ten city problem would require $5 \times 5 \times 181{,}440 \times 1$ microseconds to execute. This is approximately 4.5 seconds. Even if our machine were 100 times faster, we would still require approximately 0.045 seconds of CPU time. (The reader may compute the time for 30 cities if so inclined.) In many situations, such as telephone call routing, traffic control, project management, battlefield logistics, and real-time radar-imaging, "good enough" solutions, produced quickly, rather than absolute best are acceptable. This kind of approach is not the particular forte of the existing generation of machines.

Being able to process solutions to such problems faster, to clone human experts in short supply, as well as to address problems, the complexity of which lie completely outside of the scope of the existing generation of systems, has spurred efforts in several different directions in terms of computer architecture and systems design. Least radical are the efforts to continue to enhance the existing generation of machines, making them faster and increasing their data storage capacity with more memory, and so on. This can be considered analogous to the development of the piston engine in the evolution of the aviation industry. These engines followed a path of continuous development up to the turbo propellor driven era, and while there are still tasks for which these engines are still most suitable, it took a radical departure in engine design to develop the multi-thousand pound thrust of the jet engine to match the task of hurtling several hundred people through our skies in a steel and duraluminum cylinder at 600 miles per hour. Trends similar to this can now be seen in the computer domain in the form of massively parallel computers (also called transputers). These machines represent a fairly radical departure from the Von Neumann approach in that their architectures are designed to process instructions, to send data to and receive data from memory, in a parallel rather than in a sequential fashion. As such, although they are still very much in the embryonic stage of development, and require completely new operating system software to be developed, they are potentially very much faster and more powerful than the more conventional Von Neumann counterpart, or ever likely to be, despite continuing improvements in smaller geometry, faster semiconductor technology (see Figure 17-1).

With the advent of EEPROM semiconductor technology, non-volatile electrically erasable/programmable read only (mostly) memory, another aspect of AI—development of systems with the ability to "learn" from and adapt to their environment begins to be possible, if only on a small scale and in a very modest way. An example of this is the use of EEPROM memory in under the hood automotive environments where an engine's varying isostoichiometric parameters are "learned" in situ and stored for use as required in the future when similar conditions are encountered. A more mundane example is the storing of information which prescribes the position, height, and inclination, etc. of the driver's seat. This is still far removed from our definition of artificial intelligence offered below, regardless of which architecture is employed.

Artificial intelligence represents the marshalling and application of knowledge in the realms of computer science and the human brain towards the design, development, construction, and application of machines capable of learning from (as

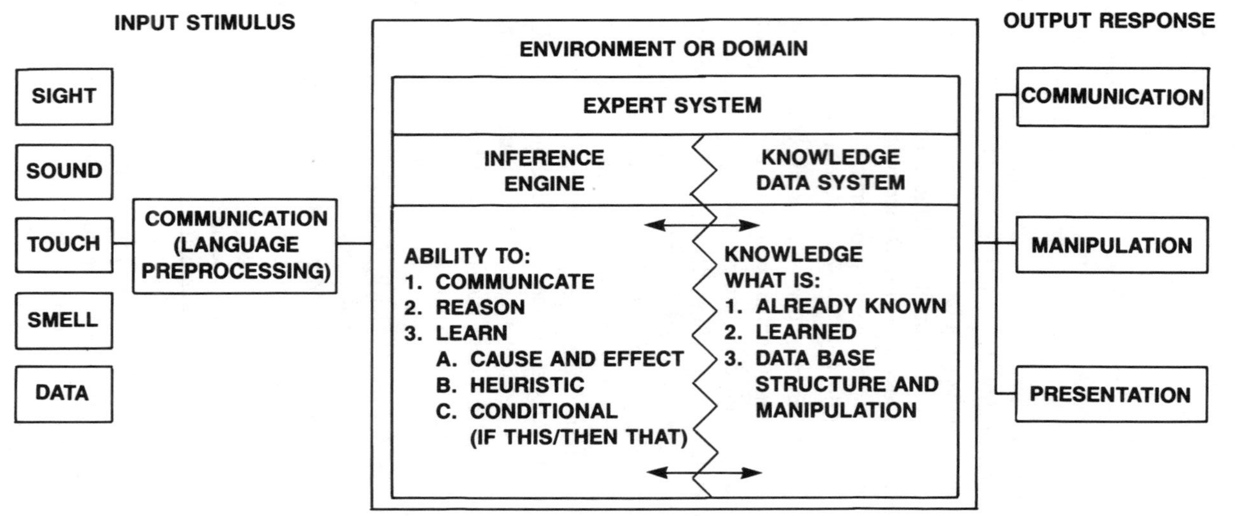

Figure 17-1 Expert System

opposed to being taught—programmed). They do so by interacting bidirectionally with their environment through sight, sound (oral conversational language), touch, taste, and smell. Their purpose is to develop and apply a "universe" of knowledge and experience data base with which to replace, exceed, or enhance the human intellectual contribution to tasks in academia, industry, commerce, and other areas of human endeavor.

The third and by far the most ambitious direction being pursued is that of so called "neural network computers." This approach is inspired by what we know, or at least what we think we know, of the anatomy and behavior of the human brain. Unlike the other approaches, which employ fixed architectures in the sense that the interconnections between the various functions in the system; the central processor, the ROM, RAM, I/O, and so on are not dynamically reconfigurable, the neural network approach is modeled on the brain's apparent ability to "rewire" itself as it were, according to the task being performed. From this observation, the hypothesis that the brain's ability is not so much a function of the number of "processors" or speed but of the number of possible interconnections, was developed. This is perceived by some researchers to be an important clue in leading to a better understanding of how the human brain works; how it receives, processes, and memorizes information from its environment, how it learns and reasons, and so on. (Some of us are willing to take the Creator's work for granted, others must know how and why.) The experts are by no means unanimous that this line of thought will lead to the desired end result and it is indeed ironic that we should use the brain as a model to design and develop machines to fulfill tasks which the brain cannot, but following clues, any clues, is probably better than waiting for divine inspiration, so let's join the faithful and review what we know (or think we know), about our model. We best get our arms around natural intelligence before we claim to have a synthetic substitute, if for no other purpose than being able to calibrate such "artificially intelligent" machines as are eventually made available against a standard. Pessimistically, we may not learn anything useful in helping us to create these "thinking" machines, but we may learn much about ourselves in the process. Whether it comes packaged in its original form or in tin boxes, human intelligence is still our primary resource in industry and it can surely do no harm to know more of its character. Before inquiring into both the natural and synthetic varieties too deeply, however, it might help our purpose if we first establish some perspective by briefly reviewing the evolution, scope, and current stage of development of artificial intelligence in general and of expert systems in particular, from the work first done in the mid-1950s up to the present day.

In the early days, what little work was being done was confined, as is typically the case in the evolution of new scientific and commercial disciplines, to major university research laboratories. The work then was limited in its depth and scope, not only by a dearth of interested and suitably qualified researchers, but by the need to support much of the development work with the only kind of computers which were then available, extremely large, and therefore very expensive, single user, batch processing mainframe machines. Driven by a need to improve the productivity of this arrangement, of both man and machine and the communication interface thereof, rather than as targeted end products of Artificial Intelligence research in their own right, multitask operating systems capable of supporting time sharing applications and higher level languages such as LISP began to emerge as derived benefit by-products. At this stage, computers and computing was still very much a "black art," practiced by but a few computer science specialists and expert assembly level language programmers programming their machines in languages far removed from conversational english and as such, the focus of much of the work tended to be confined to highly esoteric applications. Even then, in an era when anything and everything was thought possible, extravagant claims were being made that within ten years these machines would be as ''intelligent'' as humans and perhaps as a result of this euphoria, many technical and philosophical red herrings were pursued up blind alleys. With the passage of time however and nothing tangible appearing to support these claims, expectations began to be scaled back and more serious and thoughtful directions began to be pursued. When the true magnitude of the task became apparent, the tried and trusted scientific method of breaking up a task into smaller components brought the full scope of the work into a structured perspective. In doing so, we now know that to continue to make steady if not spectacular progress, we must first develop our understanding of these components in their own right, at the same time dealing with the challenge of integrating them into useful systems. The boundaries which had been previously drawn were far too narrow. Replicating a brain in a glass jar is in itself a mammoth task, integrating it into the overall system in which it functions, the human body and its environment, is mind boggling. Only when effort was concentrated on very narrow, specific elements of this total task of understanding the individual components and processes of the brain did real progress begin to be made. A specific example of practical success using this approach in dealing with the kind of problem common to many businesses, managing mix for short cycle time manufacturing in a complex environment is XCON, developed by the Digital Equipment Corporation.

XCON—EXPERT CONFIGURER

Managing mix to maximize revenue and reducing manufacturing cycle times to shorten product lead time in order to accommodate uncertainty, rather than relying on inventory, are opportunities available to any manufacturing enterprise, especially those whose product portfolio consists of variations round a common core product. (In the semiconductor industry context, gate arrays, ROMS, and single chip MCUs fall into this category.) XCON is probably a classic illustration of how Expert Systems can be used to exploit such an opportunity to maximum advantage. (There is no question that Digital Equipment Corporation, the system owners and developers, is being rewarded by the market.)

In 1978, building on R1, an expert system kernel originally developed by John McDermott at Carnegie Mellon University. DEC has since enhanced and applied this work to the problem of configuring VAX and PDP11/23 computers to almost invariably unique, customer specifications. As is so typical of a successfully growing business, with increasing volume and widening product portfolio proliferation, DEC's manual process of agreeing configurations with customers, processing these through the order entry cycle and subsequently building them to conformance back in the factories was beginning to show signs of stress. XCON's contribution in this task is to verify whether an order specification can be built in the factory, supported in the field and if so, how to configure these components architecturally and connect them together generating bills of material in the process. If customer specifications cannot be configured, XCON describes and documents why not and how to correct the problem. In use since 1980, this system runs a program with over 2000 rules on a VAX 11/780 machine and has analyzed 20,000 unique configurations. The system currently operates at up to 98 percent accuracy. (The experts are not unanimous in considering the number of rules in a program as a figure of merit, the higher the number implying the greater the power. There are those who take the view that the power of a system should reside in the inference engine, in cause and effect models used in the core of the system, not as knowledge incumbent in the domain data base and the quantity of rules is not therefore, a meaningful correlation to power.) In this context—logical inferences per second (LIPS) is a more meaningful figure of merit.

The program suite has since been expanded to include XSEL (Expert Selector) a package designed to interactively assist customers, using a portable terminal in their own premises, to configure systems of their choice and XSITE (Expert Siter), to comprehend and redefine if necessary, the environmental considerations such as air conditioning and power requirements, cable routing lengths, and so on. These programs, both of which are still currently under development, operate interactively and are being further enhanced with IMACS, a program designed to manage the flow of work within a plant and ILOG, a module designed to facilitate coordinating the shipment of material from many manufacturing plants located throughout the world to the customer's site.

From work of this nature, principles underlying successful efforts in expert systems have begun to emerge to guide the efforts of others. We can now begin to formulate, and answer, some of the important questions with regard to these systems. Why, for example (or where) do we need, or think we need, expert systems? What in fact, is an expert system? How is or should it be developed? What is its scope? Can it replace all that has gone before or should its use be confined to some narrowly defined segment of the manufacturing task? (Perhaps the very first question should be can the need for an expert system be avoided by designing the target task out of the process? Nothing, after all, is so futile as to do well, that which should not be done at all.)

In an industrial context, as customer expectations and demand for variety increase, as products and manufacturing processes become much more complex, the burden of processing information prior to processing product also increases. The work of DEC and others demonstrates that this part of the task at least can greatly benefit from expert systems. Observations drawn from these efforts are beginning to provide answers to these questions, in establishing principles to guide the efforts of others. In DEC's case, the need was obvious. With a successfully defined product (having correctly defined what business they are in and what it takes to be successful in that business), their manual system was close to being overwhelmed by opportunity. The task they had to deal with was one of a recurrent nature. The input parameters sets, selected from a "universe" of options, were almost invariably unique combinations, the output likewise, but the basic process in the cycle remained the same. This process was also highly interactive, involving more than one human "expert." The scope extended from customer definition of the product configuration to producing a model on paper back in the factory with all of its attendant documentation. They had human experts to deal with this who got it right most of the time, but they were a resource in increasingly short supply. Much of the later development of XCON was conducted in situ where continuous access to these experts was assured, where the real-life operating environment could shape the evolution of the final product. It was not a turnkey product, designed and developed offsite and then installed to replace that which had already existed. In developing the system, the human experts were thoroughly interrogated by the "knowledge engineers" and their knowledge characterized as they performed, the number of iterations to get it eventually right being of particular interest. Earlier attempts had failed due to inadequacies in the existing manual system which had to be corrected. (Discovering flaws in the existing system is frequently one of the early benefits of any form of attempt to automate!) That the total system is built in independent modules which are subsequently assembled together was also significant. What can be observed from this in terms of defining the kind of problems to which expert systems can be applied and the approach which should be followed in their development? Specifically, what kind of tasks lend themselves to this kind of treatment? What are the characteristics of a human expert? Can generic design rules for such efforts be established?

ADAPTED FROM ARTIFICIAL INTELLIGENCE SYMPOSIUM, 1986

Characteristics of tasks suitable for replacement by ES.

- **The task does in fact require the services of an expert.**
- **The task domain has a high payoff or is of a highly recurrent nature.**
- **The task is primarily cognitive—not algorithmic—or if so, the mathematical equation is not known.**
- **The knowledge required to perform the task already exists—but may be unstructured or ill defined.**
- **The knowledge of the task may be represented by rules or heuristics.**
- **The skill required of the task is routinely taught to neophytyes and practiced by them albeit inefficiently.**
- **A large amount of human expertise is required.**
- **Recognized human experts already exist.**
- **These experts are demonstrably better than amateurs in performing the task.**
- **The task requires no common sense.**
- **It is not possible to define a totally comprehensive specification in writing.**
- **The need to better execute the task, manage change, and/or proliferation is apparent.**

Characteristics of the human expert.

- **Usually specializes in relatively narrow fields of knowledge.**
- **Solves simple problems easily.**
- **Can explain what is done—why, how.**
- **Judges the reliability of their own conclusions.**
- **Knows when they are outside of the realms of their particular domain.**
- **Communicates fluently with other experts.**
- **Learns from experience.**
- **Adjusts approach to suit the problem.**
- **Transfers knowledge from one domain to another.**
- **Reasons, on many levels—rule of thumb, mathematical models, simulations.**
- **Amateurs become experts incrementally—a gradual process.**

Expert system design rules.

- **The inference "engine" and data base should be independent modules (inference engine should be transportable to other systems).**
- **The inference "engine" should be no more complicated than is absolutely necessary.**

- **Knowledge should be represented in the most uniform possible way.**
- **Redundancy should be exploited.**
- **Power is incumbent in the knowledge.**
- **The system should be able to deal with knowledge which is ill defined and unstructured.**
- **The system must be flexible and transportable (open ended).**
- **Redundancy—overlapping knowledge domains of several experts.**

One, only slightly frivolous definition of an expert is someone who knows more and more about less and less, until eventually they know everything about nothing. There is at least a germ of truth in this popular definition which, in conjunction with what we have already established, can be used to build a definition of an expert system. To summarize, whereas artificial intelligence deals with a very broad spectrum of research and development activities—computer vision, robotics, natural language interfacing, speech synthesis, and recognition—an expert system is simply a rule based, problem solving, computer system in which the knowledge of an expert is encoded in the software program—in effect, a form of intellectual cloning. Abstract "feelings" can't be integrated into such knowledge data bases. A practical distinction between AI and ES is that an expert system has to be "taught" or programmed whereas an AI system will have an inate ability to "learn" of its own accord, albeit it must be "taught" how to learn. There have been, as yet, no attempts to instill the qualities distinctive in making us human such as integrity, loyalty, compassion, morality, emotion in these machines, only "pure" logic, offering reason not clouded by emotion.

Expert Systems: A Definition

An Expert System is the end product of the process of identifying, formalizing, encoding, and applying the knowledge of human experts as the basis for a high performance computer program to replicate and distribute expertise.

Many of the commercially available products in the field of expert systems are simply the next logically progressive step in the natural evolution in computer applications, developing programs to execute tasks which are normally performed by experts. The much more ambitious developments in AI however, are to a far greater degree, being modelled on what we know, or think we know, about the processes of the brain—memory, reasoning, how we learn, and so on and this model is now reviewed.

THE HUMAN BRAIN AS A MODEL

Structural Analogies

Since our particular purpose in reviewing what is known about the brain is not in simply gaining knowledge for its own sake, although this is never a bad motive, but to try and identify and pursue clues which might lead us towards developing computer systems, both hardware and software, capable of satisfying the above definition in realizing artifically intelligent and expert systems, we shall follow a similar approach to that which we followed in developing our understanding of CIM, starting at the most fundamental level, semiconductor physics in the case of CIM and the nerve cell or neuron in the case of the brain. We shall then proceed through each successive stage up to and including the end product at the system level. After all, a brain, like a CPU, is only part, albeit a very important part, of a larger system, the human body. At each stage, we shall pause in our search for clues to try and establish what parallels if any, can be identified and developed. Significant milestones in our roadmap, lending structure to our task in the form of staging posts, might be as follows:

Semiconductor Physics	Neural Biophysics
Diode	Neuron
Transistor	Synapses
Logic Elements	"Columns"
Input/Output Peripherals	The Five Senses
The Status Register	Consciousness
Higher Order Functions	Memory, Reasoning, Learning
Bits and Byte	Phonemes and Morphemes
Protocol	Speech
Applications Software	Task specific regions of the brain—speech, reason, memory and so on
Operating System	The Reticular Formation
Networks	The Central Nervous System
Total System	Homo Sapiens

Historical Perspective

Before the age of reason—or at least informed thinking

Ever since the ancient Greeks, who believed that thought was "the soul's walk abroad," people have pondered the mysteries of the brain. Do we have a soul? If so, where does it reside? What is mind? Are brain and mind separate—or like matter and gravity—indivisible? What is intelligence? How do we think? What knowledge, if any, do we come equipped with at birth? What do we subsequently learn and how? What role, if any does culture and education play in making us what we are—is the mind of the primitive savage different from that of civilized man? Contrary to early cultures, who believed that intelligence resided in the heart, Hippocrates first conjectured, correctly as it transpired, that thought and emotion originated in the brain. Aristotle thought that the brain was nothing more than a radiator whose function was to cool the hot blood welling up from the heart. Plato perceived the soul to be immortal, moving from body to body, that the cerebral cortex was merely a protective covering for the brain. The four "humors" of the body, black bile, yellow bile, phlegm, and blood were believed to constitute the essential chemistry of the brain and body, providing the basis of the ancient medical practice of bleeding the sick to restore health by adjusting the balance of these fluids. The life force—the liver, fed by the intestines, produced a "natural spirit" that flowed to the heart where it was refined into vital spirit, mixed with pneuma in the brain to become animal spirit in the rete mirabile, a network of blood vessels found only in hoofed animals—subsequently shown by anatomist Andreas Vesalius to not even exist in the human body. It was he who refuted *In De Humani Fabrica Corpus* (The Structure of the Human Body), published in 1543, the notion that the separate mental faculties of imagination, cognition, memory, and judgment resided in the four ventricles of the brain. Descarte selected the pineal gland purely on the basis that it was the only singular organ in the brain as the residing place of the soul. The pseudoscience of phrenology, inaccurately if not erroneously linking mental faculties to regions of the brain based on the shape and contours of the head, flourished then fell from grace in the mid-eighteen century. Flourens, using the scalpel to test the claims of phrenology popularized by Gall, while confirming the general conclusion, refuted the specific relationships of function and location. Bernard pioneered new vivisectionalist techniques and established the idea that the body fluids could effect emotional behavior. Mesmerism, the forerunner of hypnotism, reached a peak in fashionability before it too was discredited.

All of the aforementioned are symptomatic of attempts to explain, in familiar terms, things we do not understand. As is so often the case, scientific progress depends on progress in many separate disciplines to explain the whole phenomena—including the need to escape the harness of the prevailing conventional ''wisdom,'' dogma, and tradition. Gradually the body of scientific knowledge accumulates to the point where explanations need no longer be based simply on speculation, although this is still relied on to a great extent in explaining the complete operation of the brain. Over the course of time, as is so often the case in development of knowledge, observation and reason began to replace speculation and mythology. Galen, a second century Greek physician, was the first to theorize that the ''power of movement and sensation flows from the brain.'' Swendenborg located and defined the motor cortex and theorized that ''when the mind is heated by passion, the lungs likewise boil up'' correctly linking respiration to brain activity and not heart beat. Cortugno discovered that shock-absorbing cerebro spinal fluid filled the ventricles of the heart and not as was until then believed, animal fluid. Charles Edouard Brown-Seqaurd showed that the glands of the body produced hormones. Galvani demonstrated the relationship between electricity and muscle contraction in frog's legs. Not until the invention of the microscope, made possible by Anton Van Leeuwenhoek, who was able to produce lenses of remarkable clarity, the electro-encephalograph by Hans Hensberger, demonstrating the existence of electrical activity in the brain, and developments in other fields, could scientific observation, hypothesis, and experiment instead of speculation, become the basis of further knowledge. Throughout history we have continued to revise theories of our understanding of the brain, progressively discovering ''nuggets of truth'' but never finding the mother lode of complete comprehension.

Driving Force

We now know primarily from the work of Charles Darwin that the evolution of the brain is not random and haphazard process but that it is guided by a purpose, a driving force, that it is goal orientated. The paramount goal is survival of the species, perpetuated from generation to generation through the DNA molecules contained in the genes, by a process of natural selection over countless cycles of trial and error, searching for the attributes most suited to ensuring survival in adapting to any particular environment. This goal is too remote and impersonal for us to relate to at a conscious level. Needs, however, are things we can all individually relate to and Maslow showed how we pursue this goal in our daily lives, how it is that we haul ourselves, cycle by cycle, along the evolutionary path, each life contributing in an infinitessimally small way, for good or ill, to the grand design, continuously attempting to satisfy a hierarchy of needs subordinate to this goal.

At the most basic level, the first plateau in this hierarchy of needs are the physiological needs of hunger, thirst, warmth, sleep, sex—those arising in the most primitive centers of our reptilian brain—with us since we first crawled, or slithered, out of the primordial soup. But, unlike other species, satisfaction of these most basic and recurring needs does not bring permanent contentment. It simply opens up a vacuum—new, higher order needs then assert themselves—in the form of the need for security. When we are well fed, our thirst quenched, we then seek safety—our prehistoric predecessors happy to accept some dark and dusty cave—which we relinquish when the more basic need of hunger reasserts itself. But yet again, even with a full stomach, a new need emerges—the craving for the company of our fellows, for which we are again willing to leave the security of our cave, at least long enough to find someone to share it with. But still we are not satisfied. It is not enough to satisfy our gregarious nature with company. What others think of us as individuals, the esteem in which we are held, then becomes an important need—yet again to be satisfied. Having clawed our way thus far up the hierarchy, we are then free to give reign to nobler thoughts, originating, not in the reptilian or premammalian regions of the brain, but in the most recently evolved miracle of evolution—the cerebral cortex. It is here that we ruminate on our raison d'etre, our purpose in life—to satisfy the need, which Maslow called self-actualization but perhaps more descriptively—self-fulfillment.

In this context, we begin to understand our motivative process—that of attempting to satisfy needs, and that we are kept on the path of biologically evolutionary virtue by pleasure and pain—positive and negative reinforcement, adherence to the righteous path rewarded by pleasure, and deviation punished with pain. If we attain our immediate goal, we are satisfied—albeit only temporarily. If we fail, or are impeded, we get frustrated, or angry even violent. These are simply ways of mustering our resources and bringing more intellectual horsepower to bear on achieving the objective. This is the underlying theme of the learning process—the motivation. It is on this theme, more or less, that the brain evolves. If then, we are to have machines capable of learning, do we have to endow them with similar needs. How can we "motivate" computers to learn? Even if we could, do we know enough of the learning process mechanics to imbue machines with this capacity. With this in mind, let's see what we think we know of this process in the human brain. To what extent can we answer the following questions? How does our brain develop physiologically and pyschologically? What is intelligence? What faculties and knowledge do we come equipped with? What do we subsequently learn? How do we remember what we have learned? How do we apply what we have learned to reason and create? What, if anything, is encoded in genes and passed on to the following generations?

The Physiological Development of the Brain

The development of the brain as a distinct organ first becomes apparent in the human embryo about three weeks after conception, when it begins to form from a single sheet of about 100,000 cells on the upper back. Growing at the incredible rate of 250,000 cells per minute, these cells provide the blueprint for subsequent growth and development by producing DNA (deoxynucleic acid) containing the genetic masterplan code, from within their nuclei. Closing in upon itself as it develops, the sheet forms itself into a tube, the upper part dividing to form the four cavities of the brain (ventricles), the lower part ultimately developing into the spinal chord. As the cells continue to divide and multiply, they migrate towards the center of this tube, the cells destined to become nerve cells (neurons) eventually exhausting their ability to produce DNA and cease dividing. Each cell's ultimate destination, the region of the brain where it will finally reside, seems to be prescribed by specialized cells called glial cells populating the inner surfaces of the ventricles, from which long tendrils extend into the neural tube wall and by which neurons selectively haul themselves along to their destination. The cells then form specific associations with other similar cells, keying in on marking molecules on the surface, forming the distinct, task specific, regions of the brain. It is hypothesized that these marking molecules may also determine the order in which neurons link together and the type of connections, called synaptic junctions, they form with other neurons. Each neuron is in itself an infinitely small switch with thousands of input terminals called dendrites, a cell body and one output terminal called an axon. These are capable of connecting with other cells and communicating with other cells by means of electro/chemical action—the transistors in our computer analogy.

Insulating all but the synapses of the neuron cells from each other by producing myelin to coat and protect the neurons and tendrils, the glial cells, outnumbering the neuron cells ten to one, provide cohesion in maintaining the spatial relationship between neurons and the blood vessels of the brain, providing the nerve cells with nourishment and disposing of waste products. By the time this divide and multiply process has run its full course, the fully developed brain will weigh approximately three pounds, two pounds of which will be the cerebrum, source of thought and creativity to which we shall return later, and will contain somewhere in the order of 10 billion neurons and possibly as many as 10 thousand billion potential interconnections.

Potential would seem to be the operative word here. Until it was demonstrated by Ramon y Cajal, using a staining technique developed by Golgi, that each neuron is a distinct, stand alone entity, it was believed that the neurons were connected to each other in a fixed arrangement (the reticular theory). It is now known that the interconnecting patterns are not fixed at any instant in time or process but that they are "programmable" (the neural doctrine), the specific interconnecting configuration at any instant apparently a function of the nature of the data required to be processed. In contrast, semiconductor technology is capable of producing no more than one million transistor switches on one monolithic piece of silicon and these only in a fixed interconnect pattern. While each individual transistor can be switched on and off individually, the interconnecting configurations are programmable only during the design stage and cannot be reconfigured on the fly at run time. In terms of scale and flexibility, this obviously falls far short of that which the brain is capable. The software required to control even this less than comparable hardware in emulating the human brain is even less remotely feasible with today's technology.

While the brain is our central processor as it were, the signals which it processes, other than those originating within the brain itself, arrive from sensor cells distributed all over the human body. These cells, through which we are interfaced to our environment, transmit their signals to the brain via nerve fibers, converging at the base of the brain in a region called the medulla oblongata. This is analogous to a computer's input/output mechanism. This region, considered to be the most primitive part of the brain, and regulating such things as heartbeat, breathing, swallowing, and blood pressure, is the major junction of nerve fibers between the body and the brain. The pineal gland, the system clock in our computer analogy, is synchronized to the sun in producing our circadian rythmn and regulates the metabolism of body and brain helping us distinguish night from day. It is located in the region of the hypothalamus. Light from the sun, or nowadays from an artificial source, passes through the iris of the eye and strikes this gland, stimulating it to secrete the hormone melanine, influencing memory, the immune system, and regulating the degree to which we feel fatigued. (This is presumably one organ we would wish not to replicate in our intelligent machines, since we would surely prefer that they work continuously without rest.)

Signals requiring an immediate response, such as those designed to alert us to potential danger, are processed in a specialized area called the reticular formation, the natural equivalent of a computer system's priority interrupt circuitry. This is the seat of the "reptilian" or "premammalian" brain as described by Paul McLean in his "3-stage tribune" brain, the starting point in Jackson's description of evolution as a "passage from the most automatic to most voluntary functional centers of the brain," residing in the cerebral cortex immediately beneath the skull. These three evolutionary centers are described as: (1) lowest—brain stem components, (2) the middle center, and (3) the highest—motor and sensory area of cerebral cortex where consciousness resides. An intermediate stage, the cerebellum, often described as the lesser brain, governing movement, processing signals from the nerve endings in muscles and from motor sensors in the brain. It is also thought possible that the cerebellum (the system status and control registers) might play a role in emotional development and control, modulating passion with reason. So convoluted that 85 percent of its surface is hidden, the cerebellum consists of three layers of cells and interconnecting nerve fibers, the middle layer called Purkinje cells, perhaps among the most complex of all neurons. With the highest density of synaptic connections in the nervous system, messages shuttled to and fro in the white threads of the arbor vitae to all parts of the brain and body. Protruding from the vermis, part of the cerebellum controling balance, posture, muscle tone, are three organs called peduncles, two of which connect to the medulla and pons transmitting signals to the cerebellum from incoming afferents. Emanating from here in both directions, upwards into the brain itself and downwards in countless tributaries dispersed all over the body, is the system data bus, 12 pairs of motor and sensory cranial nerves. These are:

1. The olefactory nerves of the nose, in which the sensors of our sense of smell reside.

2. The optic nerve, transmitting light images captured by the iris of the eyes and transmitted across the afferent pathway to their designation, the primary visual cortex at the back of the brain. Cells here are specialized, some responding only to particular shades of color, or movement in a specific direction only, or light arriving only at a certain angle. Some cells seem to respond primarily to signals arriving from one eye, others to both.

3. The occulomotor nerve controls the blinking and focussing muscles of the eyeball.

4. The trochlear controls downward and outward movement of the eye.

5. The trigeminal controls chewing muscles and sensations in the face.

6. The abducens controls focusing of the eyes.

7. The facial nerves control movement in that countenance.

8. The accoustic facilitates the transmission of sound impulses and controlling balance.

9. The glossopharyngeal supplies sensation to the back of the mouth cavity and back of the tongue, controlling also, some of the muscles required for speech.

10. The vagus enervates movement of the aesophagus and larynx, slowing heart rate, stimulating stomach acid production, controlling movement of the bowel, and several muscles of the neck.

11. The spinal accessory contributes to the action of the vagus nerve in controlling the bowel and also several muscles of the neck.

12. The hypoglossal controls tongue and throat movement and also some of the muscles involved in speech.

Radiating outwards and upwards from the brain stem, above the cerebellum and deep within the core of the upper hemispheres of the cerebral cortex, reside the four ventricles of the brain, historically but erroneously held to be the dwelling place of imagination, judgement, cognition, and memory respectively. Instead the source of nourishment for the brain's myriad of cells in the form of cerebro spinal fluid, absorbed into the blood stream and renewed several times a day. Many of the organs managing the chemistry and metabolism of the body and brain are clustered in this region. The vermis—an organ contributing to the control of balance, muscle tone, and posture. The peduncles—extending from the vermis, regulating incoming and outgoing nerve impulse. The four colliculae—relay stations for sight and sound impulses through which flows dopamine, guarding against muscle rigidity and tremor. The hypothalamus—synthesizer of hormones controlling growth, temperature, water balance, and sexual behavior. These hormones flow into the pituitary gland where they are stored and subsequently released into the blood stream in a controlled manner. The thalami—two glands which are involved in regulating consciousness, concentrating signals from virtually all over the body and then transmitting them on to the cerebrum. The paired limbic lobes—joined by the fornix, constitute the limbic system—the emotional brain—seat of pain and pleasure—the pre-mammalian brain mentioned earlier. Connecting this neural galaxy are three main groups of nerve fibers called: (1) the projection fibers or corona radiata, emanating upwards and outwards from the brain stem to the hinter regions of the cortex; (2) association fibers, including the cunilingam, linking different regions of the same hemisphere; and (3) the corpus callosum—joining the cerebral hemispheres. Evidence for each hemisphere being essentially self-sufficient has been provided from postoperative studies of patients suffering from severe epilepsy in whose brains this organ was surgically severed. The patients seemed to suffer no impairment of normal ability. Such split brain patients can perform two tasks simultaneously and seem to have two realms of consciousness—in effect, dual brain states or minds.

Residing immediately beneath the skull and enclosing virtually all of the rest of the brain, is the cerebral cortex—our intellectual brain. Within its quarter inch thick by 2.5 square feet volume are contained approximately ten billion pyramidal, stellate, and spindle cells in six layers, connected by 10 thousand miles/cubic inch of nerve fibers, involving possibly a trillion connections. Divided from front to rear by the longitudinal sulcus, a deep cleft in its structure, the cortex is also divided from left to right by the central sulcus. Forward of this, towards the forehead, the body's motor functions are located in the frontal lobe—a band of nerve tissue arching over the head from ear to ear. The frontal lobe is believed to be the domain of our foresight and planning skills. Immediately behind the central sulcus in a region called the parietal lobe lies the sensory cells that respond to signals from all of our five senses. At the back of the brain, immediately above the back of the neck, is the occipital lobe within which is located the visual cortex—as far removed form the eyes as possible. While we still do not understand all of the processes involved, most if not all of the task specific regions of the brain and cortex have been identified, at least those involved in tangible functions—body movement, facial expression, and so on.

Much less well defined are the higher order mental functions. Of these, the ones of greatest interest to the artificial intelligence research community are those of speech, memory, and reason. With regard to speech, three areas involved in its production have been identified. Broca's area—located between the lateral fissure and the lower portion of the motor cortex controlling the muscles of the face and throat necessary for the articulation of speech and Wernicke's area—located below the lateral fissure, next to the sensory cortex. The third area, the angular gyrus, is involved in managing the relationships between words read with words heard and spoken—with the symbols used by the mind. While there is good reason to believe that the brain is specialized for speech, observations of individuals sustaining brain damage in these areas has also shown evidence of other regions of the brain compensating for damage in these areas—especially if the damage occurs before the age of puberty. While the anatomy and chemistry of the brain are intriguing, in the context of artificial research, what is most interesting and of potentially greatest relevance, is the interdependence and specialization of each hemisphere, and the task specialized regions within these hemispheres—the symbiotic synergism of the brain.

Structure of the Brain—The Task Specific Regions

Nature in her infinite wisdom has endowed the human race with not one brain, but two, or at least two apparently identical hemispheres joined by a massive data bus of nerve fibers—a neural bridge—called the corpus callosum, from which millions of nerve fibers radiate to most areas of the cortex. (To be on the horns of a dilema—to be in two minds on something—may be more than literally true.) Appearance is where the similarity ends however, each hemisphere specializing in different tasks, with further specialization within each hemisphere. The left hemisphere controlling the right side of body, is analytical, dealing with literacy and numeracy, taking ideas apart—dissecting them in a sequential manner. Here, in the realm of convergent thinking, reside our verbal, reading, writing, mathematical, language, scientific skills—those matters requiring linear and logical treatment. The right hand side, controlling the left side of the body, is conceptual—skilled in integrating information and ideals together in a holistic way, grasping relationships in a single step. This is the realm of divergent thinking, of spacial and pattern recognition, generating the mental images associated with objects perceived by the senses. Joined by corpus callosum—the network of nerve fibers uniting the special powers of both hemispheres—each hemisphere specializes in its respective tasks—an early manifestation of Adam Smith's principle of division of labor. It is now widely accepted that the corpus callosum exists largely to unify attention and awareness and to allow the two hemispheres to share memory and learning.

An intriguing paradox, our dual brain regionally localized by function shows much evidence of built-in redundancy. Supporting the view that the human brain has more capacity than is used, people recovering from brain damage—children with hydroencephally—water on the brain—show remarkable compensatory powers. In our early formative years both hemispheres may be engaged in a fight for dominance normally won by the left hand side, accounting for the preponderance of right handedness. It is believed that the cause of at least some language disorders are due to situations in which neither hemisphere succeeded in asserting dominance during development.

Psychological Development

Every single human being on earth is the end product of a couple of billion years of evolution, a process of learning by countless cycles of trial and error over the course of eons, over which is superimposed for those of us in the developed countries at least, the exposure to several hundred years of organized knowledge, followed by a couple of decades of individual development towards adulthood in our particular childhood environments. Paul McLean, in his "Three Stage Tribune Brain" theory of evolution, has suggested a framework consisting of three stages:

1. Reptilian—cold blooded survival instincts/the basic drives the pimordial soup—the first step in Maslow's hierarchy of needs!

2. Paleomammalian—emotion/effective feelings/e.g.; mammals nursing young—the second and third stages, residing in the limbic system.

3. Neomammalian—the thinking brain with all three linked together by strong neurological ties "tempering reason with emotion."

The brain may stop developing organically by about age 20 but evidence exist for on-going "emotional" development beyond this.

PROCESSES OF THE BRAIN

Contemporary Theories of Operation

To fully understand the human brain, we need to understand not only what it does, why it does what it does but also how. The what and why are the realm of the psychologist. The how is the realm of the pure physical scientist. Up to this point, we have taken a very clinical view in trying to understand how. Even our cursory inquiry would not be complete unless we address the what and why of the brain function. It is perhaps indicative of how little we know of the brain and its processes that there appear to be as many theories attempting to explain its operation as there are "experts." Some of the more popular theories are as follows:

Edelman's "primary repertoire" theorizes that the brain functions by "constant recycling of impulses among its many circuits." Signals are initially detected by groups of 50 to 10,000 neuron cells called "feature" detectors which in being exercised frequently, lead to a "secondary repertoire" of knowledge. These circuits, believed to be programmed from birth to recognize codes, correspond perhaps to the building blocks, the logic elements in a computer system.

Holographic theory—based on the observation that given just a part of an image, the whole can be reconstructed by the brain.

Empiricism—this theory postulates that we all start life with a clean slate, as it were, which is subsequently written on by life's experiences.

Agents and agencies—a common approach in trying to unravel the mysteries of the human brain is to start with observed effects and try to identify underlying causes. Linguists in this field start at the macro level of language and then try to disassemble it to its least indivisible components in order to understand its content and structure at the most minute level. This is much like the approach we used in the physical sciences in understanding matter, peeling back the layers, as it were, down through molecules, then atoms to the sub-atomic particles at the core. Marvin Minsky, in his excellent book *The Society of Mind* (Simon and Schuster, New York), departs from this approach starting instead at the micro level and building upwards and outwards. Using what he calls **agents**, he develops a model of the brain which provides plausible answers to many of our questions about the brain in general and what we call mind in particular. In his words "This book tries to explain how the mind works. How can intelligence emerge from non-intelligence. To answer that, we'll show that each mind is made up of many small processes called agents, each of which is mindless by itself. Each by itself can only do simple things which of themselves require no thought or intelligence. It is the process of these agents acting in concert which gives rise to intelligence." Again in Minsky's words, "to explain the mind we have to show that the mind is made of mindless stuff."

Minsky's view is that the brain builds a pyramid of skills as we grow, the base consisting of lots of little unrelated skills, each acquired by a process of trial and error, punished by the pain of frustration and rewarded by the pleasure of accomplishment. It then develops inter-relationships enabling it to group these lower level skills to form higher level skills—building an increasing competence, layer by layer. Almost certainly, Minsky's agents correspond to neurons or small groups of neurons acting in concert through their synaptic junctions. There are indeed striking similarities between computers and brains. In fact, Minsky's model of the society of mind did not arise primarily out of what he knows of psychology but out of his efforts to develop a computer system to simulate the child building with blocks.

Minsky begins to build his model by asking us to imagine a very young child playing with building blocks. He asks us to further imagine that the child's mind contains a host of smaller minds, which he calls **mental agents** with an agent called **builder** in control at the start. He suggests at this point that the motivation involved in the learning process is the pleasure a child gets from seeing the tower grow as each new block is added. Building a tower, however, is too complicated a task for a single agent so **builder** which has control over subordinate agents **begin, add,** and **end** which it can switch on and off as required. **Add** in turn needs help from **find, get,** and **put**. **Find** needs help from **see**. **Get** needs help from **grasp, move,** and **release**. The learning process for a child obviously begins before this point but this is the early stage of learning in a controlled interactive way with its environment. In this way the child gradually builds up a hierarchy of skills by the process of trial and error. This leads to two ways of looking at agents: (1) as a simple process which turns other agents on and off and (2) as a product of all of its subagents.

Viewed as a closed system, from the outside looking in, **builder** gives the impression that it knows how to build towers. Viewed from the inside, however, no such intelligence is apparent. Agent **see** needs to be able to recognize its blocks whatever their color, size, place, against different backgrounds, shades, light, and even when partially obscured by other blocks. Agent **more** has to be able to guide the arm and hand through complicated paths in space, yet not strike the tower or hit the child in the face. Agent **find** needs to be able to determine which blocks are still available for use. By trial and error, the child remembers which actions and sequence of events were successful and stores them for future use rather like a subroutine in computer software. Minsky then systematically develops the model to explain:

Function	How do agents work?
Embodyment	What are they made of?
Interaction	How do they communicate?
Origins	Where do the first agents come from?
Heredity	Are we all born with the same agents?
Learning	How do we make new agents and change old ones?
Character	What are the most important kind of agents?
Authority	What happens when agents disagree?
Intention	How could such a network (of agents) want or wish?
Competence	How can groups of agents do what separate agents do?
Selfness	What gives them unity or personality?
Meaning	How can they understand anything?
Sensibility	How could they have feelings and emotions?
Awareness	How could they be conscious or self-aware?

Minsky's model seems too ridiculously simple to explain something as unbelievably complex as the human brain. But then simple models are the best ones to start with in any subject we know so little about.

Behaviorism—postulated by John Watson using Pavlov's "conditioned reflex" is predicated on the assumption that action stimulates thought rather than vice versa and so the child only learns by interacting with its environment.

MENTAL FACULTIES

Intelligence

In the very broad sense, intelligence is a measure of our ability to process information about our environment in order to interact with it. The output of this process is normally action on or reaction to environment. This ability manifests itself in a range of skills, the value of any particular skill being environmentally dependent. In our computer system analogy, it is a measure of the power and flexibility of the central processor and its operating system. How well our particular application program runs, that is, performs its task, will be a function of these. The central processor lends itself to a more satisfactory definition and measurement than does the operating system. This is equally true of the skills residing in the left hemisphere of the brain, those of verbal, numerical, and reasoning skills in the realm of convergent thinking. These we think we have sufficient measure of to be able to quantify them in terms of intelligence quotient, mental age/chronological age × 100, measured by such systems as the Stanford-Binet intelligence scale scholastic apptitude test. (This is analogous to measuring the CPU in our computer system.) Such measures have proved to be reliable indicators of academic success at school but are less reliable in correlating success in later life.

To complete the range of skills embraced by intelligence, one must also include those for which the right hemisphere of the brain is responsible. Those skills such as social intelligence, musical ability, leadership, intuition, motivation, and so on. Any task requires more than just analytical competence, such as motivation, concentration, discipline, and so on. These are not so easily defined in a measurable way. Neither do we know how much of our intelligence is hereditary and how much is due to interaction with our environment. We do know that both are important. Like many species we need to cooperate to survive. To cooperate we need to communicate. To facilitate communication, we developed language, both sign and verbal. Verbal is more effective in communicating precisely, so these skills assumed predominance. We developed our other analytical skills to understand our environment even better. The left hemisphere seems to be survival oriented, inclined to avoiding pain. It seems to be risk averse. The right hemisphere seems to control our more adventurous propensities, willing to take risk in pursuit of pleasure and improving our quality of life in creature comforts and intellect.

Other ways of measuring intelligence are being pursued. Reaction time for example to flashing lights or ringing bells, the hypothesis being that the faster the response, the quicker the brain, possibly confirmed by means of EEG. Another approach seeks to find a correlation between brainwave patterns and intelligence.

Learning

Much of AI research is based on the study of child development—trying to understand how our minds develop and "grow"—the importance of strategy and error in learning process being of particular interest. One of the many questions being pondered—with what knowledge do we come equipped—what do we subsequently learn? In other words, what is genetic and what is environmental? As adults, we all have the capacity to learn but as children, at least according to one school of thought, we must first learn how to learn. There is another school of thought which believes we are biologically programmed before birth. The newborn infant seems to "know" how to suckle instinctively, that crying will lead to the relief of discomfort or hunger. But does it come already equipped with this information, or does it make this association by trial and error? This process is receiving much attention from researches in AI and ES wishing to imbue machines with comparable skills. The issue is divided broadly into two schools of thought in cognitive psychology (understanding the basic laws of the human thought process)—the interactionists led primarily by Piaget and the naturalists led by Chomsky respectively. Piaget, a biologist by training but a genetic epistemologist (the study of the origins of human knowledge) by preference, testing the hypothesis—that all knowledge derives from human actions—grouped the development of mental ability into four crucial stages.

1. From birth to two years—the sensory motor intelligence stage—a child's mind develops by exploring and interacting with its environment, gradually becoming aware of the reciprocal effect on it—the child on its environment and the environment on the child up to ten months, a child literally thinks that objects and people it can no longer see, no longer exist.

2. From two to seven years, the child begins to think of its world intuitively and symbolically, indulging in games of fantasy, conjuring up mental images, although it cannot yet mentally manipulate them developing an understanding of the relationships between quantity and shape, the concept of reversability.

3. Seven to twelve years—in the concrete operational stage—logical and abstract thinking begins to develop, the use of numbers, classifying things, categories.

4. Twelve to fifteen years—formal operation, thinks in abstractions, develops ability to reason in verbal terms, manipulates scientific equations and distinguishes between conjecture and reality, irony and double entendre. Positive self-image, so important to emotional well being, is formed by this stage.

While Piaget believes that children acquire language in stages, Chomsky on the other hand, building on the work of Levi Straus, using language as an example—believes that "there is an organizational structure—a code of rules called deep structure—more fundamental than those of the grammar we learn in school." He believes that the human brain is genetically preprogrammed for language development, hypothesizing the existence of two basic forms of "language universals"—substantive and formal, substantive universals being the most elemental sounds of speech—phonemes such as p, b, or th. Formal universals are predicated on an even more controversial assumption—that children know instinctively how the grammar of a language should be organized—that they already "know" the rules.

Memory

Memory is our record of experience. It is what gives us our sense of time. To remember is to reconstruct the essence of a state previously encountered by the brain. Via memory, we structure and classify our experiences into past, present, and future. We seem to have two, and possibly three kinds of memory, short, medium, and long term. Our brains are continuously bombarded by input signals from all of our senses—sight, sound, taste, touch, and smell. These are received by and captured in a temporary latch, much like a computer's dynamic RAM scratch pad. To prevent overload, most of these signals are screened out by an organ called the reticular formation, the basis of consciousness. The remainder, what is considered relevant to the task at hand is filtered through to our short term memory mechanism (just like signal gating in a computer) controlled by an organ called the hypocampus. Surgical removal of the hypocampus prevents the creation of long term memory.

At this point, records are restricted to only a few bits of information which is stored verbally and verbatim or as visual images if verbal is not possible. They are almost certainly electrical in nature at this point. Subliminal suggestion, banned by the FCC in 1958, short circuits the reticular formation to create long term memory called engrams. In order to transfer information in short term memory to long term memory, we invoke concentration. Records formed are not verbal and verbatim, but tend to be in terms of concept, meaning or relationship and the process is almost certainly chemical in nature. The chemical process probably involves RNA producing a protein called scotophobin from which a smaller chain of molecules called a peptide is produced. If the short term electrical pattern persists long enough for chemical action to take place an engram will be formed in long term memory. This may well be fixed arrangements of neurons explaining why the activating part can reconstruct the whole. Memory is nonserial and distributed. The brain uses symbols and tags to cross reference material and some form of gating mechanism. If the input signal and the stored anagram match, then recall results.

Language

In the early days of computing, and even to some extent today, we had to communicate with our machines in their language. To do so, we needed to understand the most elemental structure, the 1s and 0s of their binary alphabet. This was adequate when the tasks we required were simple and did not require too much in encoding our intent in arrangements of these 1s and 0s. But what we ask of our machines now places demands on this form of communication far in excess of its capability. Now we are trying a different approach, attempting to teach the machines our language so we can communicate with them in, preferably spoken, conversational English. That, after all, is how two minds most often communicate, though often the way we do so leaves much to be desired. To communicate with computers in our langauge we must understand the rules of our language at its most fundamental level (not just grammer and syntax) in order to agree upon new rules of communication. Natural language processing is probably the AI discipline being most vigorously pursued. One of the major problems that the linguists studying this is that language is not dispassionate, it has an emotional content. We fully understand the structure of the computer's language. We designed it. Not so our own, with all of its nuances, context, tone, emotional content, meaning, and so on. In language, the meaning content/intent is what matters and this depends on context, the conceptual dependency. I recall about 15 years ago an attempt to use computers to translate the English phrase "out of sight, out of mind" into Russian and back again. The translation "blind idiot" duly appeared.

It is not known where speech originates in the brain. It is believed, however, that vocabulary is distributed throughout the brain, as is also believed to be the case for memory. Where brain damage occurs, speech disorders usually result in a loss of vocabulary. Much knowledge is implied in language. Go to the airport for example. Like memory, speech needs stimulus and practice for its development. Children master their understanding of present, past, and future in that order. They build up a store of experience in the present which then migrates back from the past then extrapolates forward into the future.

SUMMARY

Expert systems and artificial intelligence are expressions most people have heard but know little about. Some are impressed by the extravagant claims being made. Many are intimidated. In this chapter, I have attempted to put both of these topics in a realistic perspective in order to help reduce this intimidation and stimulate further inquiry. On that note, I think we can safely conclude that there is a place for expert systems in industry today, although this technology is not sufficiently mature to replace the human expert, only to enhance. See Figure 17-1. Artificial intelligence, however, is quite another matter. It is a gargantuan task and we have only been able to scratch the surface. Far from being mature, this technology is still at a very early stage of development. As a result of research in this area, we shall indeed continue to see improved languages with which to communicate with our machines, better robotic vision, more powerful inference engines for expert systems, improved relational data base management systems, and so on. But so limited is our understanding of the model from which we are trying to develop, that these improvements will not be soon. It will be a very long time before we are able to communicate with our machines in conversational English or build a ''thinking'' machine. Rather than direct benefits as in the case of expert systems, it is more likely that the benefits from artificial intelligence research will be in what we learn about ourselves.

Success in modeling AI systems based on the brain requires us to really understand how the brain functions. To do so, we need to understand: (1) how each cell functions—there are billions of cells, each possibly unique, and certainly hundreds of different kinds, (2) how they are interconnected, and (3) how they interact as a system. The human brain is the end result of trillions of cycles of trial and error over a couple of billion years. Every organism that ever lived in some infinitessimally small way contributing to the process, each one a cycle of learning in evolution, with perhaps an underlying masterplan. It may require at least as many iterations and a similar time span before we have something even remotely comparable in a tin box. For this reason, AI requires the combined efforts of many specialists—neurosurgeons, physiologists, phychologists, endocrinologists, computer scientists—software/hardware, the knowledge engineers, the expert specialists, the venture capitalists, and the academic. What is needed is an engineering schematic of Homo sapiens, or an organic model of a computer, neither is likely in the next couple of centuries. When our environment changed slowly and gradually under the guiding hand of mother nature, we had time to evolve and adapt. Now that man is driving these changes to the environment, they are fast and significant. Will we have time to evolve and adapt, to learn to coexist with our ''thinking'' machines, or will we shoot ourselves in the foot before then?

Following is a representative list of artificial intelligence products.

Packaged Expert Systems

Company	Products
Applied Expert Systems Five Cambridge Center Cambridge, MA 02142 (617) 492-7322	PlanPower, designed to assist financial planners in the development of strategies for their clients and in the generation of printed plans. Runs on Xerox 1186 Lisp machines.
Boole & Babbage 510 Oakmead Pkwy. Sunnyvale, CA 94086 (408) 735-9550	DASD Advisor, a performance management tool for diagnosing mainframe computer performance problems and recommending corrective action. Runs on IBM computers under the MVS operating system.
Factron EDA 269 Mt. Hermon Rd. Scotts Valley, CA 95066 (408) 438-2880	ESP/C, an IBM PC/AT-based system to assist in custom and semicustom integrated circuit design, layout, analysis, and verification.
International Systems Services Two Grand Central Tower New York, NY 10017 (212) 972-4400	ISS Three, a computer capacity management system providing work-load forecasts and modeling of alternative configurations. Comes in two modules, one running on IBM mainframes under MVS, the other on IBM PCs.
Palladian Software Four Cambridge Center Cambridge, MA 02142 (617) 661-7171	Financial Advsior, which helps Fortune 500 companies analyze the impact of business decisions; Operations Advisor, for aiding factory managers in making production decision. Both run on Symbolics and Texas Instruments Lisp machines.
Persoft 600 West Cummings Park Woburn, MA 01801 (617) 935-0095	More (for in-house use) and More/2 (for direct mail service bureaus)—two packages for ranking names on address lists for direct mail operations. Both run on IBM mainframes.
Transcomm Data Systems 1380 Old Freeport Rd. Pittsburgh, PA 15238 (412) 963-6770	Tolas Telestream, which works with the firm's Tolas order entry and financial management system, and helps field phoned-in customer orders. Runs on Digital Equipment MicroVAX computers.
Syntelligence 1000 Hamin Ct. P.O. Box 3620 Sunnyvale, CA 94088 (408) 745-6666	Underwriting Advisor, which assists property and casualty insurance underwriters; Lending Advisor, to help commercial banks analyze the advisability of making corporate loans. Both run on Symbolics Lisp machines.

Natural—Language Processing

Company	Products
Artificial Intelligence 100 Fifth Ave. Waltham, MA02254 (617) 890-8400	Intellect, designed for English queries of database residing on IBM computers. Interfaces to a variety of database management systems. Including DB2, and has a PC-based query module.
Frey Associates Chestnut Hill Rd. Amherst, NH 03031 (603) 472-5185	Themis, which runs on Digital Equipment VAX minicomputers under the VMS operating system. Interfaces to Datatrieve or Oracle database management system.
Intelligent Business Systems 246 Church St. New Haven, CT 06510 (203) 785-0813	Easytalk, sold bundled with a Digital Equipment MicroVAX II computer and with database, accounting, word-processing, and communications software.
Natural Language 1786 Fifth St. Berkeley, CA 94710 (415) 841-3500	DataTalker, which interfaces with SQL-based database management systems such as Oracle and Ingres. Runs on Sun 3 workstations or Digital Equipment VAX computers.

Expert System Toolkits/AI Languages

Company	Products
Aion 101 University Ave. Palo Alto, CA 94301 (415) 328-9595	Aion Development Systems (ADS) and Aion Execution Systems (AES), for IBM mainframes running MVS or VM and for IBM PCs. Applications developed on PCs can run on mainframes, and vice versa.
CAM Software Westpark Bldg. 750 North 200 West Provo, UT 84601 (801) 373-4080	DCLASS, a general-purpose decision tree program to assist in capturing experts' decision logic and knowledge.
Carnegie Group 650 Commerce Ct. Station Sq. Pittsburgh, PA 15219 (412) 642-6906	Knowledge Craft, a knowledge representation and problem-solving environment; Language Craft, a tool for constructing natural-language interfaces. Both run under Common Lisp machines and on VAX computers.

Expertech (U.S. office) 650 Bair Island Rd. Suite 204 Redwood City, CA 94603 (415) 367-6293	Xi Plus, which runs on IBM PCs and compatibles and offers an English interface for creating knowledge bases and applications.
Expertelligence 559 San Ysidro Rd. Santa Barbara, CA 93108 (805) 969-7874	ExperCommonLisp and ExperProlog II languages; ExperOPS5 and ExperFacts toolkits. Designed to run on Apple Macintosh and IBM PCs, as well as Sun, Apollo, and VAX computers
Expert Systems International 1700 Walnut St. Philadelphia, PA 19103 (215) 735-8510	VAX/VMS Prolog-2, an interpreter/compiler for VAX computers; Prolog-1, a subset of the Prolog-2 language for various other computers including IBM PCs.
Franz 1141 Harbor Bay Pkwy. Alameda, CA 94501 (415) 769-5656	Extended Common Lisp, a superset of the standard; Franz Lisp Opus 43, the firm's own Lisp dialect. Both run on a variety of machines from micros to mainframes.
Gold Hill Computers 161 Harvard St. Cambridge, MA 02139 (617) 492-2071	Golden Common Lisp (GCLisp) for 286- and 386-based PCs; GCLRun for delivering PC applicatons; Concurrent Common Lisp for use on Intel's IPSC; GCLisp Network to connect PCs to Symbolics Lisp machines; and 386 HummingBoard, a PC-based Lisp processing board.
Inference 5300 W. Century Blvd. Los Angeles, CA 90045 (213) 417-7997	Automated Reasoning Tool (ART), a development environment available in a Lisp version for Symbolics, LMI, Texas Instruments, Digital Equipment, and Sun computers, and in a C version for the IBM RT PC and for DEC VAX, Sun, and Apollo computers.
IntelliCorp 1975 E. Camino Real West Mountain View, CA 94040 (415) 965-5500	Knowledge Engineering Environment (KEE), a development environment in Lisp that runs on LMI, Symbolics, Texas Instruments, Xerox, and Sun computers; SimKit, a simulation package; KEEconnection, to link KEE knowledge systems to database; intelliscope, for database search and analysis.
International Business Machines 1133 Westchester Ave. White Plains, NY 10604 (914) 696-1900	Expert System Consultation Environment (ESCE) and Expert System Development Environment (ESDE) for mainframes running MVS or VM; Lisp/VM and VM/Prolog languages.

Logicware (U.S. office) 70 Walnut St. Wellesley, MA 02181 (617) 237-2254	Twaice, A Prolog-based development environment running on IBM mainframes, as well as DEC VAX, Sun, Apollo, Tektronix, and Pyramid computers; MProlog language.
Lucid 707 Laurel St. Menlo Park, CA 94025 (415) 329-8700	Lucid Common Lisp—the standard Lisp dialect along with an embedded editor, a windowing paradigm, and debugging utilities.
Prophecy Development Two Park Plaza Boston, MA 02116 (617) 451-3430	Contessa (Contextural Expert Systems), a family of developmental tools running on Symbolics and Texas Instruments computers; Profit Tool, an applicaton to help sales and marketing staff define markets, identify prospects, and close sales.
Quintus Computer Systems 2345 Yale St. Palo Alto, CA 94306 (415) 494-3612	Quintus Prolog—the Prolog language along with a development system running on the IBM RT PC and DEC VAX, Sun, Xerox, and Apollo computers; Quintus Run-Time System, for applications delivery.
Teknowledge 1850 Embarcadero Rd. P.O. Box 10119 Palo Alto, CA 94303 (415) 424-0500	S.1, a C-based development tool running on the IBM RT PC as well as on IBM mainframe, DEC VAX, and HP 9000/300 computers, and on Unix-based workstations; M.1, a C-based development tool for IBM PCs.

Symbolic Processors

Company	Products
Integrated Inference Machines 1468 Katella Ave. Anaheim, CA 92804 (714) 978-6776	SM4500, due out this month following the completion of its beta testing. Runs a superset of Common Lisp; includes an 80286 I/O processor that can simultaneously run MS-DOS programs.
LISP Machine Inc. (LMI) 175 Cabot St. Lowell, MA 01854 (617) 458-9100	LMI Lambda series, including multiuser models; software supported includes ZetaLispPlus, LM-Prolog, ObjectLisp, common Lisp, and the Flavors and ZMACS editors.
Symbolics Eleven Cambridge Center Cambridge, MA 02142 (617) 259-3711	Symbolics 3600 series, including the 3610AE applications-delivery processor; software supported includes the Genera development environment (Common Lisp, Flavors), Prolog, Ada, Fortran, and Pascal languages, and the MACSYMA for solving mathematical problems.

Texas Instruments 12501 Research Blvd. Austin, TX 78769 (512) 250-7111	TI Explorer system running Common Lisp and Flavors, with options incuding a natural-language toolkit, a graphics development package, knowledge engineering tools, and a Prolog toolkit; also sells Personal Consultant, a development environment running on MS-DOS-compatible PCs.
Xerox Xerox Center 101 Continental Blvd. El Segundo, CA 90245 (213) 536-7000	Xerox 1100 series, working under Xerox Network System (XNS) protocols, and Common Lisp and InterLisp-D; CommonLoops Object-oriented programming; Trillium, an application package for creating better man/machine interfaces.

18

Summary and Conclusions

WORLD CLASS OR CLOSED?

"To be, or not be be? That is the question. Whether it be nobler in the mind to suffer the slings and arrows of outrageous fortune or to take arms against a sea of troubles and by opposing, end them."

If world class or closed really are the only two possible outcomes of our particular "sea of troubles," if the choice facing our manufacturing industries really is so starkly binary, then unlike the bard when he penned these words, we should be in no doubt as to which outcome we prefer. With such intense competition for share, global markets are much less tolerant than they were. There is no place for those who somehow "muddle through" anymore—ask the British. There are winners and losers, there are no runners up. Our choice is to manage change or to be managed by it, to reach out and actively confront it and turn it to our advantage, to make it work for rather than against us, or alternatively, to try to run and hide from it—but we cannot make it go away.

The rules of the game itself have changed. The stakes are much higher. There are or will be far fewer players and those of world class caliber only. The cost of failure is potentially catastrophic. If we are not willing to place our faith in the comforting notion of a postindustrial service economy or believe that the merger mania currently sweeping corporate America and Europe is the answer to our ills, then how are we to advise our captains of industry which course to take in sailing safely through the eye of the storm rather than running for port. How can we help them make our industrial supertankers more seaworthy?

A New Charter for Industry

We must, without further delay, begin to build a new charter and code of conduct to guide our businesses and business leaders and all of the underlying infrastructure, including the government and educational establishments, which support them. We must discard the old values which brought us to where we are now; complacency—we have it made; arrogance—take it or leave it; greed—me first; short term myopia—there is no life after thirty or ninety days, and so on. We must accept that we ourselves were primarily responsible for allowing the situation we now find ourselves in to develop and that we can rely only on ourselves to get us out of these difficulties. Only with this frame of mind can we "take up arms" and build a new charter to guide our steps in our journey towards world-class competence.

This new charter, to change attitudes and guide actions, must be built on the principles:

That we cannot hide behind excuses and blame others any longer. We must put the propensity to rationalize failure, blaming tough market conditions for example, behind us. Markets reward competence and punish mediocrity—that is what free markets are supposed to do! Even IBM is finally willing to acknowledge this.

That the world does not owe any individual, or enterprise, or society, a living—it has to be earned. In the final analysis, the companies we are employed by do not pay our salaries. The customer is the source of these funds, our employers are merely the distribution system. There is no benign, rich uncle banker with an unlimited source of funds.

That change is a way of life. It is now the only thing we can take for granted. Closing the shutters against the winds of change results in organizational atrophy and ossification. Opening them can be not only refreshing, it might even blow some of the cobwebs away.

That we must worship at the altar of consumer sovereignty. We are fighting a global, economic war, a war in which a thousand battles are fought every day in customers' premises throughout the world. That we are losing more of these battles than we are winning is evident in our declining market share. The customer decides who is world class and who is not and exercises his prerogative to award business accordingly. To win is to fulfill, not challenge, these continuously escalating expectations. In this respect, we would do well to remember the golden rule, "he who has the gold makes the rules".

That we must continually challenge "conventional wisdom." Over the course of time, all cultures gradually accumulate a body of knowledge based on experience. This folklore consists of values and beliefs which evolved in a given set of circumstances. When these circumstances change, the folklore can outlive its usefulness.

That we must and can learn how to compete on-shore. That there is more to competing than direct labor cost. As products and processes become more complex, as the increasing capitalization and automation of the manufacturing process proceeds, direct labor becomes a diminishing proportion of product cost in relation to material and overheads, but perhaps more importantly, there are elements of competitiveness other than product costs which we must use to our advantage.

That the process of new product introduction—definition, design, development, manufacturing, and marketing must be a distinctive competence. Nowhere are the consequences of poor decisions and less than flawless execution more serious than here. Nowhere is method and discipline more required than here.

That quality, on-time delivery, and cost must be mutually inclusive, not exclusive. To be capable of less, to optimize one at the expense of another, is to deny total satisfaction to the customer.

That we must focus our thrust and stick to our knitting. If new skills are required they must be learned—not bought. As the data processing and telecommunications industries converged, IBM, a data processing company, tried to buy telecommunications skills. AT&T, a telecommunications company, did likewise in data processing. There is little evidence to suggest in their product offerings and positions in this market that these strategies are succeeding. Digital Equipment Corporation and Nippon Electric Company, on the other hand, can demonstrate fully integrated portfolios, for which they are being rewarded by the market with higher share and stock values. Perhaps the lesson here is that if we really know what business we are in and take good care of our customers, the stock value will take care of itself.

That it is better to learn how to manage mix and maximize revenue than to only rationalize proliferation to reduce costs. Markets have always wanted variety but were denied this in the belief that the means to satisfy it did not exist and led to marketing what the factory can build strategies rather than learning to build what the market demanded. With modern manufacturing techniques, this need no longer be the case. An indispensible prerequisite to this is a fully integrated business information system built in a "universal" electronic data base and focused factories with the ability to process unique, rather than homogeneous standard product lots.

That uncertainty can and should be dealt with by means of greater responsiveness and flexibility instead of inventory. Inventory can prove to be more of a liability than an asset. The alternative approach to dealing with uncertainty, short cycle-time manufacturing and just-in-time inventory management, and so on, require much more up front effort, but have proportionately greater benefits.

That structure must follow strategy, that task oriented transfunctional organizations are much more effective in serving the customer than vertically integrated functional ones—a legacy from the days when life was simpler. There is no greater enemy to accomplishment than the one within. The Japanese sail under one flag. We still have our jolly rogers.

That we must make and meet aggressive commitments, our word must be our bond. To the Japanese, a broken commitment is a matter of integrity, to us it is "just one of those things"—we forgot; we were too busy; we did not know it was important; we did not follow through. In our system, inventory deals with the cascade effect of such broken commitments, in theirs, they do not allow themselves that "luxury."

That a business must be managed as a totally integrated system—not as disparate, self-fulfilling fiefdoms. All too often synergy is lost because the component parts of a business, encouraged by a structure in which the boundaries between fiefdoms are heavily drawn and guarded, pursue divergent goals to different priorities. Allegiance to the customer can too easily be sublimated by allegiance to other, more parochial goals. Ensuring that goals are appropriate, integrated, and properly subordinated within the appropriately focused hierarchy of goals is a matter for continuous, conscious effort, not of good luck.

That the mix of skills required is changing. Manufacturing is becoming much less labor intensive yet we still cling to direct labor as our unit of calibration against which many of our parameters are measured. The kind of step function, order of magnitude improvements in quality, cost, productivity which are required to be internationally competitive are now almost exclusively a function of indirect resources—design, process, and product engineering, and so on, not direct labor.

That we must set high standards of performance. Nowhere is our complacency more apparent than in the operating standards we set for ourselves, in delivery commitments, in product yields, and so on. Historical performance plus 10 percent perpetuates mediocracy, not excellence.

That productivity and innovation must fuel growth. We cannot rely on spending our way out of trouble anymore. We must be prepared to demonstrate convincingly that we are making best use of what we have before we ask for more. We must use brains before bucks and brawn.

That manufacturing is a strategic weapon—not a tactical one. Our course is plotted by marketing, the ship's pilot and navigator, the instructions come from the captain on the bridge, but without manufacturing, the great engine converting words into deeds, this will only be so much wishful thinking. A world-class factory is the ultimate marketing weapon.

That manufacturing is the ultimate focal point of convergence. The fulcrum, the pivotal point upon which supply and demand are ultimately reconciled, the means by which customer needs for quality, on-time delivery, and price are satisfied. The interface at which processes, equipment, methods, people, skill, information, materials, typically representing 70 percent of a company's resources are integrated, the neglect of which, perhaps more than any other function, is both the cause of our difficulties today and our hope for the future.

That high tech in itself is not yet the answer. The means to fully automate have not yet evolved to the point where this becomes a feasible solution. Balance between, and integration of, manual, mechanized, and fully automated solutions is still the order of the day and will remain so, for some time to come—even for Japanese factories! Artificial intelligence does not yet exist. The natural variety is in great abundance.

That we must stop looking for quick and easy fixes. Our malaise was a long time in the making. Our now inappropriate values and beliefs, our bad practices have become assimilated as part of our business culture. A process of change which must of necessity start at the cultural level, will be a lengthy one. Sometimes the old dam reaches the point where no amount of fingers can seal the leaks and we must build a new dam.

That we must structure our businesses for profit—at lower margins. Markets today are not only less tolerant, they are also less generous. To believe that margins will improve as markets return to buoyancy is both naive and dangerous.

That there must be no accountability without authority. One of the most respected and well worn management anecdotes, but how successful have we been in applying it?

That we must design and build quality into the product—not just inspect rejects out. Of all of our misguided good intentions, creating stand-alone quality organizations may have been our most serious. This approach encourages the belief that ownership of quality is concentrated in the department of that name, rather than being dispersed throughout the whole organization. It fosters the concentration of resources immediately prior to shipping, relying on lot sampling techniques and inspecting rejects out rather than the principle of building quality in at every step in the sequence of events, from winning and entering the order to shipping the finished product.

That we measure what is meaningful. There is a propensity to measure anything and everything which can be measured in the mistaken belief that this demonstrates control. More often than not, it simply creates clerical busy work, producing vast quantities of data, which no one ever uses and which can sometimes conceal that which should really be visible. (Inventory, including data inventory, can be evil.) All too often the essence of truth, that which is fundumentally simple, is hidden in a fog of accounting obscurity.

That training and education must become a way of life. That we must start to regard corporations at least in part, as institutes of further education. Manufacturing need not be, and in some cases no longer is a labor intensive operation with output, quality, and productivity an exclusive function of the direct labor contribution. Where resources are still required in this form, they have been relegated to the task of simply loading and unloading sophisticated, automated equipment. It is this equipment—the manner in which it is designed, operated, and maintained—which now determines productivity, quality, and cost. As such, a modern manufacturing operation requires relatively fewer people, but those of a much higher level of skill. Training and education to support the redeployment of these people must become, as it already is in so many major Japanese corporations, a way of life. In all of this, the role of the first line supervisor will change perhaps more than most, from that of taskmaster—deciding what gets done, when, how, and by whom—to that of coach, supporting self-deterministic teams of people.

That all functions need to change—not just manufacturing. The need for change in order to become more internationally competitive is by no means confined to manufacturing. It may well be that manufacturing is where the need for change is greatest, where the transition from the old order to the new will be most significant in terms of the time and effort to change existing values and beliefs, reflected in dramatically different ways of doing things, but other functions must be unavoidably affected. Change in these functions will also be necessary, not only to support these new manufacturing methods with revised capital investment procedures, accounting systems, material control systems, training, education, and so forth—but because for them too, there is always a better way. To improve overall competence, they too must carry their share of the burden.

That we employ the total person—not just human robots. As the levels of skill, education, and training of those people employed, either directly or indirectly, in the manufacturing function increases and changes, longer mutually binding time commitments than were typically required in the past when manufacturing was much simpler, will become progressively more sensible. The days when direct labor for example could be recruited off the street, given a few hours of induction training, and then turned loose on the factory floor, are behind us. We can not now afford to be so casual. Limiting a person's contribution to that of the physical dexterity of their hands alone is to employ human robots, a luxury we can no longer afford.

That there must be less management and more leadership. Where people are concerned, doing more with less means utilizing them to the limit of their willingness and ability rather than limiting their contribution to mechanical operations in the mistaken belief that that is all they can be trusted with. Where there is lack of trust, much management is required—the need for supervisors to supervise the supervisors. With more leadership and less management, this need not be so.

That there must be strategy. Simply perpetuating status quo, sustaining the existing order of things, requires little in the way of strategy and leadership; management alone suffices. What people do, how they do it, their sense of urgency will have become institutionalized. The system will have its own momentum. But in times of change, either externally induced or internally self-imposed, when it has become necessary to change the direction of this momentum, or its energy level, or its mix of components, or the target of its thrust—then the need for strategy and leadership will be at a premium, for where there is momentum, there is also inertia—the resistance to change. Leadership's first task, given the perception of the need for change, will be to defuse and overcome the negative components of change—the anxiety, reluctance, ignorance which inevitably manifest themselves in times of uncertainty and stress—by harnessing the power of the positive components.

This is the true joy in life, the being used for a purpose recognized by yourself as a mighty one; the being a force of nature instead of a feverish selfish little clod of ailments and grievances complaining that the world will not devote itself to making you happy.

I want to be thoroughly used up when I die, for the harder I work the more I live. I rejoice in life for its own sake. Life is no 'brief candle' to me. It is a sort of splendid torch which I have got hold of for the moment, and I want to make it burn as brightly as possible before handing it on to future generations.

George Bernard Shaw

Appendix A

Military Products

A CASE STUDY IN THE APPLICATION OF MODERN MANUFACTURING METHODS TO THE MANUFACTURE OF INTEGRATED CIRCUITS IN COMPLIANCE WITH MIL-M-38510F AND MIL-STD-883C SPECIFICATIONS (A TOTAL SOLUTION)

Introduction

This chapter describes how the Motorola Microprocessor Group in Oak Hill, Austin, Texas is approaching the need to develop world-class manufacturing competence in the factory of the future, today. Military products, arguably the most demanding in terms of process conformance and customer satisfaction, (quality, reliability, cost and on-time delivery), are used as a base line around which much of the work has been developed. (A review of military product qualification and conformance requirements is provided to give some perspective to the manufacturing task.)

In essence, the challenge facing our manufacturing institutions is to facilitate mix management such that the objectives of high quality, low cost and on-time delivery across a wide spectrum of products, (including but not confined to military products) with widely diverse attributes, volumes and customer requirements, are no longer compromised. The success of this will facilitate the resolution of the balance of trade problems and reverse of the erosion of the western hemisphere's industrial base. Optimizing one of these parameters at the expense of another, as has been considered necessary in the past because of historical manufacturing limitations, is no longer acceptable in a highly competitive global environment. These parameters must be mutually inclusive, not exclusive. Only **dramatic improvements in productivity**, the common underlying causal factor behind quality, cost and cycle time improvements can produce these essential end effects. Application of the means now available to do so—group technology, work cells, short cycle-time manufacturing techniques, just-in-time inventory control, and so on are then discussed at length in the context of a real-life situation. Empirical data illustrating the effects of this treatment are included. Focusing on one parameter such as volume at the expense of say mix or quality, is not only no longer acceptable, it is no longer necessary. Our empirical results are offered in support of this conclusion.

The discussion on the followng pages will be structured in the following sequence:

"Hi-Rel"—What does it mean?

Military Standards—What are they and why do they exist?

Product Attributes—What is measured and how?

Manufacturing Infrastructure

What is "Hi-Rel"?

Over the course of time, the term "Hi-Rel" has come to be used synonymously with MIL-STD-883B/C. **They are not the same thing!**

"Hi-Rel" is a **general** term, used **generically** to describe product which **can be shown** to be **more reliable** than standard product of the same device type. In the commercial domain, what is required of the product in terms of reliability performance can be **arbitrarily** defined by the user. The reliability criteria which the product meets can be **arbitrarily** specified by the supplier. A mutually acceptable specification can then be agreed.

This is not the case with military product.

In order to ensure that product meets their reliability requirements in military applications, the Military procurement authorities have rigorously defined:

1. The certification and qualification specifications which a manufacturing facility must meet.

2. The quality and reliability certification specifications which a product must meet.

3. The test methods/procedures to be employed in quantifying the quality and reliability.

4. The quality conformance standards which must be met.

5. The quality assurance procedures applied to ensure continuing reliability.

Confusion has arisen because historically, both users and suppliers have referenced MIL-STD-883B test methods and procedures in describing the reliability of their particular products—so called MIL-STD-883 screened or processed as distinct from JAN qualified product—without necessarily complying in full with the military stipulated requirements associated with fully qualified or screened products.

These anomalies, which proliferated under MIL-STD-883 revision B (31 Aug. 1977) have been emphatically prohibited under MIL-STD-883 revision C superceding 883B (25 Aug. 1983). To allow suppliers a transition time in conforming to the practicalities of the new criteria, the grandfather clause allowed product manufactured on a noncertified line before Dec. 31, 1984, to be shipped up to Dec. 31, 1985—(Subject to waivers in writing confirming customer awareness/acceptance of any/all specified non 883B/C compliance.) Many of these misunderstandings arose because of the nature of the subject. The certification, qualification and ongoing conformance criteria are elaborate, complex, and until recently, understood in full by only a few, normally outwith the manufacturing environment. Likewise the manufacturing logistics of today's semiconductor technology is equally elaborate and complex and not readily understood by procurement authorities and agents. There was a language barrier, clouded in the use of jargon not equally understood by all concerned. In using the flow chart approach described in Part 1, Chapter 4, common ground can be established in reconciling the detail requirements of MIL-STD-883C and the logisitics of manufacturing in a manner which is comprehensible/communicable and practically realizable.

Military Standards

Acknowledging the difficulties encountered by suppliers in qualifying and remaining conformant in the dynamically changing high technology semiconductor environment, the military procurement authorities have established, with assistance from the industry, a hierarchy of preference, each of which follows:

MIL-STD-454

1. JAN qualified product
   Part 1—(A)—Class S—space flight/missiles/submarines
   (B)—Class B—General Applications
   (C)—Class C—Standard Commercial product
2. JAN qualified product
   Part 2—(A)—Class S—space flight/missiles/submarines
   (B)—Class B—General Applications
   (C)—Class C—Standard Commercial Product
3. Military drawing product
4. JAN equivalent product
5. JEDEC 101 product
6. Customer controlled source control document product
7. MIL-STD-883C screened (or processed) product
8. Manufacturer's prime product
9. Normal commercial standard product

A. **Qualified Product**—Part 1 (Qualified Parts List—QPL)
   (1) Is processed within the framework of MIL-M-38510F (General specification for Military Microcircuits)—issued by D.E.S.C. (Defense Electronics Supply Center).
   (2) It must be manufactured in the United States on a manufacturing line certified by D.E.S.C. (Defense Inspection Wing).
   (3) The product must be qualified using extended reliability testing against the product specification sheet, prepared as a SLASH sheet to MIL-M-38510F before production quantities are released for shipment.
   (4) Test methods and sequence of screening operations employed in processing the product and in performing quality control assessment must conform in full to MIL-STD-883C—test methods and procedures.
   (5) Conformance documentation must be provided (see Jan qualified QPL product addendum).

B. **Qualified Product**—Part 2—Pending Qualification (Must be within two years)

C. **Military Drawing Product**—Same as qualified product except:
   (1) Product is manufactured to a registered electrical specification that is independent of manufacturer.—Controlled by D.E.S.C.
   (2) No manufacturing location constraints are imposed.

(3) Self-qualification is confirmed by certificate of compliance to D.E.S.C.

D. **JAN Equivalent Product**
   (1) Vendor manufactures product ostensibly in total compliance with requirements of MIL-M-38510F and MIL-STD-883C but:
   (2) Manufacturing line is not certified/qualified by U.S. government.
   (3) Government are not the controlling authority.

E. **JEDEC 101 Product**
   (1) Product is manufactured to a registered electrical specification (JEDEC) that is independent of manufacturer.
   (2) No government qualification or manufacturing location constraints are imposed. (Self-qualification)
   (In reality, JEDEC 101 and Military drawing product differ only in the way in which the devices are marked.)

F. **Customer Controlled SCD Product**
   (1) Customer or vendor is the controlling authority.
   (2) Product is built in conformance to a military drawing but:
   (3) Manufacturing line is not certified by the government.

G. **MIL-STD-883C Screened Product**
   (1) Manufacturing line need not be qualified but must be certified to be in compliance with MIL-M-38510.
   (2) No independent test spec required.
   (3) Product must be screened and released in full compliance with MIL-STD-883C. Production screening methods and procedures are defined in MIL-STD-883C—method 5004 and QA conformance tests in method 5005.
   (4) Only two of the three major manufacturing functions—wafer fab/assembly/test need be resident in the U.S.—Depending on S.C.D.
   (See summary comparison of product levels in Table A-1.)

MIL-M-38510F—QUALIFICATION MILESTONES

PHASE 1 — CHARACTERIZATION

1. Product characterization (electrical operating profile)
2. Process base line characterization
3. Process base line documentation
4. Correlation of product parameters with process parameters

PHASE 2 — CERTIFICATION

1. Manufacturer establishes/implements product quality assurance program.
2. Submits QAP to qualifying activity
3. Qualifying activity conducts manufacturer survey audit
4. Manufacturer submits notification of a qualification lot initiation

Table A-1 MIL-STD-454 Hierarchy

MIL-STD-454 Hierarchy

Order of Preference	Device		Cert. Line	Qual. Prod.	QPL	Slash Sheet	Manuf. USA	SCD	Control Auth.	Screen	QA Conform
1	JAN QUAL PART 1	S	GOV.	YES	YES	YES	YES	SLASH SHEET	GOVERNMENT	MIL883C 5004	MIL883C 5005
		B	GOV.	YES	YES	YES	YES	SLASH SHEET	GOVERNMENT	"	"
		C	GOV.	YES	YES	YES	YES	SLAHS SHEET	GOVERNMENT	"	"
2	JAN QUAL PART 2	S	GOV.	PEND.	NO	YES	YES	SLASH SHEET	GOVERNMENT	"	"
		B	GOV.	PEND.	NO	YES	YES	SLASH SHEET	GOVERNMENT	"	"
		C	GOV.	PEND.	NO	YES	YES	SLASH SHEET	GOVERNMENT	"	"
3	MILITARY DRAWING		3RD PARTY	YES	NO	DESC	NO	MILITARY DRAWING	GOVERNMENT	"	"
4	JAN EQUIVALENT		SELF	NO	NO	NO	NO	SLASH SHEET	VENDOR	"	"
5	JEDEC 101		SELF	NO	NO	NO	NO	VENDOR	JEDEC	"	"
6	CUSTOMER CONT. SCD		SELF	NO	NO	NO	NO	CUSTOMER	CUSTOMER	?	?
7	MIL 883C REF		SELF	NO	NO	NO	NO	CUSTOMER	CUSTOMER	"	"
8	PRIME PRODUCT		NO	NO	NO	NO	NO	VENDOR	VENDOR	?	?
9	COMMERCIAL		NO	NO	NO	NO	NO	VENDOR	VENDOR	?	?

*1 There is a further subset within JAN qualified parts specifying degrees of radiation hardness: RHA levels M, D, R and H.
*2 The hierarchy of preference below military product is ambiguous and is the author's interpretation only.
*3 Motorola is fully certified to supply military drawing and JEDEC 101 product and may pursue JAN qualification.
*4 Line items 4, 5 and 6 are approximately equal, the difference being whether the source control drawing is generated by the customer or vendor.

PHASE 3 — QUALIFICATION

1. Manufacturer submits qualifying plan
2. Qualifying source determines eligibility
3. QS provides written notification to manufacturer
4. Written notification constitutes certification class S or B

PHASE 4 — SHIPPING CONTROL

1. Groups A and B tests by each inspection lot
2. Completion of Groups C/D data

PHASE 5 — ONGOING CONFORMANCE

1. Process control notification
2. Reaudits
3. Groups A/B/C/D ongoing conformance

In facilities manufacturing commercial as well as military products, and we could argue the merits of them not being confined to military products exclusively, it makes no sense to have two sets of manufacturing standards. In adopting the military standards and methods as a common manufacturing base line, commercial products derive substantial benefits in being manufactured to the same degree of discipline. To do so in the most productive possible manner is the theme of the rest of this paper. Issues which are common to both classes of product are now addressed.

Product Attributes—Operating Profile

Product Characteristics. Figure A-1 is intended to give a general impression of the behavior of the more important device variables with temperature.

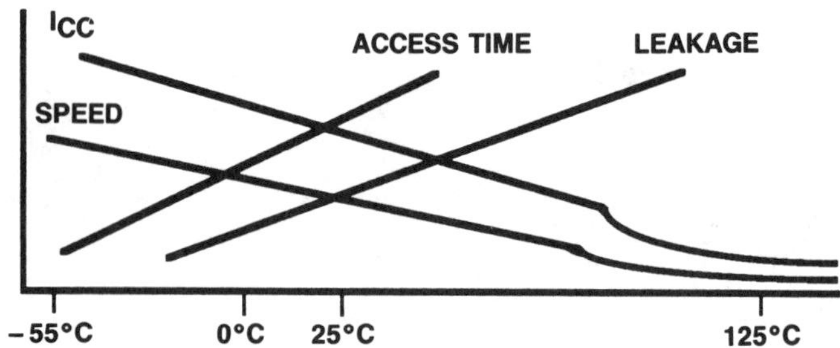

Figure A-1 Military Temperature Range

Device Operating Profile. Obviously, the more demanding the performance which is expected from a device, the less likely is the device to meet that performance. The worst possible combination is 12 MHz operation over the temperature range −55 to +125°C. Therefore, even having the capability to test the product to this specification may not result in adequate supplies of product due to the proportion from any population which can operate to this specification being small. This proportion may be seen to be batch dependent, wafer fab recipe variable. See Table A-2 and Figure A-2.

Table A-2

DEVICE YIELDS ARE FOR ILLUSTRATIVE PURPOSES ONLY

68XXX	6 MHz	8 MHz	10 MHz	12 MHz
0°C TO +70°C	95%	90%	60%	30%
0°C TO +85°C	90%	75%	40%	25%
−40°C TO +110°C	70%	60%	20%	10%
−55°C TO +125°C	50%	15%	15%	5%

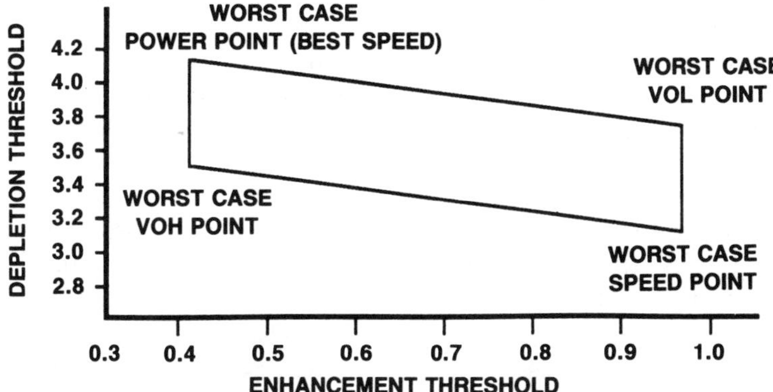

Figure A-2 Allowable Threshold Voltages Ranges for 5 V N-CH Si Gate MOS Designs

Manufacturing Infrastructure. In addition to engineering the product to meet high performance expectations, military qualified and/or military screened products are generally in short supply for the following reasons:

1. Facility certification, product qualification and process conformance is a complex, rigorous, and time consuming process.

2. Most facilities can not and indeed perhaps should not be devoted exclusively to the manufacture of military products, instead military products have to coexist with a vendors normal commercial product spectrum.

3. There tends to be a correlation between the intensity of effort applied to qualifying and remaining conformant with the level of economic activity in general and the specific status of the semiconductor industry in particular.

The first problem has been addressed by providing a vehicle which reconciles MIL-STD-883C, methods 5004 and 5005 with the manufacturing logistics in a form which is comprehensible, communicable and practically implementable. This vehicle takes the form of a flow chart (see Chapter 4) in which every step in the process from order entry to shipping the product is diagrammatically defined in the correct sequential order. The second and third difficulties have been addressed by applying some modern manufacturing principles in the form of group technology (GT), statistical process control (SPC), flexible manufacturing systems (FMS) and just-in-time (JIT) work-in-process management to the problem of managing mix in a multiproduct environment. These principles have been integrated into people, product and process modules, in effect small focused factories or work cells within a factory. Since proliferation challenges become most manifest in the screening operation, these techniques will be described in more detail in this context. (See final test.) For the time being, it will serve our purpose better to follow the chronology of manufacture.

Wafer Fabrication. Given that wafers have been manufactured on a certified line, the primary task is to identify those wafers most likely to contain die capable of operating over the full military temperature range at the desired frequency, from the total population of wafers available.

This can be achieved in one of two ways:

1. Wafers are randomly selected at the end of the wafer fabrication process on the basis of attribute values most likely to yield to the Military specification. This can be done by means of measurements of the process validation module (PVM) or process control module (PCM), up to five of which are stepped into the wafer mask set. These modules consist of configurations of transistors and aluminum or polysilicon runs, and so on, which allow direct measurements such as transistor thresholds, effective channel lengths or track resistivity to be made. The degree of sophistication in acquiring and statistically analyzing these parameter values for shape, displacement and stability of distribution can vary from one by one manual measurements to on-the-fly computer-automated measurement and analysis. In addition to being used as a selection criteria, these modules can also prove to be very informative if packaged and subjected to end-of-life testing to detect any possible parameter shift over time.

2. A less random approach is to (a) fully characterize the device operating profile at test, (b) fully characterize the wafer fab process, (c) establish correlation between device electrical parameters and wafer fab process parameters (prerequisite to statistical process control), (d) optimize recipe for yield and then, (e) target the process to that recipe. Subsequent conformance can then be assured by applying statistical process control. In either event, the objective is to get wafers to unit probe which have values of attributes most likely to yield to the ful military specification.

Unit Probe. The military specification requires these products to operate over the temperature range $-55°C$ to $+125°C$ at frequencies up to 12 MHz in the case of NMOS products. (For reasons described in Chapter 4, HCMOS products can more readily meet this specification and indeed, potentially exceed it.) Providing this test environment at unit probe presents a fairly formidable technical challenge, hot chuck at high frequency in an electrically noisy environment, but is a more economically sound approach than committing die, which have been less rigorously tested to a commercial product spec, to expensive packages, high cost assembly and final test at relatively low yield.

Assembly. This process begins by dicing (sawing) the wafer into individual die, separating the good from bad die and subsequently assembling the good die in packages. Most of the assembly operations are essentially mechanical in nature and good process control of tolerances is imperative. The sequence of operations involved is described in the flow chart referenced to earlier, the most critical being die bond, where the die is bonded to the package leadframe using a preform alloy pellet, wirebond where internal to external connections are made from the pads on the die to the leads on the package using gold wire and finally, the sealing operation where the upper and lower halves of the package are hermetically sealed together. As can be seen from the flow chart, there are process checks at almost every intermediate step in this process.

Final Test. Since most final screening or test departments are not exclusively dedicated to the screening of military products, but may be required to support a proliferation of device types, the first problem the military device encounters in the test area is one of being lost in the turbulence and cast aside into some enormous work in progress bank in preference to some other, much less painful to process device type. The most obvious extreme is that of an area required to support high volume, relatively low conformance standard products in conjunction with a spectrum of other products of increasing degrees of complexity, customization and test conformance up to and including military specifications. This problem has been dealt with at Motorola by applying group technology, focused factory (modules), flexible manufacturing systems, some degree of short cycle manufacturing (SCM) concepts and statistical process control. This approach has been developed to meet the challenge of delivering on time, every time, up to 5000 widely diverse products including military, in different quantities, in any particular manufacturing period, usually 30 days.

The next challenge which the military product has to overcome is in the test screening process per se. The equipment configuration is likely to be elaborate, consisting in the case of 16-bit products, of a very complex and expensive VLSI automatic tester and at least one test handler (for each package configuration) capable of operating accurately and repeatably over the full military temperature range. Usually the electrical interfacing arrangement of handler to tester can leave much to be desired in signal integrity. Closest physical proximity of test socket to tester is of paramount importance. These difficulties will be compounded by low or even zero yield problems if the product has not been adequately engineered such that a sufficient proportion of the total population is capable of meeting the military operating profile. Nowhere is the adage more appropriate—do it right first time—than here. If a product subsequently fails conformance gate, the probability is high that the problem existed at test system set-up time, i.e., time zero rather than during run time due to some subsequent equipment malfunction. This issue is fully discussed in the section "Engineering Hold and Short Cycle-Time Manufacturing."

Hot/Room/Cold Testing. Hot and room temperature testing pose few problems which cannot be dealt with effectively with today's equipment technology. This may not be the case however with cold testing (−55°C). Cold testing presents a unique challenge in being accurate/repeatable and productive. This problem is compounded by the fact that the capability is required for a variety of package types—dual-in-line, pin grid array and chip carrier. Whichever method is employed to fulfill the cold test requirement, be it automatic test handler, cold plate, dry ice or some form of temperature column they suffer, in varying degrees, from the problem of frosting due to moisture condensation at these low temperatures. (This is the common source of the accuracy, repeatability and productivity problems.) This phenomenon can obviously impede the correct operation of an automatic handler due to frost induced jamming. Reheating to ambient, clearing the jam and recooling to −55°C can be a very time consuming, and frustrating business. In addition to this, leakage measurements become progressively more difficult and less reliable, since the leakage paths associated with the test fixturing become difficult to isolate from the device under test and may far exceed the test limit for the device alone.

Corrective action can be taken as follows:

1. Optimize handler for cold test operation.
2. Ensure adequate capacity of nitrogen cooling tanks.
3. Provide backup nitrogen tank with quick change over T-valve.
4. Select test sockets for temperature extreme durability.
5. Apply preproduction nitrogen purge to eliminate/minimize frosting.
6. Reduce/eliminate moisture ingress paths.

7. Run handler continuously to avoid frost induced jams.

8. Eliminate/reduce need for 100 percent cold test by using cold guardband parameter limits at ambient.

MILITARY PRODUCT ACRONYMS

MIL-STD-454	Standard general requirements for electronic equipment
MIL-M-38510F	General Spec for Military Microcircuits
MIL-STD-883C	Test Methods & Procedures for Microelectronics
MIL-STD-976	Certification requirements of microcircuits
MIL-STD-1331	Parameters to be controlled for the specification of microcircuits
MIL-STD-45662	Calibration systems requirements
MIL-STD-280	Definition of item levels
MIL-STD-129	Marking for shipment and storage
MIL-STD-M-55565	Packaging of Microcircuits
FED Standard 209	Clean room and work station environment
JAN Certified Product	QPL product built on fully qualified line
J.A.N.	Joint Army Navy
D.E.S.C.	Defense Electronics Supply Center
S.C.D.	Source Control Drawings
Q.P.L.—38510—Part 1	Qualified parts list
Q.P.L.—38510—Part 2	Qualified parts list — pending
J.E.D.E.C.	Joint Electronic Devices Eng. Council
Class S	Level 1 Test—Space Flight, Missiles, Submarines (life or mission critical)
Class B	Level 2 Test—General military use
Slash Sheet	Device specification—RADC approved
R.A.D.C.	Rome Air Development Center
D.O.D.	Department of Defense
Method 5004	MIL-STD-883C 100% Production Screening Procedures
Method 5005	MIL-STD-883C LTPD Quality Conformance Procedures
LTPD	Lot Tolerance Percent Defective
AQL	Acceptable Quality Level
Group A Tests	AC/DC parameters at room/max rated temp
Group B Tests	Physical dimensions/solderability/seal quality etc.
Group C Tests	Die related test
Group D Tests	Package related tests
D.C.A.S.	Defense Contracts Administration Service
D.A.R.P.A.	Defense Advanced Research Projects Agency
N.S.A.	National Science Association
E.W.	Electronic Warfare
C^3I	Command, Control and Communications Interface
DODISS	Department of Defense Index of Specifications and Standards
A.S.T.M.	American Society for Testing and Materials
E.I.A.	Electronics Industries Association
S.T.A.N.A.G. 4093	NATO Standardization Agreement
N.Q.A.	National Qualification Authority

MIL-M-38510F (31 October, 1983)

"The manufacturer of microcircuits in compliance with this specification shall have and use production and test facilities and a quality and reliability assurance program adequate to assure successful compliance with the provisions of this specification and the detail specification. While these facilities and programs may be used for the manufacture of other than JAN microcircuits (under the provisions and limitations stated herein), any reference to the "JAN" or "J" certification mark, class S or B certification status, MIL-M-38510 or the Military part number, (or portion thereof), in such a way as to state or imply equivalency (and thereby government endorsement in connection with non-JAN product is prohibited and may be a cause for revocation of certification and/or product qualification. The individual item requirements shall be as specified herein, and in the detail specification or drawing. Only qualified (QPL-38510) microcircuits which are inspected shall be marked and delivered as JAN microcircuits. Government source inspection shall be required."

MIL-STD-883 Revision C, August 25, 1983

"Simply stated, when MIL-STD-883C (or portions thereof) is used, referenced, or advertised in relation to the processing and testing of microcircuits, its requirements shall not be subject to re-interpretation or deviation, except as specifically or clearly stated in the applicable detail specification(s).

Where device and or package characteristics prohibit implementation of the above provision, all applicable documentation shall clearly and specifically define any and all areas of nonconformance and identify them as deviations in language that is not subject to misinterpretation by the purchasing authority."

NATIONAL/INTERNATIONAL STANDARDS, ETC.—INTEGRATED CIRCUITS

USA 0 MIL-M-38510F	—General specification for military microcircuits
USA 0 MIL-STD-883C	—Test methods and procedures
USA 0 MIL-HDBK-217	—Reliability prediction of electronic equipment
USA 0 JEDEC 101	—Requirements for Class B/C microcircuits (883B/C processed)
EURO 0 CECC 90000	—Quality assessment: generic spec: integrated circuits
EURO 0 CECC 90100	—Quality assessment: sectional spec: digital monolithic IC
EURO 0 CECC 90104	—Family specification CMOS 4000B/UB digital IC
UK 0 BS9000	—General requirements for electronic components of assessed quality
UK 0 BS9400	—IC circuits of assessed quality—generic/test methods
UK 0 BS2011	—Basic environmental testing procedures
UK 0 BS3934	—Dimensions of semiconductor devices
UK 0 BS6001	—Sampling tables for inspection by attributes (identical to MIL-STD-105D)

MOS IC Military Programs Mandatory Requirements

MIL-M-38510: **United States Military General Specification for ICS**

— Manufacturing line certification
— Device specification approval; device qualification
— Maintenance of qualification, product assurance program
— Test methods, conditions specified in MIL-STD-883C

MIL-STD 883C: **United States Military Standard of Test Methods and Procedures for Micro Electronics.** It has also been adopted by most U.S. IC manufacturers as a marketing aid. It **ontensibly standardizes procurement.**

BS9000 & CECC 9000: **European General Specifications:**

— Manufacturing quality systems approval
— Device specification approval; device qualification
— Maintenance of qualification and CTR generation
— Test methods, conditions, procedures

JEDEC 101: **Introduced by JEDEC—in mid 1978** in an attempt to rationalize procurement, manufacturing and marketing of 883B Class B and C screen ICS. Lists of screening, testing, marking and QA (lot conformance) requirements.

Appendix B

Primary Test Area Product Flow

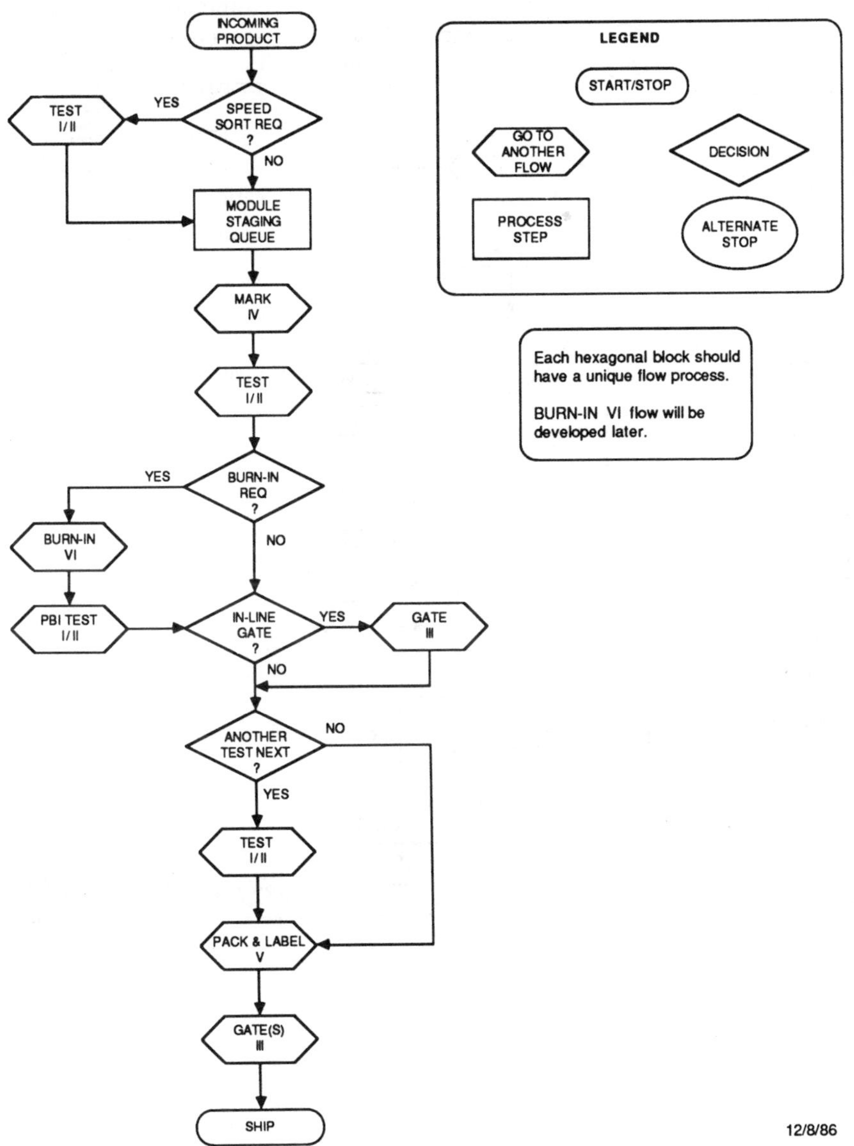

12/8/86

INCOMING PROCEDURES FLOWCHART

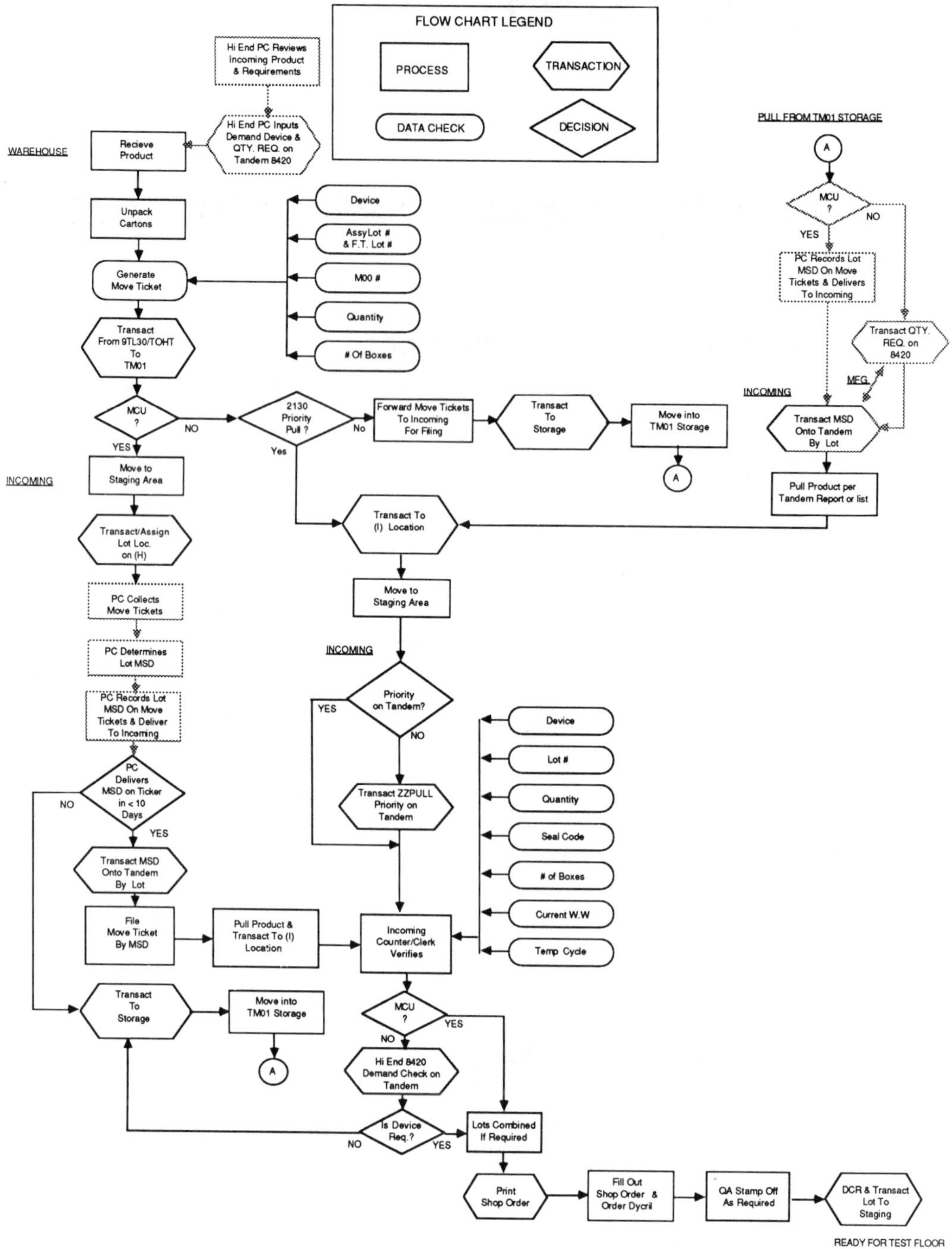

R.F.T. TEST FLOW
I. CORRELATION

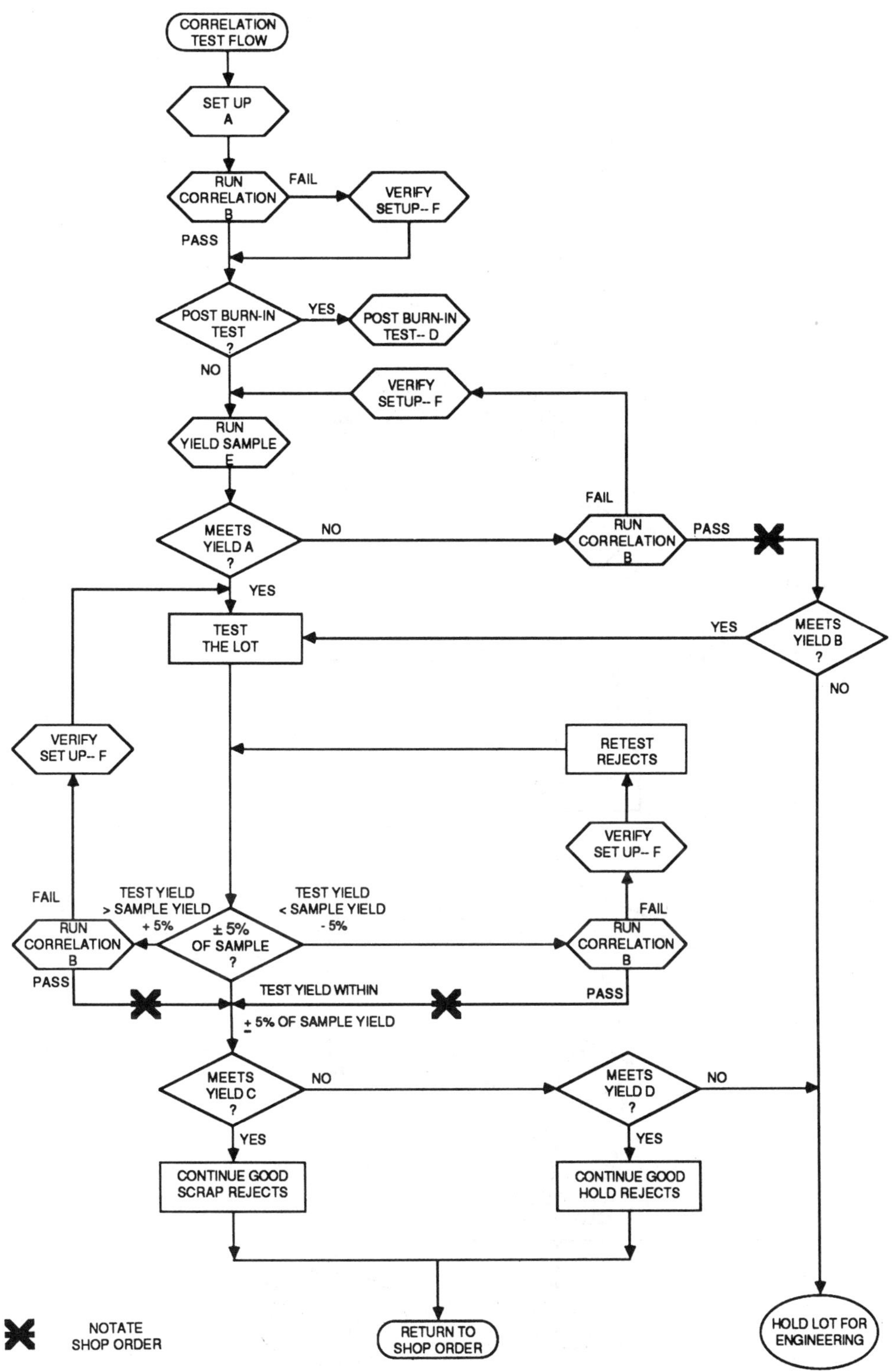

R.F.T. TEST FLOW
II. NON-CORRELATION

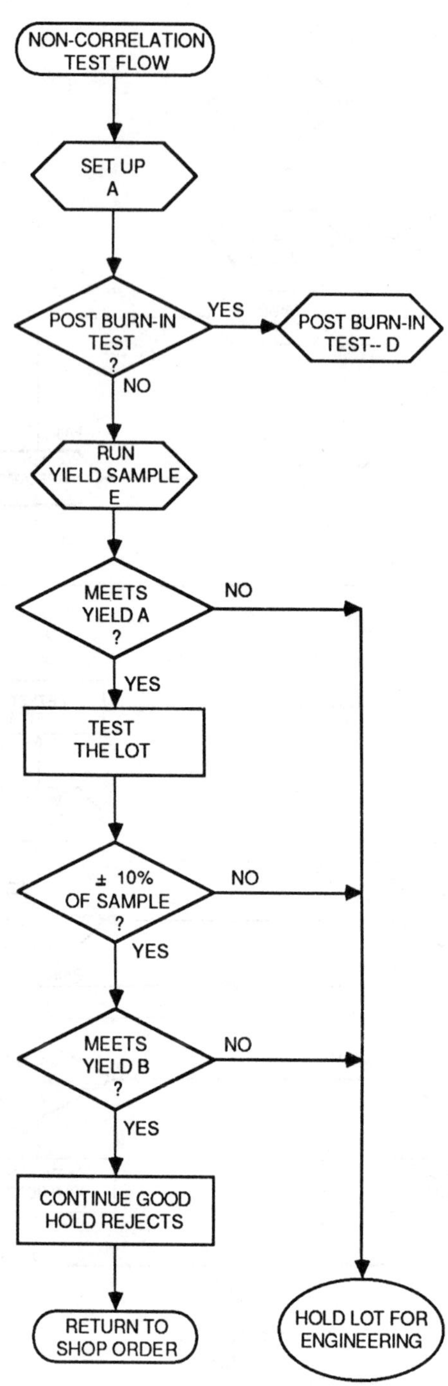

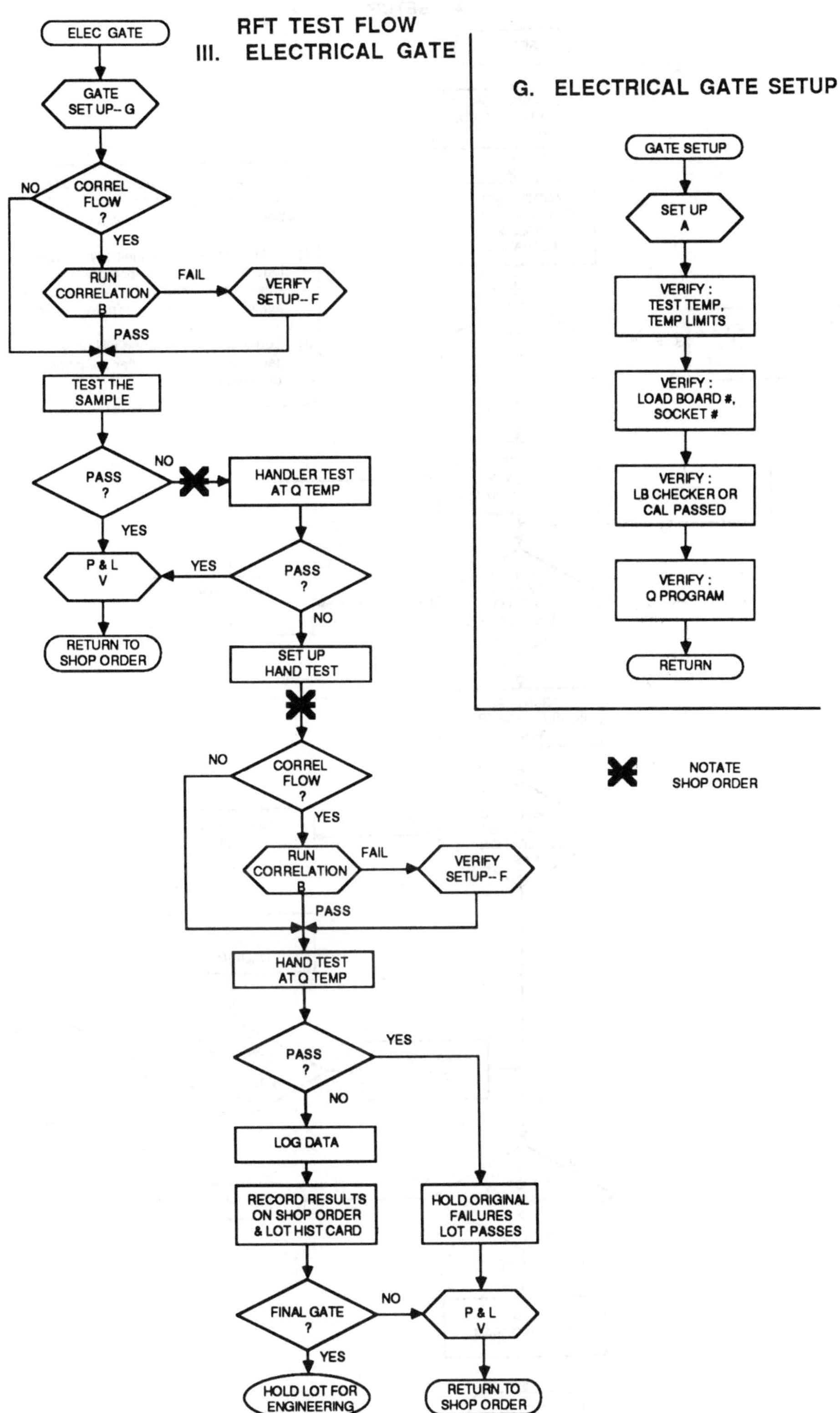

RFT TEST FLOW
III. ELECTRICAL GATE
ELEC GATE
GATE SET UP-- G
CORREL FLOW ?
NO
YES
RUN CORRELATION B
FAIL
VERIFY SETUP-- F
PASS
TEST THE SAMPLE
PASS ?
NO
HANDLER TEST AT Q TEMP
YES
P & L V
YES
PASS ?
RETURN TO SHOP ORDER
NO
SET UP HAND TEST
CORREL FLOW ?
NO
YES
RUN CORRELATION B
FAIL
VERIFY SETUP-- F
PASS
HAND TEST AT Q TEMP
PASS ?
YES
NO
LOG DATA
RECORD RESULTS ON SHOP ORDER & LOT HIST CARD
HOLD ORIGINAL FAILURES LOT PASSES
FINAL GATE ?
NO
P & L V
YES
HOLD LOT FOR ENGINEERING
RETURN TO SHOP ORDER
G. ELECTRICAL GATE SETUP
GATE SETUP
SET UP A
VERIFY : TEST TEMP, TEMP LIMITS
VERIFY : LOAD BOARD #, SOCKET #
VERIFY : LB CHECKER OR CAL PASSED
VERIFY : Q PROGRAM
RETURN
NOTATE SHOP ORDER

A. SETUP

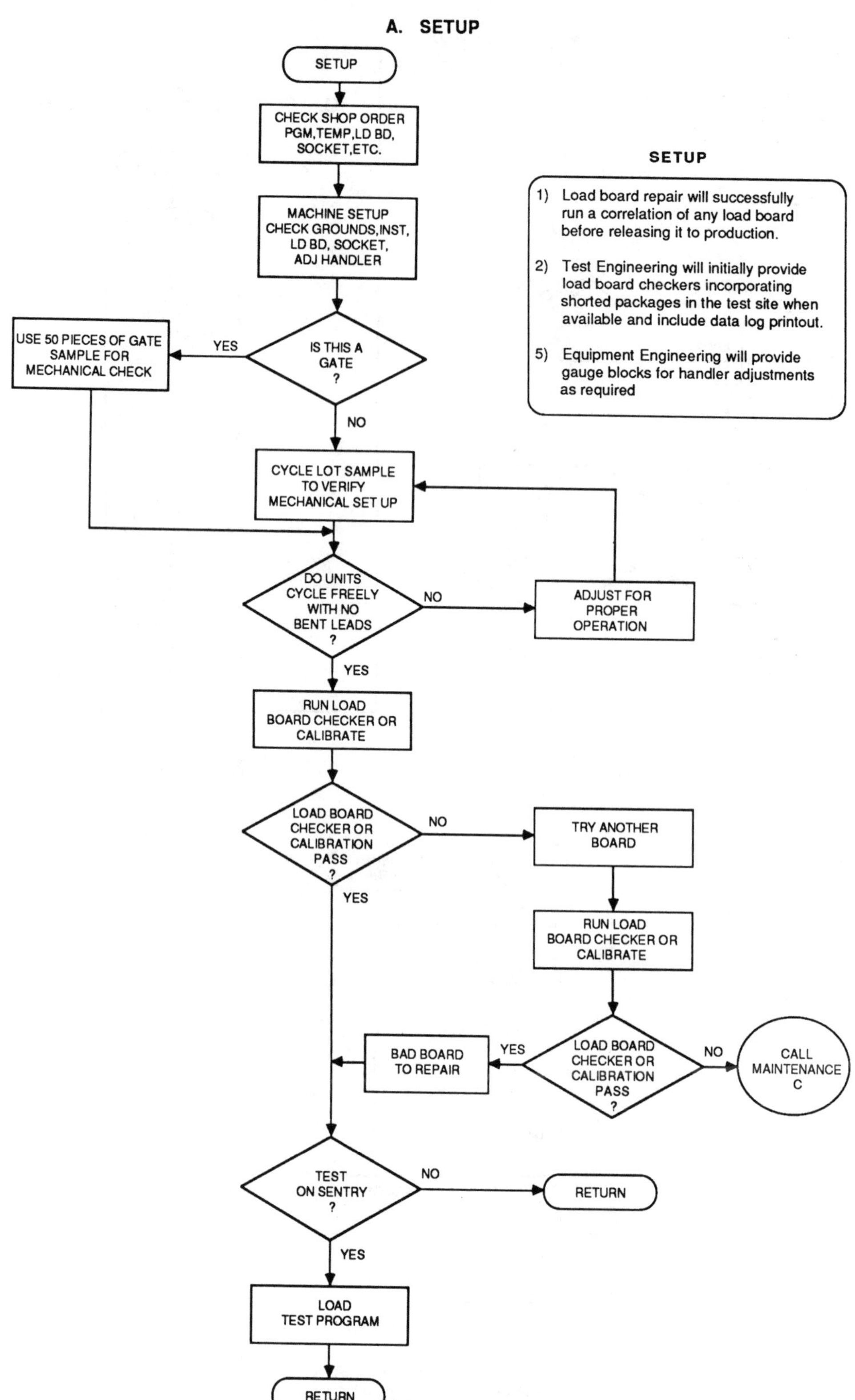

SETUP
CHECK SHOP ORDER PGM,TEMP,LD BD, SOCKET,ETC.
MACHINE SETUP CHECK GROUNDS,INST, LD BD, SOCKET, ADJ HANDLER
IS THIS A GATE ?
YES
USE 50 PIECES OF GATE SAMPLE FOR MECHANICAL CHECK
NO
CYCLE LOT SAMPLE TO VERIFY MECHANICAL SET UP
DO UNITS CYCLE FREELY WITH NO BENT LEADS ?
NO
ADJUST FOR PROPER OPERATION
YES
RUN LOAD BOARD CHECKER OR CALIBRATE
LOAD BOARD CHECKER OR CALIBRATION PASS ?
NO
TRY ANOTHER BOARD
RUN LOAD BOARD CHECKER OR CALIBRATE
LOAD BOARD CHECKER OR CALIBRATION PASS ?
YES
BAD BOARD TO REPAIR
NO
CALL MAINTENANCE C
YES
TEST ON SENTRY ?
NO
RETURN
YES
LOAD TEST PROGRAM
RETURN
SETUP
1) Load board repair will successfully run a correlation of any load board before releasing it to production.
2) Test Engineering will initially provide load board checkers incorporating shorted packages in the test site when available and include data log printout.
5) Equipment Engineering will provide gauge blocks for handler adjustments as required

B. RUN CORRELATION

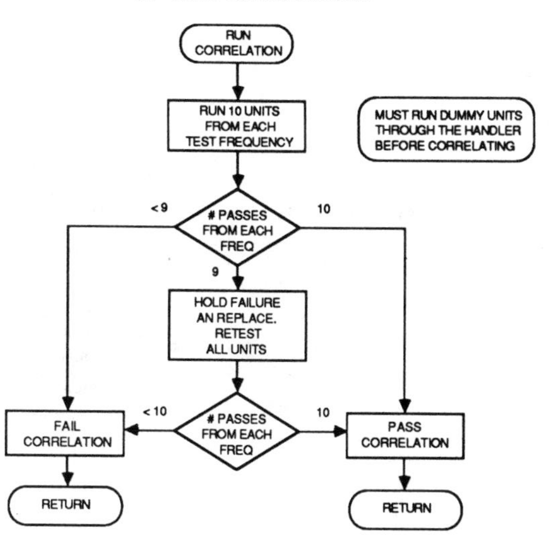

C. CALL MAINTENANCE

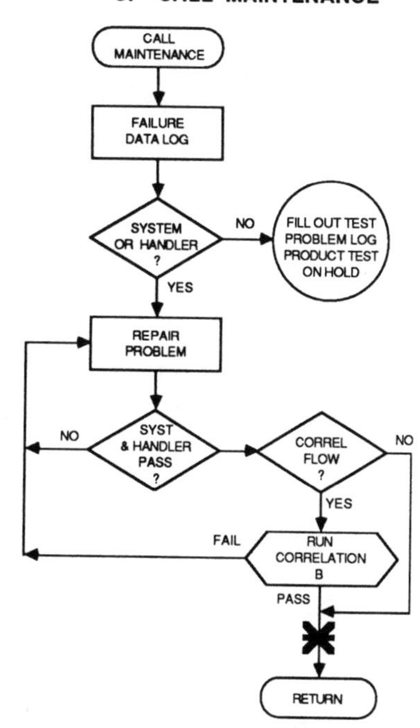

D. POST BURN-IN TEST

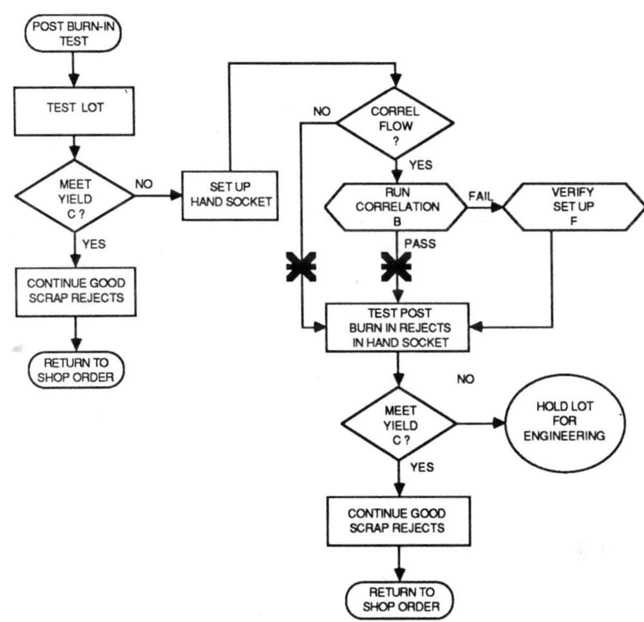

E. YIELD SAMPLE

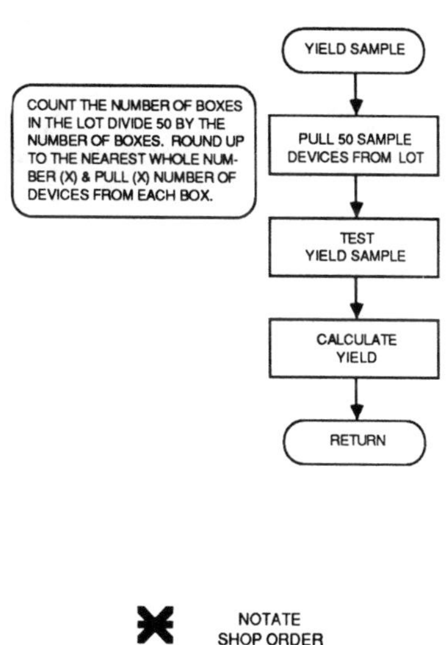

✱ NOTATE SHOP ORDER

F. VERIFY SETUP

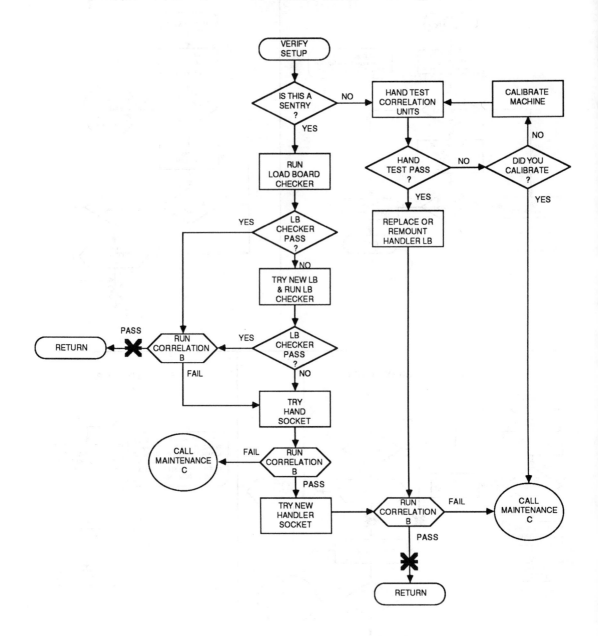

VERIFY SETUP

IS THIS A SENTRY ?

NO

HAND TEST CORRELATION UNITS

CALIBRATE MACHINE

YES

RUN LOAD BOARD CHECKER

HAND TEST PASS ?

NO

DID YOU CALIBRATE ?

NO

YES

YES

LB CHECKER PASS ?

YES

NO

REPLACE OR REMOUNT HANDLER LB

TRY NEW LB & RUN LB CHECKER

PASS

RETURN

RUN CORRELATION B

YES

LB CHECKER PASS ?

FAIL

NO

TRY HAND SOCKET

CALL MAINTENANCE C

FAIL

RUN CORRELATION B

PASS

TRY NEW HANDLER SOCKET

RUN CORRELATION B

FAIL

CALL MAINTENANCE C

PASS

RETURN

*UNDER REVISION

IV. RFT MARK

H. AUTOMATIC MARK

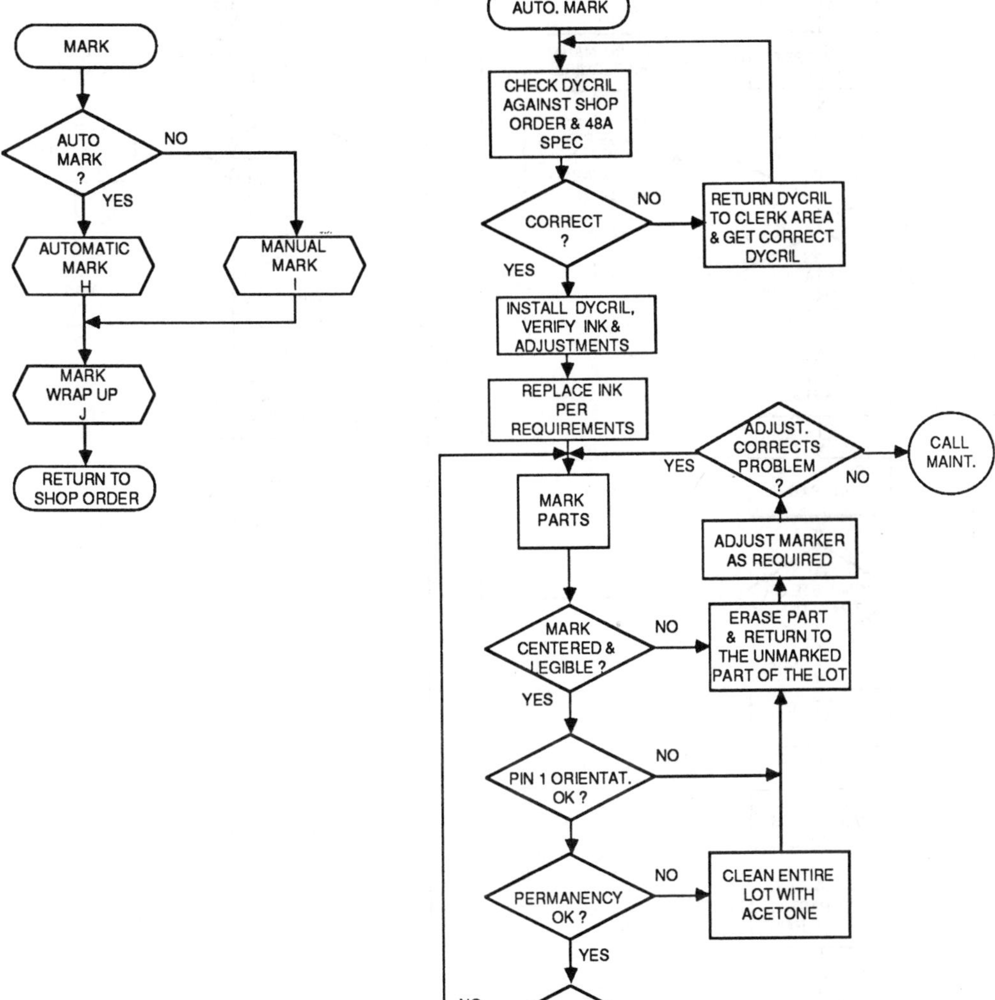

J. MANUAL MARK

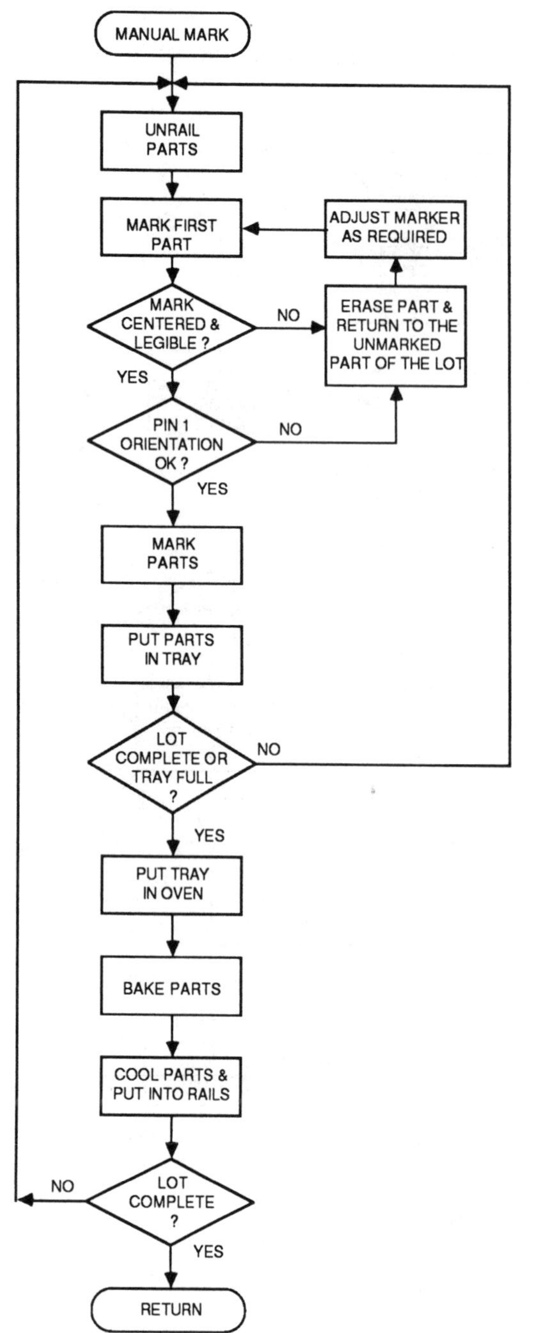

K. MARK WRAP UP

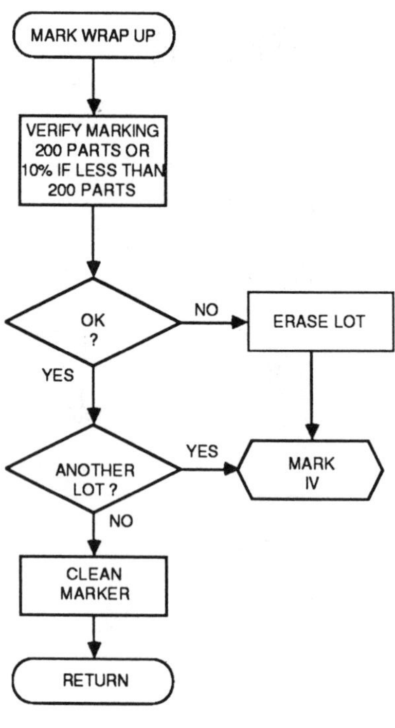

V. RFT PACK & LABEL

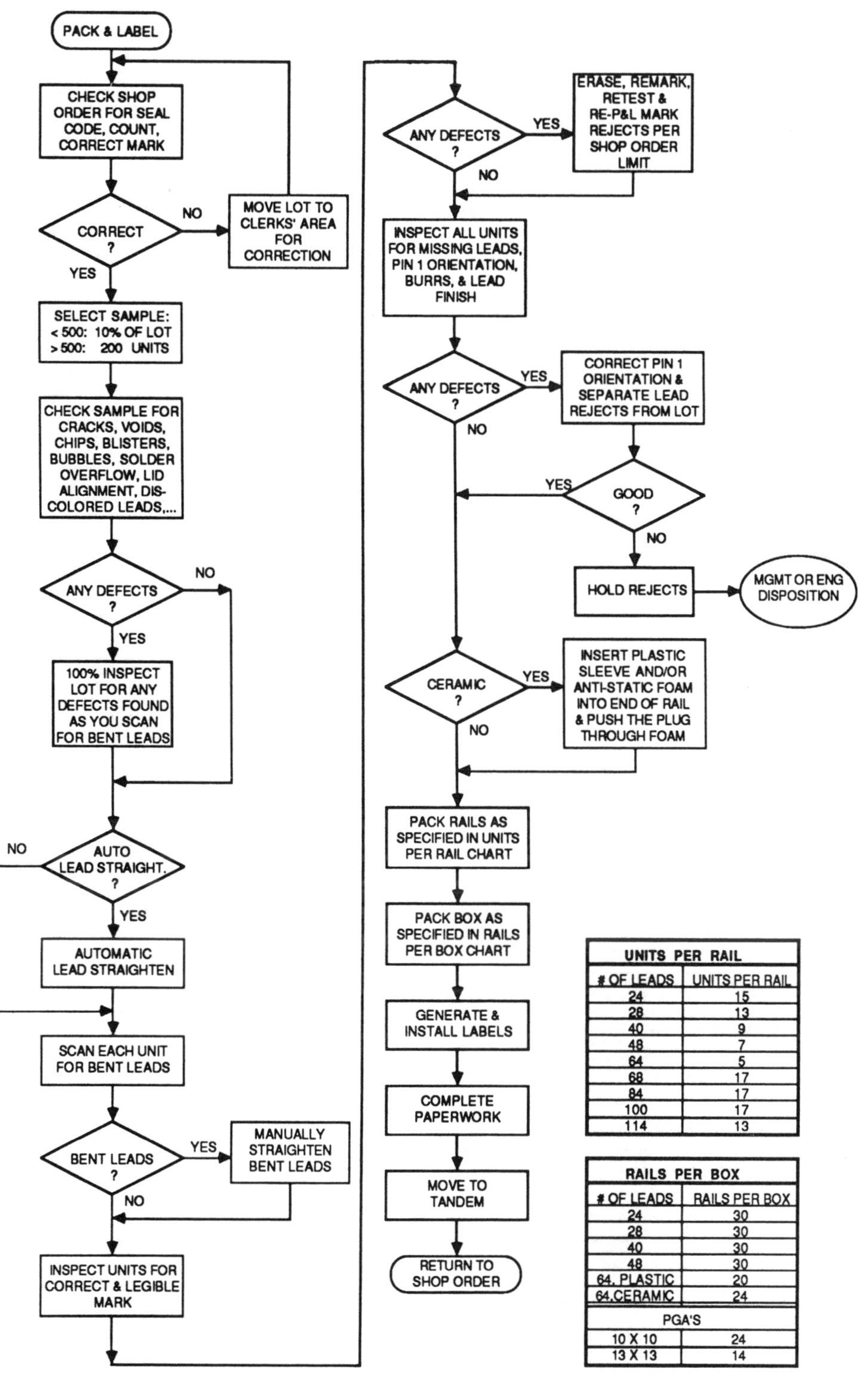
PACK & LABEL
CHECK SHOP ORDER FOR SEAL CODE, COUNT, CORRECT MARK
CORRECT ?
NO
MOVE LOT TO CLERKS' AREA FOR CORRECTION
YES
SELECT SAMPLE:
< 500: 10% OF LOT
> 500: 200 UNITS
CHECK SAMPLE FOR CRACKS, VOIDS, CHIPS, BLISTERS, BUBBLES, SOLDER OVERFLOW, LID ALIGNMENT, DIS-COLORED LEADS,...
ANY DEFECTS ?
NO
YES
100% INSPECT LOT FOR ANY DEFECTS FOUND AS YOU SCAN FOR BENT LEADS
AUTO LEAD STRAIGHT. ?
NO
YES
AUTOMATIC LEAD STRAIGHTEN
SCAN EACH UNIT FOR BENT LEADS
BENT LEADS ?
YES
MANUALLY STRAIGHTEN BENT LEADS
NO
INSPECT UNITS FOR CORRECT & LEGIBLE MARK
ANY DEFECTS ?
YES
ERASE, REMARK, RETEST & RE-P&L MARK REJECTS PER SHOP ORDER LIMIT
NO
INSPECT ALL UNITS FOR MISSING LEADS, PIN 1 ORIENTATION, BURRS, & LEAD FINISH
ANY DEFECTS ?
YES
CORRECT PIN 1 ORIENTATION & SEPARATE LEAD REJECTS FROM LOT
NO
GOOD ?
YES
NO
HOLD REJECTS
MGMT OR ENG DISPOSITION
CERAMIC ?
YES
INSERT PLASTIC SLEEVE AND/OR ANTI-STATIC FOAM INTO END OF RAIL & PUSH THE PLUG THROUGH FOAM
NO
PACK RAILS AS SPECIFIED IN UNITS PER RAIL CHART
PACK BOX AS SPECIFIED IN RAILS PER BOX CHART
GENERATE & INSTALL LABELS
COMPLETE PAPERWORK
MOVE TO TANDEM
RETURN TO SHOP ORDER

UNITS PER RAIL

# OF LEADS	UNITS PER RAIL
24	15
28	13
40	9
48	7
64	5
68	17
84	17
100	17
114	13

RAILS PER BOX

# OF LEADS	RAILS PER BOX
24	30
28	30
40	30
48	30
64, PLASTIC	20
64,CERAMIC	24
PGA'S	
10 X 10	24
13 X 13	14

WAFERS TO DIE

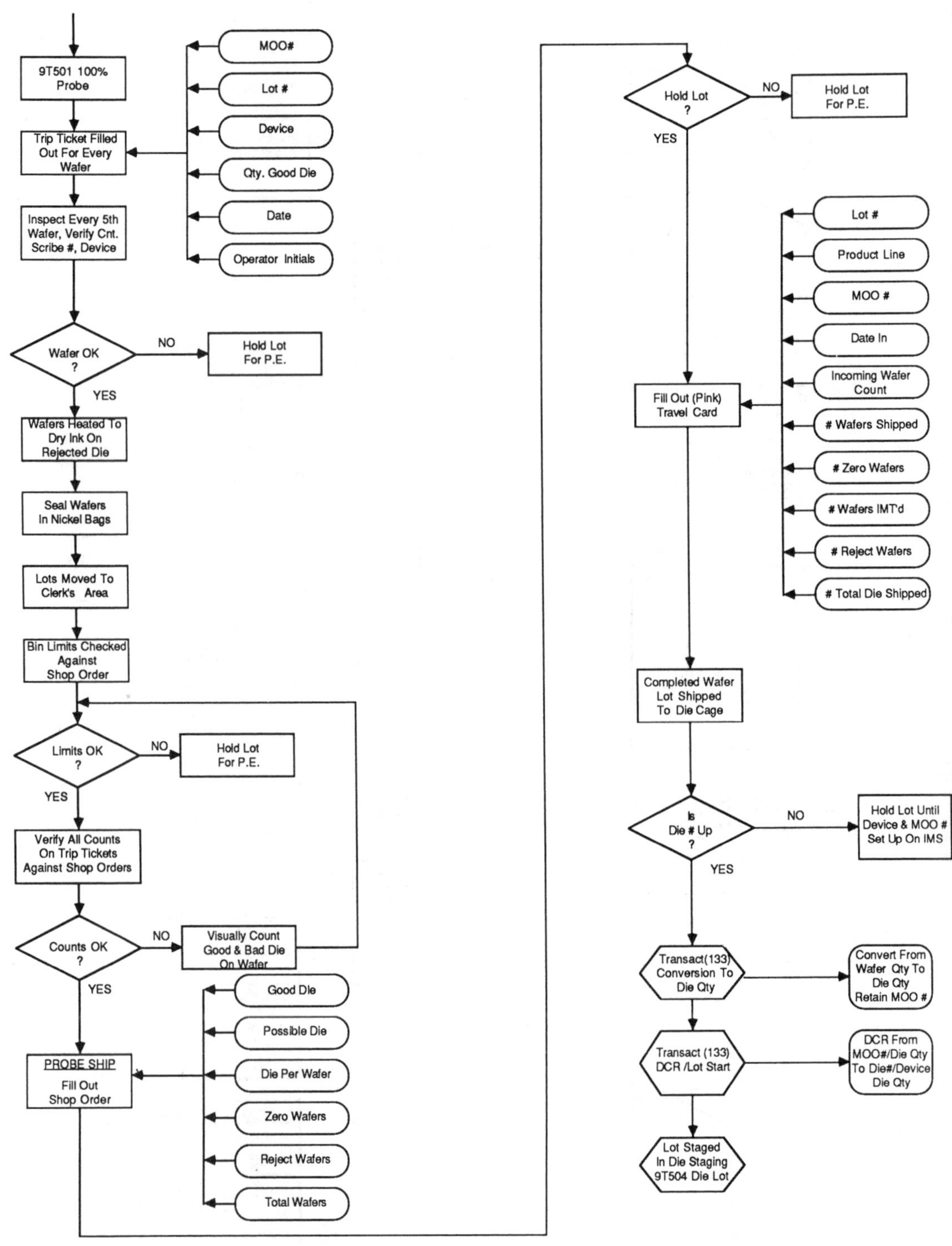

SHIPPING FROM LOT P TO THE WAREHOUSE

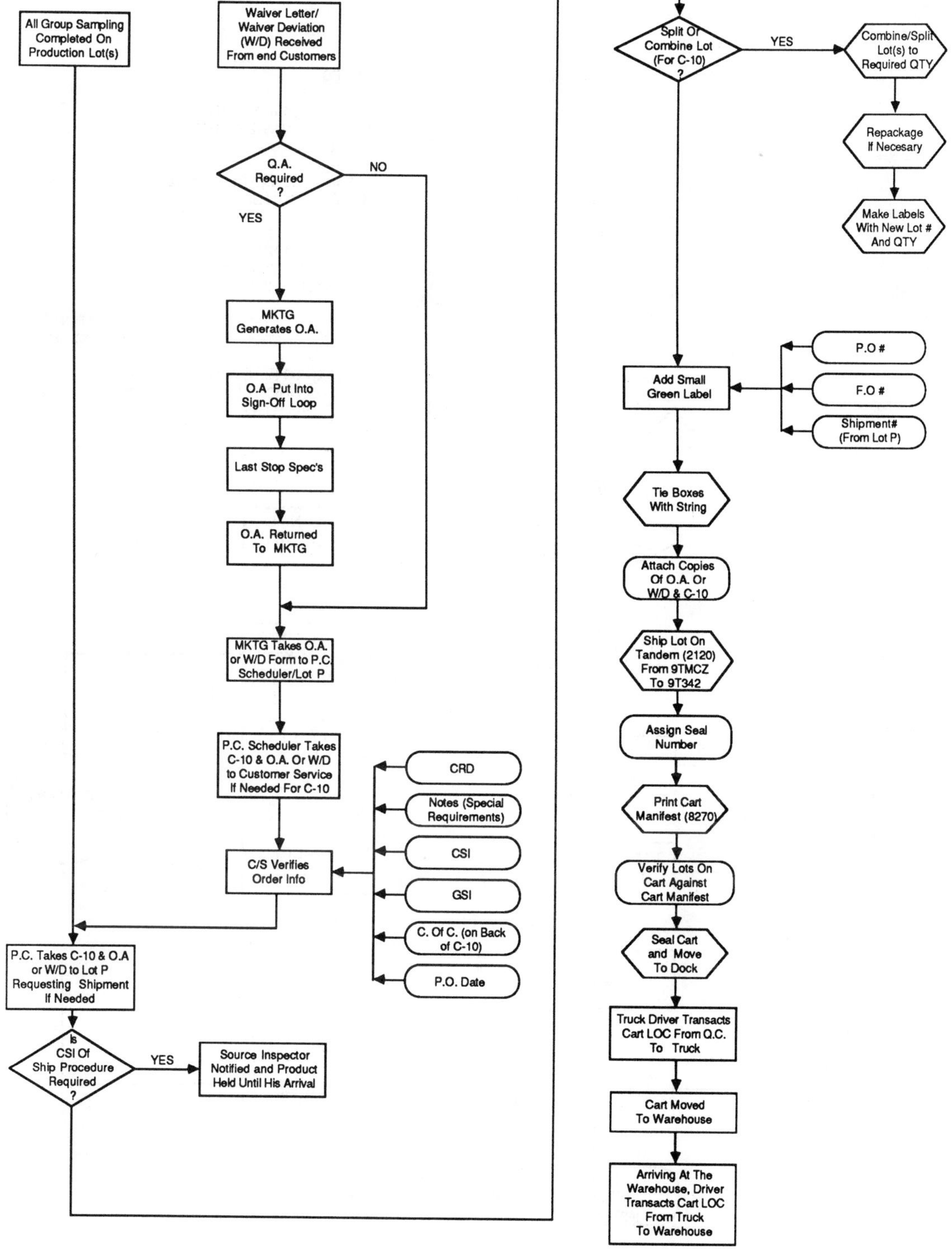

K. R.F.T. CORRELATION UNIT GENERATION

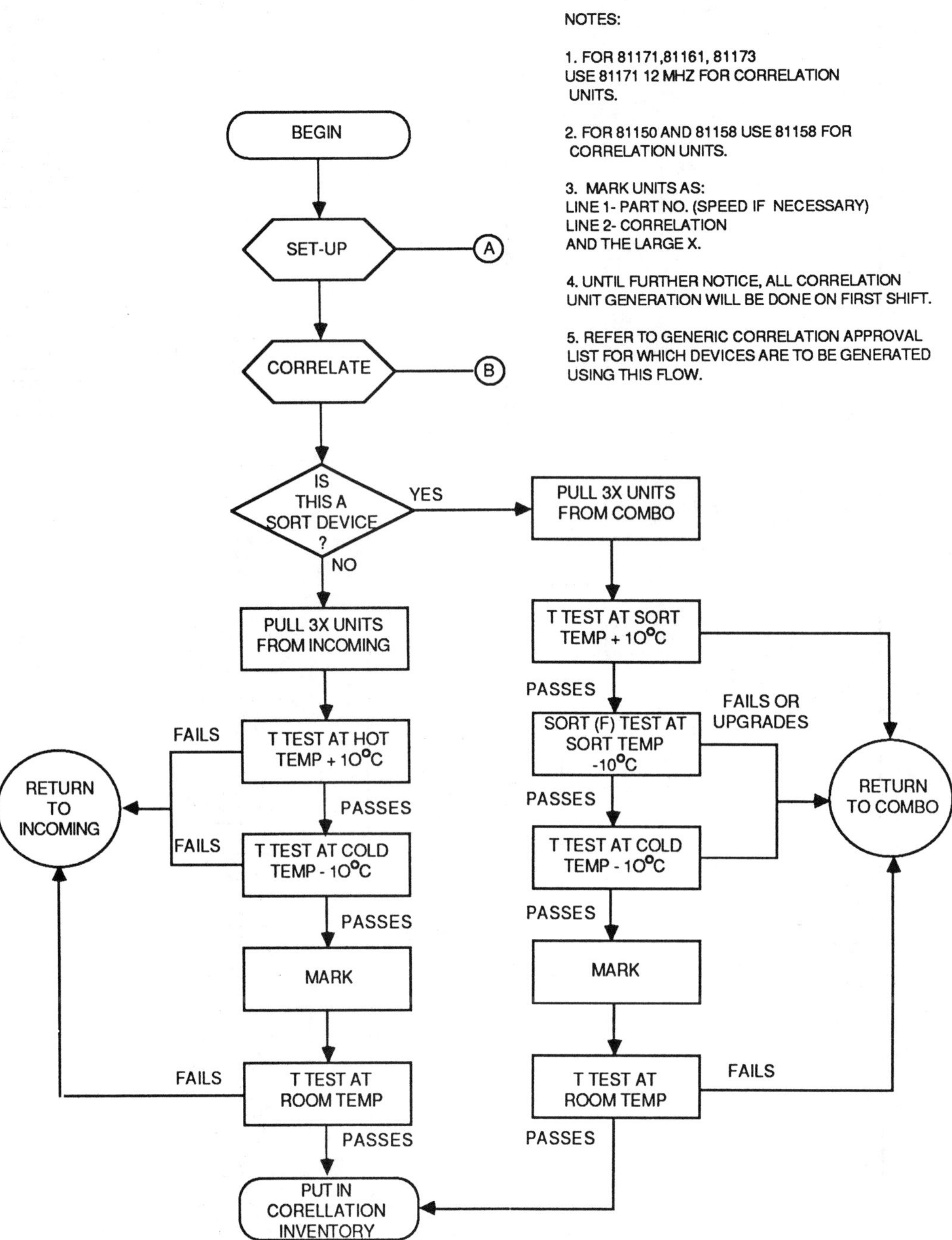

VI. BURN-IN FLOW

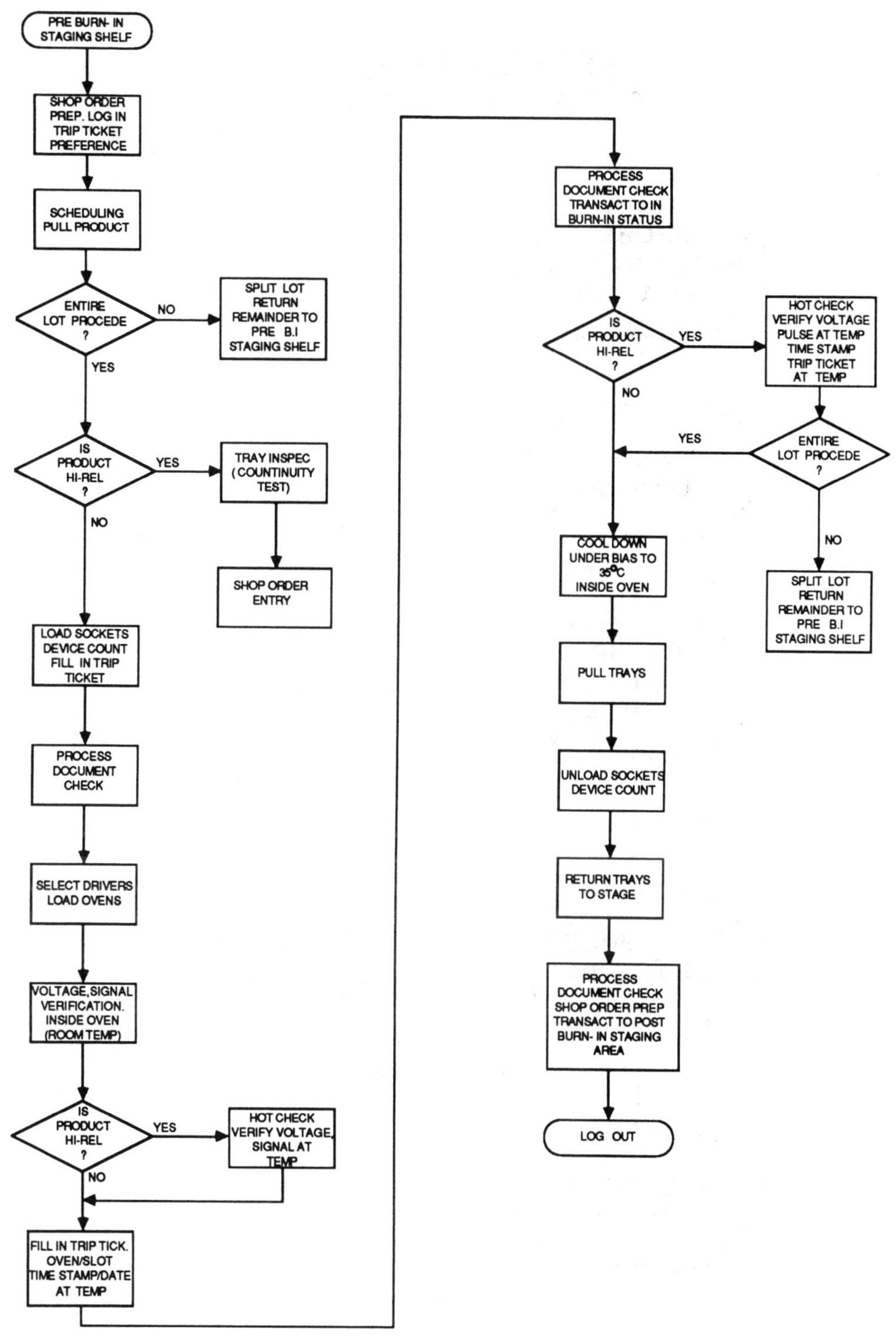

UNIT PROBE FLOW

PROBE OVERVIEW FLOWS P1 THRU P5

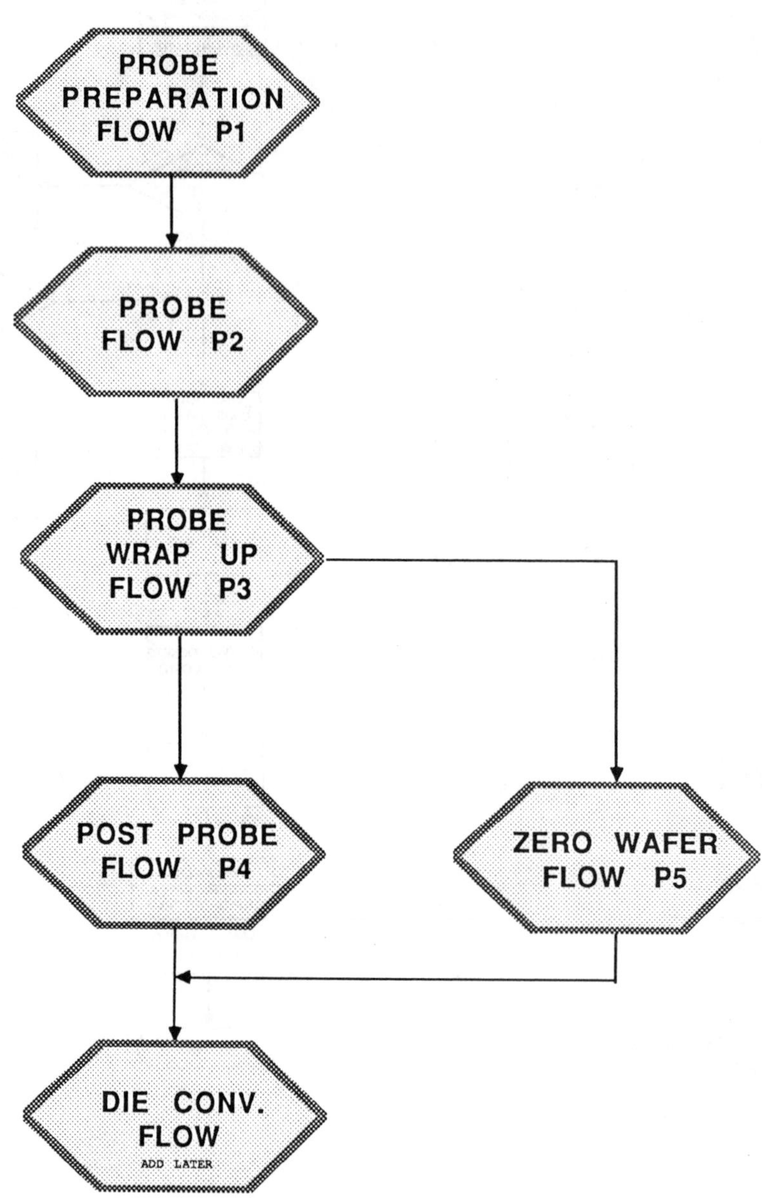

UNIT PROBE FLOW

PROBE PREPARATION FLOW P1

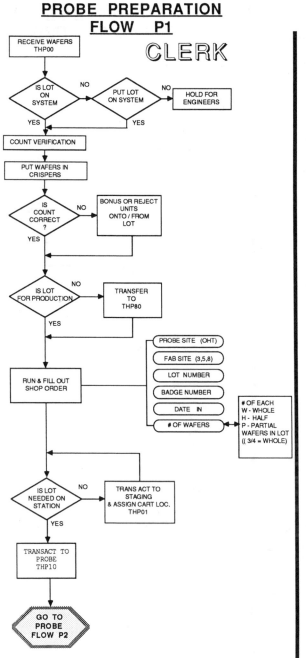

CLERK

RECEIVE WAFERS THP00

IS LOT ON SYSTEM

NO

PUT LOT ON SYSTEM

NO

HOLD FOR ENGINEERS

YES

YES

COUNT VERIFICATION

PUT WAFERS IN CRISPERS

IS COUNT CORRECT ?

NO

BONUS OR REJECT UNITS ONTO / FROM LOT

YES

IS LOT FOR PRODUCTION

NO

TRANSFER TO THP80

YES

RUN & FILL OUT SHOP ORDER

PROBE SITE (OHT)

FAB SITE (3,5,8)

LOT NUMBER

BADGE NUMBER

DATE IN

OF WAFERS

OF EACH
W - WHOLE
H - HALF
P - PARTIAL
WAFERS IN LOT
((3/4 = WHOLE)

IS LOT NEEDED ON STATION

NO

TRANS ACT TO STAGING & ASSIGN CART LOC. THP01

YES

TRANSACT TO PROBE THP10

GO TO PROBE FLOW P2

PROBE FLOW P2

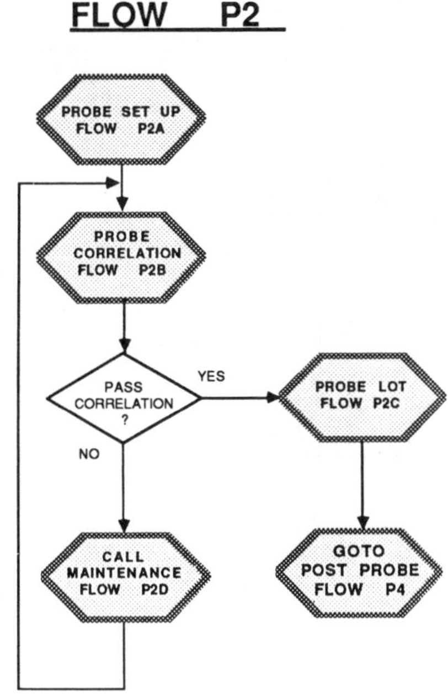

UNIT PROBE FLOW

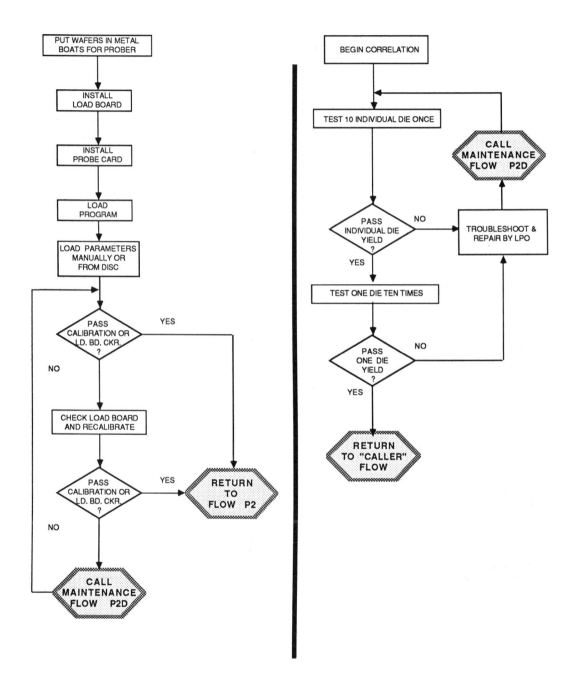

PROBE SET UP FLOW P2A

CORRELATION FLOW P2B

PUT WAFERS IN METAL BOATS FOR PROBER

INSTALL LOAD BOARD

INSTALL PROBE CARD

LOAD PROGRAM

LOAD PARAMETERS MANUALLY OR FROM DISC

PASS CALIBRATION OR LD. BD. CKR. ?

YES → RETURN TO FLOW P2

NO → CHECK LOAD BOARD AND RECALIBRATE

PASS CALIBRATION OR LD. BD. CKR. ?

YES → RETURN TO FLOW P2

NO → CALL MAINTENANCE FLOW P2D (returns to first PASS CALIBRATION OR LD. BD. CKR. ?)

BEGIN CORRELATION

TEST 10 INDIVIDUAL DIE ONCE

PASS INDIVIDUAL DIE YIELD ?

NO → TROUBLESHOOT & REPAIR BY LPO → CALL MAINTENANCE FLOW P2D (returns to TEST 10 INDIVIDUAL DIE ONCE)

YES → TEST ONE DIE TEN TIMES

PASS ONE DIE YIELD ?

NO → TROUBLESHOOT & REPAIR BY LPO

YES → RETURN TO "CALLER" FLOW

UNIT PROBE FLOW

PROBE LOT FLOW P2C

LPO

CALL MAINTENANCE FLOW P2D

PROBE WAFER
IS THIS THE FIRST OR A FIFTH WAFER ?
NO
YES
INSPECT WAFER FLOW P2E
IS IT A HIGH BIN LIMIT OR LOW YIELD WAFER ?
YES
NO
IS THIS THE THIRD CONSECUTIVE HIGH BIN LIMIT OR LOW YIELD WAFER ?
NO
YES
RUN CORRELATION FLOW P2B
ANOTHER WAFER ?
YES
NO
GET ENG. OR SUPERVISOR SIGN OFF TO CONTINUE
GO TO PROBE WRAP UP FLOW P3
PASS CORRELATION ?
YES
NO
TROUBLESHOOT AND REPAIR BY LPO
CALL MAINTENANCE FLOW P2D
WASH ANY OF LAST 3 WAFERS ?
NO
YES

DATALOG FAILURE
HDW. OR PRODUCT PROB. ?
PRODUCT
HDW.
FILL OUT DISCREPANCY REPORT & PUT LOT ON HOLD
REPAIR PROBLEM
SYSTEM OR PROBER PASS ?
NO
YES
RETURN TO "CALLER" FLOW
CONTINUE LOT ?
YES
NO
SCRAP LOT OR IMT LOT TO ENGINEERING

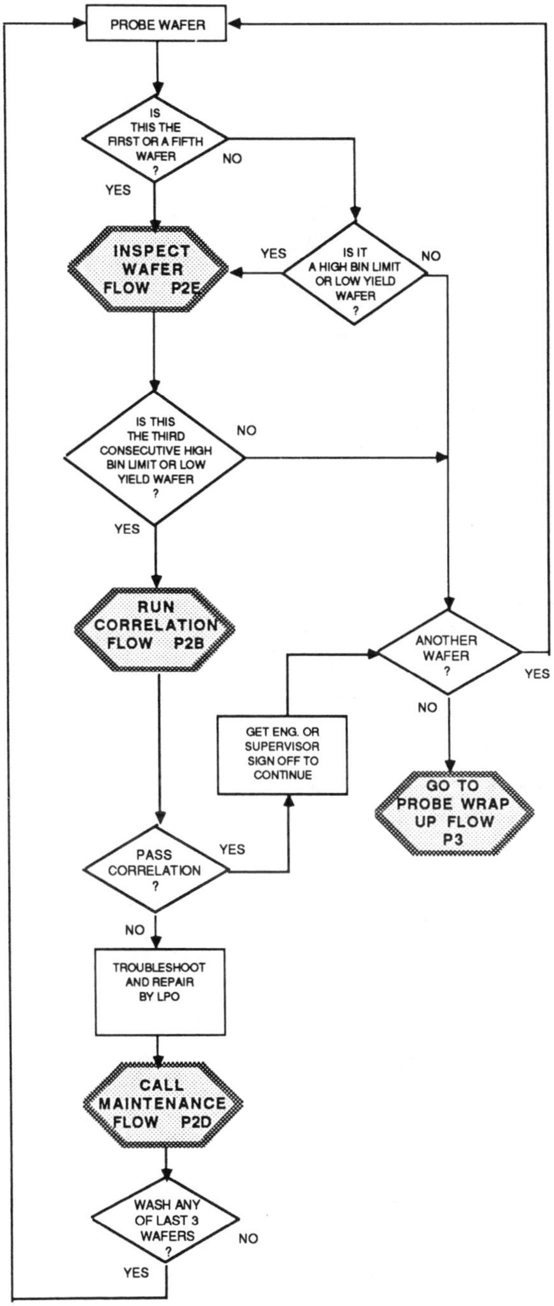

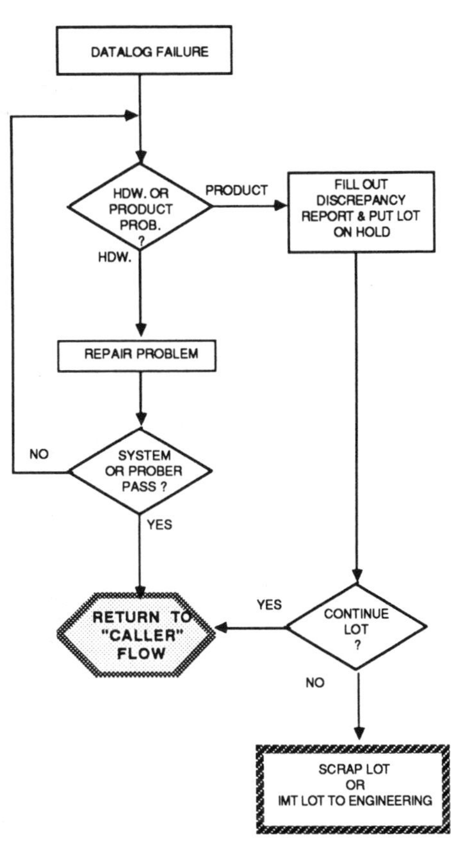

UNIT PROBE FLOW

INSPECT WAFER FLOW P2E

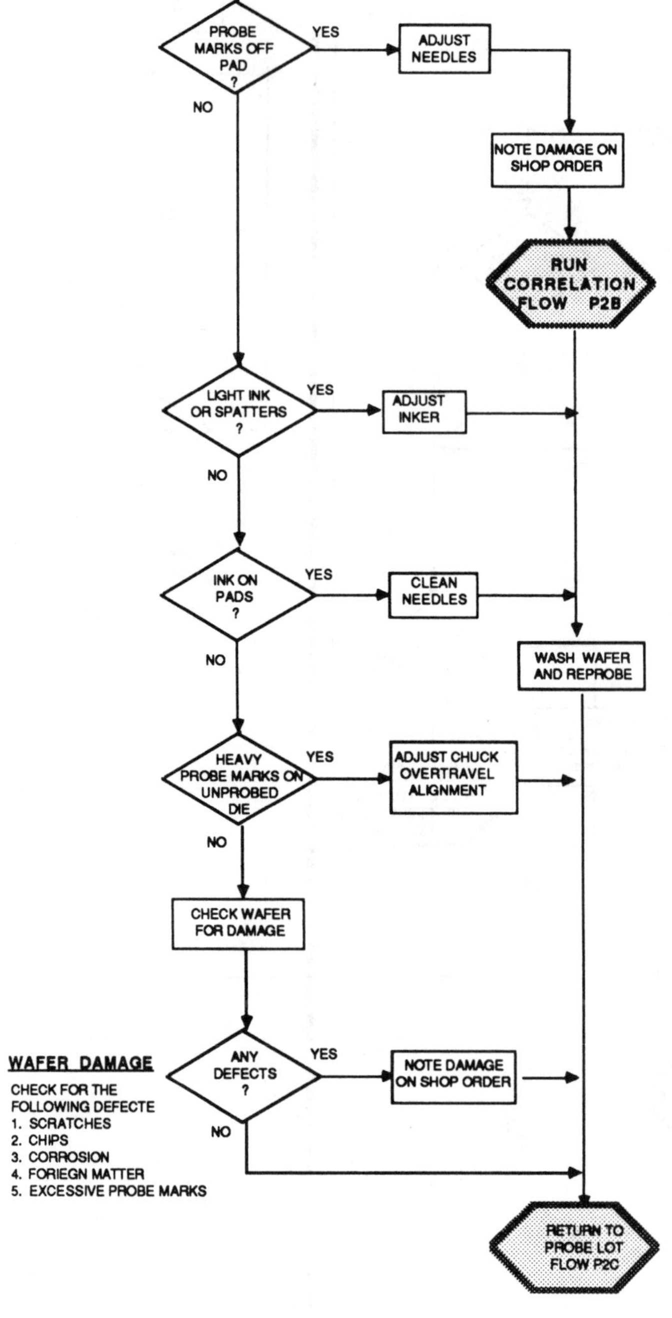

UNIT PROBE FLOW

PROBE WRAP UP

FLOW P3

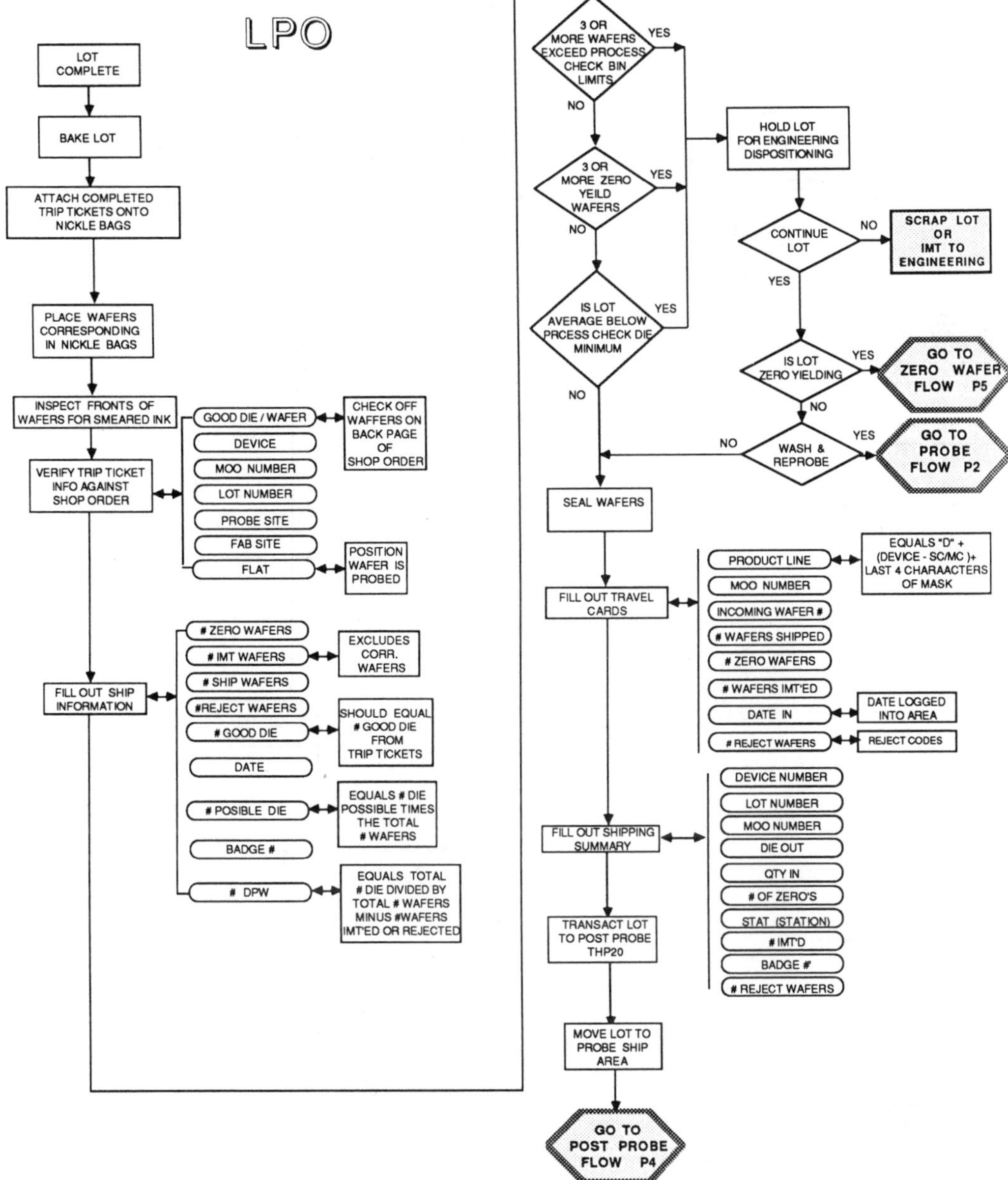

LPO
LOT COMPLETE
BAKE LOT
ATTACH COMPLETED TRIP TICKETS ONTO NICKLE BAGS
PLACE WAFERS CORRESPONDING IN NICKLE BAGS
INSPECT FRONTS OF WAFERS FOR SMEARED INK
VERIFY TRIP TICKET INFO AGAINST SHOP ORDER
GOOD DIE / WAFER
DEVICE
MOO NUMBER
LOT NUMBER
PROBE SITE
FAB SITE
FLAT
CHECK OFF WAFFERS ON BACK PAGE OF SHOP ORDER
POSITION WAFER IS PROBED
FILL OUT SHIP INFORMATION
ZERO WAFERS
IMT WAFERS
SHIP WAFERS
#REJECT WAFERS
GOOD DIE
DATE
POSIBLE DIE
BADGE #
DPW
EXCLUDES CORR. WAFERS
SHOULD EQUAL # GOOD DIE FROM TRIP TICKETS
EQUALS # DIE POSSIBLE TIMES THE TOTAL # WAFERS
EQUALS TOTAL # DIE DIVIDED BY TOTAL # WAFERS MINUS #WAFERS IMT'ED OR REJECTED
3 OR MORE WAFERS EXCEED PROCESS CHECK BIN LIMITS
YES
NO
3 OR MORE ZERO YEILD WAFERS
IS LOT AVERAGE BELOW PRCESS CHECK DIE MINIMUM
HOLD LOT FOR ENGINEERING DISPOSITIONING
CONTINUE LOT
SCRAP LOT OR IMT TO ENGINEERING
IS LOT ZERO YIELDING
GO TO ZERO WAFER FLOW P5
WASH & REPROBE
GO TO PROBE FLOW P2
SEAL WAFERS
FILL OUT TRAVEL CARDS
PRODUCT LINE
MOO NUMBER
INCOMING WAFER #
WAFERS SHIPPED
ZERO WAFERS
WAFERS IMT'ED
DATE IN
REJECT WAFERS
EQUALS "D" + (DEVICE - SC/MC)+ LAST 4 CHARAACTERS OF MASK
DATE LOGGED INTO AREA
REJECT CODES
FILL OUT SHIPPING SUMMARY
DEVICE NUMBER
LOT NUMBER
MOO NUMBER
DIE OUT
QTY IN
OF ZERO'S
STAT (STATION)
IMT'D
BADGE #
REJECT WAFERS
TRANSACT LOT TO POST PROBE THP20
MOVE LOT TO PROBE SHIP AREA
GO TO POST PROBE FLOW P4

UNIT PROBE FLOW

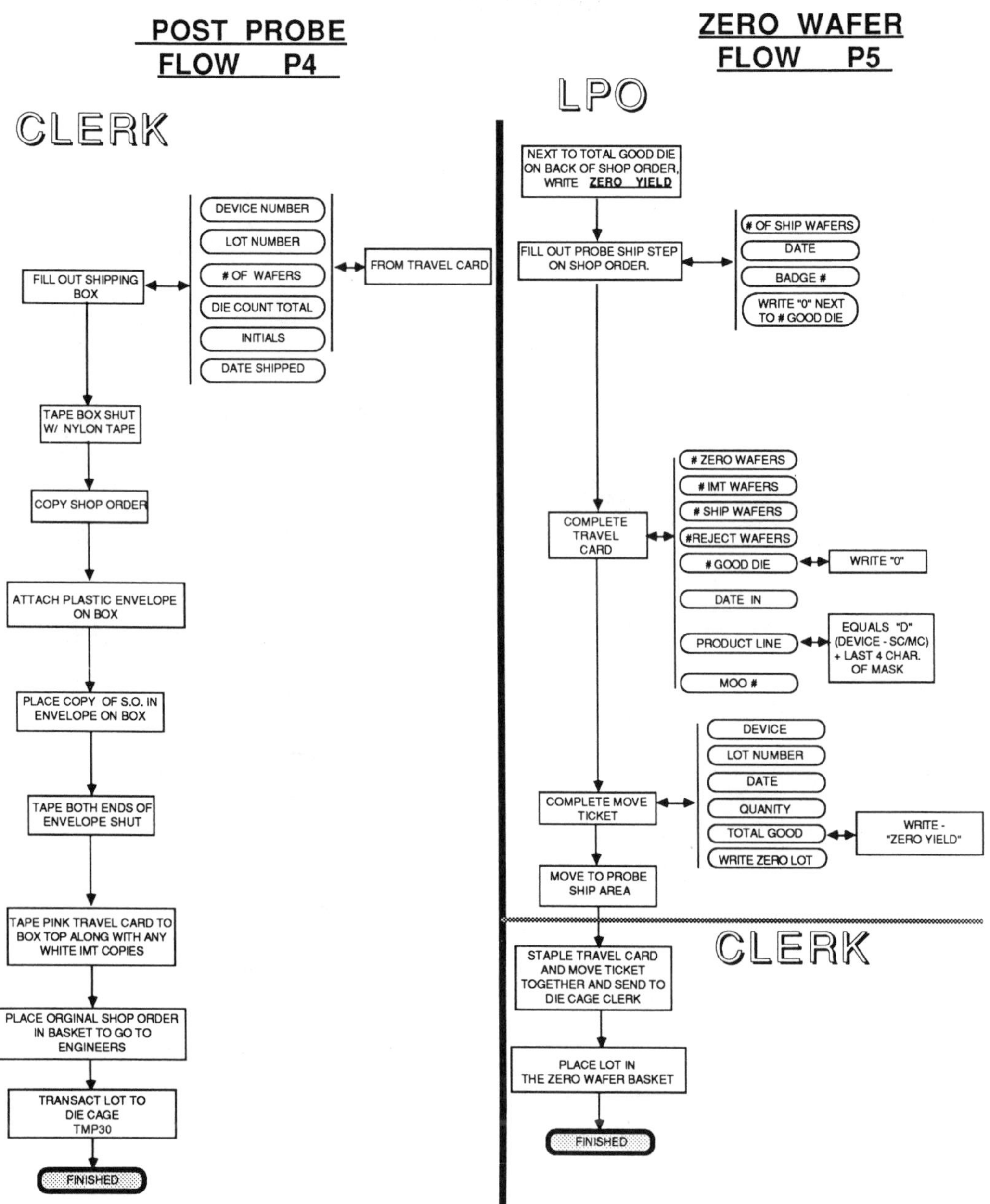

POST PROBE FLOW P4
ZERO WAFER FLOW P5
CLERK
FILL OUT SHIPPING BOX
DEVICE NUMBER
LOT NUMBER
OF WAFERS
DIE COUNT TOTAL
INITIALS
DATE SHIPPED
FROM TRAVEL CARD
TAPE BOX SHUT W/ NYLON TAPE
COPY SHOP ORDER
ATTACH PLASTIC ENVELOPE ON BOX
PLACE COPY OF S.O. IN ENVELOPE ON BOX
TAPE BOTH ENDS OF ENVELOPE SHUT
TAPE PINK TRAVEL CARD TO BOX TOP ALONG WITH ANY WHITE IMT COPIES
PLACE ORGINAL SHOP ORDER IN BASKET TO GO TO ENGINEERS
TRANSACT LOT TO DIE CAGE TMP30
FINISHED
LPO
NEXT TO TOTAL GOOD DIE ON BACK OF SHOP ORDER, WRITE ZERO YIELD
FILL OUT PROBE SHIP STEP ON SHOP ORDER.
OF SHIP WAFERS
DATE
BADGE #
WRITE "0" NEXT TO # GOOD DIE
COMPLETE TRAVEL CARD
ZERO WAFERS
IMT WAFERS
SHIP WAFERS
#REJECT WAFERS
GOOD DIE
WRITE "0"
DATE IN
PRODUCT LINE
EQUALS "D" (DEVICE - SC/MC) + LAST 4 CHAR. OF MASK
MOO #
COMPLETE MOVE TICKET
DEVICE
LOT NUMBER
DATE
QUANITY
TOTAL GOOD
WRITE - "ZERO YIELD"
WRITE ZERO LOT
MOVE TO PROBE SHIP AREA
CLERK
STAPLE TRAVEL CARD AND MOVE TICKET TOGETHER AND SEND TO DIE CAGE CLERK
PLACE LOT IN THE ZERO WAFER BASKET
FINISHED

INDEX

Acceptable quality level (AQL), 14-1
Accounting terms, 10-1, 10-2–10-8
Actual labor $, 10-4
Actual material, 10-4
Actual performance, 7-6
Allan Bradley, 15-30
Alliances, strategic, 6-39
Allowances $, 10-3
Alpha radiation immunity, 4-11
Application specific integrated circuits (ASICs), 4-5
Artificial intelligence, 17-1
ASCII (American standard code for information interchange), 15-24
Ashton-Tate, 16-27
Assembly level language, 16-22
Asynchronous transmission, 15-25
AT&T (American Telephone and Telegraph), 16-26
Average outgoing quality (AOQ), 14-2
Average Selling Price (ASP), 2-6

Backlog, 12-1
Backlog ASP $, 10-3
Backlog current $, 10-2
Backlog delinquent $, 10-2
Bandwidth, 15-26
Base price, 8-31
Baudot, 15-24
Bipolar technology, 4-1
Bipolar transistor, 4-30
Book/bill ratio $, 10-3
Bookings, 12-1
Bridges, 15-21
Budget deficit, 1-12
Buffers, 15-24
Business cycle, 1-5–1-7
Bus network architecture, 15-23, 15-28
Bysynch, 15-26

Capacity variance $, 10-7
Capital expense $, 10-7
Carrier sense multiple access (CSMA/CD), 15-28
Central processing unit (CPU), 4-5
Complementary metal oxide silicon (CMOS), 4-1, 4-33
Computer-aided design (CAD), 4-4, 16-1
Computer-aided manufacturing (CAM), 4-4, 16-1
Computer integrated manufacturing (CIM), 6-22, 15-3, 16-1
Computing milestones, 3-21
Corporation for Open Systems (COS), 16-9
Cost accounting, 9-1
Costs, 9-8–9-9
  die, 8-6
  factory, 7-3
  inventoriable, 7-2
  local standard, 7-1, 7-2, 7-5
  margin 1 (M1), 8-1, 8-7
  margin 2 (M2), 7-3, 8-2, 8-3
  test, 8-7
  wafer, 8-3
  worldwide standard (WWS), 7-1, 7-2, 7-5, 8-1
Cp, 6-34, 14-12
Cpk, 6-34, 14-12
Current, 15-8
Customer required date (CRD), 12-1
Customer satisfaction, total, 6-1
Customer to advise (CTA), 12-20
Cycle-time, 5-10, 5-12, 9-16
  short cycle-time manufacturing (SCM), 5-2, 9-1
Cyclic redundancy check (CRC), 15-26

Data base:
  distributed, 16-15
  hierarchical, 16-14
  network, 16-14
  relational, 16-15–16-16
Data base management systems (DBMS), 16-13
dBase, 16-27
DEC (Digital Equipment Corporation), 16-25
DEC/Apple, 16-26
Decoupled line flow, 6-36–6-37
Defects:
  functional, 3-12–3-13
  latent, 3-13
  parametric, 3-13
  random, 3-13
  uniform, 3-13
Deficit spending, 1-18–1-19
Demand turns $, 10-2
Direct factory overhead (DFO) $, 10-5
Direct labor tracking (DLT), 6-13
Distributed data base, 16-15
Downtime, 9-18
Duty $, 10-4

Earned labor $, 10-4
Earned material $, 10-4
EBCDIC (external binary coded decimal interchange code), 15-24
Efficiency, 8-26
Electrically erasable programmable read only memory (EEPROM), 4-4, 4-12
Electrically programmable read only memory (EPROM), 4-4, 4-6–4-7, 4-12
Experience curve, 2-22, 8-16
Expert configurer (XCON), 17-6
Expert system design rules, 17-8–17-9
Expert systems, 17-1

Factory schedule date (FSD), 12-20
Factory to advise (FTA), 12-20
Factory variance $, 10-6
Firmware, 4-7
Fiscal policy, 1-12
Forecasts, 7-5, 11-1
Fourth generation language, 16-22
Freight $, 10-3
Full-duplex, 15-24
Functional defect, 3-12–3-13
Functional manufacturing system, 5-6, 6-4

Gateways, 15-21
General Agreement on Trade and Tariffs (GATT), 1-13
General Motors, 15-29
Goals, 7-5
Gold adder $, 10-4
Gold standard, 1-3
Gramm-Rudman Act, 1-20
Gross bookings $, 10-2
Gross sales, 10-3
Gross sales ASP $, 10-3

Half-duplex, 15-24
Hamada Diagram, 1-15–1-16
HDLC, 15-26
Hierarchical data base, 16-14
Hi-Rel, A-2
Hot chuck/high frequency/inkless probe, 6-21

IBM (International Business Machines), 16-24
Incomes policy, 1-12
Index time, 9-17
Indirect factory overhead (IFO), 10-5
Initial graphics exchange specification (IGES), 16-18
Integrated business information system (IBIS), 6-10, 12-1
Integrated circuits:
  analog, 15-10
  application specific (ASICs), 4-5
  digital, 15-10
Integrated manufacturing cell (IMC), 5-7, 6-36
Integrated services digital network (ISDN), 16-9, 16-19
International Monetary Fund (IMF), 1-13
International Standards Organization (ISO), 15-29
International Trade Organization (ITO), 1-13
Inventory, 5-1
  pipeline, 5-1
  queuing, 5-1
  work in process (WIP), 5-1–5-2
Inventory adjustments, 10-6
Ion implantation, 4-3
IQs, equipment, 15-19

Job shop, 6-37
"Junk" bonds, 1-34
Just-in-case (JIC) manufacturing method, 5-5
Just-in-time (JIT) manufacturing method, 5-2, 5-5

Keynes, John Maynard, 1-8

Latchup, 4-11
Latent defect, 3-13
Layout design rules, 4-29
Learning curve, 2-21–2-22
Linearity, 12-24
Local area network (LAN), 15-19
Longitudinal redundancy check (LRC), 15-26
Lorenz curve (*see* Pareto curve)
Lot tolerance percent defective (LTPD), 14-2

Manufacturability, 3-12
Manufacturing automation protocol (MAP), 15-29, 15-30
Manufacturing variance, 10-4
Margin (2) $, 10-6
Margin (3) $, 10-7
Margin (4) $, 10-8
Market share, 2-18–2-19, 2-22
Marshall Plan, 1-7–1-8
Mask program layer, 4-8
Masks, 4-9
Mean time before repair (MTBR), 15-6
Mean time between assist (MTBA), 15-6
Mean time between failure (MTBF), 15-6
Microcomputer unit (MCU), 4-5
Microprocessing unit (MPU), 4-5
Microsoft, 16-27
Microsoft Disc Operating System (MS-DOS), 16-10
Military product acronyms, A-10
Military products, A-1
Military standards:
  MIL-M-38510F, A-4, A-6
  MIL-STD-454, A-3–A-4
  MIL-STD-883B/C, A-2
Modular manufacturing system, 5-6–5-7, 6-9
Monetary policy, 1-12
Money supply, 1-12
MOS (metal oxide silicon) technology, 4-1
  CMOS, 4-1
  NMOS, 4-1
MOS transistor, 4-30
Motivation, 8-29–8-30
Multitasking, 16-10

National Recovery Act, 1-4
N-channel silicon-gate process, 4-16
Net bookings ASP $, 10-3
Net bookings $, 10-2
Net/gross ratio %, 10-2
Net sales ASP $, 10-3
Net sales $, 10-3
Net units sold, 10-3
Network architectures:
  bus, 15-23, 15-28
  ring, 15-23, 15-28
  star, 15-23, 15-28
Network data base, 16-14
Neural network computers, 17-5
New product design, 3-1
New product introduction, 2-8
New product pricing, 2-18
Nitride passivation, 4-4
NMOS, 4-1
Nonvolatile memory (NVM), 4-12, 4-13

On-time delivery, 12-19
Open standards interconnect (OSI), 16-9
Operating statement, 10-1
Operating systems, 16-10
Opportunity curve, 2-22
Organizational structure, 6-25–6-26
OS/2, 16-10
Overhead, 9-2

Parallel computers, 17-3
Parametric defect, 3-13
Pareto, Wilfred, 13-20
Pareto curve, 13-20
Parity, 15-26
  horizontal, 15-26
  vertical, 15-26
Participative management culture (PMC), 6-9
Parts per million (PPM), 14-2
Pattern generator (PG), 4-8
Percent defective allowable (PDA), 14-2
Period expense $, other, 10-7
Photo resist, positive, 4-3
Plasma etching, 4-4
P-N junction, 4-35
Policy:
  fiscal, 1-12
  incomes, 1-12
  monetary, 1-12
Polycrystalline silicon (poly), 4-22
Price:
  base, 8-31
  transfer, 8-30
Price volume sensitivity curve, 2-23
Procedural variance $, 10-6
Procedural variation, 8-10, 8-14, 9-2
Process base line, 4-3
Process performance index (Cpk), 6-34, 14-12
Process potential index (Cp), 6-34, 14-12
Product data exchange specifications (PDES), 16-18
Product definition data interface (PDDI), 16-18
Productivity, 8-29
Productivity variation $, 10-4
Product marketing $, 10-7
Product quality, 14-1
Product reliability, 14-1
Profitability, 2-22
Program trading, 1-34
Project evaluation and review technique (PERT) 2-7, 2-15
Projection printing, 4-3
Protocol, 15-24
Prototypes, 4-7
PS/2 (IBM), 16-10

Purchase price variation $, 10-4
Purchasing & distribution $, 10-7

R&D engineering $, 10-7
Random defect, 3-13
Rate variation $, 10-4
Read only memory (ROM), 4-5
Relational data base, 16-15–16-16
Relational data model, 16-29
Resistance, 15-8
Returns $, 10-3
Right first time (RFT), 6-18
Ring network architecture, 15-23, 15-28
ROM verification unit (RVU), 4-5

Says's Law, 1-2–1-3
Scrap & obsolescence $, 10-4
Scrap reclaim $, 10-4
Scrap RMR $, 10-6
Semiconductor milestones, 3-21
Set-up time, 9-18
Shipped turns $, 10-2
Short cyle-time manufacturing (SCM), 5-2, 9-1
Simplex, 15-24
Single chip microprocessor, 4-5
Smoot-Hauley Tariff Act, 1-2
Sputtering, 4-4
Standard change $, 10-6
Standard cost $, 10-3
Standard costs:
  local, 7-1, 7-2, 7-5
  worldwide (WWS), 7-1, 7-2, 7-5, 8-1
Standard deviation, 14-12
Standard margin 1 $, 10-3
Star network architecture, 15-23, 15-28
Statistical process control (SPC), 3-18, 14-1, 14-3, 14-11
Statistics, 14-20
Stock index futures, 1-32–1-33
Stock index options, 1-33–1-34
Stock market crash:
  of 1987, 1-16
  of 1929, 1-2–1-5
Strategic alliances, 6-39
SUN (Stanford University Network), 16-26
Synchronous transmission, 15-25
Systems application architecture (SAA), 16-10, 16-24

Task force structure, 6-26
Terrible Tuesday, *Wall Street Journal*, 1-41–1-48
Test capacity, 8-24
Throughput, 9-7, 9-18
Token ring, 15-27
Total inventoriable overhead $, 10-5
Trade deficit, 1-22–1-30
Transfer price, 8-30
Translation rate variance, 10-6
Transmission:
  asynchronous, 15-25
  synchronous, 15-25
Transmission codes, 15-24
Transport time, 9-17
Turns %, 10-2
2's complement arithmetic, 15-10

Uniform defect, 3-13
UNIX, 16-10, 16-12
Usage/mix variation $, 10-4

Valuation change $, 10-6
VMS, 16-10
Voltage, 15-8

Wafer assembly, 4-10
Wafer fabrication, 4-9
Wafer probe, 4-10
Wafer test, 4-10
Wafer variations, 10-6
Wall Street Crash (1929), 1-2–1-5
Wide area networks, 15-21
WIP zig/zag, 6-18
Work-in-process, 6-4
World Bank, 1-13

XCON (expert configurer), 17-6

Yield, 3-16
Yield variation $, 10-5